BREAK THROUGH
To improving results

D1537304

5 Reasons to Use MyMathLab
for Finite Math and Applied Calculus

1 Thousands of high-quality exercises. Algorithmic exercises of all types and difficulty levels are available to meet the needs of students with diverse mathematical backgrounds. We've also added even more conceptual exercises to the already abundant skill and application exercises.

2 Helps students help themselves. Homework isn't effective if students don't do it. MyMathLab not only grades homework, but it also does the more subtle task of providing specific feedback and guidance along the way. As an instructor, you can control the amount of guidance students receive.

Breaks the problem into manageable steps. Students enter answers along the way.

Reviews a problem like the one assigned.

Links to the appropriate section in the textbook.

Features an instructor explaining the concept.

3 Addresses gaps in prerequisite skills. Our *Getting Ready for Finite Mathematics* and *Getting Ready for Applied Calculus* content addresses gaps in prerequisite skills that can impede student success. MyMathLab identifies precise areas of weakness, then automatically provides remediation for those skills.

4 Adaptive Study Plan. MyMathLab's Adaptive Study Plan makes studying more efficient and effective. Each student's work and activity are assessed continually in real time. The data and analytics are used to provide personalized content to remediate any gaps in understanding.

5 Ready-to-Go Courses. To make it even easier for first-time users to start using MyMathLab, we have enlisted experienced instructors to create premade assignments for the Ready-to-Go Courses. You can alter these assignments at any time, but they provide a terrific starting point, right out of the box.

Since 2001, more than 15 million students at more than 1,950 colleges have used MyMathLab. Users have reported significant increases in pass rates and retention. Why? Students do more work and get targeted help when they need it. See www.mymathlab.com/success_report.html for the latest information on how schools are successfully using MyMathLab.

Learn more at www.mymathlab.com

Margaret L. Lial • Thomas W. Hungerford • John P. Holcomb, Jr.
Bernadette Mullins

Mathematics with Applications in the Management, Natural, and Social Sciences

Sixth Custom Edition for Baylor University

Taken from:
Mathematics with Applications in the Management, Natural, and Social Sciences, Eleventh Edition
by Margaret L. Lial, Thomas W. Hungerford, John P. Holcomb, Jr., and Bernadette Mullins

Cover Art: Courtesy of Pearson Learning Solutions.

Taken from:

Mathematics with Applications in the Management, Natural, and Social Sciences, Eleventh Edition
by Margaret L. Lial, Thomas W. Hungerford, John P. Holcomb, Jr., and Bernadette Mullins
Copyright © 2015, 2011, 2007, 2004 by Pearson Education, Inc.
Boston, Massachusetts 02116

This special edition published in cooperation with Pearson Learning Solutions.

All trademarks, service marks, registered trademarks, and registered service marks are the property of their respective owners and are used herein for identification purposes only.

Pearson Learning Solutions, 501 Boylston Street, Suite 900, Boston, MA 02116
A Pearson Education Company
www.pearsoned.com

Printed in the United States of America

1 2 3 4 5 6 7 8 9 10   092 18 17 16 15 14

000200010271937388

EEB

ISBN 10: 1-323-03160-X
ISBN 13: 978-1-323-03160-5

Contents

Preface

Mathematics with Applications is an applications-centered text for students in business, management, and natural and social sciences. It covers the basics of college algebra, followed by topics in finite mathematics and concluding with a treatment of applied calculus. The text can be used for a variety of different courses, and the only prerequisite is a basic course in algebra. Chapter 1 provides a thorough review of basic algebra for those students who need it. The newly added Prerequisite Skills Test (for Chapters 1–4) and Calculus Readiness Test (for Chapters 11–14) at the front of the text can help determine where remediation is needed for students with gaps in their basic algebra skills.

It has been our primary goal to present sound mathematics in an understandable manner, proceeding from the familiar to new material and from concrete examples to general rules and formulas. There is an ongoing focus on real-world problem solving, and almost every section includes relevant, contemporary applications.

New to This Edition

With each revision comes an opportunity to improve the presentation of the content in a variety of ways. This revision is no exception as we have revised and added content, updated and added new applications, fine-tuned pedagogical devices, and evaluated and enhanced the exercise sets. In addition, both the functionality of MyMathLab and the resources within it have been greatly improved and expanded for this revision. These improvements were incorporated after careful consideration and much feedback from those who teach this course regularly. Following is a list of some of the more substantive revisions made to this edition.

- **Prerequisite Diagnostic Tests:** As a way to address the often weak algebra skills that students bring to this course, two diagnostic exams are provided just prior to Chapter 1. These two diagnostics can be used in a variety of ways, depending on the expectations and goals of the course. The Prerequisite Skills Test assesses student understanding of the core skills students should have prior to starting Chapter 1. The Calculus Readiness Test is designed to diagnose any missing prerequisite algebra skills prior to starting Chapter 11. Solutions are provided in the back of the text so students can self-remediate as needed, saving valuable class time. *Getting Ready* quizzes in MyMathLab are also available as automated versions of these diagnostics.

- **Additional Figures:** An additional six graphical figures were added to Section 2.2 to help illustrate slope as part of writing the equation of a line.

- **Quadratic Functions:** In the previous edition, there were two separate sections (3.4 and 3.5) for quadratic functions and applications of quadratic functions. These two sections have been consolidated into one section for ease of teaching.

- **Implicit Differentiation and Related Rates:** By popular demand, two sections have been added: implicit differentiation and related rates. These sections include step-by-step instructions for students to find the derivative of an implicitly defined function and to find a rate of change given that two quantities are related to each other and also changing over time. Examples and exercises include applications to business such as the rates of change of the number of employees and revenue of a corporation.

- **Case Studies:** The popular culminating activities at the end of every chapter have been expanded to provide options for **extended projects** for individual students or more extensive **group work.** In addition, three of the case studies are completely new and five have been updated significantly.

- A careful and thorough review of the **correlation between examples and exercises** has been completed to ensure that students have examples to refer to when working homework exercises. A table at the start of the answers for the Review Exercises (in the Answers to Exercises section in the back of the book) tells students in which section each of the review exercises is covered.

- The **MyMathLab** course that accompanies this text has been markedly improved and expanded to include even greater coverage of the topics in this course through more exercises, videos, animations, and PowerPoint slides. In addition, answer tolerance for exercises has been checked and adjusted when necessary, and prerequisite diagnostic tools are available for personalized assessment and remediation. See the Supplements portion of this preface for more details on MyMathLab.

- **Annotated Instructor's Edition**: An invaluable resource for instructors, the Annotated Instructor's Edition (AIE) contains answers to the exercises right on the exercise set page (whenever possible). In addition, *Teaching Tips* are included in the margins to provide helpful hints for less experienced instructors.

- **Graphing Calculator** screen shots have been updated to represent the newest TI calculator, the TI-84+ C. These visuals often prove valuable even to students not using graphing calculators.

- The **exercises** are now better paired so that the even exercises require similar knowledge as the corresponding odd exercise. In addition, approximately 21 percent of the 5,436 exercises in the text are new or updated.

- Approximately 22 percent of the 641 **examples** in the text are new or updated. Many examples and exercises are based on real-world data.

- **Student Learning Objectives** for every section of the text are provided at the back of the text. These objectives describe what students should understand and be able to do after studying the section and completing the exercises.

- An **Index of Companies, Products, and Agencies** is provided to increase student interest and motivation.

Continued Pedagogical Support

- **Balanced Approach**: Multiple representations of a topic (symbolic, numerical, graphical, verbal) are given when appropriate. However, we do not believe that all representations are useful for all topics, so effective alternatives are discussed only when they are likely to increase student understanding.

- **Strong Algebra Foundation:** The text begins with four thorough chapters of college algebra that can be used in a variety of ways based on the needs of the students and the goals of the course. Take advantage of the content in these chapters as needed so students will be more successful with later topics and future courses.

- **Real-Data Examples and Explanations:** Real-data exercises have long been a popular and integral aspect of this book. A significant number of new real-data examples and exercises have also been introduced into the text. Applications are noted with the type of industry in which they fall so instructors or students can focus on applications that are in line with students' majors. (See pages 190–192.)

- **The Checkpoint Exercises** (marked with icons such as ☑1) within the body of the text provide an opportunity for students to stop, check their understanding of the specific concept at hand, and move forward with confidence. Answers to Checkpoint Exercises are located at the end of the section to encourage students to work the problems before looking at the answers. (See pages 184, 192.)

- **Cautions** ⓞ highlight common student difficulties or warn against frequently made mistakes. (See page 204.)

- **Exercises:** In addition to skill-based practice, conceptual, and application-based exercises, there are some specially marked exercises:
  Writing Exercises ✎ (see page 216)

Connection Exercises ◈ that relate current topics to earlier sections (see pages 253 and 262)

Practice Exercises from previous CPA exams (see page 242), and

Technology Required Exercises ↗ (see page 263).

- **Example/Exercise Connection**: Selected exercises include a reference back to related example(s) within the section (e.g., "See Examples 6 and 7") to facilitate what students do naturally when they use a book—i.e., look for specific examples when they get stuck on a problem. Later exercises leave this information out and provide opportunities for mixed skill practice.

- End-of-chapter materials are designed to help students prepare for exams and include a **List of Key Terms and Symbols** and **Summary of Key Concepts**, as well as a thorough set of **Chapter Review Exercises**.

- **Case Studies** appear at the end of each chapter and offer contemporary, real-world and up-to-date applications of some of the mathematics presented in the chapter. Not only do these provide an opportunity for students to see the mathematics they are learning in action, but they also provide at least a partial answer to the question, "What is this stuff good for?" These have been expanded to include options for longer-term projects if the instructor should choose to use them.

Technology

In our text, we choose to support a variety of different technologies in a way that provides greater understanding and encourages exploration of the tools students have at their disposal. The technology that is supported by this text includes graphing calculators, spreadsheets, and a variety of resources within MyMathLab.

MyMathLab: This text is not just supported by MyMathLab (MML), but rather it is enriched and expanded upon within MML. Fortunately, today's students are well-equipped to take full advantage of resources beyond the text, and the MML course for this text is especially valuable to the typical student.

- Concepts that are difficult to describe in print can be shown dynamically through video or animation, providing a visual that students may otherwise miss.

- Topics that are particularly challenging to students can be practiced, assessed, reviewed, and practiced some more through algorithmically generated homework or videos.

- Prerequisite skills that students lack can be assessed and then addressed on an individual basis using quick, pre-built assessments and personalized homework.

Although use of MML with this text is completely optional, students stand a greater chance of success if they take advantage of the many resources available to them within MML. More details as to all that MML can do are provided in the Supplements portion of this preface.

Graphing Calculators and Spreadsheets: It is assumed that all students have a calculator that will handle exponential and logarithmic functions. Beyond that, however, graphing calculator and spreadsheet references are highlighted in the text so that those who use the technology can easily incorporate it and those who do not can easily omit it. Examples and exercises that require some sort of technology are marked with the icon ↗, making it obvious where technology is being included.

Instructors who routinely use technology in their courses will find more than enough material to satisfy their needs. Here are some of the features they may want to incorporate into their courses:

- **Examples and Exercises marked with** ↗ A number of examples show students how various features of graphing calculators and spreadsheets can be applied to the topics in this book. Exercises marked with the same icon give students a chance to practice particular skills using technology.

- **Technology Tips:** These are placed at appropriate points in the text to inform students of various features of their graphing calculator, spreadsheet, or other computer programs. Note that Technology Tips designed for TI-84+ C also apply to the TI-84+, TI-83, and TI-Nspire.

- **Appendix A: Graphing Calculators:** This appendix consists of a brief introduction to the relevant features of the latest TI-84+ C graphing calculator. An outline of the appendix is on page 859, and the full appendix is available online in MyMathLab and at www.mathstatsresources.com.
- A **Graphing Calculator Manual** and **Excel Spreadsheet Manual** are also available within MyMathLab. These manuals provide students with the support they need to make use of the latest versions of graphing calculators and Excel 2013.

Course Flexibility

The content of the text is divided into three parts:

- College Algebra (Chapters 1–4)
- Finite Mathematics (Chapters 5–10)
- Applied Calculus (Chapters 11–14)

This coverage of the material offers flexibility, making the book appropriate for a variety of courses, including:

- Finite Mathematics and Applied Calculus (one year or less). Use the entire book; cover topics from Chapters 1–4 as needed before proceeding to further topics.
- Finite Mathematics (one semester or two quarters). Use as much of Chapters 1–4 as needed, and then go into Chapters 5–10 as time permits and local needs require.
- Applied Calculus (one semester or quarter). Cover the precalculus topics in Chapters 1–4 as necessary, and then use Chapters 11–14.
- College Algebra with Applications (one semester or quarter). Use Chapters 1–8, with Chapters 7 and 8 being optional.

Pearson regularly produces custom versions of this text (and its accompanying MyMath-Lab course) to address the needs of specific course sequences. Custom versions can be produced for even smaller-enrollment courses due to advances in digital printing. Please contact your local Pearson representative for more details.

Chapter interdependence is as follows:

Chapter		Prerequisite
1	Algebra and Equations	None
2	Graphs, Lines, and Inequalities	Chapter 1
3	Functions and Graphs	Chapters 1 and 2
4	Exponential and Logarithmic Functions	Chapter 3
5	Mathematics of Finance	Chapter 4
6	Systems of Linear Equations and Matrices	Chapters 1 and 2
7	Linear Programming	Chapters 3 and 6
8	Sets and Probability	None
9	Counting, Probability Distributions, and Further Topics in Probability	Chapter 8
10	Introduction to Statistics	Chapter 8
11	Differential Calculus	Chapters 1–4
12	Applications of the Derivative	Chapter 11
13	Integral Calculus	Chapters 11 and 12
14	Multivariate Calculus	Chapters 11–13

Student Supplements

Student's Solutions Manual

- By Salvatore Sciandra, Niagara County Community College
- This manual contains detailed carefully worked out solutions to all odd-numbered section exercises and all Chapter Review and Case exercises.

ISBN 13: 978-0-321-92492-6
ISBN 10: 0-321-92492-4

Graphing Calculator Manual (downloadable)

- By Victoria Baker, Nicholls State University
- Contains detailed instruction for using the TI-83/TI-83+/TI-84+ C.
- Instructions are organized by topic.
- Available in MyMathLab.

Excel Spreadsheet Manual (downloadable)

- By Stela Pudar-Hozo, Indiana University—Northwest
- Contains detailed instructions for using Excel 2013.
- Instructions are organized by topic.
- Available in MyMathLab.

Instructor Supplements

Annotated Instructor's Edition

- The AIE contains answers to all exercises in the text on the exercise set page whenever possible.
- In addition, Teaching Tips are provided in the margin to give less-experienced instructors a cue as to where students typically struggle.

ISBN 13: 978-0-321-92961-7
ISBN 10: 0-321-92961-6

Instructor's Solutions Manual (downloadable)

- By Salvatore Sciandra, Niagara County Community College
- This manual contains detailed solutions to all text exercises, suggested course outlines, and a chapter interdependence chart.
- Available through www.pearsonhighered.com/irc or in MyMathLab.

Printable Test Bank (downloadable)

- By David Bridge, University of Central Oklahoma
- This test bank includes four alternate tests per chapter that parallel the text's Chapter Tests.
- Available through www.pearsonhighered.com/irc or in MyMathLab.

Media Supplements

MyMathLab® Online Course (access code required)

MyMathLab delivers **proven results** in helping individual students succeed.

- MyMathLab has a consistently positive impact on the quality of learning in higher education math instruction. MyMathLab can be successfully implemented in any environment—lab-based, hybrid, fully online, traditional—and demonstrates the quantifiable difference that integrated usage has on student retention, subsequent success, and overall achievement.
- MyMathLab's comprehensive online gradebook automatically tracks your students' results on tests, quizzes, homework, and in the study plan. You can use the gradebook to quickly intervene if your students have trouble, or to provide positive feedback on a job well done. The data within MyMathLab is easily exported to a variety of spreadsheet programs, such as Microsoft Excel. You can determine which points of data you want to export, and then analyze the results to determine success.

MyMathLab provides **engaging experiences** that personalize, stimulate, and measure learning for each student.

- **Continuously Adaptive:** Adaptive learning functionality analyzes student work and points them toward resources that will maximize their learning.
- **Exercises:** The homework and practice exercises in MyMathLab are correlated to the exercises in the textbook, and they regenerate algorithmically to give students unlimited opportunity for practice and mastery. The software offers immediate, helpful feedback when students enter incorrect answers.
- **Chapter-Level, Just-in-Time Remediation:** Students receive remediation only for those skills that they have not yet mastered through *Getting Ready* diagnostics and content, and personalized homework.

- **Multimedia Learning Aids:** Exercises include guided solutions, sample problems, animations, videos, and eText clips for extra help at point-of-use.
- **Expert Tutoring:** Although many students describe the whole of MyMathLab as "like having your own personal tutor," students using MyMathLab do have access to live tutoring from Pearson, from qualified math and statistics instructors who provide tutoring sessions for students via MyMathLab.

And, MyMathLab comes from a **trusted partner** with educational expertise and an eye on the future.

- Knowing that you are using a Pearson product means knowing that you are using quality content. That means that our eTexts are accurate and our assessment tools work.
- Whether you are just getting started with MyMathLab, or have a question along the way, we're here to help you learn about our technologies and how to incorporate them into your course.

To learn more about how MyMathLab combines proven learning applications with powerful assessment, visit www.mymathlab.com or contact your Pearson representative.

MyMathLab® Ready to Go Course (access code required)

These new Ready to Go courses provide students with all the same great MyMathLab features, but make it easier for instructors to get started. Each course includes pre-assigned homework and quizzes to make creating a course even simpler. In addition, these Ready to Go courses include a course-level "Getting Ready" diagnostic that helps pinpoint student weaknesses in prerequisite skills. Ask your Pearson representative about the details for this particular course or to see a copy of this course.

MathXL® Online Course (access code required)

MathXL® is the homework and assessment engine that runs MyMathLab. (MyMathLab is MathXL plus a learning management system.)

With MathXL, instructors can:

- Create, edit, and assign online homework and tests using algorithmically generated exercises correlated at the objective level to the textbook.
- Create and assign their own online exercises and import TestGen tests for added flexibility.
- Maintain records of all student work tracked in MathXL's online gradebook.

With MathXL, students can:

- Take chapter tests in MathXL and receive personalized study plans and/or personalized homework assignments based on their test results.
- Use the study plan and/or the homework to link directly to tutorial exercises for the objectives they need to study.
- Access supplemental animations and video clips directly from selected exercises.

MathXL is available to qualified adopters. For more information, visit our website at www.mathxl.com, or contact your Pearson representative.

New! Video Lectures with Optional Subtitles

The video lectures for this text are available in MyMathLab, making it easy and convenient for students to watch the videos from computers at home or on campus, or from their smart phones! The videos feature engaging chapter summaries and worked-out examples. The videos have **optional English subtitles;** they can easily be turned on or off for individual student needs.

PowerPoint® Lecture Slides

These slides present key concepts and definitions from the text. They are available in MyMathLab or at www.pearsonhighered.com/irc.

TestGen®

TestGen® (www.pearsoned.com/testgen) enables instructors to build, edit, print, and administer tests using a computerized bank of questions developed to cover all the objectives of the text. TestGen is algorithmically based, allowing instructors to create multiple but equivalent versions of the same question or test with the click of a button. Instructors can also modify test bank questions or add new questions. The software and testbank are available for download from Pearson Education's online catalog.

Acknowledgments

The authors wish to thank the following reviewers for their thoughtful feedback and helpful suggestions without which we could not continue to improve this text.

Hossein A. Abbasi, Bloomsburg University

Zachary J. Abernathy, Winthrop University

Sasha Anderson, Fresno City College

Sviatoslav Archava, East Carolina University

Peter Barendse, Boston University

Linda Estes Barton, Ball State University

Jaromir J. Becan, University of Texas at San Antonio

Shari Beck, Navarro College

Elizabeth Bowman, The University of Alabama in Huntsville

Dwayne C. Brown, University of South Carolina Lancaster

Priscilla Chaffe-Stengel, California State University, Fresno

Michelle Cook, Stephen F. Austin State University

Michael Dixon, Midland College

Edward D. Esparza, University of Texas at San Antonio

Mark Goldstein, West Virginia Community College

Ronald D. Hagan, The University of Tennessee

Timothy Huber, University of Texas–Pan American

Mary Jackson, Brookhaven College

Patricia Kan, Cleveland State University

Timothy Kohl, Boston University

Ronald E. Kutz, Western Connecticut State University

Gregory L. Macklin, Delaware Technical Community College

Marna Mozeff, Drexel University

Charles Odion, Houston Community College

Lindsay Packer, Metropolitan State University of Denver

David Rangel, Northeast Texas Community College

Aaron Rosenberg, Folsom Lake College

Sharon M. Saxton, Cascadia Community College

Zachary Sharon, The University of Texas at San Antonio

Robin Gayer Sirkis, Delaware Technical Community College

Pam Stogsdill, Bossier Parish Community College

Karel Stroethoff, University of Montana

Frank Viviano, Bossier Parish Community College

Cassandra Wright, Stephen F. Austin State University

Cong-Cong Xing, Nicholls State University

Xinyun Zhu, The University of Texas of the Permian Basin

A special thanks goes to Jason Stone for his help in developing the Prerequisite Skills Test. Additionally, we gratefully acknowledge Birmingham-Southern College and Cleveland State University for their whole-hearted suport of the Eleventh Edition.

We also wish to thank our accuracy checkers, who did an excellent job of checking both text and exercise answers: Paul Lorczak and Douglas Ewert. Thanks also to the supplements authors: Salvatore Sciandra, David Bridge, Victoria Baker, and Stela Pudar-Hozo.

We want to thank the staff of Pearson Education for their assistance with, and contributions to this book, particularly Greg Tobin, Deirdre Lynch, Jennifer Crum, Jeff Weidenaar, Sherry Berg, Sheila Spinney, Chere Bemelmans, Joanne Wendelken, Caitlin Crain, and Jean Choe. Finally, we wish to express our appreciation to Kelly Ricci of Aptara Corporation, who was a pleasure to work with.

Thomas W. Hungerford
John P. Holcomb, Jr.
Bernadette Mullins

To the Student

The key to succeeding in this course is to remember that **mathematics is not a spectator sport.** You can't expect to learn mathematics without *doing* mathematics any more than you could learn to swim without getting wet. You must take an active role, making use of all the resources at your disposal: your instructor, your fellow students, this book, and the supplements that accompany it. Following are some general tips on how to be successful in the course, and some specific tips on how to get the most out of this text and supplementary resources.

Ask Questions! Remember the words of the great Hillel: "The bashful do not learn." There is no such thing as a "dumb question" (assuming, of course, that you have read the book and your class notes and attempted the homework). Your instructor will welcome questions that arise from a serious effort on your part. So get your money's worth: Ask questions!

Read the Book Interactively! There is more to a math textbook than just the exercise sets. Each section introduces topics carefully with many examples—both mathematical and contextual. Take note of the "Caution" and "Note" comments, and bookmark pages with key definitions or formulas. After reading the example, try the ***Checkpoint Exercise*** that follows it in the margin to check your understanding of the concept. This will help you solidify your understanding or diagnose if you do not fully understand the concept. The answers to the Checkpoint exercises are right after the homework exercises in each section. Resist the temptation to flip to the answer until you've worked the problem completely!

Take Advantage of the Supplementary Material! Both within and outside the text, there are many resources at your disposal. Take the time to interact with them and determine which resources suit your learning style the best.

- If your instructor allows the use of graphing calculators and/or spreadsheets, work through the examples and exercises marked with the ⬈. Some instructors may make this material part of the course, whereas others will not require you to use technology. For those who use technology, there is a *Graphing Calculator Appendix* that covers the basics of calculator use and provides a number of helpful programs for working with some of the topics in the text. An outline of the appendix is on page 859, and the full appendix is available in MyMathLab. In addition, there are ***Technology Tips*** throughout the text that describe the proper menu or keys to use for various procedures on a graphing calculator. Note that Technology Tips for the TI-84+ C also apply to TI-83+, TI-Nspire, and usually TI-83.
- MyMathLab has a variety of types of resources at your disposal including videos and PowerPoints for every section of the text, example-level videos, animations to help visualize difficult concepts, unlimited practice and assessment on newly learned or prerequisite skills, and access to the *Student Solutions Manual, Graphing Calculator Manual* and *Excel Spreadsheet Manual,* a variety of helpful reference cards, and links to useful websites like Texas Instruments.

Do Your Homework! Whether it is paper/pencil homework or assigned online, you must practice what you have learned. Remember, math is not a spectator sport! This is your opportunity to practice those essential skills needed for passing this course, and for applying in future courses or your career.

We wish you the best in your efforts with this course, in future courses, and beyond school.

Prerequisite Skills Test*

The following test is unlike your typical math test. Rather than testing your skills after you have worked on them, this test assesses skills that you should know from previous course-work and will use in this class. It is intended to diagnose any areas that you may need to remediate. Take advantage of the results of this test by checking your answers in Appendix D. The full solutions are included to remind you of the steps to answer the problem.

Find the most simplified answer for the given problems involving fractions:

1. $\dfrac{5}{2} - 6 =$

2. $\dfrac{1}{2} \div \dfrac{2}{5} =$

3. $\dfrac{1}{3} \div 3 =$

Simplify the given expression, keeping in mind the appropriate order of operations:

4. $7 + 2 - 3(2 \div 6) =$

5. $\dfrac{2 \times 3 + 12}{1 + 5} - 1 =$

Indicate whether each of the statements is true or false:

6. $\dfrac{4 + 3}{3} = 5$

7. $\dfrac{5}{7} + \dfrac{7}{5} = 1$

8. $\dfrac{3}{5} + 1 = \dfrac{6}{5}$

Translate each of the following written expressions into a corresponding mathematical statement. If possible, solve for the unknown value or values.

9. Alicia has n pairs of shoes. Manuel has two more pairs of shoes than Alicia. How many pairs of shoes does Manuel have?

10. David's age and Selina's age, when added together, equals 42. Selena is 6 years older than David. What are David's and Selina's ages?

Solve the following problem.

11. The price of a sweater, originally sold for $72, is reduced by 20%. What is the new sale price of the sweater?

---

*Full Solutions to this test are provided in the back of the text.

Given the following rectangular coordinate system, graph and label the following points:

12. A: $(3, -2)$ B: $(4, 0)$ C: $(-2, -3)$

13. D: $(3, 5)$ E: $(-1, 4)$ F: $(-4, -5)$

Round the following values as indicated:

14. **(a)** 4.27659 to the nearest tenth

  (b) 245.984 to the nearest unit (whole number)

15. **(a)** 16.38572 to the nearest hundredth

  (b) 1,763,304.42 to the nearest thousand

Write the number that corresponds with the given numerical statement:

16. **(a)** The Company's liabilities totaled 34 million dollars.

  (b) The total of investments was 2.2 thousand dollars.

17. **(a)** The population of a country is 17 hundred thousand.

  (b) The cost of the new airport could run as high as three and a quarter billion dollars.

Answer the following. If there is no solution, indicate that there is no solution and provide a reason.

18. $\dfrac{5}{0} =$

19. A car is traveling 60 miles per hour. Is the car traveling at 1 mile per minute?

20. Which number is greater, -9 or -900?

Calculus Readiness Test*

1. Subtract the polynomials: $(7x^4 - 8x^3 + 2x^2 - 3) - (9x^4 - 2x^2 + 5x + 6)$.

2. Add the rational functions: $\dfrac{-6}{3x + 4} + \dfrac{2}{x}$.

3. Find the product: $(3x + 7)(5x - 8)$.

4. Find the product: $(7x + 3)(6x^2 + x - 8)$.

5. Simplify: $\dfrac{(x^5y^{-5})^3}{(x^2\sqrt{y})^6}$.

6. Multiply out and simplify: $(8x - 9)^2$.

7. Factor: $9x^2 - 49$.

8. Solve for x: $9x - 4 = 8 + 7(x - 5)$.

9. Solve for x: $3x^2 + 2x + 8 = 20x - 7$.

10. Solve the inequality for x: $x^2 - x - 6 < 0$.

11. Solve for x: $5e^{x-3} - 1 = 9$.

12. Solve for x: $\ln(5x + 1) = 2$.

13. Given that $f(x) = 5x^3 - 3x^2 + 9x + 60$, find $f(-2)$.

14. Given that $f(x) = 6x^2 - 7x - 20$, solve $f(x) = 0$.

15. Find an equation of a line through the point $(8, -3)$ with slope -5.

---

*Full Solutions to this test are provided in the back of the text.

Algebra and Equations

1

CHAPTER

CHAPTER OUTLINE

Mathematics is widely used in business, finance, and the biological, social, and physical sciences, from developing efficient production schedules for a factory to mapping the human genome. Mathematics also plays a role in determining interest on a loan from a bank, the growth of traffic on websites, and the study of falling objects. See Exercises 61 and 67 on page 51 and Exercise 63 on page 59.

Algebra and equations are the basic mathematical tools for handling many applications. Your success in this course will depend on your having the algebraic skills presented in this chapter.

1.1 The Real Numbers

Only real numbers will be used in this book.[*] The names of the most common types of real numbers are as follows.

The Real Numbers

Natural (counting) numbers	$1, 2, 3, 4, \ldots$
Whole numbers	$0, 1, 2, 3, 4, \ldots$

---

[*]Not all numbers are real numbers. For example, $\sqrt{-1}$ is a number that is *not* a real number.

Integers	$\ldots, -3, -2, -1, 0, 1, 2, 3, \ldots$
Rational numbers	All numbers that can be written in the form p/q, where p and q are integers and $q \neq 0$
Irrational numbers	Real numbers that are not rational

As you can see, every natural number is a whole number, and every whole number is an integer. Furthermore, every integer is a rational number. For instance, the integer 7 can be written as the fraction $\frac{7}{1}$ and is therefore a rational number.

One example of an irrational number is π, the ratio of the circumference of a circle to its diameter. The number π can be approximated as $\pi \approx 3.14159$ ($\approx$ means "is approximately equal to"), but there is no rational number that is exactly equal to π.

Example 1   What kind of number is each of the following?

(a) 6

Solution   The number 6 is a natural number, a whole number, an integer, a rational number, and a real number.

(b) $\dfrac{3}{4}$

Solution   This number is rational and real.

(c) 3π

Solution   Because π is not a rational number, 3π is irrational and real.

All real numbers can be written in decimal form. A rational number, when written in decimal form, is either a terminating decimal, such as .5 or .128, or a repeating decimal, in which some block of digits eventually repeats forever, such as 1.3333 . . . or 4.7234234234 . . . .[†] Irrational numbers are decimals that neither terminate nor repeat.

When a calculator is used for computations, the answers it produces are often decimal *approximations* of the actual answers; they are accurate enough for most applications. To ensure that your final answer is as accurate as possible,

> *you should not round off any numbers during long calculator computations.*

It is usually OK to round off the final answer to a reasonable number of decimal places once the computation is finished.

The important basic properties of the real numbers are as follows.

Properties of the Real Numbers

For all real numbers, a, b, and c, the following properties hold true:

Commutative properties	$a + b = b + a$ and $ab = ba$.
Associative properties	$(a + b) + c = a + (b + c)$ and $(ab)c = a(bc)$.

✓ **Checkpoint 1**

Name all the types of numbers that apply to the following.

(a) -2

(b) $-5/8$

(c) $\pi/5$

Answers to Checkpoint exercises are found at the end of the section.

---

[*]The use of Checkpoint exercises is explained in the "To the Student" section preceding this chapter.
[†]Some graphing calculators have a FRAC key that automatically converts some repeating decimals to fraction form.

Identity properties	There exists a unique real number 0, called the **additive identity,** such that

$$a + 0 = a \quad \text{and} \quad 0 + a = a.$$

There exists a unique real number 1, called the **multiplicative identity,** such that

$$a \cdot 1 = a \quad \text{and} \quad 1 \cdot a = a.$$

Inverse properties	For each real number a, there exists a unique real number $-a$, called the **additive inverse** of a, such that

$$a + (-a) = 0 \quad \text{and} \quad (-a) + a = 0.$$

If $a \neq 0$, there exists a unique real number $1/a$, called the **multiplicative inverse** of a, such that

$$a \cdot \frac{1}{a} = 1 \quad \text{and} \quad \frac{1}{a} \cdot a = 1.$$

Distributive property	$a(b + c) = ab + ac \quad \text{and} \quad (b + c)a = ba + ca.$

The next five examples illustrate the properties listed in the preceding box.

Example 2   The commutative property says that the order in which you add or multiply two quantities doesn't matter.

(a) $(6 + x) + 9 = 9 + (6 + x) = 9 + (x + 6)$ **(b)** $5 \cdot (9 \cdot 8) = (9 \cdot 8) \cdot 5$

Example 3   When the associative property is used, the order of the numbers does not change, but the placement of parentheses does.

(a) $4 + (9 + 8) = (4 + 9) + 8$ **(b)** $3(9x) = (3 \cdot 9)x$ ✓2

✓ Checkpoint 2

Name the property illustrated in each of the following examples.

(a) $(2 + 3) + 9 = (3 + 2) + 9$

(b) $(2 + 3) + 9 = 2 + (3 + 9)$

(c) $(2 + 3) + 9 = 9 + (2 + 3)$

(d) $(4 \cdot 6)p = (6 \cdot 4)p$

(e) $4(6p) = (4 \cdot 6)p$

Example 4   By the identity properties,

(a) $-8 + 0 = -8$ **(b)** $(-9) \cdot 1 = -9.$

TECHNOLOGY TIP To enter -8 on a calculator, use the negation key (labeled (−) or +/−), *not* the subtraction key. On most one-line scientific calculators, key in 8 +/−. On graphing calculators or two-line scientific calculators, key in either (−) 8 or +/− 8.

✓ Checkpoint 3

Name the property illustrated in each of the following examples.

(a) $2 + 0 = 2$

(b) $-\frac{1}{4} \cdot (-4) = 1$

(c) $-\frac{1}{4} + \frac{1}{4} = 0$

(d) $1 \cdot \frac{2}{3} = \frac{2}{3}$

Example 5   By the inverse properties, the statements in parts (a) through (d) are true.

(a) $9 + (-9) = 0$ **(b)** $-15 + 15 = 0$

(c) $-8 \cdot \left(\frac{1}{-8}\right) = 1$ **(d)** $\frac{1}{\sqrt{5}} \cdot \sqrt{5} = 1$

NOTE There is no real number x such that $0 \cdot x = 1$, so 0 has no multiplicative inverse. ✓3

Example 6   By the distributive property,

(a) $9(6 + 4) = 9 \cdot 6 + 9 \cdot 4$

(b) $3(x + y) = 3x + 3y$

(c) $-8(m + 2) = (-8)(m) + (-8)(2) = -8m - 16$

(d) $(5 + x)y = 5y + xy.$ ✓4

Order of Operations

Some complicated expressions may contain many sets of parentheses. To avoid ambiguity, the following procedure should be used.

✓ **Checkpoint 4**

Use the distributive property to complete each of the following.

(a) $4(-2 + 5)$

(b) $2(a + b)$

(c) $-3(p + 1)$

(d) $(8 - k)m$

(e) $5x + 3x$

> ### Parentheses
>
> Work separately above and below any fraction bar. Within each set of parentheses or square brackets, start with the innermost set and work outward.

Example 7   Simplify: $[(3 + 2) - 7]5 + 2([6 \cdot 3] - 13).$

Solution   On each segment, work from the inside out:

$$[(3 + 2) - 7]5 - 2([6 \cdot 3] - 13)$$
$$= [5 - 7]5 + 2(18 - 13)$$
$$= [-2]5 + 2(5)$$
$$= -10 + 10 = 0.$$

Does the expression $2 + 4 \times 3$ mean

$$(2 + 4) \times 3 = 6 \times 3 = 18?$$

Or does it mean

$$2 + (4 \times 3) = 2 + 12 = 14?$$

To avoid this ambiguity, mathematicians have adopted the following rules (which are also followed by almost all scientific and graphing calculators).

> ### Order of Operations
>
> **1.** Find all powers and roots, working from left to right.
>
> **2.** Do any multiplications or divisions in the order in which they occur, working from left to right.
>
> **3.** Finally, do any additions or subtractions in the order in which they occur, working from left to right.
>
> If sets of parentheses or square brackets are present, use the rules in the preceding box within each set, working from the innermost set outward.

According to these rules, multiplication is done *before* addition, so $2 + 4 \times 3 = 2 + 12 = 14$. Here are some additional examples.

Example 8   Use the order of operations to evaluate each expression if $x = -2$, $y = 5$, and $z = -3$.

(a) $-4x^2 - 7y + 4z$

Solution   Use parentheses when replacing letters with numbers:

$$-4x^2 - 7y + 4z = -4(-2)^2 - 7(5) + 4(-3)$$
$$= -4(4) - 7(5) + 4(-3) = -16 - 35 - 12 = -63.$$

(b) $\dfrac{2(x - 5)^2 + 4y}{z + 4} = \dfrac{2(-2 - 5)^2 + 4(5)}{-3 + 4}$

$$= \frac{2(-7)^2 + 20}{1}$$

$$= 2(49) + 20 = 118.$$ ✓₅

✓ Checkpoint 5

Evaluate the following if $m = -5$ and $n = 8$.

(a) $-2mn - 2m^2$

(b) $\dfrac{4(n - 5)^2 - m}{m + n}$

Example 9   Use a calculator to evaluate

$$\frac{-9(-3) + (-5)}{3(-4) - 5(2)}.$$

Solution   Use extra parentheses (shown here in blue) around the numerator and denominator when you enter the number in your calculator, and be careful to distinguish the negation key from the subtraction key.

numerator   denominator

$(-9\,(-3) + (-5))/(3\,(-4) - 5(2))$

Negation key   Subtraction key

If you don't get -1 as the answer, then you are entering something incorrectly. ✓₆

✓ Checkpoint 6

Use a calculator to evaluate the following.

(a) $4^2 \div 8 + 3^2 \div 3$

(b) $[-7 + (-9)] \cdot (-4) - 8(3)$

(c) $\dfrac{-11 - (-12) - 4 \cdot 5}{4(-2) - (-6)(-5)}$

(d) $\dfrac{36 \div 4 \cdot 3 \div 9 + 1}{9 \div (-6) \cdot 8 - 4}$

Square Roots

There are two numbers whose square is 16, namely, 4 and -4. The positive one, 4, is called the **square root** of 16. Similarly, the square root of a nonnegative number d is defined to be the *nonnegative* number whose square is d; this number is denoted $\sqrt{d}$. For instance,

$$\sqrt{36} = 6 \text{ because } 6^2 = 36, \quad \sqrt{0} = 0 \text{ because } 0^2 = 0, \text{ and}$$
$$\sqrt{1.44} = 1.2 \text{ because } (1.2)^2 = 1.44.$$

No negative number has a square root that is a real number. For instance, there is no real number whose square is -4, so -4 has no square root.

     Every nonnegative real number has a square root. Unless an integer is a perfect square (such as $64 = 8^2$), its square root is an irrational number. A calculator can be used to obtain a rational approximation of these square roots.

⬈ TECHNOLOGY TIP

On one-line scientific calculators, $\sqrt{40}$ is entered as 40 $\sqrt{\ }$. On graphing calculators and two-line scientific calculators, key in $\sqrt{\ }$40 ENTER (or EXE).

Example 10   Estimate each of the given quantities. Verify your estimates with a calculator.

(a) $\sqrt{40}$

Solution   Since $6^2 = 36$ and $7^2 = 49$, $\sqrt{40}$ must be a number between 6 and 7. A typical calculator shows that $\sqrt{40} \approx 6.32455532$.

Checkpoint 7

Estimate each of the following.
(a) $\sqrt{73}$
(b) $\sqrt{22} + 3$
(c) Confirm your estimates in parts (a) and (b) with a calculator.

Checkpoint 8

Draw a number line, and graph the numbers $-4, -1, 0, 1, 2.5,$ and $13/4$ on it.

(b) $5\sqrt{7}$

Solution $\sqrt{7}$ is between 2 and 3 because $2^2 = 4$ and $3^2 = 9$, so $5\sqrt{7}$ must be a number between $5 \cdot 2 = 10$ and $5 \cdot 3 = 15$. A calculator shows that $5\sqrt{7} \approx 13.22875656.$

CAUTION If c and d are positive real numbers, then $\sqrt{c + d}$ is *not* equal to $\sqrt{c} + \sqrt{d}$. For example, $\sqrt{9 + 16} = \sqrt{25} = 5$, but $\sqrt{9} + \sqrt{16} = 3 + 4 = 7.$

The Number Line

The real numbers can be illustrated geometrically with a diagram called a **number line.** Each real number corresponds to exactly one point on the line and vice versa. A number line with several sample numbers located (or **graphed**) on it is shown in Figure 1.1. ☑8

$$-\frac{2}{3} \quad \frac{1}{2} \quad \sqrt{2} \qquad \pi$$

Number line from -4 to 4

Figure 1.1

When comparing the sizes of two real numbers, the following symbols are used.

Symbol	Read	Meaning
$a < b$	a is less than b.	a lies to the *left* of b on the number line.
$b > a$	b is greater than a.	b lies to the *right* of a on the number line.

Note that $a < b$ means the same thing as $b > a$. The inequality symbols are sometimes joined with the equals sign, as follows.

Symbol	Read	Meaning
$a \leq b$	a is less than or equal to b.	either $a < b$ or $a = b$
$b \geq a$	b is greater than or equal to a.	either $b > a$ or $b = a$

TECHNOLOGY TIP

If your graphing calculator has inequality symbols (usually located on the TEST menu), you can key in statements such as "5 < 12" or "−2 ≥ 3." When you press ENTER, the calculator will display 1 if the statement is true and 0 if it is false.

Only one part of an "either . . . or" statement needs to be true for the entire statement to be considered true. So the statement $3 \leq 7$ is true because $3 < 7$, and the statement $3 \leq 3$ is true because $3 = 3$.

Example 11   Write *true* or *false* for each of the following.

(a) $8 < 12$

Solution   This statement says that 8 is less than 12, which is true.

(b) $-6 > -3$

Solution   The graph in Figure 1.2 shows that -6 is to the *left* of -3. Thus, $-6 < -3$, and the given statement is false.

Number line from -6 to 0

Figure 1.2

(c) $-2 \leq -2$

Solution   Because $-2 = -2$, this statement is true.

Checkpoint 9

Write *true* or *false* for the following.
(a) $-9 \leq -2$
(b) $8 > -3$
(c) $-14 \leq -20$

A number line can be used to draw the graph of a set of numbers, as shown in the next few examples.

> **Example 12**   Graph all real numbers x such that $1 < x < 5$.
>
> **Solution**   This graph includes all the real numbers between 1 and 5, not just the integers. Graph these numbers by drawing a heavy line from 1 to 5 on the number line, as in Figure 1.3. Parentheses at 1 and 5 show that neither of these points belongs to the graph.

✓ **Checkpoint 10**

Graph all real numbers x such that

(a) $-5 < x < 1$

(b) $4 < x < 7$.

Figure 1.3

A set that consists of all the real numbers between two points, such as $1 < x < 5$ in Example 12, is called an **interval.** A special notation called **interval notation** is used to indicate an interval on the number line. For example, the interval including all numbers x such that $-2 < x < 3$ is written as $(-2, 3)$. The parentheses indicate that the numbers -2 and 3 are *not* included. If -2 and 3 are to be included in the interval, square brackets are used, as in $[-2, 3]$. The following chart shows several typical intervals, where $a < b$.

Intervals

Inequality	Interval Notation	Explanation
$a \le x \le b$	$[a, b]$	Both a and b are included.
$a \le x < b$	$[a, b)$	a is included; b is not.
$a < x \le b$	$(a, b]$	b is included; a is not.
$a < x < b$	(a, b)	Neither a nor b is included.

Interval notation is also used to describe sets such as the set of all numbers x such that $x \ge -2$. This interval is written $[-2, \infty)$. The set of all real numbers is written $(-\infty, \infty)$ in interval notation.

> **Example 13**   Graph the interval $[-2, \infty)$.
>
> **Solution**   Start at -2 and draw a heavy line to the right, as in Figure 1.4. Use a square bracket at -2 to show that -2 itself is part of the graph. The symbol ∞, read "infinity," *does not* represent a number. This notation simply indicates that *all* numbers greater than -2 are in the interval. Similarly, the notation $(-\infty, 2)$ indicates the set of all numbers x such that $x < 2$.

✓ **Checkpoint 11**

Graph all real numbers x in the given interval.

(a) $(-\infty, 4]$

(b) $[-2, 1]$

Figure 1.4

Absolute Value

The **absolute value** of a real number a is the distance from a to 0 on the number line and is written $|a|$. For example, Figure 1.5 shows that the distance from 9 to 0 on the number line is 9, so we have $|9| = 9$. The figure also shows that $|-9| = 9$, because the distance from -9 to 0 is also 9.

Figure 1.5

The facts that $|9| = 9$ and $|-9| = 9 = -(-9)$ suggest the following algebraic definition of absolute value.

> ### Absolute Value
>
> For any real number a,
>
> $$|a| = a \qquad \text{if } a \geq 0$$
> $$|a| = -a \qquad \text{if } a < 0.$$

The first part of the definition shows that $|0| = 0$ (because $0 \geq 0$). It also shows that the absolute value of any positive number a is the number itself, so $|a|$ is positive in such cases. The second part of the definition says that the absolute value of a negative number a is the *negative* of a. For instance, if $a = -5$, then $|-5| = -(-5) = 5$. So $|-5|$ is positive. The same thing works for any negative number—that is, its absolute value (the negative of a negative number) is positive. Thus, we can state the following:

For every nonzero real number a, the number $|a|$ is positive.

✓**Checkpoint 12**

Find the following.

(a) $|-6|$

(b) $-|7|$

(c) $-|-2|$

(d) $|-3-4|$

(e) $|2-7|$

Example 14   Evaluate $|8 - 9|$.

Solution   First, simplify the expression within the absolute-value bars:

$$|8 - 9| = |-1| = 1. \ ✓_{12}$$

1.1 Exercises

In Exercises 1 and 2, label the statement true or false. (See Example 1.)

1. Every integer is a rational number.

2. Every real number is an irrational number.

3. The decimal expansion of the irrational number π begins 3.141592653589793 . . . . Use your calculator to determine which of the following rational numbers is the best approximation for the irrational number π:
$$\frac{22}{7}, \quad \frac{355}{113}, \quad \frac{103,993}{33,102}, \quad \frac{2,508,429,787}{798,458,000}.$$
Your calculator may tell you that some of these numbers are equal to π, but that just indicates that the number agrees with π for as many decimal places as your calculator can handle (usually 10–14). No rational number is exactly equal to π.

Identify the properties that are illustrated in each of the following. (See Examples 2–6.)

4. $0 + (-7) = -7 + 0$

5. $6(t + 4) = 6t + 6 \cdot 4$

6. $3 + (-3) = (-3) + 3$

7. $-5 + 0 = -5$

8. $(-4) \cdot \left(\dfrac{-1}{4} \right) = 1$

9. $8 + (12 + 6) = (8 + 12) + 6$

10. $1 \cdot (-20) = -20$

11. How is the additive inverse property related to the additive identity property? the multiplicative inverse property to the multiplicative identity property?

12. Explain the distinction between the commutative and associative properties.

Evaluate each of the following if $p = -2, q = 3,$ and $r = -5$. (See Examples 7–9.)

13. $-3(p + 5q)$

14. $2(q - r)$

15. $\dfrac{q + r}{q + p}$

16. $\dfrac{3q}{3p - 2r}$

Business *The nominal annual percentage rate (APR) reported by lenders has the formula APR = 12r, where r is the monthly interest rate. Find the APR when*

17. $r = 3.8$ **18.** $r = 0.8$

Find the monthly interest rate r when

19. $APR = 11$ **20.** $APR = 13.2$

Evaluate each expression, using the order of operations given in the text. (See Examples 7–9.)

21. $3 - 4 \cdot 5 + 5$

22. $8 - (-4)^2 - (-12)$

23. $(4 - 5) \cdot 6 + 6$

24. $\dfrac{2(3 - 7) + 4(8)}{4(-3) + (-3)(-2)}$

25. $8 - 4^2 - (-12)$

26. $-(3 - 5) - [2 - (3^2 - 13)]$

27. $\dfrac{2(-3) + 3/(-2) - 2/(-\sqrt{16})}{\sqrt{64} - 1}$

28. $\dfrac{6^2 - 3\sqrt{25}}{\sqrt{6^2 + 13}}$

Use a calculator to help you list the given numbers in order from smallest to largest. (See Example 10.)

29. $\dfrac{189}{37}, \ \dfrac{4587}{691}, \ \sqrt{47}, \ 6.735, \ \sqrt{27}, \ \dfrac{2040}{523}$

30. $\dfrac{385}{117}, \ \sqrt{10}, \ \dfrac{187}{63}, \ \pi, \ \sqrt{\sqrt{85}}, \ 2.9884$

Express each of the following statements in symbols, using $<, >, \le,$ *or* $\ge$.

31. 12 is less than 18.5.

32. -2 is greater than -20.

33. x is greater than or equal to 5.7.

34. y is less than or equal to -5.

35. z is at most 7.5.

36. w is negative.

Fill in the blank with $<, =,$ *or* $>$ *so that the resulting statement is true.*

37. -6 _____ -2 **38.** $3/4$ _____ .75

39. 3.14 _____ π **40.** $1/3$ _____ .33

Fill in the blank so as to produce two equivalent statements. For example, the arithmetic statement "a is negative" is equivalent to the geometric statement "the point a lies to the left of the point 0."

Arithmetic Statement	Geometric Statement
41. $a \ge b$	_____
42. _____	a lies c units to the right of b
43. _____	a lies between b and c, and to the right of c
44. a is positive	

Graph the given intervals on a number line. (See Examples 12 and 13.)

45. $(-8, -1)$ **46.** $[-1, 10]$

47. $(-2, 3]$ **48.** $[-2, 2)$

49. $(-2, \infty)$ **50.** $(-\infty, -2]$

Evaluate each of the following expressions (see Example 14).

51. $|-9| - |-12|$

52. $|8| - |-4|$

53. $-|-4| - |-1 - 14|$

54. $-|6| - |-12 - 4|$

In each of the following problems, fill in the blank with either $=, <,$ *or* $>$, *so that the resulting statement is true.*

55. $|5|$ _____ $|-5|$

56. $-|-4|$ _____ $|4|$

57. $|10 - 3|$ _____ $|3 - 10|$

58. $|6 - (-4)|$ _____ $|-4 - 6|$

59. $|-2 + 8|$ _____ $|2 - 8|$

60. $|3| \cdot |-5|$ _____ $|3(-5)|$

61. $|3 - 5|$ _____ $|3| - |5|$

62. $|-5 + 1|$ _____ $|-5| + |1|$

Write the expression without using absolute-value notation.

63. $|a - 7|$ if $a < 7$ **64.** $|b - c|$ if $b \ge c$

65. If a and b are any real numbers, is it always true that $|a + b| = |a| + |b|$? Explain your answer.

66. If a and b are any two real numbers, is it always true that $|a - b| = |b - a|$? Explain your answer.

67. For which real numbers b does $|2 - b| = |2 + b|$? Explain your answer.

68. Health Data from the National Health and Nutrition Examination Study estimates that 95% of adult heights (inches) are in the following ranges for females and males. (Data from: www.cdc.gov/nchs/nhanes.htm.)

Females	63.5 ± 8.4
Males	68.9 ± 9.3

Express the ranges as an absolute-value inequality in which x is the height of the person.

Business *The Consumer Price Index (CPI) tracks the cost of a typical sample of a consumer goods. The following table shows the percentage increase in the CPI for each year in a 10-year period.*

Year	2003	2004	2005	2006	2007
% Increase in CPI	2.3	2.7	2.5	3.2	4.1

Year	2008	2009	2010	2011	2012
% Increase in CPI	0.1	2.7	1.5	3.0	1.7

Let r denote the yearly percentage increase in the CPI. For each of the following inequalities, find the number of years during the given period that r satisfied the inequality. (Data from: U.S. Bureau of Labor Statistics.)

69. $r > 3.2$

70. $r < 3.2$

71. $r \leq 3.2$

72. $r \leq 1.5$

73. $r \geq 2.1$

74. $r \geq 1.3$

Finance   *The table presents the 2012 percent change in the stock price for six well-known companies. (Data from: finance.yahoo.com.)*

Company	Percent Change
American Express	+36.5
Coca-Cola	+3.4
ExxonMobil	+0.6
Hewlett-Packard	−46.5
IBM	+4.4
McDonald's	−10.8

Suppose that we wish to determine the difference in percent change between two of the companies in the table and we are interested only in the magnitude, or absolute value, of this difference. Then we subtract the two entries and find the absolute value. For example, the difference in percent change of stock price for American Express and McDonald's is $|36.5\% - (-10.8\%)| = 47.3\%$.

Find the absolute value of the difference between the two indicated changes in stock price.

75. Coca-Cola and Hewlett-Packard

76. IBM and McDonald's

77. ExxonMobil and IBM

78. American Express and ExxonMobil

79. McDonald's and Hewlett-Packard

80. IBM and Coca-Cola

Finance   *The following graph shows the per capita amount of disposable income (in thousands of dollars) in the United States. (Data from: U.S. Bureau of Economic Analysis.)*

For each of the following, determine the years for which the expression is true where x is the per capita disposable income.

81. $|x - 35{,}000| > 1000$

82. $|x - 32{,}000| > 3500$

83. $|x - 36{,}500| \leq 2200$

84. $|x - 31{,}500| \leq 4400$

✓ Checkpoint Answers

1. (a) Integer, rational, real

(b) Rational, real

(c) Irrational, real

2. (a) Commutative property

(b) Associative property

(c) Commutative property

(d) Commutative property

(e) Associative property

3. (a) Additive identity property

(b) Multiplicative inverse property

(c) Additive inverse property

(d) Multiplicative identity property

4. (a) $4(-2) + 4(5) = 12$ (b) $2a + 2b$

(c) $-3p - 3$ (d) $8m - km$

(e) $(5 + 3)x = 8x$

5. (a) 30   (b) $\dfrac{41}{3}$

6. (a) 5   (b) 40

(c) $\dfrac{19}{38} = \dfrac{1}{2} = .5$ (d) $-\dfrac{1}{4} = -.25$

7. (a) Between 8 and 9

(b) Between 7 and 8

(c) 8.5440; 7.6904

8.

9. (a) True   (b) True   (c) False

10. (a)   (b)

11. (a)   (b)

12. (a) 6   (b) −7

(c) −2   (d) 7

(e) 5

1.2 Polynomials

Polynomials are the fundamental tools of algebra and will play a central role in this course. In order to do polynomial arithmetic, you must first understand exponents. So we begin with them. You are familiar with the usual notation for squares and cubes, such as:

$$5^2 = 5 \cdot 5 \quad \text{and} \quad 6^3 = 6 \cdot 6 \cdot 6.$$

We now extend this convenient notation to other cases.

If n is a natural number and a is any real number, then

a^n denotes the product $a \cdot a \cdot a \cdots a$ (n factors).

The number a is the **base,** and the number n is the **exponent.**

Example 1 4^6, which is read "four to the sixth," or "four to the sixth power," is the number

$$4 \cdot 4 \cdot 4 \cdot 4 \cdot 4 \cdot 4 = 4096.$$

Similarly, $(-5)^3 = (-5)(-5)(-5) = -125$, and

$$\left(\frac{3}{2}\right)^4 = \frac{3}{2} \cdot \frac{3}{2} \cdot \frac{3}{2} \cdot \frac{3}{2} = \frac{81}{16}.$$

Example 2 Use a calculator to approximate the given expressions.

(a) $(1.2)^8$

Solution Key in 1.2 and then use the x^y key (labeled $\wedge$ on some calculators); finally, key in the exponent 8. The calculator displays the (exact) answer 4.29981696.

(b) $\left(\frac{12}{7}\right)^{23}$

Solution Don't compute 12/7 separately. Use parentheses and key in (12/7), followed by the x^y key and the exponent 23 to obtain the approximate answer 242,054.822. ✓₁

⊘ CAUTION A common error in using exponents occurs with expressions such as $4 \cdot 3^2$. The exponent of 2 applies only to the base 3, so that

$$4 \cdot 3^2 = 4 \cdot 3 \cdot 3 = 36.$$

On the other hand,

$$(4 \cdot 3)^2 = (4 \cdot 3)(4 \cdot 3) = 12 \cdot 12 = 144,$$

so

$$4 \cdot 3^2 \neq (4 \cdot 3)^2.$$

Be careful to distinguish between expressions like -2^4 and $(-2)^4$:

$$-2^4 = -(2^4) = -(2 \cdot 2 \cdot 2 \cdot 2) = -16$$
$$(-2)^4 = (-2)(-2)(-2)(-2) = 16,$$

so

$$-2^4 \neq (-2)^4. ✓₂$$

✓ **Checkpoint 1**

Evaluate the following.

(a) 6^3

(b) 5^{12}

(c) 1^9

(d) $\left(\frac{7}{5}\right)^8$

✓ **Checkpoint 2**

Evaluate the following.

(a) $3 \cdot 6^2$

(b) $5 \cdot 4^3$

(c) -3^6

(d) $(-3)^6$

(e) $-2 \cdot (-3)^5$

By the definition of an exponent,

$$3^4 \cdot 3^2 = (3 \cdot 3 \cdot 3 \cdot 3)(3 \cdot 3) = 3^6.$$

Since $6 = 4 + 2$, we can write the preceding equation as $3^4 \cdot 3^2 = 3^{4+2}$. This result suggests the following fact, which applies to any real number a and natural numbers m and n.

Multiplication with Exponents

To multiply a^m by a^n, *add* the exponents:

$$a^m \cdot a^n = a^{m+n}.$$

Example 3   Verify each of the following simplifications.

(a) $7^4 \cdot 7^6 = 7^{4+6} = 7^{10}$

(b) $(-2)^3 \cdot (-2)^5 = (-2)^{3+5} = (-2)^8$

(c) $(3k)^2 \cdot (3k)^3 = (3k)^5$

(d) $(m + n)^2 \cdot (m + n)^5 = (m + n)^7$ ☑3

The multiplication property of exponents has a convenient consequence. By definition,

$$(5^2)^3 = 5^2 \cdot 5^2 \cdot 5^2 = 5^{2+2+2} = 5^6.$$

Note that $2 + 2 + 2$ is $3 \cdot 2 = 6$. This is an example of a more general fact about any real number a and natural numbers m and n.

Power of a Power

To find a power of a power, $(a^m)^n$, *multiply* the exponents:

$$(a^m)^n = a^{mn}.$$

Example 4   Verify the following computations.

(a) $(x^3)^4 = x^{3 \cdot 4} = x^{12}$.

(b) $[(-3)^5]^3 = (-3)^{5 \cdot 3} = (-3)^{15}$.

(c) $[(6z)^4]^4 = (6z)^{4 \cdot 4} = (6z)^{16}$. ☑4

It will be convenient to give a zero exponent a meaning. If the multiplication property of exponents is to remain valid, we should have, for example, $3^5 \cdot 3^0 = 3^{5+0} = 3^5$. But this will be true only when $3^0 = 1$. So we make the following definition.

Zero Exponent

If a is any nonzero real number, then

$$a^0 = 1.$$

For example, $6^0 = 1$ and $(-9)^0 = 1$. Note that 0^0 is *not* defined.

Polynomials

A **polynomial** is an algebraic expression such as

$$5x^4 + 2x^3 + 6x, \qquad 8m^3 + 9m^2 + \frac{3}{2}m + 3, \qquad -10p, \qquad \text{or} \qquad 8.$$

The letter used is called a **variable,** and a polynomial is a sum of **terms** of the form

$$(\text{constant}) \times (\text{nonnegative integer power of the variable}).$$

We assume that $x^0 = 1$, $m^0 = 1$, etc., so terms such as 3 or 8 may be thought of as $3x^0$ and $8x^0$, respectively. The constants that appear in each term of a polynomial are called the **coefficients** of the polynomial. The coefficient of x^0 is called the **constant term.**

Example 5   Identify the coefficients and the constant term of the given polynomials.

(a) $5x^2 - x + 12$

Solution   The coefficients are 5, -1, and 12, and the constant term is 12.

(b) $7x^3 + 2x - 4$

Solution   The coefficients are 7, 0, 2, and -4, because the polynomial can be written $7x^3 + 0x^2 + 2x - 4$. The constant term is -4.

A polynomial that consists only of a constant term, such as 15, is called a **constant polynomial.** The **zero polynomial** is the constant polynomial 0. The **degree** of a polynomial is the *exponent* of the highest power of x that appears with a *nonzero* coefficient, and the nonzero coefficient of this highest power of x is the **leading coefficient** of the polynomial. For example,

Polynomial	Degree	Leading Coefficient	Constant Term
$6x^7 + 4x^3 + 5x^2 - 7x + 10$	7	6	10
$-x^4 + 2x^3 + \frac{1}{2}$	4	-1	$\frac{1}{2}$
x^3	3	1	0
12	0	12	12

The degree of the zero polynomial is *not defined*, since no exponent of x occurs with nonzero coefficient. First-degree polynomials are often called **linear polynomials.** Second- and third-degree polynomials are called **quadratics** and **cubics**, respectively.

✓ **Checkpoint 6**

Find the degree of each polynomial.

(a) $x^4 - x^2 + x + 5$

(b) $7x^5 + 6x^3 - 3x^8 + 2$

(c) 17

(d) 0

Addition and Subtraction

Two terms having the same variable with the same exponent are called **like terms;** other terms are called **unlike terms.** Polynomials can be added or subtracted by using the distributive property to combine like terms. Only like terms can be combined. For example,

$$12y^4 + 6y^4 = (12 + 6)y^4 = 18y^4$$

and

$$-2m^2 + 8m^2 = (-2 + 8)m^2 = 6m^2.$$

The polynomial $8y^4 + 2y^5$ has unlike terms, so it cannot be further simplified.

In more complicated cases of addition, you may have to eliminate parentheses, use the commutative and associative laws to regroup like terms, and then combine them.

Example 6   Add the following polynomials.

(a) $(8x^3 - 4x^2 + 6x) + (3x^3 + 5x^2 - 9x + 8)$

Solution $8x^3 - 4x^2 + 6x + 3x^3 + 5x^2 - 9x + 8$ Eliminate parentheses.

$\quad = \underbrace{(8x^3 + 3x^3)} + \underbrace{(-4x^2 + 5x^2)} + \underbrace{(6x - 9x)} + 8$ Group like terms.

$\quad = 11x^3 + x^2 - 3x + 8$ Combine like terms.

(b) $(-4x^4 + 6x^3 - 9x^2 - 12) + (-3x^3 + 8x^2 - 11x + 7)$

Solution

$\quad -4x^4 + 6x^3 - 9x^2 - 12 - 3x^3 + 8x^2 - 11x + 7$ Eliminate parentheses.

$\quad = -4x^4 + \underbrace{(6x^3 - 3x^3)} + \underbrace{(-9x^2 + 8x^2)} - 11x + \underbrace{(-12 + 7)}$ Group like terms.

$\quad = -4x^4 + 3x^3 - x^2 - 11x - 5$ Combine like terms.

Care must be used when parentheses are preceded by a minus sign. For example, we know that

$$-(4 + 3) = -(7) = -7 = -4 - 3.$$

If you simply delete the parentheses in $-(4 + 3)$, you obtain $-4 + 3 = -1$, which is the wrong answer. This fact and the preceding examples illustrate the following rules.

Rules for Eliminating Parentheses

Parentheses preceded by a plus sign (or no sign) may be deleted.

Parentheses preceded by a minus sign may be deleted *provided that* the sign of every term within the parentheses is changed.

Example 7   Subtract: $(2x^2 - 11x + 8) - (7x^2 - 6x + 2)$.

Solution $2x^2 - 11x + 8 - 7x^2 + 6x - 2$ Eliminate parentheses.

$\quad = (2x^2 - 7x^2) + (-11x + 6x) + (8 - 2)$ Group like terms.

$\quad = -5x^2 - 5x + 6$ Combine like terms.

✓**Checkpoint 7**

Add or subtract as indicated.

(a) $(-2x^2 + 7x + 9)$
$+ (3x^2 + 2x - 7)$

(b) $(4x + 6) - (13x - 9)$

(c) $(9x^3 - 8x^2 + 2x)$
$- (9x^3 - 2x^2 - 10)$

Multiplication

The distributive property is also used to multiply polynomials. For example, the product of $8x$ and $6x - 4$ is found as follows:

$$8x(6x - 4) = 8x(6x) - 8x(4) \qquad \text{Distributive property}$$
$$= 48x^2 - 32x \qquad x \cdot x = x^2$$

Example 8   Use the distributive property to find each product.

(a) $2p^3(3p^2 - 2p + 5) = 2p^3(3p^2) + 2p^3(-2p) + 2p^3(5)$
$\qquad\qquad\qquad = 6p^5 - 4p^4 + 10p^3$

✓**Checkpoint 8**

Find the following products.

(a) $-6r(2r - 5)$

(b) $(8m + 3) \cdot (m^4 - 2m^2 + 6m)$

(b) $(3k - 2)(k^2 + 5k - 4) = 3k(k^2 + 5k - 4) - 2(k^2 + 5k - 4)$
$\qquad\qquad\qquad\qquad\qquad = 3k^3 + 15k^2 - 12k - 2k^2 - 10k + 8$
$\qquad\qquad\qquad\qquad\qquad = 3k^3 + 13k^2 - 22k + 8$

Example 9 The product $(2x - 5)(3x + 4)$ can be found by using the distributive property twice:

$$(2x - 5)(3x + 4) = 2x(3x + 4) - 5(3x + 4)$$
$$= \underline{2x \cdot 3x} + \underline{2x \cdot 4} + \underline{(-5) \cdot 3x} + \underline{(-5) \cdot 4}$$
$$= 6x^2 \quad + \quad 8x \quad - \quad 15x \quad - \quad 20$$
$$= 6x^2 \quad - \quad \quad 7x \quad \quad - \quad 20$$

Observe the pattern in the second line of Example 9 and its relationship to the terms being multiplied:

$$(2x - 5)(3x + 4) = 2x \cdot 3x + 2x \cdot 4 + (-5) \cdot 3x + (-5) \cdot 4$$

First terms

$(2x - 5)(3x + 4)$ Outside terms

$(2x - 5)(3x + 4)$ Inside terms

$(2x - 5)(3x + 4)$ Last terms

This pattern is easy to remember by using the acronym **FOIL** (**F**irst, **O**utside, **I**nside, **L**ast). The FOIL method makes it easy to find products such as this one mentally, without the necessity of writing out the intermediate steps.

Example 10 Use FOIL to find the product of the given polynomials.

(a) $(3x + 2)(x + 5) = 3x^2 \quad + \quad 15x \quad + \quad 2x \quad + \quad 10 = 3x^2 + 17x + 10$

              First   Outside   Inside   Last

(b) $(x + 3)^2 = (x + 3)(x + 3) = x^2 + 3x + 3x + 9 = x^2 + 6x + 9$

(c) $(2x + 1)(2x - 1) = 4x^2 - 2x + 2x - 1 = 4x^2 - 1$ ☑ 9

✓ **Checkpoint 9**

Use FOIL to find these products.

(a) $(5k - 1)(2k + 3)$

(b) $(7z - 3)(2z + 5)$

Applications

In business, the *revenue* from the sales of an item is given by

Revenue = (price per item) × (number of items sold).

The *cost* to manufacture and sell these items is given by

Cost = Fixed Costs + Variable Costs,

where the fixed costs include such things as buildings and machinery (which do not depend on how many items are made) and variable costs include such things as labor and materials (which vary, depending on how many items are made). Then

Profit = Revenue − Cost.

Example 11 **Business** A manufacturer of scientific calculators sells calculators for $12 each (wholesale) and can produce a maximum of 150,000. The variable cost of producing x thousand calculators is $6995x - 7.2x^2$ dollars, and the fixed costs for the manufacturing operation are $230,000. If x thousand calculators are manufactured and sold, find expressions for the revenue, cost, and profit.

Solution If x thousand calculators are sold at $12 each, then

$$\text{Revenue} = (\text{price per item}) \times (\text{number of items sold})$$
$$R = 12 \times 1000x = 12{,}000x,$$

✓ **Checkpoint 10**

Suppose revenue is given by $7x^2 - 3x$, fixed costs are $500, and variable costs are given by $3x^2 + 5x - 25$. Write an expression for

(a) Cost

(b) Profit

where $x \le 150$ (because only 150,000 calculators can be made). The variable cost of making x thousand calculators is $6995x - 7.2x^2$, so that

$$\text{Cost} = \text{Fixed Costs} + \text{Variable Costs},$$
$$C = 230{,}000 + (6995x - 7.2x^2) \quad (x \le 150).$$

Therefore, the profit is given by

$$P = R - C = 12{,}000x - (230{,}000 + 6995x - 7.2x^2)$$
$$= 12{,}000x - 230{,}000 - 6995x + 7.2x^2$$
$$P = 7.2x^2 + 5005x - 230{,}000 \quad (x \le 150). \quad ✓_{10}$$

1.2 Exercises

Use a calculator to approximate these numbers. (See Examples 1 and 2.)

1. 11.2^6

2. $(-6.54)^{11}$

3. $(-18/7)^6$

4. $(5/9)^7$

5. Explain how the value of -3^2 differs from $(-3)^2$. Do -3^3 and $(-3)^3$ differ in the same way? Why or why not?

6. Describe the steps used to multiply 4^3 and 4^5. Is the product of 4^3 and 3^4 found in the same way? Explain.

Simplify each of the given expressions. Leave your answers in exponential notation. (See Examples 3 and 4.)

7. $4^2 \cdot 4^3$

8. $(-4)^4 \cdot (-4)^6$

9. $(-6)^2 \cdot (-6)^5$

10. $(2z)^5 \cdot (2z)^6$

11. $[(5u)^4]^7$

12. $(6y)^3 \cdot [(6y)^5]^4$

List the degree of the given polynomial, its coefficients, and its constant term. (See Example 5.)

13. $6.2x^4 - 5x^3 + 4x^2 - 3x + 3.7$

14. $6x^7 + 4x^6 - x^3 + x$

State the degree of the given polynomial.

15. $1 + x + 2x^2 + 3x^3$

16. $5x^4 - 4x^5 - 6x^3 + 7x^4 - 2x + 8$

Add or subtract as indicated. (See Examples 6 and 7.)

17. $(3x^3 + 2x^2 - 5x) + (-4x^3 - x^2 - 8x)$

18. $(-2p^3 - 5p + 7) + (-4p^2 + 8p + 2)$

19. $(-4y^2 - 3y + 8) - (2y^2 - 6y + 2)$

20. $(7b^2 + 2b - 5) - (3b^2 + 2b - 6)$

21. $(2x^3 + 2x^2 + 4x - 3) - (2x^3 + 8x^2 + 1)$

22. $(3y^3 + 9y^2 - 11y + 8) - (-4y^2 + 10y - 6)$

Find each of the given products. (See Examples 8–10.)

23. $-9m(2m^2 + 6m - 1)$

24. $2a(4a^2 - 6a + 8)$

25. $(3z + 5)(4z^2 - 2z + 1)$

26. $(2k + 3)(4k^3 - 3k^2 + k)$

27. $(6k - 1)(2k + 3)$

28. $(8r + 3)(r - 1)$

29. $(3y + 5)(2y + 1)$

30. $(5r - 3s)(5r - 4s)$

31. $(9k + q)(2k - q)$

32. $(.012x - .17)(.3x + .54)$

33. $(6.2m - 3.4)(.7m + 1.3)$

34. $2p - 3[4p - (8p + 1)]$

35. $5k - [k + (-3 + 5k)]$

36. $(3x - 1)(x + 2) - (2x + 5)^2$

Business *Find expressions for the revenue, cost, and profit from selling x thousand items. (See Example 11.)*

Item Price	Fixed Costs	Variable Costs
37. $5.00	$200,000	$1800x$
38. $8.50	$225,000	$4200x$

39. Business Beauty Works sells its cologne wholesale for $9.75 per bottle. The variable costs of producing x thousand bottles is $-3x^2 + 3480x - 325$ dollars, and the fixed costs of manufacturing are $260,000. Find expressions for the revenue, cost, and profit from selling x thousand items.

40. Business A self-help guru sells her book *Be Happy in 45 Easy Steps* for $23.50 per copy. Her fixed costs are $145,000 and she estimates the variable cost of printing, binding, and distribution is given by $-4.2x^2 + 3220x - 425$ dollars. Find expressions for the revenue, cost, and profit from selling x thousand copies of the book.

Work these problems.

Business *The accompanying bar graph shows the net earnings (in millions of dollars) of the Starbucks Corporation. The polynomial*

$$-1.48x^4 + 50.0x^3 - 576x^2 + 2731x - 4027$$

gives a good approximation of Starbucks's net earnings in year x, where x = 3 corresponds to 2003, x = 4 to 2004, and so on (3 ≤ x ≤ 12). For each of the given years,

(a) use the bar graph to determine the net earnings;

(b) use the polynomial to determine the net earnings.

(Data from: www.morningstar.com.)

41. 2003   **42.** 2007

43. 2010   **44.** 2012

Assuming that the polynomial approximation in Exercises 41–44 remains accurate in later years, use it to estimate Starbucks's net earnings in each of the following years.

45. 2013   **46.** 2014   **47.** 2015

48. Do the estimates in Exercises 45–47 seem plausible? Explain.

Economics *The percentage of persons living below the poverty line in the United States in year x is approximated by the polynomial* $-.0057x^4 + .157x^3 - 1.43x^2 + 5.14x + 6.3$, *where x = 0 corresponds to the year 2000. Determine whether each of the given statements is true or false. (Data from: U.S. Census Bureau, Current Population Survey, Annual Social and Economic Supplements.)*

49. The percentage living in poverty was higher than 13% in 2004.

50. The percentage living in poverty was higher than 14% in 2010.

51. The percentage living in poverty was higher in 2003 than 2006.

52. The percentage living in poverty was lower in 2009 than 2008.

Health *According to data from a leading insurance company, if a person is 65 years old, the probability that he or she will live for another x years is approximated by the polynomial*

$$1 - .0058x - .00076x^2.$$

(Data from: Ralph DeMarr, University of New Mexico.)

Find the probability that a 65-year-old person will live to the following ages.

53. 75 (that is, 10 years past 65)   **54.** 80

55. 87   **56.** 95

57. Physical Science One of the most amazing formulas in all of ancient mathematics is the formula discovered by the Egyptians to find the volume of the frustum of a square pyramid, as shown in the following figure:

The volume of this pyramid is given by

$$(1/3)h \cdot (a^2 + ab + b^2),$$

where b is the length of the base, a is the length of the top, and h is the height. (Data from: H. A. Freebury, *A History of Mathematics* [New York: MacMillan Company, 1968].)

(a) When the Great Pyramid in Egypt was partially completed to a height h of 200 feet, b was 756 feet and a was 314 feet. Calculate its volume at this stage of construction.

(b) Try to visualize the figure if a = b. What is the resulting shape? Find its volume.

(c) Let a = b in the Egyptian formula and simplify. Are the results the same?

58. Physical Science Refer to the formula and the discussion in Exercise 57.

(a) Use the expression $(1/3)h(a^2 + ab + b^2)$ to determine a formula for the volume of a pyramid with a square base b and height h by letting a = 0.

(b) The Great Pyramid in Egypt had a square base of length 756 feet and a height of 481 feet. Find the volume of the Great Pyramid. Compare it with the volume of the 273-foot-tall Louisiana Superdome, which has an approximate volume of 125 million cubic feet. (Data from: Louisiana Superdome [www.superdome.com].)

(c) The Superdome covers an area of 13 acres. How many acres does the Great Pyramid cover? (*Hint:* 1 acre = 43,560 ft².)

59. Suppose one polynomial has degree 3 and another also has degree 3. Find all possible values for the degree of their

(a) sum;

(b) difference;

(c) product.

Business *Use the table feature of a graphing calculator or use a spreadsheet to make a table of values for the profit function in Example 11, with x = 0, 5, 10, . . . , 150. Use the table to answer the following questions.*

60. What is the profit or loss (negative profit) when 25,000 calculators are sold? when 60,000 are sold? Explain these answers.

61. Approximately how many calculators must be sold in order for the company to make a profit?

62. What is the profit from selling 100,000 calculators? 150,000 calculators?

✓ **Checkpoint Answers**

1. (a) 216   (b) 244,140,625
   (c) 1   (d) 14.75789056

2. (a) 108   (b) 320   (c) −729
   (d) 729   (e) 486

3. (a) 5^9 (b) $(-3)^{14}$ (c) $(5p)^{10}$

4. (a) 6^{21} (b) $(4k)^{30}$

5. (a) 1   (b) 1   (c) 1   (d) −1

6. (a) 4   (b) 8   (c) 0   (d) Not defined

7. (a) $x^2 + 9x + 2$
   (b) $-9x + 15$
   (c) $-6x^2 + 2x + 10$

8. (a) $-12r^2 + 30r$
   (b) $8m^5 + 3m^4 - 16m^3 + 42m^2 + 18m$

9. (a) $10k^2 + 13k - 3$ (b) $14z^2 + 29z - 15$

10. (a) $C = 3x^2 + 5x + 475$ (b) $P = 4x^2 - 8x - 475$

1.3 Factoring

The number 18 can be written as a product in several ways: $9 \cdot 2, (-3)(-6), 1 \cdot 18$, etc. The numbers in each product $(9, 2, -3$, etc.) are called **factors,** and the process of writing 18 as a product of factors is called **factoring.** Thus, factoring is the reverse of multiplication.

Factoring of polynomials is a means of simplifying many expressions and of solving certain types of equations. As is the usual custom, factoring of polynomials in this text will be restricted to finding factors with *integer* coefficients (otherwise there may be an infinite number of possible factors).

Greatest Common Factor

The algebraic expression $15m + 45$ is made up of two terms: $15m$ and 45. Each of these terms has 15 as a factor. In fact, $15m = 15 \cdot m$ and $45 = 15 \cdot 3$. By the distributive property,

$$15m + 45 = 15 \cdot m + 15 \cdot 3 = 15(m + 3).$$

Both 15 and $m + 3$ are factors of $15m + 45$. Since 15 divides evenly into all terms of $15m + 45$ and is the largest number that will do so, it is called the **greatest common factor** for the polynomial $15m + 45$. The process of writing $15m + 45$ as $15(m + 3)$ is called **factoring out** the greatest common factor.

Example 1   Factor out the greatest common factor.

(a) $12p - 18q$

Solution   Both $12p$ and $18q$ are divisible by 6, and

$$12p - 18q = 6 \cdot 2p - 6 \cdot 3q$$
$$= 6(2p - 3q).$$

(b) $8x^3 - 9x^2 + 15x$

Solution   Each of these terms is divisible by x:

$$8x^3 - 9x^2 + 15x = (8x^2) \cdot x - (9x) \cdot x + 15 \cdot x$$
$$= x(8x^2 - 9x + 15).$$

(c) $5(4x - 3)^3 + 2(4x - 3)^2$

Solution   The quantity $(4x - 3)^2$ is a common factor. Factoring it out gives

$$5(4x - 3)^3 + 2(4x - 3)^2 = (4x - 3)^2[5(4x - 3) + 2]$$
$$= (4x - 3)^2(20x - 15 + 2)$$
$$= (4x - 3)^2(20x - 13). \text{ ✓}$$

✓ **Checkpoint 1**

Factor out the greatest common factor.

(a) $12r + 9k$
(b) $75m^2 + 100n^2$
(c) $6m^4 - 9m^3 + 12m^2$
(d) $3(2k + 1)^3 + 4(2k + 1)^4$

Factoring Quadratics

If we multiply two first-degree polynomials, the result is a quadratic. For instance, using FOIL, we see that $(x + 1)(x - 2) = x^2 - x - 2$. Since factoring is the reverse of multiplication, factoring quadratics requires using FOIL backward.

Example 2 Factor $x^2 + 9x + 18$.

Solution We must find integers b and d such that

$$x^2 + 9x + 18 = (x + b)(x + d)$$
$$= x^2 + dx + bx + bd$$
$$x^2 + 9x + 18 = x^2 + (b + d)x + bd.$$

Since the constant coefficients on each side of the equation must be equal, we must have $bd = 18$; that is, b and d are factors of 18. Similarly, the coefficients of x must be the same, so that $b + d = 9$. The possibilities are summarized in this table:

Factors b, d of 18	Sum $b + d$
$18 \cdot 1$	$18 + 1 = 19$
$9 \cdot 2$	$9 + 2 = 11$
$6 \cdot 3$	$6 + 3 = 9$

There is no need to list negative factors, such as $(-3)(-6)$, because their sum is negative. The table suggests that 6 and 3 will work. Verify that

$$(x + 6)(x + 3) = x^2 + 9x + 18.$$ ✓₂

✓**Checkpoint 2**

Factor the following.
(a) $r^2 + 7r + 10$
(b) $x^2 + 4x + 3$
(c) $y^2 + 6y + 8$

Example 3 Factor $x^2 + 3x - 10$.

Solution As in Example 2, we must find factors b and d whose product is -10 (the constant term) and whose sum is 3 (the coefficient of x). The following table shows the possibilities.

Factors b, d of -10	Sum $b + d$
$1(-10)$	$1 + (-10) = -9$
$(-1)10$	$-1 + 10 = 9$
$2(-5)$	$2 + (-5) = -3$
$(-2)5$	$-2 + 5 = 3$

The only factors with product -10 and sum 3 are -2 and 5. So the correct factorization is

$$x^2 + 3x - 10 = (x - 2)(x + 5),$$

as you can readily verify.

It is usually not necessary to construct tables as was done in Examples 2 and 3—you can just mentally check the various possibilities. The approach used in Examples 2 and 3 (with minor modifications) also works for factoring quadratic polynomials whose leading coefficient is not 1.

Example 4 Factor $4y^2 - 11y + 6$.

Solution We must find integers a, b, c, and d such that

$$4y^2 - 11y + 6 = (ay + b)(cy + d)$$
$$= acy^2 + ady + bcy + bd$$
$$4y^2 - 11y + 6 = acy^2 + (ad + bc)y + bd.$$

Since the coefficients of y^2 must be the same on both sides, we see that $ac = 4$. Similarly, the constant terms show that $bd = 6$. The positive factors of 4 are 4 and 1 or 2 and 2. Since the middle term is negative, we consider only negative factors of 6. The possibilities are -2 and -3 or -1 and -6. Now we try various arrangements of these factors until we find one that gives the correct coefficient of y:

$$(2y - 1)(2y - 6) = 4y^2 - 14y + 6 \qquad \text{Incorrect}$$
$$(2y - 2)(2y - 3) = 4y^2 - 10y + 6 \qquad \text{Incorrect}$$
$$(y - 2)(4y - 3) = 4y^2 - 11y + 6. \qquad \text{Correct}$$

The last trial gives the correct factorization. ☑3

✓ **Checkpoint 3**

Factor the following.

(a) $x^2 - 4x + 3$

(b) $2y^2 - 5y + 2$

(c) $6z^2 - 13z + 6$

Example 5   Factor $6p^2 - 7pq - 5q^2$.

Solution   Again, we try various possibilities. The positive factors of 6 could be 2 and 3 or 1 and 6. As factors of -5, we have only -1 and 5 or -5 and 1. Try different combinations of these factors until the correct one is found:

$$(2p - 5q)(3p + q) = 6p^2 - 13pq - 5q^2 \qquad \text{Incorrect}$$
$$(3p - 5q)(2p + q) = 6p^2 - 7pq - 5q^2. \qquad \text{Correct}$$

So $6p^2 - 7pq - 5q^2$ factors as $(3p - 5q)(2p + q)$. ☑4

✓ **Checkpoint 4**

Factor the following.

(a) $r^2 - 5r - 14$

(b) $3m^2 + 5m - 2$

(c) $6p^2 + 13pq - 5q^2$

📄 **NOTE** In Examples 2–4, we chose positive factors of the positive first term. Of course, we could have used two negative factors, but the work is easier if positive factors are used.

Example 6   Factor $x^2 + x + 3$.

Solution   There are only two ways to factor 3, namely, $3 = 1 \cdot 3$ and $3 = (-1)(-3)$. They lead to these products:

$$(x + 1)(x + 3) = x^2 + 4x + 3 \qquad \text{Incorrect}$$
$$(x - 1)(x - 3) = x^2 - 4x + 3. \qquad \text{Incorrect}$$

Therefore, this polynomial cannot be factored.

Factoring Patterns

In some cases, you can factor a polynomial with a minimum amount of guesswork by recognizing common patterns. The easiest pattern to recognize is the *difference of squares*.

$$x^2 - y^2 = (x + y)(x - y). \qquad \text{Difference of squares}$$

To verify the accuracy of the preceding equation, multiply out the right side.

Example 7   Factor each of the following.

(a) $4m^2 - 9$

Solution   Notice that $4m^2 - 9$ is the difference of two squares, since $4m^2 = (2m)^2$ and $9 = 3^2$. Use the pattern for the difference of two squares, letting $2m$ replace x and 3 replace y. Then the pattern $x^2 - y^2 = (x + y)(x - y)$ becomes

$$4m^2 - 9 = (2m)^2 - 3^2$$
$$= (2m + 3)(2m - 3).$$

(b) $128p^2 - 98q^2$

Solution First factor out the common factor of 2:

$$128p^2 - 98q^2 = 2(64p^2 - 49q^2)$$
$$= 2[(8p)^2 - (7q)^2]$$
$$= 2(8p + 7q)(8p - 7q).$$

(c) $x^2 + 36$

Solution The *sum* of two squares cannot be factored. To convince yourself of this, check some possibilities:

$$(x + 6)(x + 6) = (x + 6)^2 = x^2 + 12x + 36;$$
$$(x + 4)(x + 9) = x^2 + 13x + 36.$$

(d) $(x - 2)^2 - 49$

Solution Since $49 = 7^2$, this is a difference of two squares. So it factors as follows:

$$(x - 2)^2 - 49 = (x - 2)^2 - 7^2$$
$$= [(x - 2) + 7][(x - 2) - 7]$$
$$= (x + 5)(x - 9). \quad ✓_5$$

✓ **Checkpoint 5**

Factor the following.

(a) $9p^2 - 49$

(b) $y^2 + 100$

(c) $(x + 3)^2 - 64$

Another common pattern is the *perfect square*. Verify each of the following factorizations by multiplying out the right side.

$$x^2 + 2xy + y^2 = (x + y)^2$$
$$x^2 - 2xy + y^2 = (x - y)^2$$

Perfect Squares

Whenever you have a quadratic whose first and last terms are squares, it *may* factor as a perfect square. The key is to look at the middle term. To have a perfect square whose first and last terms are x^2 and y^2, the middle term must be $\pm 2xy$. To avoid errors, always check this.

Example 8   Factor each polynomial, if possible.

(a) $16p^2 - 40pq + 25q^2$

Solution The first and last terms are squares, namely, $16p^2 = (4p)^2$ and $25q^2 = (5q)^2$. So the second perfect-square pattern, with $x = 4p$ and $y = 5q$, might work. To have a perfect square, the middle term $-40pq$ must equal $-2(4p)(5q)$, which it does. So the polynomial factors as

$$16p^2 - 40pq + 25q^2 = (4p - 5q)(4p - 5q),$$

as you can easily verify.

(b) $9u^2 + 5u + 1$

Solution Again, the first and last terms are squares: $9u^2 = (3u)^2$ and $1 = 1^2$. The middle term is positive, so the first perfect-square pattern might work, with $x = 3u$ and $y = 1$. To have a perfect square, however, the middle term would have to be $2(3u) \cdot 1 = 6u$, which is *not* the middle term of the given polynomial. So it is not a perfect square—in fact, it cannot be factored.

(c) $169x^2 + 104xy^2 + 16y^4$

Solution   This polynomial may be factored as $(13x + 4y^2)^2$, since $169x^2 = (13x)^2$, $16y^4 = (4y^2)^2$, and $2(13x)(4y^2) = 104xy^2$. ✔₆

Checkpoint 6

Factor.

(a) $4m^2 + 4m + 1$

(b) $25z^2 - 80zt + 64t^2$

(c) $9x^2 + 15x + 25$

Example 9   Factor each of the given polynomials.

(a) $12x^2 - 26x - 10$

Solution   Look first for a greatest common factor. Here, the greatest common factor is 2: $12x^2 - 26x - 10 = 2(6x^2 - 13x - 5)$. Now try to factor $6x^2 - 13x - 5$. Possible factors of 6 are 3 and 2 or 6 and 1. The only factors of -5 are -5 and 1 or 5 and -1. Try various combinations. You should find that the quadratic factors as $(3x + 1)(2x - 5)$. Thus,

$$12x^2 - 26x - 10 = 2(3x + 1)(2x - 5).$$

(b) $4z^2 + 12z + 9 - w^2$

Solution   There is no common factor here, but notice that the first three terms can be factored as a perfect square:

$$4z^2 + 12z + 9 - w^2 = (2z + 3)^2 - w^2.$$

Written in this form, the expression is the difference of squares, which can be factored as follows:

$$(2z + 3)^2 - w^2 = [(2z + 3) + w][(2z + 3) - w]$$
$$= (2z + 3 + w)(2z + 3 - w).$$

(c) $16a^2 - 100 - 48ac + 36c^2$

Solution   Factor out the greatest common factor of 4 first:

$$16a^2 - 100 - 48ac + 36c^2 = 4[4a^2 - 25 - 12ac + 9c^2]$$

$$= 4[(4a^2 - 12ac + 9c^2) - 25] \quad \text{Rearrange terms and group.}$$

$$= 4[(2a - 3c)^2 - 25] \quad \text{Factor.}$$

$$= 4(2a - 3c + 5)(2a - 3c - 5) \quad \text{Factor the difference of squares.} ✔_7$$

Checkpoint 7

Factor the following.

(a) $6x^2 - 27x - 15$

(b) $9r^2 + 12r + 4 - t^2$

(c) $18 - 8xy - 2y^2 - 8x^2$

⊙ CAUTION   Remember always to look first for a greatest common factor.

Higher Degree Polynomials

Polynomials of degree greater than 2 are often difficult to factor. However, factoring is relatively easy in two cases: *the difference and the sum of cubes.* By multiplying out the right side, you can readily verify each of the following factorizations.

$$x^3 - y^3 = (x - y)(x^2 + xy + y^2) \quad \text{Difference of cubes}$$
$$x^3 + y^3 = (x + y)(x^2 - xy + y^2) \quad \text{Sum of cubes}$$

Example 10   Factor each of the following polynomials.

(a) $k^3 - 8$

Solution   Since $8 = 2^3$, use the pattern for the difference of two cubes to obtain

$$k^3 - 8 = k^3 - 2^3 = (k - 2)(k^2 + 2k + 4).$$

(b) $m^3 + 125$

Solution $m^3 + 125 = m^3 + 5^3 = (m + 5)(m^2 - 5m + 25)$

(c) $8k^3 - 27z^3$

Solution $8k^3 - 27z^3 = (2k)^3 - (3z)^3 = (2k - 3z)(4k^2 + 6kz + 9z^2)$ ✓8

✓ **Checkpoint 8**

Factor the following.

(a) $a^3 + 1000$

(b) $z^3 - 64$

(c) $1000m^3 - 27z^3$

Substitution and appropriate factoring patterns can sometimes be used to factor higher degree expressions.

Example 11 Factor the following polynomials.

(a) $x^8 + 4x^4 + 3$

Solution The idea is to make a substitution that reduces the polynomial to a quadratic or cubic that we can deal with. Note that $x^8 = (x^4)^2$. Let $u = x^4$. Then

$$x^8 + 4x^4 + 3 = (x^4)^2 + 4x^4 + 3 \quad \text{Power of a power}$$
$$= u^2 + 4u + 3 \quad \text{Substitute } x^4 = u.$$
$$= (u + 3)(u + 1) \quad \text{Factor}$$
$$= (x^4 + 3)(x^4 + 1). \quad \text{Substitute } u = x^4.$$

(b) $x^4 - y^4$

Solution Note that $x^4 = (x^2)^2$, and similarly for the y term. Let $u = x^2$ and $v = y^2$. Then

$$x^4 - y^4 = (x^2)^2 - (y^2)^2 \quad \text{Power of a power}$$
$$= u^2 - v^2 \quad \text{Substitute } x^2 = u \text{ and } y^2 = v.$$
$$= (u + v)(u - v) \quad \text{Difference of squares}$$
$$= (x^2 + y^2)(x^2 - y^2) \quad \text{Substitute } u = x^2 \text{ and } v = y^2.$$
$$= (x^2 + y^2)(x + y)(x - y). \quad \text{Difference of squares}$$ ✓9

✓ **Checkpoint 9**

Factor each of the following.

(a) $2x^4 + 5x^2 + 2$

(b) $3x^4 - x^2 - 2$

Once you understand Example 11, you can often factor without making explicit substitutions.

Example 12 Factor $256k^4 - 625m^4$.

Solution Use the difference of squares twice, as follows:

$$256k^4 - 625m^4 = (16k^2)^2 - (25m^2)^2$$
$$= (16k^2 + 25m^2)(16k^2 - 25m^2)$$
$$= (16k^2 + 25m^2)(4k + 5m)(4k - 5m).$$ ✓10

✓ **Checkpoint 10**

Factor $81x^4 - 16y^4$.

1.3 Exercises

Factor out the greatest common factor in each of the given polynomials. (See Example 1.)

1. $12x^2 - 24x$

2. $5y - 65xy$

3. $r^3 - 5r^2 + r$

4. $t^3 + 3t^2 + 8t$

5. $6z^3 - 12z^2 + 18z$

6. $5x^3 + 55x^2 + 10x$

7. $3(2y - 1)^2 + 7(2y - 1)^3$

8. $(3x + 7)^5 - 4(3x + 7)^3$

9. $3(x + 5)^4 + (x + 5)^6$

10. $3(x + 6)^2 + 6(x + 6)^4$

Factor the polynomial. (See Examples 2 and 3.)

11. $x^2 + 5x + 4$

12. $u^2 + 7u + 6$

13. $x^2 + 7x + 12$

14. $y^2 + 8y + 12$

15. $x^2 + x - 6$

16. $x^2 + 4x - 5$

17. $x^2 + 2x - 3$

18. $y^2 + y - 12$

19. $x^2 - 3x - 4$

20. $u^2 - 2u - 8$

21. $z^2 - 9z + 14$

22. $w^2 - 6w - 16$

23. $z^2 + 10z + 24$

24. $r^2 + 16r + 60$

Factor the polynomial. (See Examples 4–6.)

25. $2x^2 - 9x + 4$

26. $3w^2 - 8w + 4$

27. $15p^2 - 23p + 4$

28. $8x^2 - 14x + 3$

29. $4z^2 - 16z + 15$

30. $12y^2 - 29y + 15$

31. $6x^2 - 5x - 4$

32. $12z^2 + z - 1$

33. $10y^2 + 21y - 10$

34. $15u^2 + 4u - 4$

35. $6x^2 + 5x - 4$

36. $12y^2 + 7y - 10$

Factor each polynomial completely. Factor out the greatest common factor as necessary. (See Examples 2–9.)

37. $3a^2 + 2a - 5$

38. $6a^2 - 48a - 120$

39. $x^2 - 81$

40. $x^2 + 17xy + 72y^2$

41. $9p^2 - 12p + 4$

42. $3r^2 - r - 2$

43. $r^2 + 3rt - 10t^2$

44. $2a^2 + ab - 6b^2$

45. $m^2 - 8mn + 16n^2$

46. $8k^2 - 16k - 10$

47. $4u^2 + 12u + 9$

48. $9p^2 - 16$

49. $25p^2 - 10p + 4$

50. $10x^2 - 17x + 3$

51. $4r^2 - 9v^2$

52. $x^2 + 3xy - 28y^2$

53. $x^2 + 4xy + 4y^2$

54. $16u^2 + 12u - 18$

55. $3a^2 - 13a - 30$

56. $3k^2 + 2k - 8$

57. $21m^2 + 13mn + 2n^2$

58. $81y^2 - 100$

59. $y^2 - 4yz - 21z^2$

60. $49a^2 + 9$

61. $121x^2 - 64$

62. $4z^2 + 56zy + 196y^2$

Factor each of these polynomials. (See Example 10.)

63. $a^3 - 64$

64. $b^3 + 216$

65. $8r^3 - 27s^3$

66. $1000p^3 + 27q^3$

67. $64m^3 + 125$

68. $216y^3 - 343$

69. $1000y^3 - z^3$

70. $125p^3 + 8q^3$

Factor each of these polynomials. (See Examples 11 and 12.)

71. $x^4 + 5x^2 + 6$

72. $y^4 + 7y^2 + 10$

73. $b^4 - b^2$

74. $z^4 - 3z^2 - 4$

75. $x^4 - x^2 - 12$

76. $4x^4 + 27x^2 - 81$

77. $16a^4 - 81b^4$

78. $x^6 - y^6$

79. $x^8 + 8x^2$

80. $x^9 - 64x^3$

81. When asked to factor $6x^4 - 3x^2 - 3$ completely, a student gave the following result:

$$6x^4 - 3x^2 - 3 = (2x^2 + 1)(3x^2 - 3).$$

Is this answer correct? Explain why.

82. When can the sum of two squares be factored? Give examples.

83. Explain why $(x + 2)^3$ is not the correct factorization of $x^3 + 8$, and give the correct factorization.

84. Describe how factoring and multiplication are related. Give examples.

✓**Checkpoint Answers**

1. (a) $3(4r + 3k)$ (b) $25(3m^2 + 4n^2)$
(c) $3m^2(2m^2 - 3m + 4)$ (d) $(2k + 1)^3(7 + 8k)$

2. (a) $(r + 2)(r + 5)$ (b) $(x + 3)(x + 1)$
(c) $(y + 2)(y + 4)$

3. (a) $(x - 3)(x - 1)$ (b) $(2y - 1)(y - 2)$
(c) $(3z - 2)(2z - 3)$

4. (a) $(r - 7)(r + 2)$ (b) $(3m - 1)(m + 2)$
(c) $(2p + 5q)(3p - q)$

5. (a) $(3p + 7)(3p - 7)$ (b) Cannot be factored
(c) $(x + 11)(x - 5)$

6. (a) $(2m + 1)^2$ (b) $(5z - 8t)^2$
(c) Does not factor

7. (a) $3(2x + 1)(x - 5)$
(b) $(3r + 2 + t)(3r + 2 - t)$
(c) $2(3 - 2x - y)(3 + 2x + y)$

8. (a) $(a + 10)(a^2 - 10a + 100)$
(b) $(z - 4)(z^2 + 4z + 16)$
(c) $(10m - 3z)(100m^2 + 30mz + 9z^2)$

9. (a) $(2x^2 + 1)(x^2 + 2)$
(b) $(3x^2 + 2)(x + 1)(x - 1)$

10. $(9x^2 + 4y^2)(3x + 2y)(3x - 2y)$

1.4 Rational Expressions

A **rational expression** is an expression that can be written as the quotient of two polynomials, such as

$$\frac{8}{x - 1}, \qquad \frac{3x^2 + 4x}{5x - 6}, \qquad \text{and} \qquad \frac{2y + 1}{y^4 + 8}.$$

It is sometimes important to know the values of the variable that make the denominator 0 (in which case the quotient is not defined). For example, 1 cannot be used as a replacement for x in the first expression above and 6/5 cannot be used in the second one, since these values make the respective denominators equal 0. *Throughout this section, we assume that all denominators are nonzero,* which means that some replacement values for the variables may have to be excluded. ☑₁

Simplifying Rational Expressions

A key tool for simplification is the following fact.

For all expressions P, Q, R, and S, with $Q \neq 0$ and $S \neq 0$,

$$\frac{PS}{QS} = \frac{P}{Q}. \quad \text{Cancellation Property}$$

✓ Checkpoint 1

What value of the variable makes each denominator equal 0?

(a) $\dfrac{5}{x-3}$

(b) $\dfrac{2x-3}{4x-1}$

(c) $\dfrac{x+2}{x}$

(d) Why do we need to determine these values?

Example 1 Write each of the following rational expressions in lowest terms (so that the numerator and denominator have no common factor with integer coefficients except 1 or -1).

(a) $\dfrac{12m}{-18}$

Solution Both $12m$ and -18 are divisible by 6. By the cancellation property,

$$\frac{12m}{-18} = \frac{2m \cdot 6}{-3 \cdot 6}$$

$$= \frac{2m}{-3}$$

$$= -\frac{2m}{3}.$$

(b) $\dfrac{8x+16}{4}$

Solution Factor the numerator and cancel:

$$\frac{8x+16}{4} = \frac{8(x+2)}{4} = \frac{4 \cdot 2(x+2)}{4} = \frac{2(x+2)}{1} = 2(x+2).$$

The answer could also be written as $2x + 4$ if desired.

(c) $\dfrac{k^2+7k+12}{k^2+2k-3}$

✓ Checkpoint 2

Write each of the following in lowest terms.

(a) $\dfrac{12k+36}{18}$

(b) $\dfrac{15m+30m^2}{5m}$

(c) $\dfrac{2p^2+3p+1}{p^2+3p+2}$

Solution Factor the numerator and denominator and cancel:

$$\frac{k^2+7k+12}{k^2+2k-3} = \frac{(k+4)(k+3)}{(k-1)(k+3)} = \frac{k+4}{k-1}. \quad ☑_2$$

Multiplication and Division

The rules for multiplying and dividing rational expressions are the same fraction rules you learned in arithmetic.

For all expressions P, Q, R, and S, with $Q \neq 0$ and $S \neq 0$,

$$\frac{P}{Q} \cdot \frac{R}{S} = \frac{PR}{QS}$$ Multiplication Rule

and

$$\frac{P}{Q} \div \frac{R}{S} = \frac{P}{Q} \cdot \frac{S}{R} \qquad (R \neq 0).$$ Division Rule

Example 2

(a) Multiply $\dfrac{2}{3} \cdot \dfrac{y}{5}$.

Solution Use the multiplication rule. Multiply the numerators and then the denominators:

$$\frac{2}{3} \cdot \frac{y}{5} = \frac{2 \cdot y}{3 \cdot 5} = \frac{2y}{15}.$$

The result, $2y/15$, is in lowest terms.

(b) Multiply $\dfrac{3y + 9}{6} \cdot \dfrac{18}{5y + 15}$.

Solution Factor where possible:

$$\frac{3y + 9}{6} \cdot \frac{18}{5y + 15} = \frac{3(y + 3)}{6} \cdot \frac{18}{5(y + 3)}$$

$$= \frac{3 \cdot 18(y + 3)}{6 \cdot 5(y + 3)}$$ Multiply numerators and denominators.

$$= \frac{3 \cdot 6 \cdot 3(y + 3)}{6 \cdot 5(y + 3)}$$ $18 = 6 \cdot 3$

$$= \frac{3 \cdot 3}{5}$$ Write in lowest terms.

$$= \frac{9}{5}.$$

(c) Multiply $\dfrac{m^2 + 5m + 6}{m + 3} \cdot \dfrac{m^2 + m - 6}{m^2 + 3m + 2}$.

Solution Factor numerators and denominators:

$$\frac{(m + 2)(m + 3)}{m + 3} \cdot \frac{(m - 2)(m + 3)}{(m + 2)(m + 1)}$$ Factor.

$$= \frac{(m + 2)(m + 3)(m - 2)(m + 3)}{(m + 3)(m + 2)(m + 1)}$$ Multiply.

$$= \frac{(m - 2)(m + 3)}{m + 1}$$ Lowest terms

$$= \frac{m^2 + m - 6}{m + 1}.$$ ✓ 3

✓ **Checkpoint 3**

Multiply.

(a) $\dfrac{3r^2}{5} \cdot \dfrac{20}{9r}$

(b) $\dfrac{y - 4}{y^2 - 2y - 8} \cdot \dfrac{y^2 - 4}{3y}$

Example 3

(a) Divide $\dfrac{8x}{5} \div \dfrac{11x^2}{20}$.

Solution Invert the second expression and multiply (division rule):

$$\dfrac{8x}{5} \div \dfrac{11x^2}{20} = \dfrac{8x}{5} \cdot \dfrac{20}{11x^2} \qquad \text{Invert and multiply.}$$

$$= \dfrac{8x \cdot 20}{5 \cdot 11x^2} \qquad \text{Multiply.}$$

$$= \dfrac{32}{11x}. \qquad \text{Lowest terms}$$

(b) Divide $\dfrac{9p - 36}{12} \div \dfrac{5(p - 4)}{18}$.

Solution We have

$$\dfrac{9p - 36}{12} \cdot \dfrac{18}{5(p - 4)} \qquad \text{Invert and multiply.}$$

$$= \dfrac{9(p - 4)}{12} \cdot \dfrac{18}{5(p - 4)} \qquad \text{Factor.}$$

$$= \dfrac{27}{10}. \qquad \text{Cancel, multiply, and write in lowest terms.} \quad \boxed{4}$$

✓ **Checkpoint 4**

Divide.

(a) $\dfrac{5m}{16} \div \dfrac{m^2}{10}$

(b) $\dfrac{2y - 8}{6} \div \dfrac{5y - 20}{3}$

(c) $\dfrac{m^2 - 2m - 3}{m(m + 1)} \div \dfrac{m + 4}{5m}$

Addition and Subtraction

As you know, when two numerical fractions have the same denominator, they can be added or subtracted. The same rules apply to rational expressions.

For all expressions P, Q, R, with $Q \neq 0$,

$$\dfrac{P}{Q} + \dfrac{R}{Q} = \dfrac{P + R}{Q} \qquad \text{Addition Rule}$$

and

$$\dfrac{P}{Q} - \dfrac{R}{Q} = \dfrac{P - R}{Q}. \qquad \text{Subtraction Rule}$$

Example 4   Add or subtract as indicated.

(a) $\dfrac{4}{5k} + \dfrac{11}{5k}$

Solution Since the denominators are the same, we add the numerators:

$$\dfrac{4}{5k} + \dfrac{11}{5k} = \dfrac{4 + 11}{5k} = \dfrac{15}{5k} \qquad \text{Addition rule}$$

$$= \dfrac{3}{k}. \qquad \text{Lowest terms}$$

(b) $\dfrac{2x^2 + 3x + 1}{x^5 + 1} - \dfrac{x^2 - 7x}{x^5 + 1}$

Solution   The denominators are the same, so we subtract numerators, paying careful attention to parentheses:

$$\dfrac{2x^2 + 3x + 1}{x^5 + 1} - \dfrac{x^2 - 7x}{x^5 + 1} = \dfrac{(2x^2 + 3x + 1) - (x^2 - 7x)}{x^5 + 1} \qquad \text{Subtraction rule}$$

$$= \dfrac{2x^2 + 3x + 1 - x^2 - (-7x)}{x^5 + 1} \qquad \text{Subtract numerators.}$$

$$= \dfrac{2x^2 + 3x + 1 - x^2 + 7x}{x^5 + 1}$$

$$= \dfrac{x^2 + 10x + 1}{x^5 + 1}. \qquad \text{Simplify the numerator.}$$

When fractions do not have the same denominator, you must first find a common denominator before you can add or subtract. A common denominator is a denominator that has each fraction's denominator as a factor.

Example 5   Add or subtract as indicated.

(a) $\dfrac{7}{p^2} + \dfrac{9}{2p} + \dfrac{1}{3p^2}$

Solution   These three denominators are different, so we must find a common denominator that has each of p^2, $2p$, and $3p^2$ as factors. Observe that $6p^2$ satisfies these requirements. Use the cancellation property to rewrite each fraction as one that has $6p^2$ as its denominator and then add them:

$$\dfrac{7}{p^2} + \dfrac{9}{2p} + \dfrac{1}{3p^2} = \dfrac{6 \cdot 7}{6 \cdot p^2} + \dfrac{3p \cdot 9}{3p \cdot 2p} + \dfrac{2 \cdot 1}{2 \cdot 3p^2} \qquad \text{Cancellation property}$$

$$= \dfrac{42}{6p^2} + \dfrac{27p}{6p^2} + \dfrac{2}{6p^2}$$

$$= \dfrac{42 + 27p + 2}{6p^2} \qquad \text{Addition rule}$$

$$= \dfrac{27p + 44}{6p^2}. \qquad \text{Simplify.}$$

(b) $\dfrac{k^2}{k^2 - 1} - \dfrac{2k^2 - k - 3}{k^2 + 3k + 2}$

Solution   Factor the denominators to find a common denominator:

$$\dfrac{k^2}{k^2 - 1} - \dfrac{2k^2 - k - 3}{k^2 + 3k + 2} = \dfrac{k^2}{(k + 1)(k - 1)} - \dfrac{2k^2 - k - 3}{(k + 1)(k + 2)}.$$

A common denominator here is $(k + 1)(k - 1)(k + 2)$, because each of the preceding denominators is a factor of this common denominator. Write each fraction with the common denominator:

$$\frac{k^2}{(k+1)(k-1)} - \frac{2k^2 - k - 3}{(k+1)(k+2)}$$

$$= \frac{k^2(k+2)}{(k+1)(k-1)(k+2)} - \frac{(2k^2 - k - 3)(k-1)}{(k+1)(k-1)(k+2)}$$

$$= \frac{k^3 + 2k^2 - (2k^2 - k - 3)(k-1)}{(k+1)(k-1)(k+2)} \qquad \text{Subtract fractions.}$$

$$= \frac{k^3 + 2k^2 - (2k^3 - 3k^2 - 2k + 3)}{(k+1)(k-1)(k+2)} \qquad \text{Multiply } (2k^2 - k - 3)(k-1).$$

$$= \frac{k^3 + 2k^2 - 2k^3 + 3k^2 + 2k - 3}{(k+1)(k-1)(k+2)} \qquad \text{Polynomial subtraction}$$

$$= \frac{-k^3 + 5k^2 + 2k - 3}{(k+1)(k-1)(k+2)}. \qquad \text{Combine terms.} \quad ✓_5$$

✓**Checkpoint 5**

Add or subtract.

(a) $\dfrac{3}{4r} + \dfrac{8}{3r}$

(b) $\dfrac{1}{m-2} - \dfrac{3}{2(m-2)}$

(c) $\dfrac{p+1}{p^2-p} - \dfrac{p^2-1}{p^2+p-2}$

Complex Fractions

Any quotient of rational expressions is called a **complex fraction.** Complex fractions are simplified as demonstrated in Example 6.

Example 6   Simplify the complex fraction

$$\frac{6 - \dfrac{5}{k}}{1 + \dfrac{5}{k}}.$$

Solution   Multiply both numerator and denominator by the common denominator k:

$$\frac{6 - \dfrac{5}{k}}{1 + \dfrac{5}{k}} = \frac{k\left(6 - \dfrac{5}{k}\right)}{k\left(1 + \dfrac{5}{k}\right)} \qquad \text{Multiply by } \dfrac{k}{k}.$$

$$= \frac{6k - k\left(\dfrac{5}{k}\right)}{k + k\left(\dfrac{5}{k}\right)} \qquad \text{Distributive property}$$

$$= \frac{6k - 5}{k + 5}. \qquad \text{Simplify.}$$

1.4 Exercises

Write each of the given expressions in lowest terms. Factor as necessary. (See Example 1.)

1. $\dfrac{8x^2}{56x}$

2. $\dfrac{27m}{81m^3}$

3. $\dfrac{25p^2}{35p^3}$

4. $\dfrac{18y^4}{24y^2}$

5. $\dfrac{5m+15}{4m+12}$

6. $\dfrac{10z+5}{20z+10}$

7. $\dfrac{4(w-3)}{(w-3)(w+6)}$

8. $\dfrac{-6(x+2)}{(x+4)(x+2)}$

9. $\dfrac{3y^2 - 12y}{9y^3}$

10. $\dfrac{15k^2 + 45k}{9k^2}$

11. $\dfrac{m^2 - 4m + 4}{m^2 + m - 6}$

12. $\dfrac{r^2 - r - 6}{r^2 + r - 12}$

13. $\dfrac{x^2 + 2x - 3}{x^2 - 1}$

14. $\dfrac{z^2 + 4z + 4}{z^2 - 4}$

Multiply or divide as indicated in each of the exercises. Write all answers in lowest terms. (See Examples 2 and 3.)

15. $\dfrac{3a^2}{64} \cdot \dfrac{8}{2a^3}$

16. $\dfrac{2u^2}{8u^4} \cdot \dfrac{10u^3}{9u}$

17. $\dfrac{7x}{11} \div \dfrac{14x^3}{66y}$

18. $\dfrac{6x^2y}{2x} \div \dfrac{21xy}{y}$

19. $\dfrac{2a+b}{3c} \cdot \dfrac{15}{4(2a+b)}$

20. $\dfrac{4(x+2)}{w} \cdot \dfrac{3w^2}{8(x+2)}$

21. $\dfrac{15p-3}{6} \div \dfrac{10p-2}{3}$

22. $\dfrac{2k+8}{6} \div \dfrac{3k+12}{3}$

23. $\dfrac{9y-18}{6y+12} \cdot \dfrac{3y+6}{15y-30}$

24. $\dfrac{12r+24}{36r-36} \div \dfrac{6r+12}{8r-8}$

25. $\dfrac{4a+12}{2a-10} \div \dfrac{a^2-9}{a^2-a-20}$

26. $\dfrac{6r-18}{9r^2+6r-24} \cdot \dfrac{12r-16}{4r-12}$

27. $\dfrac{k^2-k-6}{k^2+k-12} \cdot \dfrac{k^2+3k-4}{k^2+2k-3}$

28. $\dfrac{n^2-n-6}{n^2-2n-8} \div \dfrac{n^2-9}{n^2+7n+12}$

29. In your own words, explain how to find the least common denominator of two fractions.

30. Describe the steps required to add three rational expressions. You may use an example to illustrate.

Add or subtract as indicated in each of the following. Write all answers in lowest terms. (See Example 4.)

31. $\dfrac{2}{7z} - \dfrac{1}{5z}$

32. $\dfrac{4}{3z} - \dfrac{5}{4z}$

33. $\dfrac{r+2}{3} - \dfrac{r-2}{3}$

34. $\dfrac{3y-1}{8} - \dfrac{3y+1}{8}$

35. $\dfrac{4}{x} + \dfrac{1}{5}$

36. $\dfrac{6}{r} - \dfrac{3}{4}$

37. $\dfrac{1}{m-1} + \dfrac{2}{m}$

38. $\dfrac{8}{y+2} - \dfrac{3}{y}$

39. $\dfrac{7}{b+2} + \dfrac{2}{5(b+2)}$

40. $\dfrac{4}{3(k+1)} + \dfrac{3}{k+1}$

41. $\dfrac{2}{5(k-2)} + \dfrac{5}{4(k-2)}$

42. $\dfrac{11}{3(p+4)} - \dfrac{5}{6(p+4)}$

43. $\dfrac{2}{x^2-4x+3} + \dfrac{5}{x^2-x-6}$

44. $\dfrac{3}{m^2-3m-10} + \dfrac{7}{m^2-m-20}$

45. $\dfrac{2y}{y^2+7y+12} - \dfrac{y}{y^2+5y+6}$

46. $\dfrac{-r}{r^2-10r+16} - \dfrac{3r}{r^2+2r-8}$

In each of the exercises in the next set, simplify the complex fraction. (See Example 6.)

47. $\dfrac{1 + \dfrac{1}{x}}{1 - \dfrac{1}{x}}$

48. $\dfrac{2 - \dfrac{2}{y}}{2 + \dfrac{2}{y}}$

49. $\dfrac{\dfrac{1}{x+h} - \dfrac{1}{x}}{h}$

50. $\dfrac{\dfrac{1}{(x+h)^2} - \dfrac{1}{x^2}}{h}$

Work these problems.

Natural Science *Each figure in the following exercises is a dartboard. The probability that a dart which hits the board lands in the shaded area is the fraction*

$$\frac{\text{area of the shaded region}}{\text{area of the dartboard}}.$$

(a) *Express the probability as a rational expression in x. (Hint: Area formulas are given in Appendix B.)*

(b) *Then reduce the expression to lowest terms.*

51.

52.

53.

54.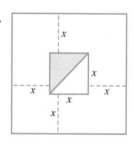

Business *In Example 11 of Section 1.2, we saw that the cost C of producing x thousand calculators is given by*

$$C = -7.2x^2 + 6995x + 230{,}000 \quad (x \le 150).$$

55. Write a rational expression that gives the average cost per calculator when x thousand are produced. (*Hint:* The average cost is the total cost C divided by the number of calculators produced.)

56. Find the average cost per calculator for each of these production levels: 20,000, 50,000, and 125,000.

Business *The cost (in millions of dollars) for a 30-second ad during the TV broadcast of the Superbowl can be approximated by*

$$\frac{.314x^2 - 1.399x + 15.0}{x + 1}$$

where x = 6 corresponds to the year 2006. (Data from: forbes.com and espn.com.)

57. How much did an ad cost in 2010?

58. How much did an ad cost in 2012?

59. If this trend continues, will the cost of an ad reach $5 million by 2018?

60. If this trend continues, when will the cost of an ad reach $6 million?

Health Economics *The average company cost per hour of an employee's health insurance in year x is approximated by*

$$\frac{.265x^2 + 1.47x + 3.63}{x + 2},$$

where x = 0 corresponds to the year 2000. (Data from: U.S. Bureau of Labor Statistics.)

61. What is the hourly health insurance cost in 2011?

62. What is the hourly health insurance cost in 2012?

63. Assuming that this model remains accurate and that an employee works 2100 hours per year, what is the annual company cost of her health care insurance in 2015?

64. Will annual costs reach $10,000 by 2020?

✓**Checkpoint Answers**

1. (a) 3   (b) 1/4   (c) 0

(d) Because division by 0 is undefined

2. (a) $\dfrac{2(k + 3)}{3}$ or $\dfrac{2k + 6}{3}$

(b) $3(1 + 2m)$ or $3 + 6m$ (c) $\dfrac{2p + 1}{p + 2}$

3. (a) $\dfrac{4r}{3}$ (b) $\dfrac{y - 2}{3y}$

4. (a) $\dfrac{25}{8m}$ (b) $\dfrac{1}{5}$ (c) $\dfrac{5(m - 3)}{m + 4}$

5. (a) $\dfrac{41}{12r}$ (b) $\dfrac{-1}{2(m - 2)}$ (c) $\dfrac{-p^3 + p^2 + 4p + 2}{p(p - 1)(p + 2)}$

1.5 Exponents and Radicals

Exponents were introduced in Section 1.2. In this section, the definition of exponents will be extended to include negative exponents and rational-number exponents such as 1/2 and 7/3.

Integer Exponents

Positive-integer and zero exponents were defined in Section 1.2, where we noted that

$$a^m \cdot a^n = a^{m+n}$$

for nonnegative integers m and n. Now we develop an analogous property for quotients. By definition,

$$\frac{6^5}{6^2} = \frac{6 \cdot 6 \cdot 6 \cdot 6 \cdot 6}{6 \cdot 6} = 6 \cdot 6 \cdot 6 = 6^3.$$

Because there are 5 factors of 6 in the numerator and 2 factors of 6 in the denominator, the quotient has $5 - 2 = 3$ factors of 6. In general, we can make the following statement, which applies to any real number a and nonnegative integers m and n with $m > n$.

Division with Exponents

To divide a^m by a^n, *subtract* the exponents:

$$\frac{a^m}{a^n} = a^{m-n}.$$

Example 1   Compute each of the following.

(a) $\dfrac{5^7}{5^4} = 5^{7-4} = 5^3$.

(b) $\dfrac{(-8)^{10}}{(-8)^5} = (-8)^{10-5} = (-8)^5$.

(c) $\dfrac{(3c)^9}{(3c)^3} = (3c)^{9-3} = (3c)^6$.

✓ **Checkpoint 1**

Evaluate each of the following.

(a) $\dfrac{2^{14}}{2^5}$

(b) $\dfrac{(-5)^9}{(-5)^5}$

(c) $\dfrac{(xy)^{17}}{(xy)^{12}}$

When an exponent applies to the product of two numbers, such as $(7 \cdot 19)^3$, use the definitions carefully. For instance,

$$(7 \cdot 19)^3 = (7 \cdot 19)(7 \cdot 19)(7 \cdot 19) = 7 \cdot 7 \cdot 7 \cdot 19 \cdot 19 \cdot 19 = 7^3 \cdot 19^3.$$

In other words, $(7 \cdot 19)^3 = 7^3 \cdot 19^3$. This is an example of the following fact, which applies to any real numbers a and b and any nonnegative-integer exponent n.

Product to a Power

To find $(ab)^n$, apply the exponent to *every* term inside the parentheses:

$$(ab)^n = a^n b^n.$$

🛇 **CAUTION** A common mistake is to write an expression such as $(2x)^5$ as $2x^5$, rather than the correct answer $(2x)^5 = 2^5 x^5 = 32x^5$.

Analogous conclusions are valid for quotients (where a and b are any real numbers with $b \neq 0$ and n is a nonnegative-integer exponent).

Quotient to a Power

To find $\left(\dfrac{a}{b}\right)^n$, apply the exponent to both numerator and denominator:

$$\left(\frac{a}{b}\right)^n = \frac{a^n}{b^n}.$$

Example 2   Compute each of the following.

(a) $(5y)^3 = 5^3 y^3 = 125y^3$ Product to a power

(b) $(c^2 d^3)^4 = (c^2)^4 (d^3)^4$ Product to a power

  $= c^8 d^{12}$ Power of a power

(c) $\left(\dfrac{x}{2}\right)^6 = \dfrac{x^6}{2^6} = \dfrac{x^6}{64}$ Quotient to a power

(d) $\left(\dfrac{a^4}{b^3}\right)^3 = \dfrac{(a^4)^3}{(b^3)^3}$ Quotient to a power

  $= \dfrac{a^{12}}{b^9}$ Power of a power

(e) $\left(\dfrac{(rs)^3}{r^4}\right)^2$

Solution   Use several of the preceding properties in succession:

$$\left(\frac{(rs)^3}{r^4}\right)^2 = \left(\frac{r^3 s^3}{r^4}\right)^2 \qquad \text{Product to a power in numerator}$$

$$= \left(\frac{s^3}{r}\right)^2 \qquad \text{Cancel.}$$

$$= \frac{(s^3)^2}{r^2} \qquad \text{Quotient to a power}$$

$$= \frac{s^6}{r^2}. \qquad \text{Power of a power in numerator}$$

As is often the case, there is another way to reach the last expression. You should be able to supply the reasons for each of the following steps:

$$\left(\frac{(rs)^3}{r^4}\right)^2 = \frac{[(rs)^3]^2}{(r^4)^2} = \frac{(rs)^6}{r^8} = \frac{r^6 s^6}{r^8} = \frac{s^6}{r^2}.$$

Checkpoint 2

Compute each of the following.

(a) $(3x)^4$

(b) $(r^2 s^5)^6$

(c) $\left(\dfrac{2}{z}\right)^5$

(d) $\left(\dfrac{3a^5}{(ab)^3}\right)^2$

Negative Exponents

The next step is to define negative-integer exponents. If they are to be defined in such a way that the quotient rule for exponents remains valid, then we must have, for example,

$$\frac{3^2}{3^4} = 3^{2-4} = 3^{-2}.$$

However,

$$\frac{3^2}{3^4} = \frac{3 \cdot 3}{3 \cdot 3 \cdot 3 \cdot 3} = \frac{1}{3^2},$$

which suggests that 3^{-2} should be defined to be $1/3^2$. Thus, we have the following definition of a negative exponent.

Negative Exponent

If n is a natural number, and if $a \neq 0$, then

$$a^{-n} = \frac{1}{a^n}.$$

Checkpoint 3

Evaluate the following.

(a) 6^{-2}

(b) -6^{-3}

(c) -3^{-4}

(d) $\left(\dfrac{5}{8}\right)^{-1}$

Example 3   Evaluate the following.

(a) $3^{-2} = \dfrac{1}{3^2} = \dfrac{1}{9}.$

(b) $5^{-4} = \dfrac{1}{5^4} = \dfrac{1}{625}.$

(c) $x^{-1} = \dfrac{1}{x^1} = \dfrac{1}{x}.$

(d) $-4^{-2} = -\dfrac{1}{4^2} = -\dfrac{1}{16}.$

(e) $\left(\dfrac{3}{4}\right)^{-1} = \dfrac{1}{\left(\dfrac{3}{4}\right)^1} = \dfrac{1}{\dfrac{3}{4}} = \dfrac{4}{3}.$

There is a useful property that makes it easy to raise a fraction to a negative exponent. Consider, for example,

$$\left(\frac{2}{3}\right)^{-4} = \frac{1}{\left(\frac{2}{3}\right)^4} = \frac{1}{\left(\frac{2^4}{3^4}\right)} = 1 \cdot \frac{3^4}{2^4} = \left(\frac{3}{2}\right)^4.$$

This example is easily generalized to the following property (in which a/b is a nonzero fraction and n a positive integer).

Inversion Property

$$\left(\frac{a}{b}\right)^{-n} = \left(\frac{b}{a}\right)^n.$$

Example 4   Use the inversion property to compute each of the following.

(a) $\left(\frac{2}{5}\right)^{-3} = \left(\frac{5}{2}\right)^3 = \frac{5^3}{2^3} = \frac{125}{8}.$

(b) $\left(\frac{3}{x}\right)^{-5} = \left(\frac{x}{3}\right)^5 = \frac{x^5}{3^5} = \frac{x^5}{243}.$ ✔️4

When keying in negative exponents on a calculator, be sure to use the negation key (labeled $(-)$ or $+/-$), not the subtraction key. Calculators normally display answers as decimals, as shown in Figure 1.6. Some graphing calculators have a FRAC key that converts these decimals to fractions, as shown in Figure 1.7.

Figure 1.6

Figure 1.7

✓ **Checkpoint 4**

Compute each of the following.

(a) $\left(\frac{5}{8}\right)^{-1}$

(b) $\left(\frac{1}{2}\right)^{-5}$

(c) $\left(\frac{a^2}{b}\right)^{-3}$

🖊 **TECHNOLOGY TIP**
The FRAC key is in the MATH menu of TI graphing calculators. A FRAC program for other graphing calculators is in the Program Appendix. Fractions can be displayed on some graphing calculators by changing the number display format (in the MODES menu) to "fraction" or "exact."

Roots and Rational Exponents

There are two numbers whose square is 16: 4 and -4. As we saw in Section 1.1, the positive one, 4, is called the *square root* (or second root) of 16. Similarly, there are two numbers whose fourth power is 16: 2 and -2. We call 2 the **fourth root** of 16. This suggests the following generalization.

If n is even, the ***n*th root of a** is the positive real number whose nth power is a.

All nonnegative numbers have nth roots for every natural number n, but *no negative number has a real, even nth root*. For example, there is no real number whose square is -16, so -16 has no square root.

We say that the **cube root** (or third root) of 8 is 2 because $2^3 = 8$. Similarly, since $(-2)^3 = -8$, we say that -2 is the cube root of -8. Again, we can make the following generalization.

> If n is odd, the **nth root of a** is the real number whose nth power is a.

Every real number has an nth root for every *odd* natural number n.

We can now define rational exponents. If they are to have the same properties as integer exponents, we want $a^{1/2}$ to be a number such that

$$(a^{1/2})^2 = a^{1/2} \cdot a^{1/2} = a^{1/2+1/2} = a^1 = a.$$

Thus, $a^{1/2}$ should be a number whose square is a, and it is reasonable to *define* $a^{1/2}$ to be the square root of a (if it exists). Similarly, $a^{1/3}$ is defined to be the cube root of a, and we have the following definition.

> If a is a real number and n is a positive integer, then
>
> $$a^{1/n} \text{ is defined to be the } n\text{th root of } a \text{ (if it exists).}$$

Example 5   Examine the reasoning used to evaluate the following roots.

(a) $36^{1/2} = 6$ because $6^2 = 36$.

(b) $100^{1/2} = 10$ because $10^2 = 100$.

(c) $-(225^{1/2}) = -15$ because $15^2 = 225$.

(d) $625^{1/4} = 5$ because $5^4 = 625$.

(e) $(-1296)^{1/4}$ is not a real number.

(f) $-1296^{1/4} = -6$ because $6^4 = 1296$.

(g) $(-27)^{1/3} = -3$ because $(-3)^3 = -27$.

(h) $-32^{1/5} = -2$ because $2^5 = 32$. ✓5

✓ Checkpoint 5

Evaluate the following.

(a) $16^{1/2}$

(b) $16^{1/4}$

(c) $-256^{1/2}$

(d) $(-256)^{1/2}$

(e) $-8^{1/3}$

(f) $243^{1/5}$

A calculator can be used to evaluate expressions with fractional exponents. Whenever it is easy to do so, enter the fractional exponents in their equivalent decimal form. For instance, to find $625^{1/4}$, enter $625^{.25}$ into the calculator. When the decimal equivalent of a fraction is an infinitely repeating decimal, however, it is best to enter the fractional exponent directly. If you use a shortened decimal approximation (such as $.333$ for $1/3$), you will not get the correct answers. Compare the incorrect answers in Figure 1.9 with the correct ones in Figure 1.8.

$27^{\frac{1}{3}}$
 	
                3
	$27^{.333}$
	
	        2.996705973

Figure 1.8   Figure 1.9

For other rational exponents, the symbol $a^{m/n}$ should be defined so that the properties for exponents still hold. For example, by the product property, we want

$$(a^{1/3})^2 = a^{1/3} \cdot a^{1/3} = a^{1/3+1/3} = a^{2/3}.$$

This result suggests the following definition.

For all integers m and all positive integers n, and for all real numbers a for which $a^{1/n}$ is a real number,

$$a^{m/n} = (a^{1/n})^m.$$

Example 6   Verify each of the following calculations.

(a) $27^{2/3} = (27^{1/3})^2 = 3^2 = 9$.

(b) $32^{2/5} = (32^{1/5})^2 = 2^2 = 4$.

(c) $64^{4/3} = (64^{1/3})^4 = 4^4 = 256$.

(d) $25^{3/2} = (25^{1/2})^3 = 5^3 = 125$. ✓ 6

✓ **Checkpoint 6**

Evaluate the following.

(a) $16^{3/4}$

(b) $25^{5/2}$

(c) $32^{7/5}$

(d) $100^{3/2}$

🛑 **CAUTION** When the base is negative, as in $(-8)^{2/3}$, some calculators produce an error message. On such calculators, you should first compute $(-8)^{1/3}$ and then square the result; that is, compute $[(-8)^{1/3}]^2$.

Since every terminating decimal is a rational number, decimal exponents now have a meaning. For instance, $5.24 = \frac{524}{100}$, so $3^{5.24} = 3^{524/100}$, which is easily approximated by a calculator (Figure 1.10).

Rational exponents were defined so that one of the familiar properties of exponents remains valid. In fact, it can be proved that *all* of the rules developed earlier for integer exponents are valid for rational exponents. The following box summarizes these rules, which are illustrated in Examples 7–9.

```
3^5.24
          316.3117863
524
3^100
          316.3117863
```

Figure 1.10

Properties of Exponents

For any rational numbers m and n, and for any real numbers a and b for which the following exist,

(a) $a^m \cdot a^n = a^{m+n}$ Product property

(b) $\dfrac{a^m}{a^n} = a^{m-n}$ Quotient property

(c) $(a^m)^n = a^{mn}$ Power of a power

(d) $(ab)^m = a^m \cdot b^m$ Product to a power

(e) $\left(\dfrac{a}{b}\right)^m = \dfrac{a^m}{b^m}$ Quotient to a power

(f) $a^0 = 1$ Zero exponent

(g) $a^{-n} = \dfrac{1}{a^n}$ Negative exponent

(h) $\left(\dfrac{a}{b}\right)^{-n} = \left(\dfrac{b}{a}\right)^n$.   Inversion property

The power-of-a-power property provides another way to compute $a^{m/n}$ (when it exists):

$$a^{m/n} = a^{m(1/n)} = (a^m)^{1/n}. \tag{1}$$

For example, we can now find $4^{3/2}$ in two ways:

$$4^{3/2} = (4^{1/2})^3 = 2^3 = 8 \qquad \text{or} \qquad 4^{3/2} = (4^3)^{1/2} = 64^{1/2} = 8.$$

Definition of $a^{m/n}$ Statement (1)

Example 7   Simplify each of the following expressions.

(a) $7^{-4} \cdot 7^6 = 7^{-4+6} = 7^2 = 49.$ Product property

(b) $5x^{2/3} \cdot 2x^{1/4} = 10x^{2/3}x^{1/4}$

$\qquad\qquad = 10x^{2/3+1/4}$ Product property

$\qquad\qquad = 10x^{11/12}.$ $\dfrac{2}{3} + \dfrac{1}{4} = \dfrac{8}{12} + \dfrac{3}{12} = \dfrac{11}{12}$

(c) $\dfrac{9^{14}}{9^{-6}} = 9^{14-(-6)} = 9^{20}.$ Quotient property

(d) $\dfrac{c^5}{2c^{4/3}} = \dfrac{1}{2} \cdot \dfrac{c^5}{c^{4/3}}$

$\qquad\quad = \dfrac{1}{2}c^{5-4/3}$ Quotient property

$\qquad\quad = \dfrac{1}{2}c^{11/3} = \dfrac{c^{11/3}}{2}.$ $5 - \dfrac{4}{3} = \dfrac{15}{3} - \dfrac{4}{3} = \dfrac{11}{3}$

(e) $\dfrac{27^{1/3} \cdot 27^{5/3}}{27^3} = \dfrac{27^{1/3+5/3}}{27^3}$ Product property

$\qquad\qquad = \dfrac{27^2}{27^3} = 27^{2-3}$ Quotient property

$\qquad\qquad = 27^{-1} = \dfrac{1}{27}.$ Definition of negative exponent ✓7

✓ **Checkpoint 7**

Simplify each of the following.

(a) $9^7 \cdot 9^{-5}$

(b) $3x^{1/4} \cdot 5x^{5/4}$

(c) $\dfrac{8^7}{8^{-3}}$

(d) $\dfrac{5^{2/3} \cdot 5^{-4/3}}{5^2}$

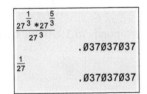

Figure 1.11

You can use a calculator to check numerical computations, such as those in Example 7, by computing the left and right sides separately and confirming that the answers are the same in each case. Figure 1.11 shows this technique for part (e) of Example 7.

Example 8   Perform the indicated operations.

(a) $(2^{-3})^{-4/7} = 2^{(-3)(-4/7)} = 2^{12/7}.$ Power of a power

(b) $\left(\dfrac{3m^{5/6}}{y^{3/4}}\right)^2 = \dfrac{(3m^{5/6})^2}{(y^{3/4})^2}$ Quotient to a power

$\qquad\qquad = \dfrac{3^2(m^{5/6})^2}{(y^{3/4})^2}$ Product to a power

$\qquad\qquad = \dfrac{9m^{(5/6)2}}{y^{(3/4)2}}$ Power of a power

$\qquad\qquad = \dfrac{9m^{5/3}}{y^{3/2}}.$ $\dfrac{5}{6} \cdot 2 = \dfrac{10}{6} = \dfrac{5}{3}$ and $\dfrac{3}{4} \cdot 2 = \dfrac{3}{2}$

(c) $m^{2/3}(m^{7/3} + 2m^{1/3}) = m^{2/3}m^{7/3} + m^{2/3}2m^{1/3}$ Distributive property

$\qquad\qquad = m^{2/3+7/3} + 2m^{2/3+1/3} = m^3 + 2m.$ Product rule ✓8

✓ **Checkpoint 8**

Simplify each of the following.

(a) $(7^{-4})^{-2} \cdot (7^4)^{-2}$

(b) $\dfrac{c^4 c^{-1/2}}{c^{3/2}d^{1/2}}$

(c) $a^{5/8}(2a^{3/8} + a^{-1/8})$

Example 9   Simplify each expression in parts (a)–(c). Give answers with only positive exponents.

(a) $\dfrac{(m^3)^{-2}}{m^4} = \dfrac{m^{-6}}{m^4} = m^{-6-4} = m^{-10} = \dfrac{1}{m^{10}}.$

(b) $6y^{2/3} \cdot 2y^{-1/2} = 12y^{2/3-1/2} = 12y^{1/6}.$

(c) $\dfrac{x^{1/2}(x-2)^{-3}}{5(x-2)} = \dfrac{x^{1/2}}{5} \cdot \dfrac{(x-2)^{-3}}{x-2} = \dfrac{x^{1/2}}{5} \cdot (x-2)^{-3-1}$

$\quad = \dfrac{x^{1/2}}{5} \cdot \dfrac{1}{(x-2)^4} = \dfrac{x^{1/2}}{5(x-2)^4}.$

(d) Write $a^{-1} + b^{-1}$ as a single quotient.

Solution   Be careful here. $a^{-1} + b^{-1}$ does *not* equal $(a+b)^{-1}$; the exponent properties deal only with products and quotients, not with sums. However, using the definition of negative exponents and addition of fractions, we have

$$a^{-1} + b^{-1} = \frac{1}{a} + \frac{1}{b} = \frac{b+a}{ab}. \quad ✓_9$$

We can use some functions of the form ax^b where both a and b are constants and b is also an exponent.

Example 10   **Social Science**   The total number of students (in millions) attending institutes of higher education can be approximated by the function

$$5.8x^{0.357} \quad (x \geq 10),$$

where $x = 10$ corresponds to the year 1990. Find the approximate number of students enrolled in higher education in 2012. (Data from: U.S. National Center for Education Statistics.)

Solution   Since 2012 is 22 years after 1990 and $x = 10$ corresponds to 1990, we have that $x = 22 + 10 = 32$ corresponds to 2012. We then obtain

$$5.8(32)^{0.357} \approx 20.0 \text{ million students.} \quad ✓_{10}$$

Radicals

Earlier, we denoted the nth root of a as $a^{1/n}$. An alternative notation for nth roots uses the radical symbol $\sqrt[n]{}$.

If n is an even natural number and $a \geq 0$, or if n is an odd natural number,

$$\sqrt[n]{a} = a^{1/n}.$$

In the radical expression $\sqrt[n]{a}$, a is called the *radicand* and n is called the *index*. When $n = 2$, the familiar square-root symbol $\sqrt{a}$ is used instead of $\sqrt[2]{a}$.

Example 11   Simplify the following radicals.

(a) $\sqrt[4]{16} = 16^{1/4} = 2.$

(b) $\sqrt[5]{-32} = -2.$

(c) $\sqrt[3]{1000} = 10.$

(d) $\sqrt[6]{\dfrac{64}{729}} = \left(\dfrac{64}{729}\right)^{1/6} = \dfrac{64^{1/6}}{729^{1/6}} = \dfrac{2}{3}. \quad ✓_{11}$

✓ **Checkpoint 9**

Simplify the given expressions. Give answers with only positive exponents.

(a) $(3x^{2/3})(2x^{-1})(y^{-1/3})^2$

(b) $\dfrac{(t^{-1})^2}{t^{-5}}$

(c) $\left(\dfrac{2k^{1/3}}{p^{5/4}}\right)^2 \cdot \left(\dfrac{4k^{-2}}{p^5}\right)^{3/2}$

(d) $x^{-1} - y^{-2}$

✓ **Checkpoint 10**

Assuming the model from Example 10 remains accurate, find the number of students for 2015.

✓ **Checkpoint 11**

Simplify.

(a) $\sqrt[3]{27}$

(b) $\sqrt[4]{625}$

(c) $\sqrt[6]{64}$

(d) $\sqrt[3]{\dfrac{64}{125}}$

Recall that $a^{m/n} = (a^{1/n})^m$ by definition and $a^{m/n} = (a^m)^{1/n}$ by statement **(1)** on page 36 (provided that all terms are defined). We translate these facts into radical notation as follows.

For all rational numbers m/n and all real numbers a for which $\sqrt[n]{a}$ exists,
$$a^{m/n} = (\sqrt[n]{a})^m \quad \text{or} \quad a^{m/n} = \sqrt[n]{a^m}.$$

Notice that $\sqrt[n]{x^n}$ cannot be written simply as x when n is even. For example, if $x = -5$, then
$$\sqrt{x^2} = \sqrt{(-5)^2} = \sqrt{25} = 5 \neq x.$$
However, $|-5| = 5$, so that $\sqrt{x^2} = |x|$ when x is -5. This relationship is true in general.

For any real number a and any natural number n,
$$\sqrt[n]{a^n} = |a| \quad \text{if } n \text{ is even}$$
and
$$\sqrt[n]{a^n} = a \quad \text{if } n \text{ is odd.}$$

To avoid the difficulty that $\sqrt[n]{a^n}$ is not necessarily equal to a, we shall assume that all variables in radicands represent only nonnegative numbers, as they usually do in applications. The properties of exponents can be written with radicals as follows.

For all real numbers a and b, and for positive integers n for which all indicated roots exist,

(a) $\sqrt[n]{a} \cdot \sqrt[n]{b} = \sqrt[n]{ab}$ and

(b) $\dfrac{\sqrt[n]{a}}{\sqrt[n]{b}} = \sqrt[n]{\dfrac{a}{b}}$ $(b \neq 0)$.

Example 12 Simplify the following expressions.

(a) $\sqrt{6} \cdot \sqrt{54} = \sqrt{6 \cdot 54} = \sqrt{324} = 18.$

Alternatively, simplify $\sqrt{54}$ first:
$$\sqrt{6} \cdot \sqrt{54} = \sqrt{6} \cdot \sqrt{9 \cdot 6}$$
$$= \sqrt{6} \cdot 3\sqrt{6} = 3 \cdot 6 = 18.$$

(b) $\sqrt{\dfrac{7}{64}} = \dfrac{\sqrt{7}}{\sqrt{64}} = \dfrac{\sqrt{7}}{8}.$

(c) $\sqrt{75} - \sqrt{12}.$

Solution Note that $12 = 4 \cdot 3$ and that 4 is a perfect square. Similarly, $75 = 25 \cdot 3$ and 25 is a perfect square. Consequently,

$$\sqrt{75} - \sqrt{12} = \sqrt{25 \cdot 3} - \sqrt{4 \cdot 3} \qquad \text{Factor.}$$
$$= \sqrt{25}\sqrt{3} - \sqrt{4}\sqrt{3} \qquad \text{Property (a)}$$
$$= 5\sqrt{3} - 2\sqrt{3} = 3\sqrt{3}. \qquad \text{Simplify.} \quad \boxed{12}$$

✓**Checkpoint 12**

Simplify.

(a) $\sqrt{3} \cdot \sqrt{27}$

(b) $\sqrt{\dfrac{3}{49}}$

(c) $\sqrt{50} + \sqrt{72}$

⊙ **CAUTION** When a and b are nonzero real numbers,

$$\sqrt[n]{a + b} \text{ is \textbf{NOT} equal to } \sqrt[n]{a} + \sqrt[n]{b}.$$

For example,

$$\sqrt{9 + 16} = \sqrt{25} = 5, \text{ but } \sqrt{9} + \sqrt{16} = 3 + 4 = 7,$$

so $\sqrt{9 + 16} \neq \sqrt{9} + \sqrt{16}$.

Multiplying radical expressions is much like multiplying polynomials.

> **Example 13**   Perform the following multiplications.
>
> **(a)** $(\sqrt{2} + 3)(\sqrt{8} - 5) = \sqrt{2}(\sqrt{8}) - \sqrt{2}(5) + 3\sqrt{8} - 3(5)$ FOIL
> $$= \sqrt{16} - 5\sqrt{2} + 3(2\sqrt{2}) - 15$$
> $$= 4 - 5\sqrt{2} + 6\sqrt{2} - 15$$
> $$= -11 + \sqrt{2}.$$
>
> **(b)** $(\sqrt{7} - \sqrt{10})(\sqrt{7} + \sqrt{10}) = (\sqrt{7})^2 - (\sqrt{10})^2$
> $$= 7 - 10 = -3. \;\; \boxed{13}$$

✓**Checkpoint 13**

Multiply.

(a) $(\sqrt{5} - \sqrt{2})(3 + \sqrt{2})$

(b) $(\sqrt{3} + \sqrt{7})(\sqrt{3} - \sqrt{7})$

Rationalizing Denominators and Numerators

Before the invention of calculators, it was customary to **rationalize the denominators** of fractions (that is, write equivalent fractions with no radicals in the denominator), because this made many computations easier. Although there is no longer a computational reason to do so, rationalization of denominators (and sometimes numerators) is still used today to simplify expressions and to derive useful formulas.

> **Example 14**   Rationalize each denominator.
>
> **(a)** $\dfrac{4}{\sqrt{3}}$
>
> **Solution**   The key is to multiply by 1, with 1 written as a radical fraction:
> $$\frac{4}{\sqrt{3}} = \frac{4}{\sqrt{3}} \cdot 1 = \frac{4}{\sqrt{3}} \cdot \frac{\sqrt{3}}{\sqrt{3}} = \frac{4\sqrt{3}}{3}.$$
>
> **(b)** $\dfrac{1}{3 - \sqrt{2}}$
>
> **Solution**   The same technique works here, using $1 = \dfrac{3 + \sqrt{2}}{3 + \sqrt{2}}$:
> $$\frac{1}{3 - \sqrt{2}} = \frac{1}{3 - \sqrt{2}} \cdot 1 = \frac{1}{3 - \sqrt{2}} \cdot \frac{3 + \sqrt{2}}{3 + \sqrt{2}} = \frac{3 + \sqrt{2}}{(3 - \sqrt{2})(3 + \sqrt{2})}$$
> $$= \frac{3 + \sqrt{2}}{9 - 2} = \frac{3 + \sqrt{2}}{7}. \;\; \boxed{14}$$

✓**Checkpoint 14**

Rationalize the denominator.

(a) $\dfrac{2}{\sqrt{5}}$

(b) $\dfrac{1}{2 + \sqrt{3}}$

> **Example 15**   Rationalize the numerator of
> $$\frac{2 + \sqrt{5}}{1 + \sqrt{3}}.$$
>
> **Solution**   As in Example 14(b), we must write 1 as a suitable fraction. Since we want to rationalize the numerator here, we multiply by the fraction $1 = \dfrac{2 - \sqrt{5}}{2 - \sqrt{5}}$:

$$\frac{2 + \sqrt{5}}{1 + \sqrt{3}} = \frac{2 + \sqrt{5}}{1 + \sqrt{3}} \cdot \frac{2 - \sqrt{5}}{2 - \sqrt{5}} = \frac{4 - 5}{2 - \sqrt{5} + 2\sqrt{3} - \sqrt{3}\sqrt{5}}$$

$$= \frac{-1}{2 - \sqrt{5} + 2\sqrt{3} - \sqrt{15}}.$$

1.5 Exercises

Perform the indicated operations and simplify your answer. (See Examples 1 and 2.)

1. $\dfrac{7^5}{7^3}$

2. $\dfrac{(-6)^{14}}{(-6)^6}$

3. $(4c)^2$

4. $(-2x)^4$

5. $\left(\dfrac{2}{x}\right)^5$

6. $\left(\dfrac{5}{xy}\right)^3$

7. $(3u^2)^3(2u^3)^2$

8. $\dfrac{(5v^2)^3}{(2v)^4}$

Perform the indicated operations and simplify your answer, which should not have any negative exponents. (See Examples 3 and 4.)

9. 7^{-1}

10. 10^{-3}

11. -6^{-5}

12. $(-x)^{-4}$

13. $(-y)^{-3}$

14. $\left(\dfrac{1}{6}\right)^{-2}$

15. $\left(\dfrac{4}{3}\right)^{-2}$

16. $\left(\dfrac{x}{y^2}\right)^{-2}$

17. $\left(\dfrac{a}{b^3}\right)^{-1}$

18. Explain why $-2^{-4} = -1/16$, but $(-2)^{-4} = 1/16$.

Evaluate each expression. Write all answers without exponents. Round decimal answers to two places. (See Examples 5 and 6.)

19. $49^{1/2}$

20. $8^{1/3}$

21. $(5.71)^{1/4}$

22. $12^{5/2}$

23. $-64^{2/3}$

24. $-64^{3/2}$

25. $(8/27)^{-4/3}$

26. $(27/64)^{-1/3}$

Simplify each expression. Write all answers using only positive exponents. (See Example 7.)

27. $\dfrac{5^{-3}}{4^{-2}}$

28. $\dfrac{7^{-4}}{7^{-3}}$

29. $4^{-3} \cdot 4^6$

30. $9^{-9} \cdot 9^{10}$

31. $\dfrac{4^{10} \cdot 4^{-6}}{4^{-4}}$

32. $\dfrac{5^{-4} \cdot 5^6}{5^{-1}}$

Simplify each expression. Assume all variables represent positive real numbers. Write answers with only positive exponents. (See Examples 8 and 9.)

33. $\dfrac{z^6 \cdot z^2}{z^5}$

34. $\dfrac{k^6 \cdot k^9}{k^{12}}$

35. $\dfrac{3^{-1}(p^{-2})^3}{3p^{-7}}$

36. $\dfrac{(5x^3)^{-2}}{x^4}$

37. $(q^{-5}r^3)^{-1}$

38. $(2y^2z^{-2})^{-3}$

39. $(2p^{-1})^3 \cdot (5p^2)^{-2}$

40. $(4^{-1}x^3)^{-2} \cdot (3x^{-3})^4$

41. $(2p)^{1/2} \cdot (2p^3)^{1/3}$

42. $(5k^2)^{3/2} \cdot (5k^{1/3})^{3/4}$

43. $p^{2/3}(2p^{1/3} + 5p)$

44. $3x^{3/2}(2x^{-3/2} + x^{3/2})$

45. $\dfrac{(x^2)^{1/3}(y^2)^{2/3}}{3x^{2/3}y^2}$

46. $\dfrac{(c^{1/2})^3(d^3)^{1/2}}{(c^3)^{1/4}(d^{1/4})^3}$

47. $\dfrac{(7a)^2(5b)^{3/2}}{(5a)^{3/2}(7b)^4}$

48. $\dfrac{(4x)^{1/2}\sqrt{xy}}{x^{3/2}y^2}$

49. $x^{1/2}(x^{2/3} - x^{4/3})$

50. $x^{1/2}(3x^{3/2} + 2x^{-1/2})$

51. $(x^{1/2} + y^{1/2})(x^{1/2} - y^{1/2})$ **52.** $(x^{1/3} + y^{1/2})(2x^{1/3} - y^{3/2})$

Match the rational-exponent expression in Column I with the equivalent radical expression in Column II. Assume that x is not zero.

I	II
53. $(-3x)^{1/3}$	(a) $\dfrac{3}{\sqrt[3]{x}}$
54. $-3x^{1/3}$	(b) $-3\sqrt[3]{x}$
55. $(-3x)^{-1/3}$	(c) $\dfrac{1}{\sqrt[3]{3x}}$
56. $-3x^{-1/3}$	(d) $\dfrac{-3}{\sqrt[3]{x}}$
57. $(3x)^{1/3}$	(e) $3\sqrt[3]{x}$
58. $3x^{-1/3}$	(f) $\sqrt[3]{-3x}$
59. $(3x)^{-1/3}$	(g) $\sqrt[3]{3x}$
60. $3x^{1/3}$	(h) $\dfrac{1}{\sqrt[3]{-3x}}$

Simplify each of the given radical expressions. (See Examples 11–13.)

61. $\sqrt[3]{125}$

62. $\sqrt[6]{64}$

63. $\sqrt[4]{625}$

64. $\sqrt[7]{-128}$

65. $\sqrt{63}\sqrt{7}$

66. $\sqrt[3]{81} \cdot \sqrt[3]{9}$

67. $\sqrt{81 - 4}$

68. $\sqrt{49 - 16}$

69. $\sqrt{5}\sqrt{15}$

70. $\sqrt{8}\sqrt{96}$

71. $\sqrt{50} - \sqrt{72}$

72. $\sqrt{75} + \sqrt{192}$

73. $5\sqrt{20} - \sqrt{45} + 2\sqrt{80}$ **74.** $(\sqrt{3} + 2)(\sqrt{3} - 2)$

75. $(\sqrt{5} + \sqrt{2})(\sqrt{5} - \sqrt{2})$

76. What is wrong with the statement $\sqrt[3]{4} \cdot \sqrt[3]{4} = 4$?

Rationalize the denominator of each of the given expressions. (See Example 14.)

77. $\dfrac{3}{1 - \sqrt{2}}$

78. $\dfrac{2}{1 + \sqrt{5}}$

79. $\dfrac{9 - \sqrt{3}}{3 - \sqrt{3}}$

80. $\dfrac{\sqrt{3} - 1}{\sqrt{3} - 2}$

Rationalize the numerator of each of the given expressions. (See Example 15.)

81. $\dfrac{3 - \sqrt{2}}{3 + \sqrt{2}}$

82. $\dfrac{1 + \sqrt{7}}{2 - \sqrt{3}}$

The following exercises are applications of exponentiation and radicals.

83. Business The theory of economic lot size shows that, under certain conditions, the number of units to order to minimize total cost is

$$x = \sqrt{\frac{kM}{f}},$$

where k is the cost to store one unit for one year, f is the (constant) setup cost to manufacture the product, and M is the total number of units produced annually. Find x for the following values of f, k, and M.

(a) $k = \$1, f = \$500, M = 100{,}000$

(b) $k = \$3, f = \$7, M = 16{,}700$

(c) $k = \$1, f = \$5, M = 16{,}800$

84. Health The threshold weight T for a person is the weight above which the risk of death increases greatly. One researcher found that the threshold weight in pounds for men aged 40–49 is related to height in inches by the equation $h = 12.3T^{1/3}$. What height corresponds to a threshold of 216 pounds for a man in this age group?

Business *The annual domestic revenue (in billions of dollars) generated by the sale of movie tickets can be approximated by the function*

$$8.19x^{0.096} \quad (x \geq 1),$$

where $x = 1$ corresponds to 2001. Assuming the model remains accurate, approximate the revenue in the following years. (Data from: www.the-numbers.com.)

85. 2010   **86.** 2013

87. 2015   **88.** 2018

Health *The age-adjusted death rates per 100,000 people for diseases of the heart can be approximated by the function*

$$262.5x^{-.156} \quad (x \geq 1),$$

where $x = 1$ corresponds to 2001. Assuming the model continues to be accurate, find the approximate age-adjusted death rate for

the following years. (Data from: U.S. National Center for Health Statistics.)

89. 2011   **90.** 2013   **91.** 2017   **92.** 2020

Social Science *The number of students receiving financial aid from the federal government in the form of Pell Grants (in millions) can be approximated by the function*

$$3.96x^{0.239} \quad (x \geq 1),$$

where $x = 1$ corresponds to the year 2001. Assuming the model remains accurate, find the number of students receiving a Pell Grant for the following years. (Data from: www.finaid.org.)

93. 2005   **94.** 2010   **95.** 2013   **96.** 2018

Health *A function that approximates the number (in millions) of CT scans performed annually in the United States is*

$$3.5x^{1.04} \quad (x \geq 5),$$

where $x = 5$ corresponds to 1995. Find the approximate number of CT scans performed in the following years. (Data from: The Wall Street Journal.)

97. 1998   **98.** 2005   **99.** 2012   **100.** 2013

✓ Checkpoint Answers

1. (a) 2^9 (b) $(-5)^4$ (c) $(xy)^5$

2. (a) $81x^4$ (b) $r^{12}s^{30}$ (c) $\dfrac{32}{z^5}$ (d) $\dfrac{9a^4}{b^6}$

3. (a) $1/36$ (b) $-1/216$ (c) $-1/81$ (d) $8/5$

4. (a) $8/5$ (b) 32 (c) b^3/a^6

5. (a) 4 (b) 2 (c) -16

    (d) Not a real number   (e) -2 (f) 3

6. (a) 8 (b) 3125 (c) 128 (d) 1000

7. (a) 81 (b) $15x^{3/2}$ (c) 8^{10}

    (d) $5^{-8/3}$ or $1/5^{8/3}$

8. (a) 1 (b) $c^2/d^{1/2}$ (c) $2a + a^{1/2}$

9. (a) $\dfrac{6}{x^{1/3}y^{2/3}}$ (b) t^3

    (c) $32/(p^{10}k^{7/3})$ (d) $\dfrac{y^2 - x}{xy^2}$

10. About 20.6 million

11. (a) 3 (b) 5 (c) 2 (d) $4/5$

12. (a) 9 (b) $\dfrac{\sqrt{3}}{7}$ (c) $11\sqrt{2}$

13. (a) $3\sqrt{5} + \sqrt{10} - 3\sqrt{2} - 2$ (b) -4

14. (a) $\dfrac{2\sqrt{5}}{5}$ (b) $2 - \sqrt{3}$

1.6 First-Degree Equations

An **equation** is a statement that two mathematical expressions are equal; for example,

$$5x - 3 = 13, \qquad 8y = 4, \qquad \text{and} \qquad -3p + 5 = 4p - 8$$

are equations.

The letter in each equation is called the variable. This section concentrates on **first-degree equations,** which are equations that involve only constants and the first power of the variable. All of the equations displayed above are first-degree equations, but neither of the following equations is of first degree:

$$2x^2 = 5x + 6 \qquad \text{(the variable has an exponent greater than 1);}$$
$$\sqrt{x + 2} = 4 \qquad \text{(the variable is under the radical).}$$

A **solution** of an equation is a number that can be substituted for the variable in the equation to produce a true statement. For example, substituting the number 9 for x in the equation $2x + 1 = 19$ gives

$$2x + 1 = 19$$
$$2(9) + 1 \stackrel{?}{=} 19 \qquad \text{Let } x = 9.$$
$$18 + 1 = 19. \qquad \text{True}$$

This true statement indicates that 9 is a solution of $2x + 1 = 19$. ✓₁

The following properties are used to solve equations.

✓ **Checkpoint 1**

Is -4 a solution of the equations in parts (a) and (b)?

(a) $3x + 5 = -7$

(b) $2x - 3 = 5$

(c) Is there more than one solution of the equation in part (a)?

Properties of Equality

1. The same number may be added to or subtracted from both sides of an equation:

$$\text{If } a = b, \text{ then } a + c = b + c \text{ and } a - c = b - c.$$

2. Both sides of an equation may be multiplied or divided by the same nonzero number:

$$\text{If } a = b \text{ and } c \neq 0, \text{ then } ac = bc \text{ and } \frac{a}{c} = \frac{b}{c}.$$

Example 1   Solve the equation $5x - 3 = 12$.

Solution   Using the first property of equality, add 3 to both sides. This isolates the term containing the variable on one side of the equation:

$$5x - 3 = 12$$
$$5x - 3 + 3 = 12 + 3 \qquad \text{Add 3 to both sides.}$$
$$5x = 15.$$

Now arrange for the coefficient of x to be 1 by using the second property of equality:

$$5x = 15$$
$$\frac{5x}{5} = \frac{15}{5} \qquad \text{Divide both sides by 5.}$$
$$x = 3.$$

✓ **Checkpoint 2**

Solve the following.

(a) $3p - 5 = 19$

(b) $4y + 3 = -5$

(c) $-2k + 6 = 2$

The solution of the original equation, $5x - 3 = 12$, is 3. Check the solution by substituting 3 for x in the original equation. ✓₂

Example 2   Solve $2k + 3(k - 4) = 2(k - 3)$.

Solution   First, simplify the equation by using the distributive property on the left-side term $3(k - 4)$ and right-side term $2(k - 3)$:

$$2k + 3(k - 4) = 2(k - 3)$$
$$2k + 3k - 12 = 2(k - 3) \qquad \text{Distributive property}$$
$$2k + 3k - 12 = 2k - 6 \qquad \text{Distributive property}$$
$$5k - 12 = 2k - 6. \qquad \text{Collect like terms on left side.}$$

One way to proceed is to add $-2k$ to both sides:

$$5k - 12 + (-2k) = 2k - 6 + (-2k) \qquad \text{Add } -2k \text{ to both sides.}$$
$$3k - 12 = -6$$
$$3k - 12 + 12 = -6 + 12 \qquad \text{Add 12 to both sides.}$$
$$3k = 6$$
$$\frac{1}{3}(3k) = \frac{1}{3}(6) \qquad \text{Multiply both sides by } \frac{1}{3}.$$
$$k = 2.$$

The solution is 2. Check this result by substituting 2 for k in the original equation. ✓₃

✓ Checkpoint 3

Solve the following.

(a) $3(m - 6) + 2(m + 4)$
     $= 4m - 2$

(b) $-2(y + 3) + 4y$
     $= 3(y + 1) - 6$

Example 3   **Business**   The percentage y of U.S. households owning Individual Retirement Accounts (IRAs) in year x is approximated by the equation

$$0.096(x - 2000) = 15y - 5.16.$$

Assuming this equation remains valid, use a calculator to determine when 44% of households will own an IRA. (Data from: ProQuest Statistical Abstract of the United States: 2013.)

Solution   Since 44% = .44, let $y = .44$ in the equation and solve for x. To avoid any rounding errors in the intermediate steps, it is often a good idea to do all the algebra first, before using the calculator:

$$0.096(x - 2000) = 15y - 5.16$$
$$0.096(x - 2000) = 15 \cdot .44 - 5.16 \qquad \text{Substitute } y = .44$$
$$.096x - .096 \cdot 2000 = 15 \cdot .44 - 5.16 \qquad \text{Distributive property}$$
$$.096x = 15 \cdot .44 - 5.16 + .096 \cdot 2000 \qquad \text{Add } .096 \cdot 2000 \text{ to both sides.}$$
$$x = \frac{15 \cdot .44 - 5.16 + .096 \cdot 2000}{.096} \qquad \text{Divide both sides by .096}$$

```
15*.44-5.16+.096*2000
              .096
                    2015
```

Figure 1.12

Now use a calculator to determine that $x = 2015$, as shown in Figure 1.12. So 44% of households will own an IRA in 2015. ✓₄

The next three examples show how to simplify the solution of first-degree equations involving fractions. We solve these equations by multiplying both sides of the equation by a *common denominator.* This step will eliminate the fractions.

✓ Checkpoint 4

In Example 3, in what year will 48% of U.S. households own an IRA?

Example 4   Solve

$$\frac{r}{10} - \frac{2}{15} = \frac{3r}{20} - \frac{1}{5}.$$

Solution   Here, the denominators are 10, 15, 20, and 5. Each of these numbers is a factor of 60; therefore, 60 is a common denominator. Multiply both sides of the equation by 60:

$$60\left(\frac{r}{10} - \frac{2}{15}\right) = 60\left(\frac{3r}{20} - \frac{1}{5}\right)$$

$$60\left(\frac{r}{10}\right) - 60\left(\frac{2}{15}\right) = 60\left(\frac{3r}{20}\right) - 60\left(\frac{1}{5}\right) \qquad \text{Distributive property}$$

$$6r - 8 = 9r - 12$$

$$6r - 8 + (-6r) + 12 = 9r - 12 + (-6r) + 12 \qquad \text{Add } -6r \text{ and 12 to both sides.}$$

$$4 = 3r$$

$$r = \frac{4}{3}. \qquad \text{Multiply both sides by 1/3.}$$

✓ Checkpoint 5

Solve the following.

(a) $\dfrac{x}{2} - \dfrac{x}{4} = 6$

(b) $\dfrac{2x}{3} + \dfrac{1}{2} = \dfrac{x}{4} - \dfrac{9}{2}$

Check this solution in the original equation.

⚠ CAUTION Multiplying *both* sides of an *equation* by a number to eliminate fractions is valid. But multiplying a single fraction by a number to simplify it is not valid. For instance, multiplying $\dfrac{3x}{8}$ by 8 *changes* it to $3x$, which is *not equal* to $\dfrac{3x}{8}$.

The second property of equality (page 43) applies only to *nonzero* quantities. Multiplying or dividing both sides of an equation by a quantity involving the variable (which might be zero for some values) may lead to an **extraneous solution**—that is, a number that does not satisfy the original equation. To avoid errors in such situations, always *check your solutions in the original equation.*

Example 5   Solve

$$\frac{4}{3(k+2)} - \frac{k}{3(k+2)} = \frac{5}{3}.$$

Solution   Multiply both sides of the equation by the common denominator $3(k+2)$. Here, $k \neq -2$, since $k = -2$ would give a 0 denominator, making the fraction undefined. So, we have

$$3(k+2) \cdot \frac{4}{3(k+2)} - 3(k+2) \cdot \frac{k}{3(k+2)} = 3(k+2) \cdot \frac{5}{3}.$$

Simplify each side and solve for k:

$$4 - k = 5(k+2)$$

$$4 - k = 5k + 10 \qquad \text{Distributive property}$$

$$4 - k + k = 5k + 10 + k \qquad \text{Add } k \text{ to both sides.}$$

$$4 = 6k + 10$$

$$4 + (-10) = 6k + 10 + (-10) \qquad \text{Add } -10 \text{ to both sides.}$$

$$-6 = 6k$$

$$-1 = k. \qquad \text{Multiply both sides by } \frac{1}{6}.$$

The solution is -1. Substitute -1 for k in the original equation as a check:

$$\frac{4}{3(-1+2)} - \frac{-1}{3(-1+2)} \overset{?}{=} \frac{5}{3}$$

$$\frac{4}{3} - \frac{-1}{3} \overset{?}{=} \frac{5}{3}$$

✓ Checkpoint 6

Solve the equation

$$\frac{5p+1}{3(p+1)} = \frac{3p-3}{3(p+1)} + \frac{9p-3}{3(p+1)}.$$

$$\frac{5}{3} = \frac{5}{3}.$$

The check shows that -1 is the solution.

Example 6   Solve

$$\frac{3x - 4}{x - 2} = \frac{x}{x - 2}.$$

Solution   Multiplying both sides by $x - 2$ produces

$$3x - 4 = x$$
$$2x - 4 = 0 \qquad \text{Subtract } x \text{ from both sides.}$$
$$2x = 4 \qquad \text{Add 4 to both sides.}$$
$$x = 2. \qquad \text{Divide both sides by 2.}$$

Substituting 2 for x in the original equation produces fractions with 0 denominators. Since division by 0 is not defined, $x = 2$ is an extraneous solution. So the original equation has no solution. ✓7

Sometimes an equation with several variables must be solved for one of the variables. This process is called **solving for a specified variable.**

Example 7   Solve for x: $3(ax - 5a) + 4b = 4x - 2$.

Solution   Use the distributive property to get

$$3ax - 15a + 4b = 4x - 2.$$

Treat x as the variable and the other letters as constants. Get all terms with x on one side of the equation and all terms without x on the other side:

$$3ax - 4x = 15a - 4b - 2 \qquad \text{Isolate terms with } x \text{ on the left.}$$
$$(3a - 4)x = 15a - 4b - 2 \qquad \text{Distributive property}$$
$$x = \frac{15a - 4b - 2}{3a - 4} \qquad \text{Multiply both sides by } \frac{1}{3a - 4}.$$

The final equation is solved for x, as required. ✓8

Absolute-Value Equations

Recall from Section 1.1 that the absolute value of a number a is either a or $-a$, whichever one is nonnegative. For instance, $|4| = 4$ and $|-7| = -(-7) = 7$.

Example 8   Solve $|x| = 3$.

Solution   Since $|x|$ is either x or $-x$, the equation says that

$$x = 3 \qquad \text{or} \qquad -x = 3$$
$$x = -3.$$

The solutions of $|x| = 3$ are 3 and -3.

Example 9   Solve $|p - 4| = 2$.

Solution   Since $|p - 4|$ is either $p - 4$ or $-(p - 4)$, we have

$$p - 4 = 2 \qquad \text{or} \qquad -(p - 4) = 2$$
$$p = 6 \qquad\qquad -p + 4 = 2$$
$$-p = -2$$
$$p = 2,$$

so that 6 and 2 are possible solutions. Checking them in the original equation shows that both are solutions. ✓9

✓ **Checkpoint 7**

Solve each equation.

(a) $\dfrac{3p}{p + 1} = 1 - \dfrac{3}{p + 1}$

(b) $\dfrac{8y}{y - 4} = \dfrac{32}{y - 4} - 3$

✓ **Checkpoint 8**

Solve for x.

(a) $2x - 7y = 3xk$

(b) $8(4 - x) + 6p = -5k - 11yx$

✓ **Checkpoint 9**

Solve each equation.

(a) $|y| = 9$

(b) $|r + 3| = 1$

(c) $|2k - 3| = 7$

Example 10   Solve $|4m - 3| = |m + 6|$.

Solution   To satisfy the equation, the quantities in absolute-value bars must either be equal or be negatives of one another. That is,

$$4m - 3 = m + 6 \quad \text{or} \quad 4m - 3 = -(m + 6)$$
$$3m = 9 \qquad\qquad 4m - 3 = -m - 6$$
$$m = 3 \qquad\qquad 5m = -3$$
$$m = -\frac{3}{5}.$$

Check that the solutions for the original equation are 3 and $-3/5$. ✓10

✓ **Checkpoint 10**

Solve each equation.

(a) $|r + 6| = |2r + 1|$

(b) $|5k - 7| = |10k - 2|$

Applications

One of the main reasons for learning mathematics is to be able to use it to solve practical problems. There are no hard-and-fast rules for dealing with real-world applications, except perhaps to use common sense. However, you will find it much easier to deal with such problems if you do not try to do everything at once. After reading the problem carefully, attack it in stages, as suggested in the following guidelines.

Solving Applied Problems

Step 1   Read the problem carefully, focusing on the facts you are given and the unknown values you are asked to find. Look up any words you do not understand. You may have to read the problem more than once, until you understand exactly what you are being asked to do.

Step 2   Identify the unknown. (If there is more than one, choose one of them, and see Step 3 for what to do with the others.) Name the unknown with some variable that you *write down*. Many students try to skip this step. They are eager to get on with the writing of the equation. But this is an important step. If you do not know what the variable represents, how can you write a meaningful equation or interpret a result?

Step 3   Decide on a variable expression to represent any other unknowns in the problem. For example, if x represents the width of a rectangle, and you know that the length is one more than twice the width, then *write down* the fact that the length is $1 + 2x$.

Step 4   Draw a sketch or make a chart, if appropriate, showing the information given in the problem.

Step 5   Using the results of Steps 1–4, write an equation that expresses a condition that must be satisfied.

Step 6   Solve the equation.

Step 7   Check the solution in the words of the *original problem*, not just in the equation you have written.

Example 11   **Finance**   A financial manager has $15,000 to invest for her company. She plans to invest part of the money in tax-free bonds at 5% interest and the remainder in taxable bonds at 8%. She wants to earn $1020 per year in interest from the investments. Find the amount she should invest at each rate.

Solution

Step 1 We are asked to find how much of the $15,000 should be invested at 5% and how much at 8%, in order to earn the required interest.

Step 2 Let x represent the amount to be invested at 5%.

Step 3 After x dollars are invested, the remaining amount is $15,000 - x$ dollars, which is to be invested at 8%.

Step 4 Interest for one year is given by rate × amount invested. For instance, 5% of x dollars is $.05x$. The given information is summarized in the following chart.

Investment	Amount Invested	Interest Rate	Interest Earned in One Year
Tax-free bonds	x	5% = .05	$.05x$
Taxable bonds	$15,000 - x$	8% = .08	$.08(15,000 - x)$
Totals	15,000		1020

Step 5 Because the total interest is to be $1020, the last column of the table shows that

$$.05x + .08(15,000 - x) = 1020.$$

Step 6 Solve the preceding equation as follows:

$$.05x + .08(15,000 - x) = 1020$$
$$.05x + .08(15,000) - .08x = 1020$$
$$.05x + 1200 - .08x = 1020$$
$$-.03x = -180$$
$$x = 6000.$$

The manager should invest $6000 at 5% and $15,000 - $6000 = $9000 at 8%.

Step 7 Check these results in the original problem. If $6000 is invested at 5%, the interest is .05(6000) = $300. If $9000 is invested at 8%, the interest is .08(9000) = $720. So the total interest is $300 + $720 = $1020 as required ☑11

✓ **Checkpoint 11**

An investor owns two pieces of property. One, worth twice as much as the other, returns 6% in annual interest, while the other returns 4%. Find the value of each piece of property if the total annual interest earned is $8000.

Example 12 **Business** Spotify and Rhapsody are digital music streaming services. In 2012, *Time* magazine reported that Spotify acquired in 7 business quarters (a quarter is a 3-month period) the same number of users as Rhapsody acquired in 11 years (44 quarters). Spotify's average rate of user acquisition per quarter was 120,000 more than Rhapsody's average rate per quarter. Find the average rate of user acquisition per quarter for each company.

Solution

Step 1 We must find Spotify's user acquisition rate and Rhapsody's user acquisition rate.

Step 2 Let x represent Rhapsody's rate.

Step 3 Since Spotify's rate is 120,000 users per quarter faster than Rhapsody's, its rate is $x + 120,000$.

Step 4 In general, the number of users can be found by the formula:

Number of users = number of quarters × rate of users per quarter

So, for Rhapsody, number of users = $44x$ and for

Spotify, the number of users = $7(x + 120,000)$

We can collect these facts to make a chart, which organizes the information given in the problem.

	Quarters		Rate	Number of Users
Rhapsody	44		x	$44x$
Spotify	7	·	$x + 120{,}000$	$7(x + 120{,}000)$

Step 5   Because both companies obtained the *same number of users*, the equation is

$$44x = 7(x + 120{,}000).$$

Step 6   If we distribute the 7 through the quantity on the right side of the equation, we obtain

$$44x = 7x + 840{,}000$$

$$37x = 840{,}000 \qquad \text{Add } -7x \text{ to each side.}$$

$$x \approx 22{,}703 \qquad \text{Divide each side by 37.}$$

Step 7   Since x represents Rhapsody's rate, Rhapsody acquired, on average, 22,702 users per quarter. Spotify's rate is $x + 120{,}000$, or $22{,}702 + 120{,}000 = 142{,}702$ users per quarter. ✓12

✓**Checkpoint 12**

In Example 12, suppose Spotify had taken 12 quarters and Rhapsody had taken 40 quarters to reach the same number of users. Assuming that Spotify acquired users at a rate 100,000 per quarter more than Rhapsody, find the average rate at which

(a)   Rhapsody had acquired users.

(b)   Spotify had acquired users.

Example 13   **Business**   An oil company needs to fill orders for 89-octane gas, but has only 87- and 93-octane gas on hand. The octane rating is the percentage of isooctane in the standard fuel. How much of each type should be mixed together to produce 100,000 gallons of 89-octane gas?

Solution

Step 1   We must find how much 87-octane gas and how much 93-octane gas are needed for the 100,000 gallon mixture.

Step 2   Let x be the amount of 87-octane gas.

Step 3   Then $100{,}000 - x$ is the amount of 93-octane gas.

Step 4   We can summarize the relevant information in a chart.

Type of Gas	Quantity	% Isooctane	Amount of Isooctane
87-octane	x	87%	$.87x$
93-octane	$100{,}000 - x$	93%	$.93(100{,}000 - x)$
Mixture	100,000	89%	$.89(100{,}000)$

Step 5   The amount of isooctane satisfies this equation:

$$.87x + .93(100{,}000 - x) = .89(100{,}000).$$

Step 6   Solving this equation yields

$$.87x + 93{,}000 - .93x = .89(100{,}000) \qquad \text{Distribute the left side.}$$

$$.87x + 93{,}000 - .93x = 89{,}000 \qquad \text{Multiply on the right side.}$$

$$-.06x = -4000 \qquad \text{Combine terms and add } -93{,}000 \text{ to each side.}$$

$$x = \frac{-4000}{-.06} \approx 66{,}667.$$

Step 7   So the distributor should mix 66,667 gallons of 87-octane gas with $100{,}000 - 66{,}667 = 33{,}333$ gallons of 93-octane gas. Then the amount of isooctane in the mixture is

$$.87(66{,}667) + .93(33{,}333)$$

$$\approx 58{,}000 + 31{,}000$$

$$= 89{,}000.$$

✓**Checkpoint 13**

How much 89-octane gas and how much 94-octane gas are needed to produce 1500 gallons of 91-octane gas?

Hence, the octane rating of the mixture is $\dfrac{89{,}000}{100{,}000} = .89$ as required. ✓13

1.6 Exercises

Solve each equation. (See Examples 1–6.)

1. $3x + 8 = 20$

2. $4 - 5y = 19$

3. $.6k - .3 = .5k + .4$

4. $2.5 + 5.04m = 8.5 - .06m$

5. $2a - 1 = 4(a + 1) + 7a + 5$

6. $3(k - 2) - 6 = 4k - (3k - 1)$

7. $2[x - (3 + 2x) + 9] = 3x - 8$

8. $-2[4(k + 2) - 3(k + 1)] = 14 + 2k$

9. $\dfrac{3x}{5} - \dfrac{4}{5}(x + 1) = 2 - \dfrac{3}{10}(3x - 4)$

10. $\dfrac{4}{3}(x - 2) - \dfrac{1}{2} = 2\left(\dfrac{3}{4}x - 1\right)$

11. $\dfrac{5y}{6} - 8 = 5 - \dfrac{2y}{3}$

12. $\dfrac{x}{2} - 3 = \dfrac{3x}{5} + 1$

13. $\dfrac{m}{2} - \dfrac{1}{m} = \dfrac{6m + 5}{12}$

14. $-\dfrac{3k}{2} + \dfrac{9k - 5}{6} = \dfrac{11k + 8}{k}$

15. $\dfrac{4}{x - 3} - \dfrac{8}{2x + 5} + \dfrac{3}{x - 3} = 0$

16. $\dfrac{5}{2p + 3} - \dfrac{3}{p - 2} = \dfrac{4}{2p + 3}$

17. $\dfrac{3}{2m + 4} = \dfrac{1}{m + 2} - 2$

18. $\dfrac{8}{3k - 9} - \dfrac{5}{k - 3} = 4$

Use a calculator to solve each equation. Round your answer to the nearest hundredth. (See Example 3.)

19. $9.06x + 3.59(8x - 5) = 12.07x + .5612$

20. $-5.74(3.1 - 2.7p) = 1.09p + 5.2588$

21. $\dfrac{2.63r - 8.99}{1.25} - \dfrac{3.90r - 1.77}{2.45} = r$

22. $\dfrac{8.19m + 2.55}{4.34} - \dfrac{8.17m - 9.94}{1.04} = 4m$

Solve each equation for x. (See Example 7.)

23. $4(a + x) = b - a + 2x$

24. $(3a - b) - bx = a(x - 2)$ $(a \neq -b)$

25. $5(b - x) = 2b + ax$ $(a \neq -5)$

26. $bx - 2b = 2a - ax$

Solve each equation for the specified variable. Assume that all denominators are nonzero. (See Example 7.)

27. $PV = k$ for V

28. $i = prt$ for p

29. $V = V_0 + gt$ for g

30. $S = S_0 + gt^2 + k$ for g

31. $A = \dfrac{1}{2}(B + b)h$ for B

32. $C = \dfrac{5}{9}(F - 32)$ for F

Solve each equation. (See Examples 8–10.)

33. $|2h - 1| = 5$

34. $|4m - 3| = 12$

35. $|6 + 2p| = 10$

36. $|-5x + 7| = 15$

37. $\left|\dfrac{5}{r - 3}\right| = 10$

38. $\left|\dfrac{3}{2h - 1}\right| = 4$

Solve the following applied problems.

Health   *According to the American Heart Association, the number y of brain neurons (in billions) that are lost in a stroke lasting x hours is given by $y = \dfrac{x}{8}$. Find the length of the stroke for the given number of neurons lost.*

39. 1,250,000,000

40. 2,400,000,000

Natural Science   *The equation that relates Fahrenheit temperature F to Celsius temperature C is*

$$C = \dfrac{5}{9}(F - 32).$$

Find the Fahrenheit temperature corresponding to these Celsius temperatures.

41. -5

42. -15

43. 22

44. 36

Finance   *The gross federal debt y (in trillions of dollars) in year x is approximated by*

$$y = 1.16x + 1.76,$$

where x is the number of years after 2000. Assuming the trend continues, in what year will the federal debt be the given amount? (Data from: U.S. Office of Management and Budget.)

45. $13.36 trillion

46. $16.84 trillion

47. $19.16 trillion

48. $24.96 trillion

Health Economics   *The total health care expenditures E in the United States (in trillions of dollars) can be approximated by*

$$E = .118x + 1.45,$$

where x is the number of years after 2000. Assuming the trend continues, determine the year in which health care expenditures are at the given level. (*Data from: U.S. Centers for Medicare and Medicaid Services.*)

49. $2.63 trillion **50.** $2.866 trillion

51. $3.338 trillion **52.** $3.574 trillion

Finance *The percentage y (written as a decimal) of U.S. households who owned Roth Individual Retirement Accounts (IRAs) in year x is given by the equation*

$$.09(x - 2004) = 12y - 1.44.$$

Find the year in which the given percentage of U.S. households own a Roth IRA. (Data from: Proquest Statistical Abstract of the United States: 2013.)

53. 18.0% **54.** 19.5%

55. 21% **56.** 23.25%

Finance *The total amount A (in millions of dollars) donated within a state for charitable contributions claimed on individual federal tax returns can be modeled by the function*

$$A = 4.35x - 12$$

where x is the total number of returns filed (in thousands) for the state. For the given amounts A donated, determine the number of returns that were filed within the following states. (Data from: Proquest Statistical Abstract of the United States: 2013.)

57. California: $A = \$20,777$ million

58. New York: $A = \$13,732$ million

59. Texas: $A = \$13,360$ million

60. Florida: $A = \$9596$ million

Business *When a loan is paid off early, a portion of the finance charge must be returned to the borrower. By one method of calculating the finance charge (called the rule of 78), the amount of unearned interest (finance charge to be returned) is given by*

$$u = f \cdot \frac{n(n + 1)}{q(q + 1)},$$

where u represents unearned interest, f is the original finance charge, n is the number of payments remaining when the loan is paid off, and q is the original number of payments. Find the amount of the unearned interest in each of the given cases.

61. Original finance charge = $800, loan scheduled to run 36 months, paid off with 18 payments remaining

62. Original finance charge = $1400, loan scheduled to run 48 months, paid off with 12 payments remaining

Business *Solve the following investment problems. (See Example 11.)*

63. Joe Gonzalez received $52,000 profit from the sale of some land. He invested part at 5% interest and the rest at 4% interest. He earned a total of $2290 interest per year. How much did he invest at 5%?

64. Weijen Luan invests $20,000 received from an insurance settlement in two ways: some at 6% and some at 4%. Altogether, she makes $1040 per year in interest. How much is invested at 4%?

65. Maria Martinelli bought two plots of land for a total of $120,000. On the first plot, she made a profit of 15%. On the second, she lost 10%. Her total profit was $5500. How much did she pay for each piece of land?

66. Suppose $20,000 is invested at 5%. How much additional money must be invested at 4% to produce a yield of 4.8% on the entire amount invested?

Solve the given applied problems. (See Example 12.)

According to data from comScore.com, two social media sites, Tumblr.com and Pinterest.com, acquired the same number of unique visitors in 2012. Tumblr.com took 63 months to acquire these visitors while Pinterest.com took 30 months. Pinterest's rate of visitor growth was 450,000 more a month, on average, than Tumblr's average growth per month.

67. Find the average rate of growth of Tumblr.com.

68. Find the average rate of growth of Pinterest.com.

69. Approximately how many unique visitors did Tumblr.com acquire in 63 months?

70. Approximately how many unique visitors did Pinterest.com acquire in 30 months?

Natural Science *Using the same assumptions about octane ratings as in Example 13, solve the following problems.*

71. How many liters of 94-octane gasoline should be mixed with 200 liters of 99-octane gasoline to get a mixture that is 97-octane gasoline?

72. A service station has 92-octane and 98-octane gasoline. How many liters of each gasoline should be mixed to provide 12 liters of 96-octane gasoline for a chemistry experiment?

Solve the following applied problems.

73. **Business** A major car rental firm charges $78 a day for a full-size car in Tampa, Florida, with unlimited mileage. Another firm offers a similar car for $55 a day plus 22 cents per mile. How far must you drive in a day in order for the cost to be the same for both vehicles?

74. **Business** A car radiator contains 8.5 quarts of fluid, 35% of which is antifreeze. How much fluid should be drained and replaced with pure (100%) antifreeze in order that the new mixture be 65% antifreeze?

Business *Massachusetts has a graduated fine system for speeding, meaning you can pay a base fine and then have more charges added on top. For example, the base fine for speeding is $100. But that is just the start. If you are convicted of going more than 10 mph over the speed limit, add $10 for each additional mph you were traveling over the speed limit plus 10 mph. Thus, the amount of the fine y (in dollars) for driving x miles over the speed limit (when the speed limit is 65 miles per hour) can be represented as*

$$y = 10(x - 75) + 100, \quad x \geq 75.$$

(Data from: www.dmv.org.)

75. If Paul was fined $180 for speeding, how fast was he going?

76. If Sarah was fined $120 for speeding, how fast was she going?

Jack borrowed his father's luxury car and promised to return it with a full tank of premium gas, which costs $3.80 per gallon. From experience, he knows that he needs 15.5 gallons. He has, however, only $50 (and no credit card). He decides to get as much premium as possible and fill the remainder of the tank with regular gas, which costs $3.10 per gallon.

77. How much of each type of gas should he get?

78. If he has $53, how much of each type of gas should he get?

✓ Checkpoint Answers

1. (a) Yes   (b) No   (c) No

2. (a) 8   (b) −2   (c) 2

3. (a) 8   (b) −3

4. Early 2021 ($x = 2021.25$)

5. (a) 24   (b) −12

6. 1

7. Neither equation has a solution.

8. (a) $x = \dfrac{7y}{2 - 3k}$ (b) $x = \dfrac{5k + 32 + 6p}{8 - 11y}$

9. (a) 9, −9   (b) −2, −4   (c) 5, −2

10. (a) 5, −7/3   (b) −1, 3/5

11. 6% return: $100,000; 4% return: $50,000

12. (a) 42,857 per quarter
      (b) 142,857 per quarter

13. 900 gallons of 89-octane gas; 600 gallons of 94-octane gas

1.7 Quadratic Equations

An equation that can be written in the form

$$ax^2 + bx + c = 0,$$

where a, b, and c are real numbers with $a \neq 0$, is called a **quadratic equation.** For example, each of

$$2x^2 + 3x + 4 = 0, \qquad x^2 = 6x - 9, \qquad 3x^2 + x = 6, \qquad \text{and} \qquad x^2 = 5$$

is a quadratic equation. A solution of an equation that is a real number is said to be a **real solution** of the equation.

One method of solving quadratic equations is based on the following property of real numbers.

Zero-Factor Property

If a and b are real numbers, with $ab = 0$, then $a = 0$ or $b = 0$ or both.

Example 1   Solve the equation $(x - 4)(3x + 7) = 0$.

Solution   By the zero-factor property, the product $(x - 4)(3x + 7)$ can equal 0 only if at least one of the factors equals 0. That is, the product equals zero only if $x - 4 = 0$ or $3x + 7 = 0$. Solving each of these equations separately will give the solutions of the original equation:

$$x - 4 = 0 \qquad \text{or} \qquad 3x + 7 = 0$$
$$x = 4 \qquad \text{or} \qquad 3x = -7$$
$$x = -\frac{7}{3}.$$

The solutions of the equation $(x - 4)(3x + 7) = 0$ are 4 and −7/3. Check these solutions by substituting them into the original equation. ✓₁

✓ Checkpoint 1

Solve the following equations.

(a) $(y - 6)(y + 2) = 0$

(b) $(5k - 3)(k + 5) = 0$

(c) $(2r - 9)(3r + 5) \cdot (r + 3) = 0$

Example 2   Solve $6r^2 + 7r = 3$.

Solution   Rewrite the equation as

$$6r^2 + 7r - 3 = 0.$$

Now factor $6r^2 + 7r - 3$ to get

$$(3r - 1)(2r + 3) = 0.$$

By the zero-factor property, the product $(3r - 1)(2r + 3)$ can equal 0 only if

$$3r - 1 = 0 \quad \text{or} \quad 2r + 3 = 0.$$

Solving each of these equations separately gives the solutions of the original equation:

$$3r = 1 \quad \text{or} \quad 2r = -3$$
$$r = \frac{1}{3} \qquad\qquad r = -\frac{3}{2}.$$

Verify that both $1/3$ and $-3/2$ are solutions by substituting them into the original equation. ✓₂

An equation such as $x^2 = 5$ has two solutions: $\sqrt{5}$ and $-\sqrt{5}$. This fact is true in general.

✓**Checkpoint 2**

Solve each equation by factoring.

(a) $y^2 + 3y = 10$

(b) $2r^2 + 9r = 5$

(c) $4k^2 = 9k$

> ## Square-Root Property
>
> If $b > 0$, then the solutions of $x^2 = b$ are $\sqrt{b}$ and $-\sqrt{b}$.

The two solutions are sometimes abbreviated $\pm\sqrt{b}$.

Example 3   Solve each equation.

(a) $m^2 = 17$

Solution   By the square-root property, the solutions are $\sqrt{17}$ and $-\sqrt{17}$, abbreviated $\pm\sqrt{17}$.

(b) $(y - 4)^2 = 11$

Solution   Use a generalization of the square-root property, we work as follows.

$$(y - 4)^2 = 11$$
$$y - 4 = \sqrt{11} \quad \text{or} \quad y - 4 = -\sqrt{11}$$
$$y = 4 + \sqrt{11} \qquad\qquad y = 4 - \sqrt{11}.$$

Abbreviate the solutions as $4 \pm \sqrt{11}$. ✓₃

✓**Checkpoint 3**

Solve each equation by using the square-root property.

(a) $p^2 = 21$

(b) $(m + 7)^2 = 15$

(c) $(2k - 3)^2 = 5$

When a quadratic equation cannot be easily factored, it can be solved by using the following formula, which you should memorize.*

> ## Quadratic Formula
>
> The solutions of the quadratic equation $ax^2 + bx + c = 0$, where $a \neq 0$, are given by
>
> $$x = \frac{-b \pm \sqrt{b^2 - 4ac}}{2a}.$$

---

*A proof of the quadratic formula can be found in many College Algebra books.

> ⊘ **CAUTION** When using the quadratic formula, remember that the equation must be in the form $ax^2 + bx + c = 0$. Also, notice that the fraction bar in the quadratic formula extends under *both* terms in the numerator. Be sure to add $-b$ to $\pm \sqrt{b^2 - 4ac}$ *before* dividing by $2a$.

Example 4 Solve $x^2 + 1 = 4x$.

Solution First add $-4x$ to both sides to get 0 alone on the right side:

$$x^2 - 4x + 1 = 0.$$

Now identify the values of a, b, and c. Here, $a = 1$, $b = -4$, and $c = 1$. Substitute these numbers into the quadratic formula to obtain

$$x = \frac{-(-4) \pm \sqrt{(-4)^2 - 4(1)(1)}}{2(1)}$$

$$= \frac{4 \pm \sqrt{16 - 4}}{2}$$

$$= \frac{4 \pm \sqrt{12}}{2}$$

$$= \frac{4 \pm 2\sqrt{3}}{2} \qquad \sqrt{12} = \sqrt{4 \cdot 3} = \sqrt{4} \cdot \sqrt{3} = 2\sqrt{3}$$

$$= \frac{2(2 \pm \sqrt{3})}{2} \qquad \text{Factor } 4 \pm 2\sqrt{3}.$$

$$x = 2 \pm \sqrt{3}. \qquad \text{Cancel 2.}$$

The $\pm$ sign represents the two solutions of the equation. First use $+$ and then use $-$ to find each of the solutions: $2 + \sqrt{3}$ and $2 - \sqrt{3}$. ☑ 4

Example 4 shows that the quadratic formula produces exact solutions. In many real-world applications, however, you must use a calculator to find decimal approximations of the solutions. The approximate solutions in Example 4 are

$$x = 2 + \sqrt{3} \approx 3.732050808 \qquad \text{and} \qquad x = 2 - \sqrt{3} \approx .2679491924,$$

as shown in Figure 1.13.

Example 5 **Business** Many companies in recent years saw their net earnings follow a parabolic pattern because of the recession that began in 2008. One such example is Motorola Corporation. The net earnings for Motorola Corporation E (in millions of dollars) can be approximated by the function

$$E = 545.9x^2 - 10{,}408x + 48{,}085 \quad (6 \le x \le 12),$$

where $x = 6$ corresponds to the year 2006. Use the quadratic formula and a calculator to find the year in which net earnings recovered to $1799 million. (Data from: www.morningstar.com.)

Solution To find the year x, solve the equation above when $E = 1799$:

$$545.9x^2 - 10{,}408x + 48{,}085 = E$$

$$545.9x^2 - 10{,}408x + 48{,}085 = 1799 \qquad \text{Substitute } E = 1799.$$

$$545.9x^2 - 10{,}408x + 46{,}286 = 0 \qquad \text{Subtract 1799 from both sides.}$$

To apply the quadratic formula, first compute the radical part:

$$\sqrt{b^2 - 4ac} = \sqrt{(10{,}408)^2 - 4(545.9)(46{,}286)} = \sqrt{7{,}256{,}354.4}.$$

✓ **Checkpoint 4**

Use the quadratic formula to solve each equation.

(a) $x^2 - 2x = 2$

(b) $u^2 - 6u + 4 = 0$

```
2+√3
         3.732050808
2-√3
         .2679491924
```

Figure 1.13

Figure 1.14

Then store $\sqrt{7{,}256{,}354.4}$ (which we denote by M) in the calculator memory. (Check your instruction manual for how to store and recall numbers.) By the quadratic formula, the exact solutions of the equation are

$$x = \frac{-b \pm \sqrt{b^2 - 4ac}}{2a} = \frac{-b \pm M}{2a} = \frac{-(-10{,}408) \pm M}{2(545.9)} = \frac{10{,}408 \pm M}{1091.8}.$$

Figure 1.14 shows that the approximate solutions are

$$\frac{10{,}408 + M}{1091.8} \approx 12.0 \qquad \frac{10{,}408 - M}{1091.8} \approx 7.1.$$

Since we were told that net earnings had recovered, we use the solution later in time and $x = 12$ corresponds to 2012. ☑5

✓Checkpoint 5

Use the equation of Example 5 to find the year in which net earnings were first −$140 million dollars.

Example 6   Solve $9x^2 - 30x + 25 = 0$.

Solution   Applying the quadratic formula with $a = 9$, $b = -30$, and $c = 25$, we have

$$x = \frac{-(-30) \pm \sqrt{(-30)^2 - 4(9)(25)}}{2(9)}$$

$$= \frac{30 \pm \sqrt{900 - 900}}{18} = \frac{30 \pm 0}{18} = \frac{30}{18} = \frac{5}{3}.$$

Therefore, the given equation has only one real solution. The fact that the solution is a rational number indicates that this equation could have been solved by factoring.

✓ TECHNOLOGY TIP

You can approximate the solutions of quadratic equations on a graphing calculator by using a quadratic formula program (see the Program Appendix) or using a built-in quadratic equation solver if your calculator has one. Then you need only enter the values of the coefficients a, b, and c to obtain the approximate solutions.

Example 7   Solve $x^2 - 6x + 10 = 0$.

Solution   Apply the quadratic formula with $a = 1$, $b = -6$, and $c = 10$:

$$x = \frac{-(-6) \pm \sqrt{(-6)^2 - 4(1)(10)}}{2(1)}$$

$$= \frac{6 \pm \sqrt{36 - 40}}{2}$$

$$= \frac{6 \pm \sqrt{-4}}{2}.$$

Since no negative number has a square root in the real-number system, $\sqrt{-4}$ is not a real number. Hence, the equation has no real solutions. ☑6

Examples 4–7 show that the number of solutions of the quadratic equation $ax^2 + bx + c = 0$ is determined by $b^2 - 4ac$, the quantity under the radical, which is called the **discriminant** of the equation. ☑7

✓Checkpoint 6

Solve each equation.
(a) $9k^2 - 6k + 1 = 0$
(b) $4m^2 + 28m + 49 = 0$
(c) $2x^2 - 5x + 5 = 0$

✓Checkpoint 7

Use the discriminant to determine the number of real solutions of each equation.
(a) $x^2 + 8x + 3 = 0$
(b) $2x^2 + x + 3 = 0$
(c) $x^2 - 194x + 9409 = 0$

The Discriminant

The equation $ax^2 + bx + c = 0$ has either two, or one, or no real solutions.

If $b^2 - 4ac > 0$, there are two real solutions. (*Examples 4 and 5*)
If $b^2 - 4ac = 0$, there is one real solution. (*Example 6*)
If $b^2 - 4ac < 0$, there are no real solutions. (*Example 7*)

Applications

Quadratic equations arise in a variety of settings, as illustrated in the next set of examples. Example 8 depends on the following useful fact from geometry.

The Pythagorean Theorem

In a right triangle with legs of lengths a and b and hypotenuse of length c,

$$a^2 + b^2 = c^2.$$

Example 8   **Business** The size of a flat screen television is the diagonal measurement of its screen. The height of the screen is approximately 63% of its width. Kathy claims that John's 39-inch flat screen has only half of the viewing area that her 46-inch flat screen television has. Is Kathy right?

Solution   First, find the area of Kathy's screen. Let x be its width. Then its height is 63% of x (that is, $.63x$, as shown in Figure 1.15). By the Pythagorean theorem,

$$x^2 + (.63x)^2 = 46^2$$
$$x^2 + .3969x^2 = 2116 \qquad \text{Expand } (.63x)^2 \text{ and } 46^2.$$
$$(1 + .3969)x^2 = 2116 \qquad \text{Distributive property}$$
$$1.3969x^2 = 2116$$
$$x^2 = 1514.78 \qquad \text{Divide both sides by 1.3969.}$$
$$x = \pm\sqrt{1514.78} \qquad \text{Square-root property}$$
$$x \approx \pm 38.9.$$

Figure 1.15

We can ignore the negative solution, since x is a width. Thus, the width is 38.9 inches and the height is $.63x = .63(38.9) \approx 24.5$ inches, so the area is

$$\text{Area} = \text{width} \times \text{height} = 38.9 \times 24.5 = 953.1 \text{ square inches.}$$

Next we find the area of John's television in a similar manner. Let y be the width of John's television. Then its height is 63% of y. By the Pythagorean theorem,

$$y^2 + (.63y)^2 = 39^2$$
$$y^2 + .3969y^2 = 1521 \qquad \text{Expand } (.63y)^2 \text{ and } 39^2.$$
$$(1 + .3969)y^2 = 1521 \qquad \text{Distributive property}$$
$$1.3969y^2 = 1521$$
$$y^2 = 1088.84 \qquad \text{Divide both sides by 1.3969.}$$
$$y = \pm\sqrt{1088.84} \qquad \text{Square-root property}$$
$$y \approx \pm 33.0.$$

Again, we can ignore the negative solution, since y is a width. Thus, the width is 33.0 inches and the height is $.63y = .63(33.0) \approx 20.8$ inches, so the area is

$$\text{Area} = \text{width} \times \text{height} = 33.0 \times 20.8 = 686.4 \text{ square inches.}$$

Since half of 953.1 square inches (the area of Kathy's television) is 476.55 square inches, Kathy is wrong because John's viewing area is 686.4 square inches. ✓ 8

✓**Checkpoint 8**

If John's television was only a 26-inch flat screen television, would Kathy have been right?

Example 9   **Business** A landscape architect wants to make an exposed gravel border of uniform width around a small shed behind a company plant. The shed is 10 feet by 6 feet. He has enough gravel to cover 36 square feet. How wide should the border be?

Solution   A sketch of the shed with border is given in Figure 1.16. Let x represent the width of the border. Then the width of the large rectangle is $6 + 2x$, and its length is $10 + 2x$.

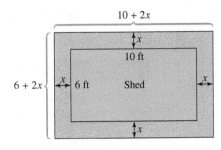

Figure 1.16

We must write an equation relating the given areas and dimensions. The area of the large rectangle is $(6 + 2x)(10 + 2x)$. The area occupied by the shed is $6 \cdot 10 = 60$. The area of the border is found by subtracting the area of the shed from the area of the large rectangle. This difference should be 36 square feet, giving the equation

$$(6 + 2x)(10 + 2x) - 60 = 36.$$

Solve this equation with the following sequence of steps:

$$60 + 32x + 4x^2 - 60 = 36 \qquad \text{Multiply out left side.}$$
$$4x^2 + 32x - 36 = 0 \qquad \text{Simplify.}$$
$$x^2 + 8x - 9 = 0 \qquad \text{Divide both sides by 4.}$$
$$(x + 9)(x - 1) = 0 \qquad \text{Factor.}$$
$$x + 9 = 0 \quad \text{or} \quad x - 1 = 0 \qquad \text{Zero-factor property.}$$
$$x = -9 \quad \text{or} \qquad x = 1.$$

The number -9 cannot be the width of the border, so the solution is to make the border 1 foot wide. ✓ 9

✓ **Checkpoint 9**

The length of a picture is 2 inches more than the width. It is mounted on a mat that extends 2 inches beyond the picture on all sides. What are the dimensions of the picture if the area of the mat is 99 square inches?

Example 10 **Physical Science**   If an object is thrown upward, dropped, or thrown downward and travels in a straight line subject only to gravity (with wind resistance ignored), the height h of the object above the ground (in feet) after t seconds is given by

$$h = -16t^2 + v_0 t + h_0,$$

where h_0 is the height of the object when $t = 0$ and v_0 is the initial velocity at time $t = 0$. The value of v_0 is taken to be positive if the object moves upward and negative if it moves downward. Suppose that a golf ball is thrown downward from the top of a 625-foot-high building with an initial velocity of 65 feet per second. How long does it take to reach the ground?

Solution   In this case, $h_0 = 625$ (the height of the building) and $v_0 = -65$ (negative because the ball is thrown downward). The object is on the ground when $h = 0$, so we must solve the equation

$$h = -16t^2 + v_0 t + h_0$$
$$0 = -16t^2 - 65t + 625. \qquad \text{Let } h = 0, v_0 = -65, \text{ and } h_0 = 625.$$

Using the quadratic formula and a calculator, we see that

$$t = \frac{-(-65) \pm \sqrt{(-65)^2 - 4(-16)(625)}}{2(-16)} = \frac{65 \pm \sqrt{44{,}225}}{-32} \approx \begin{cases} -8.60 \\ \text{or} \\ 4.54 \end{cases}$$

Only the positive answer makes sense in this case. So it takes about 4.54 seconds for the ball to reach the ground.

In some applications, it may be necessary to solve an equation in several variables for a specific variable.

Example 11 Solve $v = mx^2 + x$ for x. (Assume that m and v are positive.)

Solution The equation is quadratic in x because of the x^2 term. Before we use the quadratic formula, we write the equation in standard form:

$$v = mx^2 + x$$
$$0 = mx^2 + x - v.$$

Let $a = m$, $b = 1$, and $c = -v$. Then the quadratic formula gives

$$x = \frac{-1 \pm \sqrt{1^2 - 4(m)(-v)}}{2m}$$

$$x = \frac{-1 \pm \sqrt{1 + 4mv}}{2m}. \quad \checkmark_{10}$$

✓ **Checkpoint 10**

Solve each of the given equations for the indicated variable. Assume that all variables are positive.

(a) $k = mp^2 - bp$ for p

(b) $r = \dfrac{APk^2}{3}$ for k

1.7 Exercises

Use factoring to solve each equation. (See Examples 1 and 2.)

1. $(x + 4)(x - 14) = 0$
2. $(p - 16)(p - 5) = 0$
3. $x(x + 6) = 0$
4. $x^2 - 2x = 0$
5. $2z^2 = 4z$
6. $x^2 - 64 = 0$
7. $y^2 + 15y + 56 = 0$
8. $k^2 - 4k - 5 = 0$
9. $2x^2 = 7x - 3$
10. $2 = 15z^2 + z$
11. $6r^2 + r = 1$
12. $3y^2 = 16y - 5$
13. $2m^2 + 20 = 13m$
14. $6a^2 + 17a + 12 = 0$
15. $m(m + 7) = -10$
16. $z(2z + 7) = 4$
17. $9x^2 - 16 = 0$
18. $36y^2 - 49 = 0$
19. $16x^2 - 16x = 0$
20. $12y^2 - 48y = 0$

Solve each equation by using the square-root property. (See Example 3.)

21. $(r - 2)^2 = 7$
22. $(b + 4)^2 = 27$
23. $(4x - 1)^2 = 20$
24. $(3t + 5)^2 = 11$

Use the quadratic formula to solve each equation. If the solutions involve square roots, give both the exact and approximate solutions. (See Examples 4–7.)

25. $2x^2 + 7x + 1 = 0$
26. $3x^2 - x - 7 = 0$
27. $4k^2 + 2k = 1$
28. $r^2 = 3r + 5$
29. $5y^2 + 5y = 2$
30. $2z^2 + 3 = 8z$
31. $6x^2 + 6x + 4 = 0$
32. $3a^2 - 2a + 2 = 0$
33. $2r^2 + 3r - 5 = 0$
34. $8x^2 = 8x - 3$
35. $2x^2 - 7x + 30 = 0$
36. $3k^2 + k = 6$
37. $1 + \dfrac{7}{2a} = \dfrac{15}{2a^2}$
38. $5 - \dfrac{4}{k} - \dfrac{1}{k^2} = 0$

Use the discriminant to determine the number of real solutions of each equation. You need not solve the equations.

39. $25t^2 + 49 = 70t$
40. $9z^2 - 12z = 1$
41. $13x^2 + 24x - 5 = 0$
42. $20x^2 + 19x + 5 = 0$

Use a calculator and the quadratic formula to find approximate solutions of each equation. (See Example 5.)

43. $4.42x^2 - 10.14x + 3.79 = 0$
44. $3x^2 - 82.74x + 570.4923 = 0$
45. $7.63x^2 + 2.79x = 5.32$
46. $8.06x^2 + 25.8726x = 25.047256$

Solve the following problems. (See Example 3.)

47. **Physical Science** According to the Federal Aviation Administration, the maximum recommended taxiing speed x (in miles per hour) for a plane on a curved runway exit is given by $R = .5x^2$, where R is the radius of the curve (in feet). Find the maximum taxiing speed for planes on such exits when the radius of the exit is

    (a) 450 ft　　　(b) 615 ft　　　(c) 970 ft

48. **Social Science** The enrollment E in public colleges and universities (in millions) is approximated by $E = .011x^2 + 10.7$ where x is the number of years since 1990. Find the year when enrollment is the following. (Data from: ProQuest Statistical Abstract of the United States: 2013.)

    (a) 14.7 million　　　(b) 17.6 million

49. **Social Science** The number of traffic fatalities F (in thousands) where a driver involved in the crash had a blood alcohol level of .08 or higher can be approximated by the function

    $$F = -.079x^2 + .46x + 13.3 \quad (0 \le x \le 10),$$

    where $x = 0$ corresponds to the year 2000. Determine in what year the number of fatalities is approximately the given number. (Data from: National Highway Traffic Safety Administration.)

    (a) 12,600　　　(b) 11,000

50. Finance The total assets A of private and public pension funds (in trillions of dollars) can be approximated by the function

$$A = .237x^2 - 3.96x + 28.2 \quad (6 \le x \le 11),$$

where $x = 6$ corresponds to the year 2006. (Data from: Board of Governors of the Federal Reserve System.)

(a) What were the assets in 2008?

(b) What year after 2008 produced $12.3 trillion in assets?

51. Finance The assets A of public pension funds (in trillions of dollars) can be approximated by the function

$$A = .169x^2 - 2.85x + 19.6 \quad (6 \le x \le 11),$$

where $x = 6$ corresponds to the year 2006. (Data from: Board of Governors of the Federal Reserve System.)

(a) What were the assets in 2009?

(b) What year before 2008 produced $7.9 trillion in assets?

52. Business The net income for Apple A (in billions) can be approximated by the function

$$A = .877x^2 - 9.33x + 23.4 \quad (6 \le x \le 12),$$

where $x = 6$ corresponds to 2006. Find the year in which net income was the following. (Data from: www.morningstar.com.)

(a) $17.8 billion

(b) $37.7 billion

Solve the following problems. (See Examples 8 and 9).

53. Physical Science A 13-foot-long ladder leans on a wall, as shown in the accompanying figure. The bottom of the ladder is 5 feet from the wall. If the bottom is pulled out 2 feet farther from the wall, how far does the top of the ladder move down the wall? [*Hint:* Draw pictures of the right triangle formed by the ladder, the ground, and the wall before and after the ladder is moved. In each case, use the Pythagorean theorem to find the distance from the top of the ladder to the ground.]

5 ft

54. Physical Science A 15-foot-long pole leans against a wall. The bottom is 9 feet from the wall. How much farther should the bottom be pulled away from the wall so that the top moves the same amount down the wall?

55. Physical Science Two trains leave the same city at the same time, one going north and the other east. The eastbound train travels 20 mph faster than the northbound one. After 5 hours, the trains are 300 miles apart. Determine the speed of each train, using the following steps.

(a) Let x denote the speed of the northbound train. Express the speed of the eastbound train in terms of x.

(b) Write expressions that give the distance traveled by each train after 5 hours.

(c) Use part (b) and the fact that the trains are 300 miles apart after 5 hours to write an equation. (A diagram of the situation may help.)

(d) Solve the equation and determine the speeds of the trains.

56. Physical Science Chris and Josh have received walkie-talkies for Christmas. If they leave from the same point at the same time, Chris walking north at 2.5 mph and Josh walking east at 3 mph, how long will they be able to talk to each other if the range of the walkie-talkies is 4 miles? Round your answer to the nearest minute.

57. Physical Science An ecology center wants to set up an experimental garden. It has 300 meters of fencing to enclose a rectangular area of 5000 square meters. Find the length and width of the rectangle as follows.

(a) Let $x = $ the length and write an expression for the width.

(b) Write an equation relating the length, width, and area, using the result of part (a).

(c) Solve the problem.

58. Business A landscape architect has included a rectangular flower bed measuring 9 feet by 5 feet in her plans for a new building. She wants to use two colors of flowers in the bed, one in the center and the other for a border of the same width on all four sides. If she can get just enough plants to cover 24 square feet for the border, how wide can the border be?

59. Physical Science Joan wants to buy a rug for a room that is 12 feet by 15 feet. She wants to leave a uniform strip of floor around the rug. She can afford 108 square feet of carpeting. What dimensions should the rug have?

60. Physical Science In 2012, Dario Franchitti won the 500-mile Indianapolis 500 race. His speed (rate) was, on average, 92 miles per hour faster than that of the 1911 winner, Ray Haroun. Franchitti completed the race in 3.72 hours less time than Harroun. Find Harroun's and Franchitti's rates to the nearest tenth.

Physical Science *Use the height formula in Example 10 to work the given problems. Note that an object that is dropped (rather than thrown downward) has initial velocity $v_0 = 0$.*

61. How long does it take a baseball to reach the ground if it is dropped from the top of a 625-foot-high building? Compare the answer with that in Example 10.

62. After the baseball in Exercise 61 is dropped, how long does it take for the ball to fall 196 feet? (*Hint:* How high is the ball at that time?)

63. You are standing on a cliff that is 200 feet high. How long will it take a rock to reach the ground if

(a) you drop it?

(b) you throw it downward at an initial velocity of 40 feet per second?

(c) How far does the rock fall in 2 seconds if you throw it downward with an initial velocity of 40 feet per second?

64. A rocket is fired straight up from ground level with an initial velocity of 800 feet per second.

(a) How long does it take the rocket to rise 3200 feet?

(b) When will the rocket hit the ground?

65. A ball is thrown upward from ground level with an initial velocity of 64 ft per second. In how many seconds will the ball reach the given height?

(a)   64 ft   (b)   39 ft

(c)   Why are two answers possible in part (b)?

66. Physical Science   A ball is thrown upward from ground level with an initial velocity of 100 feet per second. In how many seconds will the ball reach the given height?

(a)   50 ft   (b)   35 ft

Solve each of the given equations for the indicated variable. Assume that all denominators are nonzero and that all variables represent positive real numbers. (See Example 11.)

67. $S = \dfrac{1}{2}gt^2$ for t

68. $a = \pi r^2$ for r

69. $L = \dfrac{d^4 k}{h^2}$ for h

70. $F = \dfrac{kMv^2}{r}$ for v

71. $P = \dfrac{E^2 R}{(r + R)^2}$ for R

72. $S = 2\pi rh + 2\pi r^2$ for r

73. Solve the equation $z^4 - 2z^2 = 15$ as follows.

(a)   Let $x = z^2$ and write the equation in terms of x.

(b)   Solve the new equation for x.

(c)   Set z^2 equal to each positive answer in part (b) and solve the resulting equation.

Solve each of the given equations. (See Exercise 73.)

74. $6p^4 = p^2 + 2$

75. $2q^4 + 3q^2 - 9 = 0$

76. $4a^4 = 2 - 7a^2$

77. $z^4 - 3z^2 - 1 = 0$

78. $2r^4 - r^2 - 5 = 0$

✓ Checkpoint Answers

1. (a) $6, -2$ (b) $3/5, -5$ (c) $9/2, -5/3, -3$

2. (a) $2, -5$ (b) $1/2, -5$ (c) $9/4, 0$

3. (a) $\pm\sqrt{21}$ (b) $-7 \pm \sqrt{15}$ (c) $(3 \pm \sqrt{5})/2$

4. (a) $x = 1 + \sqrt{3}$ or $1 - \sqrt{3}$

(b) $u = 3 + \sqrt{5}$ or $3 - \sqrt{5}$

5. Late 2007

6. (a) $1/3$ (b) $-7/2$ (c) No real solutions

7. (a) 2   (b) 0   (c) 1

8. Yes, area = 304.92 sq. in.

9. 5 inches by 7 inches

10. (a) $p = \dfrac{b \pm \sqrt{b^2 + 4mk}}{2m}$

(b) $k = \pm\sqrt{\dfrac{3r}{AP}}$ or $\dfrac{\pm\sqrt{3rAP}}{AP}$

CHAPTER 1 Summary and Review

Key Terms and Symbols

1.1 $\approx$ is approximately equal to
π pi
$|a|$ absolute value of a
real number
natural (counting) number
whole number
integer
rational number
irrational number
properties of real
   numbers
order of operations
square roots
number line
interval
interval notation
absolute value

1.2 a^n a to the power n
exponent or power

multiplication with
   exponents
power of a power rule
zero exponent
base
polynomial
variable
coefficient
term
constant term
degree of a polynomial
zero polynomial
leading coefficient
quadratics
cubics
like terms
FOIL
revenue
fixed cost

variable cost
profit

1.3   factor
factoring
greatest common factor
difference of squares
perfect squares
sum and difference of cubes

1.4   rational expression
cancellation property
operations with rational
   expressions
complex fraction

1.5 $a^{1/n}$ nth root of a
$\sqrt{a}$ square root of a
$\sqrt[n]{a}$ nth root of a
properties of exponents
radical
radicand

index
rationalizing the
   denominator
rationalizing the numerator

1.6   first-degree equation
solution of an equation
properties of equality
extraneous solution
solving for a specified
   variable
absolute-value equations
solving applied problems

1.7   quadratic equation
real solution
zero-factor property
square-root property
quadratic formula
discriminant
Pythagorean theorem

Chapter 1 Key Concepts

Factoring

$x^2 + 2xy + y^2 = (x + y)^2$ $x^3 - y^3 = (x - y)(x^2 + xy + y^2)$

$x^2 - 2xy + y^2 = (x - y)^2$ $x^3 + y^3 = (x + y)(x^2 - xy + y^2)$

$x^2 - y^2 = (x + y)(x - y)$

Properties of Radicals

Let a and b be real numbers, n be a positive integer, and m be any integer for which the given relationships exist. Then

$a^{m/n} = \sqrt[n]{a^m} = (\sqrt[n]{a})^m$; $\sqrt[n]{a^n} = |a|$ if n is even; $\sqrt[n]{a^n} = a$ if n is odd;

$\sqrt[n]{a} \cdot \sqrt[n]{b} = \sqrt[n]{ab}$; $\dfrac{\sqrt[n]{a}}{\sqrt[n]{b}} = \sqrt[n]{\dfrac{a}{b}}$ ($b \neq 0$).

Properties of Exponents

Let a, b, r, and s be any real numbers for which the following exist. Then

$a^{-r} = \dfrac{1}{a^r}$ $a^0 = 1$ $\left(\dfrac{a}{b}\right)^r = \dfrac{a^r}{b^r}$

$a^r \cdot a^s = a^{r+s}$ $(a^r)^s = a^{rs}$ $a^{1/r} = \sqrt[r]{a}$

$\dfrac{a^r}{a^s} = a^{r-s}$ $(ab)^r = a^r b^r$ $\left(\dfrac{a}{b}\right)^{-r} = \left(\dfrac{b}{a}\right)^r$

Absolute Value

Assume that a and b are real numbers with $b > 0$.

The solutions of $|a| = b$ or $|a| = |b|$ are $a = b$ or $a = -b$.

Quadratic Equations

Facts needed to solve quadratic equations (in which a, b, and c are real numbers):

Factoring If $ab = 0$, then $a = 0$ or $b = 0$ or both.

Square-Root Property If $b > 0$, then the solutions of $x^2 = b$ are $\sqrt{b}$ and $-\sqrt{b}$.

Quadratic Formula The solutions of $ax^2 + bx + c = 0$ (with $a \neq 0$) are

$$x = \frac{-b \pm \sqrt{b^2 - 4ac}}{2a}.$$

Discriminant There are two real solutions of $ax^2 + bx + c = 0$ if $b^2 - 4ac > 0$, one real solution if $b^2 - 4ac = 0$, and no real solutions if $b^2 - 4ac < 0$.

Chapter 1 Review Exercises

Name the numbers from the list $-12, -6, -9/10, -\sqrt{7}, -\sqrt{4}$, $0, 1/8, \pi/4, 6$, and $\sqrt{11}$ that are

1. whole numbers   **2.** integers

3. rational numbers   **4.** irrational numbers

Identify the properties of real numbers that are illustrated in each of the following expressions.

5. $9[(-3)4] = 9[4(-3)]$

6. $7(4 + 5) = (4 + 5)7$

7. $6(x + y - 3) = 6x + 6y + 6(-3)$

8. $11 + (5 + 3) = (11 + 5) + 3$

Express each statement in symbols.

9. x is at least 9.   **10.** x is negative.

Write the following numbers in numerical order from smallest to largest.

11. $|6 - 4|, -|-2|, |8 + 1|, -|3 - (-2)|$

12. $\sqrt{7}, -\sqrt{8}, -|\sqrt{16}|, |-\sqrt{12}|$

Write the following without absolute-value bars.

13. $7 - |-8|$ **14.** $|-3| - |-9 + 6|$

Graph each of the following on a number line.

15. $x \geq -3$ **16.** $-4 < x \leq 6$

Use the order of operations to simplify each of the following.

17. $\dfrac{-9 + (-6)(-3) \div 9}{6 - (-3)}$ **18.** $\dfrac{20 \div 4 \cdot 2 \div 5 - 1}{-9 - (-3) - 12 \div 3}$

Perform each of the indicated operations.

19. $(3x^4 - x^2 + 5x) - (-x^4 + 3x^2 - 6x)$

20. $(-8y^3 + 8y^2 - 5y) - (2y^3 + 4y^2 - 10)$

21. $(5k - 2h)(5k + 2h)$ **22.** $(2r - 5y)(2r + 5y)$

23. $(3x + 4y)^2$ **24.** $(2a - 5b)^2$

Factor each of the following as completely as possible.

25. $2kh^2 - 4kh + 5k$ **26.** $2m^2n^2 + 6mn^2 + 16n^2$

27. $5a^4 + 12a^3 + 4a^2$ **28.** $24x^3 + 4x^2 - 4x$

29. $144p^2 - 169q^2$ **30.** $81z^2 - 25x^2$

31. $27y^3 - 1$ **32.** $125a^3 + 216$

Perform each operation.

33. $\dfrac{3x}{5} \cdot \dfrac{45x}{12}$

34. $\dfrac{5k^2}{24} - \dfrac{70k}{36}$

35. $\dfrac{c^2 - 3c + 2}{2c(c - 1)} \div \dfrac{c - 2}{8c}$

36. $\dfrac{p^3 - 2p^2 - 8p}{3p(p^2 - 16)} \div \dfrac{p^2 + 4p + 4}{9p^2}$

37. $\dfrac{2m^2 - 4m + 2}{m^2 - 1} \div \dfrac{6m + 18}{m^2 + 2m - 3}$

38. $\dfrac{x^2 + 6x + 5}{4(x^2 + 1)} \cdot \dfrac{2x(x + 1)}{x^2 - 25}$

Simplify each of the given expressions. Write all answers without negative exponents. Assume that all variables represent positive real numbers.

39. 5^{-3}

40. 10^{-2}

41. -8^0

42. $\left(-\dfrac{5}{6}\right)^{-2}$

43. $4^6 \cdot 4^{-3}$

44. $7^{-5} \cdot 7^{-2}$

45. $\dfrac{8^{-5}}{8^{-4}}$

46. $\dfrac{6^{-3}}{6^4}$

47. $5^{-1} + 2^{-1}$

48. $5^{-2} + 5^{-1}$

49. $\dfrac{5^{1/3} \cdot 5^{1/2}}{5^{3/2}}$

50. $\dfrac{2^{3/4} \cdot 2^{-1/2}}{2^{1/4}}$

51. $(3a^2)^{1/2} \cdot (3^2 a)^{3/2}$

52. $(4p)^{2/3} \cdot (2p^3)^{3/2}$

Simplify each of the following expressions.

53. $\sqrt[3]{27}$

54. $\sqrt[6]{-64}$

55. $\sqrt[3]{54p^3 q^5}$

56. $\sqrt[4]{64a^5 b^3}$

57. $3\sqrt{3} - 12\sqrt{12}$

58. $8\sqrt{7} + 2\sqrt{63}$

Rationalize each denominator.

59. $\dfrac{\sqrt{3}}{1 + \sqrt{2}}$

60. $\dfrac{4 + \sqrt{2}}{4 - \sqrt{5}}$

Solve each equation.

61. $3x - 4(x - 2) = 2x + 9$

62. $4y + 9 = -3(1 - 2y) + 5$

63. $\dfrac{2m}{m - 3} = \dfrac{6}{m - 3} + 4$

64. $\dfrac{15}{k + 5} = 4 - \dfrac{3k}{k + 5}$

Solve for x.

65. $8ax - 3 = 2x$

66. $b^2 x - 2x = 4b^2$

Solve each equation.

67. $\left|\dfrac{2 - y}{5}\right| = 8$

68. $|4k + 1| = |6k - 3|$

Find all real solutions of each equation.

69. $(b + 7)^2 = 5$

70. $(2p + 1)^2 = 7$

71. $2p^2 + 3p = 2$

72. $2y^2 = 15 + y$

73. $2q^2 - 11q = 21$

74. $3x^2 + 2x = 16$

75. $6k^4 + k^2 = 1$

76. $21p^4 = 2 + p^2$

Solve each equation for the specified variable.

77. $p = \dfrac{E^2 R}{(r + R)^2}$ for r

78. $p = \dfrac{E^2 R}{(r + R)^2}$ for E

79. $K = s(s - a)$ for s

80. $kz^2 - hz - t = 0$ for z

Work these problems.

81. Finance   The percent change in stock price in 2012 for retailers The Gap and J. C. Penny was +67% and −44% respectively. Find the difference in the percent change for these two companies in 2012. (Data from: money.cnn.com.)

82. Finance   The percent change in stock price in 2012 for tech companies Dell and Hewlett-Packard was −31% and −45% respectively. Find the difference in the percent change for these two companies in 2012. (Data from: money.cnn.com.)

83. Business   A new PC is on sale for 20% off. The sale price is $895. What was the original price?

84. Business   The stock price of eBay increased 68% in 2012. If the price was $51 a share at the end of 2012, at what price did it begin the year?

85. Finance   The amount of outlays O of the U.S. government per year (in trillions of dollars) can be approximated by the function

$$O = .2x + 1.5,$$

where $x = 6$ corresponds to the year 2006. Find the year in which the outlays are the following. (Data from: U.S. Office of Management and Budget.)

(a) $3.3 trillion   **(b)** $3.9 trillion

86. Business   Estimated revenue R (in billions of dollars) from the general newspaper industry can be approximated by the function

$$R = -3.6x + 64.4,$$

where $x = 6$ corresponds to the year 2006. In what year was revenue $28.4 billion? (Data from: U.S. Census Bureau.)

87. Business   The number (in millions) of new vehicles V sold or leased in the United States can be approximated by the function $V = .89x^2 - 17.9x + 139.3$ where $x = 6$ corresponds to 2006. Find the total sales for 2012. (Data from: U.S. Bureau of Transportation Statistics.)

88. Business   The total sales (in billions of dollars) of alcoholic beverages A in the United States can be approximated by the function $A = -.023x^3 + .38x^2 + 3.29x + 107$ where $x = 0$ corresponds to the year 2000. (Data from: U.S. Department of Agriculture.)

(a) Find the total sales in 2010.

(b) In what year did sales become greater than $140 billion.

89. Business The number (in millions) of flight departures F within the United States per year can be approximated by the function

$$F = \frac{0.004x^2 + 10.3x + 5.8}{x + 1},$$

where $x = 1$ corresponds to the year 2001. (Data from: U.S. Bureau of Transportation Statistics.)

(a) How many flights departed in 2009?

(b) If the trend continues, when will the number of flights exceed 10 million?

90. Business The total amount of sales from manufacturing (in trillions of dollars) within the United States M can be approximated by

$$M = \frac{.122x^2 + 5.48x + 6.5}{x + 2},$$

where $x = 1$ corresponds to the year 2001. (Data from U.S. Census Bureau.)

(a) What were the sales in 2009?

(b) In what year did sales exceed $6.0 trillion?

91. Economics The total amount (in billions of dollars) of research and development spending by the U.S. government R can be approximated by

$$R = 4.33x^{0.66},$$

where $x = 8$ corresponds to 1998. (Data from: www.nsf.gov/statistics/)

(a) Find the spending in 2000.

(b) Find the spending in 2010.

92. Economics The total number (in millions) of employees within the United States in the service-providing industry E can be approximated by

$$E = 91.5x^{0.07},$$

where $x = 10$ corresponds to the year 2000. Assume the trend continues indefinitely. (Data from: ProQuest Statistical Abstract of the United States: 2013.)

(a) How many employees will there be in the year 2015?

(b) In what year will there be more than 115 million employees?

93. Finance Kinisha borrowed $2000 from a credit union at 12% annual interest and borrowed $500 from her aunt at 7% annual interest. What single rate of interest on $2500 results in the same total amount of interest?

94. Business A butcher makes a blend of stew meat from beef that sells for $2.80 a pound and pork that sells for $3.25 a pound. How many pounds of each meat should be used to get 30 pounds of a mix that can be sold for $3.10 a pound?

95. Business The number of patents P granted for new inventions within each U.S. state in the year 2011 is approximated by

$$P = 18.2x^2 - 26.0x + 789,$$

where x is the population of the state in millions. (Data from: U.S. Patent and Trademark Office).

(a) What is the number of patents granted for the state of New York with a population of 19.47 million?

(b) Approximate the population of Illinois with its number of patents at 3806.

96. Business Within the state of California, the number (in thousands) of patents C granted for new inventions can be approximated by

$$C = .22x^2 - 1.9x + 23.0,$$

where $x = 2$ corresponds to the year 2002. (Data from: U.S. Patent and Trademark Office.)

(a) What was the number of patents issued in California for 2011?

(b) What most recent year saw California hit 24 thousand patents?

97. Business A concrete mixer needs to know how wide to make a walk around a rectangular fountain that is 10 by 15 feet. She has enough concrete to cover 200 square feet. To the nearest tenth of a foot, how wide should the walk be in order to use up all the concrete?

98. Physical Science A new homeowner needs to put up a fence to make his yard secure. The house itself forms the south boundary and the garage forms the west boundary of the property, so he needs to fence only 2 sides. The area of the yard is 4000 square feet. He has enough material for 160 feet of fence. Find the length and width of the yard (to the nearest foot).

99. Physical Science A projectile is launched from the ground vertically upward at a rate of 150 feet per second. How many seconds will it take for the projectile to be 200 feet from the ground on its downward trip?

100. Physical Science Suppose a tennis ball is thrown downward from the top of a 700-foot-high building with an initial velocity of 55 feet per second. How long does it take to reach the ground?

Case Study 1 Consumers Often Need to Just Do the Math

In the late 1960s and early 1970s researchers conducted a series of famous experiments in which children were tested regarding their ability for delayed gratification.[*] In these experiments, a child would be offered a marshmallow, cookie, or pretzel and told that if they did not eat the treat, they could have two of the treats when the researcher returned (after about 15 minutes). Of course, some children would eat the treat immediately, and others would wait and receive two of the treats.

[*]Mischel, Walter, Ebbe B. Ebbesen, and Antonette Raskoff Zeiss. (1972). "Cognitive and attentional mechanisms in delay of gratification." *Journal of Personality and Social Psychology*, pp. 204–218.

Similar studies occur in studying consumer behavior among adults. Often when making purchases, consumers will purchase an appliance that initially costs less, but in the long run costs more money when one accounts for the operating expense. Imagine trying to decide whether to buy a new furnace for $4500 that is 80% efficient versus a new furnace that is 90% efficient that costs $5700. Each furnace is expected to last at least 20 years. The furnace with the 90% efficiency is estimated to cost $1800 a year to operate, while the 80% efficiency furnace is estimated to cost $2100 a year to operate—a difference of $300 a year. Thus, the original price differential of $1200 would be made up in four years. Over the course of 16 additional years, the 90% efficiency furnace would end up saving the buyer $4800.

For other appliances, the difference in total expenditures may not be as dramatic, but can still be substantial. The energy guide tags that often accompany new appliances help make it easier for consumers "to do the math" by communicating the yearly operating costs of an appliance. For example, a Kenmore new side-by-side 25.4 cubic foot refrigerator retails for $1128. The energy guide estimates the cost of operation for a year to be $72. A similarly sized new Frigidaire refrigerator retails for $1305, and the energy guide information estimates the annual cost to be $43. Over 10 years, which refrigerator costs the consumer more money?

We can write mathematical expressions to answer this question. With an initial cost of $1128, and an annual operating cost of $72, for x years of operation the cost C for the Kenmore refrigerator is

$$C = 1128 + 72x$$

For 10 years, the Kenmore would cost $C = 1128 + 72(10) = 1848. For the Frigidaire model, the cost is

$$C = 1305 + 43x.$$

For 10 years, the Frigidaire would cost $C = 1305 + 43(10) = 1735.

Thus, the Frigidaire refrigerator costs $113 less in total costs over 10 years.

Behavior when a consumer seeks the up-front savings sounds very similar to the delayed gratification studies among children. These kinds of behavior are of interest to both psychologists and economists. The implications are also very important in the marketing of energy-efficient appliances that often do have a higher initial cost, but save consumers money over the lifetime of the product.

One tool to help consumers make the best choice in the long run is simply to take the time to "just do the math," as the common expression goes. The techniques of this chapter can be applied to do just that!

Exercises

1. On the homedepot.com website, a General Electric 40-gallon electric hot water tank retails for $218 and the estimated annual cost of operation is $508. Write an expression for the cost to buy and run the hot water tank for x years.

2. On the homedepot.com website, a General Electric 40-gallon gas hot water tank retails for $328 and the estimated annual cost of operation is $309. Write an expression for the cost to buy and run the hot water tank for x years.

3. Over ten years, does the electric or gas hot water tank cost more? By how much?

4. In how many years will the total for the two hot water tanks be equal?

5. On the Lowes website, a Maytag 25-cubic-foot refrigerator was advertised for $1529.10 with an estimated cost per month in electricity of $50 a year. Write an expression for the cost to buy and run the refrigerator for x years.

6. On the HomeDepot website, an LG Electronics 25-cubic-foot refrigerator was advertised for $1618.20 with an estimated cost per month in electricity of $44 a year. Write an expression for the cost to buy and run the refrigerator for x years.

7. Over ten years, which refrigerator (the Maytag or the LG) costs the most? By how much?

8. In how many years will the total for the two refrigerators be equal?

Extended Project

A high-end real estate developer needs to install 50 new washing machines in a building she leases to tenants (with utilities included in the monthly rent). She knows that energy-efficient front loaders cost less per year to run, but they can be much more expensive than traditional top loaders. Investigate by visiting an appliance store or using the Internet, the prices and energy efficiency of two comparable front-loading and top-loading washing machines.

1. Estimate how many years it will take for the total expenditure (including purchase and cost of use) for the 50 front-loading machines to equal the total expenditure for the 50 top-loading machines.

2. The energy guide ratings use data that is often several years old. If the owner believes that current energy costs are 20% higher than what is indicated with the energy guide, redo the calculations for (1) above and determine if it will take less time for the two total expenditures to be equal.

Graphs, Lines, and Inequalities

2

CHAPTER OUTLINE

Data from current and past events is often a useful tool in business and in the social and health sciences. Gathering data is the first step in developing mathematical models that can be used to analyze a situation and predict future performance. For examples of linear models in transportation, business, and health see Exercises 15, 16, and 21 on page 94.

Graphical representations of data are commonly used in business and in the health and social sciences. Lines, equations, and inequalities play an important role in developing mathematical models from such data. This chapter presents both algebraic and graphical methods for dealing with these topics.

2.1 Graphs

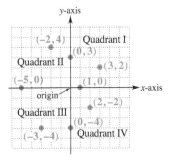

Figure 2.1

Just as the number line associates the points on a line with real numbers, a similar construction in two dimensions associates points in a plane with *ordered pairs* of real numbers. A **Cartesian coordinate system,** as shown in Figure 2.1, consists of a horizontal number line (usually called the *x*-**axis**) and a vertical number line (usually called the *y*-**axis**). The point where the number lines meet is called the **origin.** Each point in a Cartesian coordinate system is labeled with an **ordered pair** of real numbers, such as (−2, 4) or (3, 2). Several points and their corresponding ordered pairs are shown in Figure 2.1.

For the point labeled (−2, 4), for example, −2 is the *x*-**coordinate** and 4 is the *y*-**coordinate.** You can think of these coordinates as directions telling you how to move to this point from the origin: You go 2 horizontal units to the left (*x*-coordinate) and 4 vertical

✓ **Checkpoint 1**

Locate $(-1, 6)$, $(-3, -5)$, $(4, -3)$, $(0, 2)$, and $(-5, 0)$ on a coordinate system.

Answers to Checkpoint exercises are found at the end of the section.

units upward (y-coordinate). From now on, instead of referring to "the point labeled by the ordered pair $(-2, 4)$," we will say "the point $(-2, 4)$."

The x-axis and the y-axis divide the plane into four parts, or **quadrants,** which are numbered as shown in Figure 2.1. The points on the coordinate axes belong to no quadrant.

Equations and Graphs

A **solution of an equation** in two variables, such as

$$y = -2x + 3$$

or

$$y = x^2 + 7x - 2,$$

is an ordered pair of numbers such that the substitution of the first number for x and the second number for y produces a true statement.

Example 1 Which of the following are solutions of $y = -2x + 3$?

(a) $(2, -1)$

Solution This is a solution of $y = -2x + 3$ because "$-1 = -2 \cdot 2 + 3$" is a true statement.

(b) $(4, 7)$

✓ **Checkpoint 2**

Which of the following are solutions of
$$y = x^2 + 5x - 3?$$
(a) $(1, 3)$
(b) $(-2, -3)$
(c) $(-1, -7)$

Solution Since $-2 \cdot 4 + 3 = -5$, and not 7, the ordered pair $(4, 7)$ is not a solution of $y = -2x + 3$.

Equations in two variables, such as $y = -2x + 3$, typically have an infinite number of solutions. To find one, choose a number for x and then compute the value of y that produces a solution. For instance, if $x = 5$, then $y = -2 \cdot 5 + 3 = -7$, so that the pair $(5, -7)$ is a solution of $y = -2x + 3$. Similarly, if $x = 0$, then $y = -2 \cdot 0 + 3 = 3$, so that $(0, 3)$ is also a solution.

The **graph** of an equation in two variables is the set of points in the plane whose coordinates (ordered pairs) are solutions of the equation. Thus, the graph of an equation is a picture of its solutions. Since a typical equation has infinitely many solutions, its graph has infinitely many points.

Example 2 Sketch the graph of $y = -2x + 5$.

✓ **Checkpoint 3**

Graph $x = 5y$.

Solution Since we cannot plot infinitely many points, we construct a table of y-values for a reasonable number of x-values, plot the corresponding points, and make an "educated guess" about the rest. The table of values and points in Figure 2.2 suggests that the graph is a straight line, as shown in Figure 2.3.

x	$-2x + 5$
-1	7
0	5
2	1
4	-3
5	-5

Figure 2.2

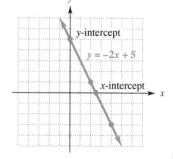

Figure 2.3

An **x-intercept** of a graph is the x-coordinate of a point where the graph intersects the x-axis. The y-coordinate of this point is 0, since it is on the axis. Consequently, to find the x-intercepts of the graph of an equation, set $y = 0$ and solve for x. For instance, in Example 2, the x-intercept of the graph of $y = -2x + 5$ (see Figure 2.3) is found by setting $y = 0$ and solving for x:

$$0 = -2x + 5$$
$$2x = 5$$
$$x = \frac{5}{2}.$$

Similarly, a **y-intercept** of a graph is the y-coordinate of a point where the graph intersects the y-axis. The x-coordinate of this point is 0. The y-intercepts are found by setting $x = 0$ and solving for y. For example, the graph of $y = -2x + 5$ in Figure 2.3 has y-intercept 5. ✓4

✓**Checkpoint 4**

Find the x- and y-intercepts of the graphs of these equations.

(a) $3x + 4y = 12$

(b) $5x - 2y = 8$

Example 3   Find the x- and y-intercepts of the graph of $y = x^2 - 2x - 8$, and sketch the graph.

Solution   To find the y-intercept, set $x = 0$ and solve for y:

$$y = x^2 - 2x - 8 = 0^2 - 2 \cdot 0 - 8 = -8.$$

The y-intercept is -8. To find the x-intercept, set $y = 0$ and solve for x.

$$x^2 - 2x - 8 = y$$
$$x^2 - 2x - 8 = 0 \qquad \text{Set } y = 0.$$
$$(x + 2)(x - 4) = 0 \qquad \text{Factor.}$$
$$x + 2 = 0 \quad \text{or} \quad x - 4 = 0 \qquad \text{Zero-factor property}$$
$$x = -2 \quad \text{or} \quad x = 4$$

The x-intercepts are -2 and 4. Now make a table, using both positive and negative values for x, and plot the corresponding points, as in Figure 2.4. These points suggest that the entire graph looks like Figure 2.5.

x	$x^2 - 2x - 8$
-3	7
-2	0
-1	-5
0	-8
1	-9
3	-5
4	0
5	7

Figure 2.4

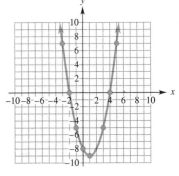

Figure 2.5

Example 4   Sketch the graph of $y = \sqrt{x + 2}$.

Solution   Notice that $\sqrt{x + 2}$ is a real number only when $x + 2 \geq 0$—that is, when $x \geq -2$. Furthermore, $y = \sqrt{x + 2}$ is always nonnegative. Hence, all points on the graph lie on or above the x-axis and on or to the right of $x = -2$. Computing some typical values, we obtain the graph in Figure 2.6.

x	$\sqrt{x+2}$
-2	0
0	$\sqrt{2} \approx 1.414$
2	2
5	$\sqrt{7} \approx 2.646$
7	3
9	$\sqrt{11} \approx 3.317$

Figure 2.6

Example 2 shows that the solution of the equation $-2x + 5 = 0$ is the x-intercept of the graph of $y = -2x + 5$. Example 3 shows that the solutions of the equation $x^2 - 2x - 8 = 0$ are the x-intercepts of the graph $y = x^2 - 2x - 8$. Similar facts hold in the general case.

Intercepts and Equations

The real solutions of a one-variable equation of the form

$$\text{expression in } x = 0$$

are the x-intercepts of the graph of

$$y = \text{same expression in } x.$$

Graph Reading

Information is often given in graphical form, so you must be able to read and interpret graphs—that is, translate graphical information into statements in English.

Example 5 **Finance** Newspapers and websites summarize activity of the S&P 500 Index in graphical form. The results for the 20 trading days for the month of December, 2012 are displayed in Figure 2.7. The first coordinate of each point on the graph is the trading day in December, and the second coordinate represents the closing price of the S&P 500 on that day. (Data from: www.morningstar.com.)

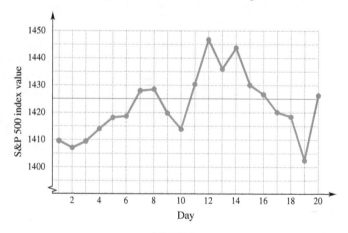

Figure 2.7

(a) What was the value of the S&P 500 Index on day 11 and day 17?

Solution The point (11, 1430) is on the graph, which means that the value of the index was 1430. The point (17, 1420) is on the graph, which means that the value of the index was 1420 on that day.

(b) On what days was the value of the index above 1425?

Solution   Look for points whose second coordinates are greater than 1425—that is, points that lie above the horizontal line through 1425 (shown in red in Figure 2.7). The first coordinates of these points are the days when the index value was above 1425. We see these days occurred on days 7, 8, 11, 12, 13, 14, 15, 16, and 20. ✓₅

The next example deals with the basic business relationship that was introduced in Section 1.2:

$$\text{Profit} = \text{Revenue} - \text{Cost}.$$

✓ **Checkpoint 5**

From Figure 2.7 determine when the S&P 500 had its highest point and its lowest point. What where the index values on those days?

Cell phones (in thousands)

Figure 2.8

Example 6   Business   Monthly revenue and costs for the Webster Cell Phone Company are determined by the number t of phones produced and sold, as shown in Figure 2.8.

(a) How many phones should be produced each month if the company is to make a profit (assuming that all phones produced are sold)?

Solution   Profit is revenue minus cost, so the company makes a profit whenever revenue is greater than cost—that is, when the revenue graph is above the cost graph. Figure 2.8 shows that this occurs between $t = 12$ and $t = 48$—that is, when 12,000 to 48,000 phones are produced. If the company makes fewer than 12,000 phones, it will lose money (because costs will be greater than revenue.) It also loses money by making more than 48,000 phones. (One reason might be that high production levels require large amounts of overtime pay, which drives costs up too much.)

(b) Is it more profitable to make 40,000 or 44,000 phones?

Solution   On the revenue graph, the point with first coordinate 40 has second coordinate of approximately 3.7, meaning that the revenue from 40,000 phones is about 3.7 million dollars. The point with first coordinate 40 on the cost graph is (40, 2), meaning that the cost of producing 40,000 phones is 2 million dollars. Therefore, the profit on 40,000 phones is about $3.7 - 2 = 1.7$ million dollars. For 44,000 phones, we have the approximate points (44, 4) on the revenue graph and (44, 3) on the cost graph. So the profit on 44,000 phones is $4 - 3 = 1$ million dollars. Consequently, it is more profitable to make 40,000 phones. ✓₆

✓ **Checkpoint 6**

In Example 6, find the profit from making

(a)   32,000 phones;

(b)   4000 phones.

 Technology and Graphs

A graphing calculator or computer graphing program follows essentially the same procedure used when graphing by hand: The calculator selects a large number of x-values (95 or more), equally spaced along the x-axis, and plots the corresponding points, simultaneously connecting them with line segments. Calculator-generated graphs are generally quite accurate, although they may not appear as smooth as hand-drawn ones. The next example illustrates the basics of graphing on a graphing calculator. (Computer graphing software operates similarly.)

Example 7   Use a graphing calculator to sketch the graph of the equation

$$2x^3 - 2y - 10x + 2 = 0.$$

Solution   *First, set the **viewing window**—the portion of the coordinate plane that will appear on the screen. Press the WINDOW key (labeled RANGE or PLOT-SETUP on some calculators) and enter the appropriate numbers, as in Figure 2.9 (which shows the screen from a TI-84+; other calculators are similar). Then the calculator will display the portion of the plane inside the dashed lines shown in Figure 2.10—that is, the points (x, y) with $-9 \le x \le 9$ and $-6 \le y \le 6$.

Figure 2.9

Figure 2.10

In Figure 2.9, we have set Xscl = 2 and Yscl = 1, which means the **tick marks** on the *x*-axis are two units apart and the tick marks on the *y*-axis are one unit apart (as shown in Figure 2.10).

Second, enter the equation to be graphed in the equation memory. To do this, you must first solve the equation for *y* (because a calculator accepts only equations of the form *y* = expression in *x*):

$$2y = 2x^3 - 10x + 2$$
$$y = x^3 - 5x + 1.$$

Now press the Y = key (labeled SYMB on some calculators) and enter the equation, using the "variable key" for *x*. (This key is labeled X, T, θ, *n* or X, θ, T or *x*-VAR, depending on the calculator.) Figure 2.11 shows the equation entered on a TI-84+; other calculators are similar. Now press GRAPH (or PLOT or DRW on some calculators), and obtain Figure 2.12.

Figure 2.11

Figure 2.12

Finally, if necessary, change the viewing window to obtain a more readable graph. It is difficult to see the *y*-intercept in Figure 2.12, so press WINDOW and change the viewing window (Figure 2.13); then press GRAPH to obtain Figure 2.14, in which the *y*-intercept at *y* = 1 is clearly shown. (It isn't necessary to reenter the equation.) ✔7

✔ **Checkpoint 7**

Use a graphing calculator to graph $y = 18x - 3x^3$ in the following viewing windows:

(a) $-10 \le x \le 10$ and $-10 \le y \le 10$ with Xscl = 1, Yscl = 1;

(b) $-5 \le x \le 5$ and $-20 \le y \le 20$ with Xscl = 1, Yscl = 5.

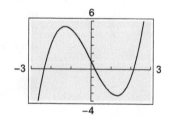

Figure 2.13

Figure 2.14

◢ **Technology Tools**

In addition to graphing equations, graphing calculators (and graphing software) provide convenient tools for solving equations and reading graphs. For example, when you have graphed an equation, you can readily determine the points the calculator plotted. Press **trace** (a cursor will appear on the graph), and use the left and right arrow keys to move the cursor along the graph. The coordinates of the point the cursor is on appear at the bottom of the screen.

Recall that the solutions of an equation, such as $x^3 - 5x + 1 = 0$, are the x-intercepts of the graph of $y = x^3 - 5x + 1$. (See the box on page 68.) A **graphical root finder** enables you to find these x-intercepts and thus to solve the equation.

✓ **Checkpoint 8**

Use a graphical root finder to approximate the third solution of the equation in Example 8.

Example 8   Use a graphical root finder to solve $x^3 - 5x + 1 = 0$.

Solution   First, graph $y = x^3 - 5x + 1$. The x-intercepts of this graph are the solutions of the equation. To find these intercepts, look for "root" or "zero" in the appropriate menu.* Check your instruction manual for the proper syntax. A typical root finder (see Figure 2.15) shows that two of the solutions (x-intercepts) are $x \approx .2016$ and $x \approx 2.1284$. For the third solution, see Checkpoint 8. ✓₈

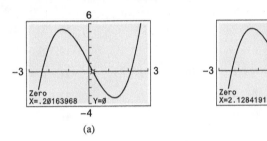

Figure 2.15

Many graphs have peaks and valleys (for instance, the graphs in Figure 2.15). A **maximum/minimum finder** provides accurate approximations of the locations of the "tops" of the peaks and the "bottoms" of the valleys.

Example 9   **Business**   The net income (in millions of dollars) for Marriott International, Inc. can be approximated by

$$6.159x^3 - 130.9x^2 + 783.4x - 749,$$

where $x = 2$ corresponds to the year 2002. In what year was the net income the highest? What was the net income that year? (Data from: www.morningstar.com.)

Solution   The graph of $y = 6.159x^3 - 130.9x^2 + 783.4x - 749$ is shown in Figure 2.16. The highest net income corresponds to the highest point on this graph. To find this point, look for "maximum" or "max" or "extremum" in the same menu as the graphical root finder. Check your instruction manual for the proper syntax. A typical maximum finder (Figure 2.17) shows that the highest point has approximate coordinates (4.29, 688.96). The first coordinate is the year and the second is the net income (in millions). So the largest net income occurred in 2004 and the net income was approximately $689 million. ✓₉

✓ **Checkpoint 9**

Use a minimum finder to locate the approximate coordinates of the lowest point on the graph in Figure 2.16.

Figure 2.16

Figure 2.17

---

*CALC on TI-84+, GRAPH MATH on TI-86, G-SOLV on Casio.

2.1 Exercises

State the quadrant in which each point lies.

1. $(1, -2), (-2, 1), (3, 4), (-5, -6)$

2. $(\pi, 2), (3, -\sqrt{2}), (4, 0), (-\sqrt{3}, \sqrt{3})$

Determine whether the given ordered pair is a solution of the given equation. (See Example 1.)

3. $(1, -3); 3x - y - 6 = 0$

4. $(2, -1); x^2 + y^2 - 6x + 8y = -15$

5. $(3, 4); (x - 2)^2 + (y + 2)^2 = 6$

6. $(1, -1); \dfrac{x^2}{2} + \dfrac{y^2}{3} = -4$

Sketch the graph of each of these equations. (See Example 2.)

7. $4y + 3x = 12$

8. $2x + 7y = 14$

9. $8x + 3y = 12$

10. $9y - 4x = 12$

11. $x = 2y + 3$

12. $x - 3y = 0$

List the x-intercepts and y-intercepts of each graph.

13.

14.

15.

16.

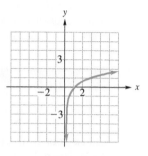

Find the x-intercepts and y-intercepts of the graph of each equation. You need not sketch the graph. (See Example 3.)

17. $3x + 4y = 12$

18. $x - 2y = 5$

19. $2x - 3y = 24$

20. $3x + y = 4$

21. $y = x^2 - 9$

22. $y = x^2 + 4$

23. $y = x^2 + x - 20$

24. $y = 5x^2 + 6x + 1$

25. $y = 2x^2 - 5x + 7$

26. $y = 3x^2 + 4x - 4$

Sketch the graph of the equation. (See Examples 2–4.)

27. $y = x^2$

28. $y = x^2 + 2$

29. $y = x^2 - 3$

30. $y = 2x^2$

31. $y = x^2 - 6x + 5$

32. $y = x^2 + 2x - 3$

33. $y = x^3$

34. $y = x^3 - 3$

35. $y = x^3 + 1$

36. $y = x^3/2$

37. $y = \sqrt{x + 4}$

38. $y = \sqrt{x - 2}$

39. $y = \sqrt{4 - x^2}$

40. $y = \sqrt{9 - x^2}$

Business   *An article in the Wall Street Journal on March 17, 2012 spoke of the increase in production of pipe tobacco as stores and consumers found that pipe tobacco is often not subject to the same taxes as cigarette tobacco. The graph below shows the production of pipe tobacco (in millions of pounds) and of roll-your-own tobacco (in millions of pounds). (Data from: Alcohol and Tobacco Tax and Trade Bureau.) (See Examples 5 and 6.)*

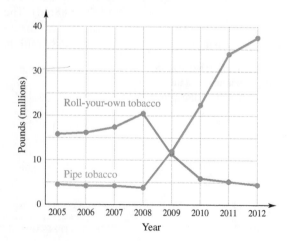

41. In what year did roll-your-own tobacco hit its peak of production? What was that peak production?

42. In what year did both roll-your-own tobacco and pipe tobacco have approximately the same level of production? How much was produced for each?

43. In what year did pipe tobacco production exceed roll-your-own tobacco by at least 25 million pounds?

44. In what years did roll-your-own tobacco production exceed pipe tobacco production by less than 10 million pounds?

Business *Use the revenue and cost graphs for the Webster Cell Phone Company in Example 6 to do Exercises 45–48.*

45. Find the approximate cost of manufacturing the given number of phones.

(a) 20,000   (b) 36,000   (c) 48,000

46. Find the approximate revenue from selling the given number of phones.

(a) 12,000   (b) 24,000   (c) 36,000

47. Find the approximate profit from manufacturing the given number of phones.

(a) 20,000   (b) 28,000   (c) 36,000

48. The company must replace its aging machinery with better, but much more expensive, machines. In addition, raw material prices increase, so that monthly costs go up by $250,000. Owing to competitive pressure, phone prices cannot be increased, so revenue remains the same. Under these new circumstances, find the approximate profit from manufacturing the given number of phones.

(a) 20,000   (b) 36,000   (c) 40,000

Business *The graph below gives the annual per-person retail availability of beef, chicken, and pork (in pounds) from 2001 to 2010. Use the graph to answer the following questions. (Data from: U.S. Department of Agriculture.)*

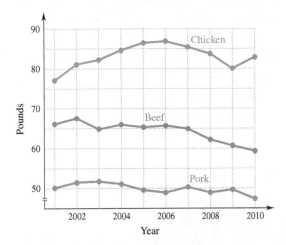

49. What is the approximate annual per-person retail availability of beef, chicken, and pork in 2010?

50. In what year was annual availability of beef the highest?

51. In what year was annual availability of chicken the lowest?

52. How much did the annual availability of beef decrease from 2001 to 2010?

Business *The graph below gives the total sales (in billions of dollars) at grocery stores within the United States from 2005 to 2015. (Years 2011–2015 are projections.) Use the graph to answer the following questions. (Data from: U.S. Census Bureau.)*

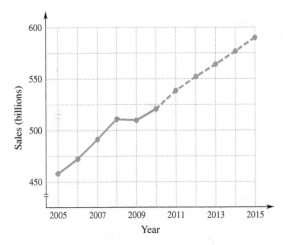

53. What were the total sales at grocery stores in 2008?

54. In what years are total sales below $525 billion (including projections)?

55. In what years are total sales above $500 billion (including projections)?

56. How much are grocery sales projected to increase from 2010 to 2015?

Business *The graph below shows the closing share prices (in dollars) for Hewlett-Packard Corporation and Intel Corporation on the 21 trading days of the month of January, 2013. Use this graph to answer the following questions.*

57. What was the approximate closing share price for Hewlett-Packard on day 21? for Intel?

58. What was the approximate closing share price for Hewlett-Packard on day 9? for Intel?

59. What was the highest closing share price for Hewlett-Packard and on what day did this occur?

60. What was the highest closing share price for Intel and on what day did this occur?

61. Was the difference in share price between the two companies ever more than $7.00?

62. Over the course of the month, what was the gain in share price for Hewlett-Packard?

✐ Use a graphing calculator to find the graph of the equation. (See Example 7.)

63. $y = x^2 + x + 1$ **64.** $y = 2 - x - x^2$

65. $y = (x - 3)^3$ **66.** $y = x^3 + 2x^2 + 2$

67. $y = x^3 - 3x^2 + x - 1$ **68.** $y = x^4 - 5x^2 - 2$

✐ Use a graphing calculator for Exercises 69–70.

69. Graph $y = x^4 - 2x^3 + 2x$ in a window with $-3 \le x \le 3$. Is the "flat" part of the graph near $x = 1$ really a horizontal line segment? (*Hint:* Use the trace feature to move along the "flat" part and watch the y-coordinates. Do they remain the same [as they should on a horizontal segment]?)

70. (a) Graph $y = x^4 - 2x^3 + 2x$ in the **standard window** (the one with $-10 \le x \le 10$ and $-10 \le y \le 10$). Use the trace feature to approximate the coordinates of the lowest point on the graph.

    (b) Use a minimum finder to obtain an accurate approximation of the lowest point. How does this compare with your answer in part (a)?

✐ Use a graphing calculator to approximate all real solutions of the equation. (See Example 8.)

71. $x^3 - 3x^2 + 5 = 0$

72. $x^3 + x - 1 = 0$

73. $2x^3 - 4x^2 + x - 3 = 0$

74. $6x^3 - 5x^2 + 3x - 2 = 0$

75. $x^5 - 6x + 6 = 0$

76. $x^3 - 3x^2 + x - 1 = 0$

✐ Use a graphing calculator to work Exercises 77–80. (See Examples 8 and 9.)

Finance *The financial assets of the mutual fund industry (in trillions of dollars) can be approximated by*

$$y = .0556x^3 - 1.286x^2 + 9.76x - 17.4,$$

where x = 5 corresponds to 2005. (Data from: Board of Governors of the Federal Reserve System.)

77. Find the maximum value of the total assets between 2005 and 2008.

78. Find the minimum value of the total assets between 2008 and 2011.

Finance *The financial assets of households (in trillions of dollars) can be approximated by*

$$y = .328x^3 - 7.75x^2 + 59.03x - 97.1,$$

where x = 5 corresponds to 2005. (Data from: Board of Governors of the Federal Reserve System.)

79. Find the minimum value of the household assets between 2007 and 2011.

80. Find the maximum value of the household assets between 2005 and 2008.

✓ Checkpoint Answers

1.

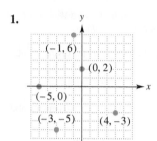

Points: $(-1, 6)$, $(0, 2)$, $(-5, 0)$, $(-3, -5)$, $(4, -3)$

2. (a) and (c)

3.

$x = 5y$

4. (a) x-intercept 4, y-intercept 3

    (b) x-intercept $8/5$, y-intercept -4

5. The highest was 1446 on day 12

    The lowest was 1407 on day 11

6. (a) About $1,200,000 (rounded)

    (b) About $-$500,000

        (that is, a loss of $500,000)

7. (a)

    (b)

8. $x \approx -2.330059$

9. $(9.88, 153.19)$

2.2 Equations of Lines

Straight lines, which are the simplest graphs, play an important role in a wide variety of applications. They are considered here from both a geometric and an algebraic point of view.

The key geometric feature of a nonvertical straight line is how steeply it rises or falls as you move from left to right. The "steepness" of a line can be represented numerically by a number called the *slope* of the line.

To see how the slope is defined, start with Figure 2.18, which shows a line passing through the two different points $(x_1, y_1) = (-5, 6)$ and $(x_2, y_2) = (4, -7)$. The difference in the two x-values,

$$x_2 - x_1 = 4 - (-5) = 9,$$

is called the **change in x.** Similarly, the **change in y** is the difference in the two y-values:

$$y_2 - y_1 = -7 - 6 = -13.$$

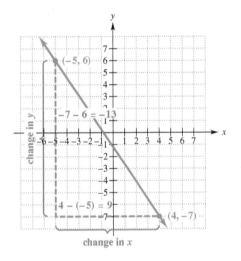

Figure 2.18

> The **slope** of the line through the two points (x_1, y_1) and (x_2, y_2), where $x_1 \neq x_2$, is defined as the quotient of the change in y and the change in x:
>
> $$\textbf{slope} = \frac{\textbf{change in } y}{\textbf{change in } x} = \frac{y_2 - y_1}{x_2 - x_1}.$$

The slope of the line in Figure 2.18 is

$$\text{slope} = \frac{-7 - 6}{4 - (-5)} = -\frac{13}{9}.$$

Using similar triangles from geometry, we can show that the slope is independent of the choice of points on the line. That is, the same value of the slope will be obtained for *any* choice of two different points on the line.

Example 1   Find the slope of the line through the points $(-6, 8)$ and $(5, 4)$.

Solution   Let $(x_1, y_1) = (-6, 8)$ and $(x_2, y_2) = (5, 4)$. Use the definition of slope as follows:

$$\text{slope} = \frac{y_2 - y_1}{x_2 - x_1} = \frac{4 - 8}{5 - (-6)} = \frac{-4}{11} = -\frac{4}{11}.$$

The slope can also by found by letting $(x_1, y_1) = (5, 4)$ and $(x_2, y_2) = (-6, 8)$. In that case,

$$\text{slope} = \frac{y_2 - y_1}{x_2 - x_1} = \frac{8 - 4}{-6 - 5} = \frac{4}{-11} = -\frac{4}{11},$$

which is the same answer.

✓ **Checkpoint 1**

Find the slope of the line through the following pairs of points.

(a) $(5, 9), (-5, -3)$

(b) $(-4, 2), (-2, -7)$

Figure 2.19

⊘ **CAUTION** When finding the slope of a line, be careful to subtract the x-values and the y-values in the same order. For example, with the points $(4, 3)$ and $(2, 9)$, if you use $9 - 3$ for the numerator, you must use $2 - 4$ (*not* $4 - 2$) for the denominator.

Example 2 Find the slope of the horizontal line in Figure 2.19.

Solution Every point on the line has the same y-coordinate, -5. Choose any two of them to compute the slope, say, $(x_1, y_1) = (-3, -5)$ and $(x_2, y_2) = (2, -5)$:

$$\text{slope} = \frac{-5 - (-5)}{2 - (-3)}$$

$$= \frac{0}{5}$$

$$= 0.$$

Example 3 What is the slope of the vertical line in Figure 2.20?

Solution Every point on the line has the same x-coordinate, 4. If we attempt to compute the slope with two of these points, say, $(x_1, y_1) = (4, -2)$ and $(x_2, y_2) = (4, 1)$, we obtain

$$\text{slope} = \frac{1 - (-2)}{4 - 4}$$

$$= \frac{3}{0}.$$

Division by 0 is not defined, so the slope of this line is undefined.

The arguments used in Examples 2 and 3 work in the general case and lead to the following conclusion.

The slope of every horizontal line is 0.
The slope of every vertical line is undefined.

Slope–Intercept Form

The slope can be used to develop an algebraic description of nonvertical straight lines. Assume that a line with slope m has y-intercept b, so that it goes through the point $(0, b)$. (See Figure 2.21.) Let (x, y) be any point on the line other than $(0, b)$. Using the definition of slope with the points $(0, b)$ and (x, y) gives

$$m = \frac{y - b}{x - 0}$$

$$m = \frac{y - b}{x}$$

$$mx = y - b \qquad \text{Multiply both sides by } x.$$

$$y = mx + b. \qquad \text{Add } b \text{ to both sides. Reverse the equation.}$$

In other words, the coordinates of any point on the line satisfy the equation $y = mx + b$.

Figure 2.20

Figure 2.21

Slope–Intercept Form

If a line has slope m and y-intercept b, then it is the graph of the equation

$$y = mx + b.$$

This equation is called the **slope–intercept form** of the equation of the line.

Example 4 Find an equation for the line with y-intercept $7/2$ and slope $-5/2$.

Solution Use the slope–intercept form with $b = 7/2$ and $m = -5/2$:

$$y = mx + b$$

$$y = -\frac{5}{2}x + \frac{7}{2}. \ ✓_2$$

> ✓**Checkpoint 2**
>
> Find an equation for the line with
> **(a)** y-intercept -3 and slope $2/3$;
> **(b)** y-intercept $1/4$ and slope $-3/2$.

Example 5 Find the equation of the horizontal line with y-intercept 3.

Solution The slope of the line is 0 (why?) and its y-intercept is 3, so its equation is

$$y = mx + b$$
$$y = 0x + 3$$
$$y = 3.$$

The argument in Example 5 also works in the general case.

If k is a constant, then the graph of the equation $y = k$ is the horizontal line with y-intercept k.

Example 6 Find the slope and y-intercept for each of the following lines.

(a) $5x - 3y = 1$

Solution Solve for y:

$$5x - 3y = 1$$
$$-3y = -5x + 1 \qquad \text{Subtract } 5x \text{ from both sides.}$$
$$y = \frac{5}{3}x - \frac{1}{3}. \qquad \text{Divide both sides by } -3.$$

This equation is in the form $y = mx + b$, with $m = 5/3$ and $b = -1/3$. So the slope is $5/3$ and the y-intercept is $-1/3$.

(b) $-9x + 6y = 2$

Solution Solve for y:

$$-9x + 6y = 2$$
$$6y = 9x + 2 \qquad \text{Add } 9x \text{ to both sides.}$$
$$y = \frac{3}{2}x + \frac{1}{3}. \qquad \text{Divide both sides by 6.}$$

The slope is $3/2$ (the coefficient of x), and the y-intercept is $1/3$. ✓$_3$

> **Checkpoint 3**
>
> Find the slope and y-intercept of
> **(a)** $x + 4y = 6$;
> **(b)** $3x - 2y = 1$.

The slope–intercept form can be used to show how the slope measures the steepness of a line. Consider the straight lines A, B, C, and D given by the following equations, where each has y-intercept 0 and slope as indicated:

$$A: y = .5x; \qquad B: y = x; \qquad C: y = 3x; \qquad D: y = 7x.$$

Slope .5 \qquad Slope 1 \qquad Slope 3 \qquad Slope 7

For these lines, Figure 2.22 shows that the bigger the slope, the more steeply the line rises from left to right. ✓ 4

✓ **Checkpoint 4**

(a) List the slopes of the following lines:
$E: y = -.3x; \quad F: y = -x;$
$G: y = -2x; \quad H: y = -5x.$

(b) Graph all four lines on the same set of axes.

(c) How are the slopes of the lines related to their steepness?

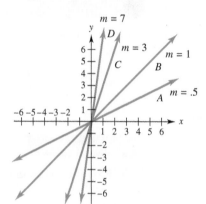

Figure 2.22

The preceding discussion and Checkpoint 4 may be summarized as follows.

Direction of Line (moving from left to right)	Slope
Upward	**Positive** (larger for steeper lines)
Horizontal	**0**
Downward	**Negative** (larger in absolute value for steeper lines)
Vertical	**Undefined**

Example 7 Sketch the graph of $x + 2y = 5$, and label the intercepts.

Solution Find the x-intercept by setting $y = 0$ and solving for x:

$$x + 2 \cdot 0 = 5$$
$$x = 5.$$

The x-intercept is 5, and (5, 0) is on the graph. The y-intercept is found similarly, by setting $x = 0$ and solving for y:

$$0 + 2y = 5$$
$$y = 5/2.$$

✓ **Checkpoint 5**

Graph the given lines and label the intercepts.

(a) $3x + 4y = 12$

(b) $5x - 2y = 8$

The y-intercept is $5/2$, and $(0, 5/2)$ is on the graph. The points $(5, 0)$ and $(0, 5/2)$ can be used to sketch the graph, as shown on the following page (Figure 2.23). ✓ 5

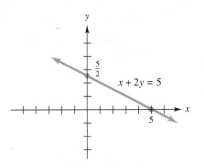

Figure 2.23

TECHNOLOGY TIP To graph a linear equation on a graphing calculator, you must first put the equation in slope–intercept form $y = mx + b$ so that it can be entered in the equation memory (called the Y = list on some calculators). Vertical lines cannot be graphed on most calculators.

Slopes of Parallel and Perpendicular Lines

We shall assume the following facts without proof. The first one is a consequence of the fact that the slope measures steepness and that parallel lines have the same steepness.

> Two nonvertical lines are **parallel** whenever they have the same slope.
>
> Two nonvertical lines are **perpendicular** whenever the product of their slopes is -1.

Example 8 Determine whether each of the given pairs of lines are *parallel*, *perpendicular*, or *neither*.

(a) $2x + 3y = 5$ and $4x + 5 = -6y$.

Solution Put each equation in slope–intercept form by solving for y:

$$3y = -2x + 5 \qquad -6y = 4x + 5$$
$$y = -\frac{2}{3}x + \frac{5}{3} \qquad y = -\frac{2}{3}x - \frac{5}{6}.$$

In each case, the slope (the coefficient of x) is $-2/3$, so the lines are parallel. See Figure 2.24(a).

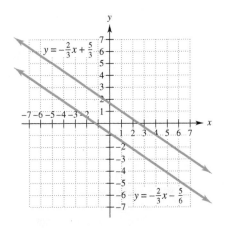

Figure 2.24(a)

(b) $3x = y + 7$ and $x + 3y = 4$.

Solution Put each equation in slope–intercept form to determine the slope of the associated line:

$$3x = y + 7 \qquad\qquad 3y = -x + 4$$

$$y = 3x - 7 \qquad\qquad y = -\frac{1}{3}x + \frac{4}{3}$$

$$\text{slope } 3 \qquad\qquad \text{slope } -1/3.$$

Since $3(-1/3) = -1$, these lines are perpendicular. See Figure 2.24(b).

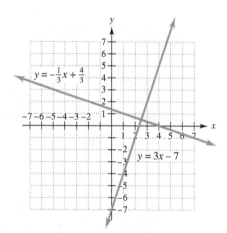

Figure 2.24(b)

(c) $x + y = 4$ and $x - 2y = 3$.

Solution Verify that the slope of the first line is -1 and the slope of the second is $1/2$. The slopes are not equal and their product is not -1, so the lines are neither parallel nor perpendicular. See Figure 2.24(c).

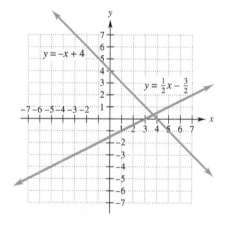

Figure 2.24(c)

✓**Checkpoint 6**

Tell whether the lines in each of the following pairs are *parallel, perpendicular,* or *neither.*

(a) $x - 2y = 6$ and $2x + y = 5$

(b) $3x + 4y = 8$ and $x + 3y = 2$

(c) $2x - y = 7$ and $2y = 4x - 5$

⬛ **TECHNOLOGY TIP** Perpendicular lines may not appear perpendicular on a graphing calculator unless you use a *square window*—a window in which a one-unit segment on the *y*-axis is the same length as a one-unit segment on the *x*-axis. To obtain such a window on most calculators, use a viewing window in which the *y*-axis is about two-thirds as long as the *x*-axis. The SQUARE (or ZSQUARE) key in the ZOOM menu will change the current window to a square window by automatically adjusting the length of one of the axes.

Point–Slope Form

The slope–intercept form of the equation of a line is usually the most convenient for graphing and for understanding how slopes and lines are related. However, it is not always the best way to *find* the equation of a line. In many situations (particularly in calculus), the slope and a point on the line are known and you must find the equation of the line. In such cases, the best method is to use the *point–slope form*, which we now explain.

Suppose that a line has slope m and that (x_1, y_1) is a point on the line. Let (x, y) represent any other point on the line. Since m is the slope, then, by the definition of slope,

$$\frac{y - y_1}{x - x_1} = m.$$

Multiplying both sides by $x - x_1$ yields

$$y - y_1 = m(x - x_1).$$

Point–Slope Form

If a line has slope m and passes through the point (x_1, y_1), then

$$\boldsymbol{y - y_1 = m(x - x_1)}$$

is the **point–slope form** of the equation of the line.

Figure 2.25

Example 9 Find the equation of the line satisfying the given conditions.

(a) Slope 2; the point $(1, 3)$ is on the line.

Solution Use the point–slope form with $m = 2$ and $(x_1, y_1) = (1, 3)$. Substitute $x_1 = 1$, $y_1 = 3$, and $m = 2$ into the point–slope form of the equation.

$$y - y_1 = m(x - x_1)$$
$$y - 3 = 2(x - 1). \qquad \text{Point–slope form}$$

For some purposes, this form of the equation is fine; in other cases, you may want to rewrite it in the slope–intercept form.

Using algebra, we obtain the slope–intercept form of this equation:

$$y - 3 = 2(x - 1)$$
$$y - 3 = 2x - 2 \qquad \text{Distributive property}$$
$$y = 2x + 1 \qquad \text{Add 3 to each side to obtain slope-intercept form.}$$

See Figure 2.25 for the graph.

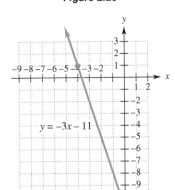

Figure 2.26

(b) Slope -3; the point $(-4, 1)$ is on the line.

Solution Use the point–slope form with $m = -3$ and $(x_1, y_1) = (-4, 1)$:

$$y - y_1 = m(x - x_1)$$
$$y - 1 = -3[x - (-4)]. \qquad \text{Point–slope form}$$

Using algebra, we obtain the slope–intercept form of this equation:

$$y - 1 = -3(x + 4)$$
$$y - 1 = -3x - 12 \qquad \text{Distributive property}$$
$$y = -3x - 11. \qquad \text{Slope–intercept form}$$

See Figure 2.26.

✓ **Checkpoint 7**

Find both the point–slope and the slope–intercept form of the equation of the line having the given slope and passing through the given point.

(a) $m = -3/5, (5, -2)$

(b) $m = 1/3, (6, 8)$

The point–slope form can also be used to find an equation of a line, given two different points on the line. The procedure is shown in the next example.

Example 10   Find an equation of the line through $(5, 4)$ and $(-10, -2)$.

Solution   Begin by using the definition of the slope to find the slope of the line that passes through the two points:

$$\text{slope} = m = \frac{-2 - 4}{-10 - 5} = \frac{-6}{-15} = \frac{2}{5}.$$

Use $m = 2/5$ and either of the given points in the point–slope form. If $(x_1, y_1) = (5, 4)$, then

$$y - y_1 = m(x - x_1)$$

$$y - 4 = \frac{2}{5}(x - 5) \qquad \text{Let } y_1 = 4, m = \frac{2}{5}, \text{ and } x_1 = 5.$$

$$y - 4 = \frac{2}{5}x - \frac{10}{5} \qquad \text{Distributive property}$$

$$y = \frac{2}{5}x + 2 \qquad \text{Add 4 to both sides and simplify.}$$

See Figure 2.27. Check that the results are the same when $(x_1, y_1) = (-10, -2)$.

Figure 2.27

Checkpoint 8

Find an equation of the line through

(a) $(2, 3)$ and $(-4, 6)$;

(b) $(-8, 2)$ and $(3, -6)$.

Vertical Lines

The equation forms we just developed do not apply to vertical lines, because the slope is not defined for such lines. However, vertical lines can easily be described as graphs of equations.

Example 11   Find the equation whose graph is the vertical line in Figure 2.28.

Solution   Every point on the line has x-coordinate -1 and hence has the form $(-1, y)$. Thus, every point is a solution of the equation $x + 0y = -1$, which is usually written simply as $x = -1$. Note that -1 is the x-intercept of the line.

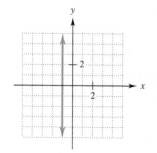

Figure 2.28

The argument in Example 11 also works in the general case.

If k is a constant, then the graph of the equation $x = k$ is the vertical line with x-intercept k.

Linear Equations

An equation in two variables whose graph is a straight line is called a **linear equation.** Linear equations have a variety of forms, as summarized in the following table.

Equation	Description
$x = k$	**Vertical line,** x-intercept k, no y-intercept, undefined slope
$y = k$	**Horizontal line,** y-intercept k, no x-intercept, slope 0
$y = mx + b$	**Slope–intercept form,** slope m, y-intercept b
$y - y_1 = m(x - x_1)$	**Point–slope form,** slope m, the line passes through (x_1, y_1)
$ax + by = c$	**General form.** If $a \neq 0$ and $b \neq 0$, the line has x-intercept c/a, y-intercept c/b, and slope $-a/b$.

Note that every linear equation can be written in general form. For example, $y = 4x - 5$ can be written in general form as $4x - y = 5$, and $x = 6$ can be written in general form as $x + 0y = 6$.

Applications

Many relationships are linear or almost linear, so that they can be approximated by linear equations.

Example 12 **Business** The world-wide sales (in billions of dollars) of men's razor blades can be approximated by the linear equation

$$y = .76x + 4.44,$$

where $x = 6$ corresponds to the year 2006. The graph appears in Figure 2.29. (Data from: *Wall Street Journal*, April 12, 2012.)

(a) What were the approximate razor sales in 2011?

Solution Substitute $x = 11$ in the equation and use a calculator to compute y:

$$y = .76x + 4.44$$
$$y = .76(11) + 4.44 = 12.80.$$

The approximate sales in 2011 were $12.8 billion.

(b) In what year did sales reach $10.5 billion?

Solution Substitute $y = 10.5$ into the equation and solve for x:

$$10.5 = .76x + 4.44$$
$$10.5 - 4.44 = .76x \qquad \text{Subtract 4.44 from each side.}$$
$$x = \frac{10.5 - 4.44}{.76} \qquad \text{Divide each side by .76 and reverse the equation.}$$
$$x = 8.0.$$

The year was 2008.

Figure 2.29

Example 13 **Education** According to the National Center for Education Statistics, the average cost of tuition and fees at public four-year universities was $3768 in the year 2000 and grew in an approximately linear fashion to $8751 in the year 2011.

(a) Find a linear equation for these data.

Solution Measure time along the x-axis and cost along the y-axis. Then the x-coordinate of each point is a year and the y-coordinate is the average cost of tuition and fees in that year. For convenience, let $x = 0$ correspond to 2000, and so $x = 11$ is 2011. Then the given data points are $(0, 3768)$ and $(11, 8751)$. The slope of the line joining these two points is

$$\frac{8751 - 3768}{11 - 0} = \frac{4983}{11} = 453.$$

Since we already know the y-intercept $b = 3768$ and the slope $m = 453$, we can write the equation as

$$y = mx + b = 453x + 3768.$$

We could also use the point-slope form with the point $(11, 8751)$, to obtain the equation of the line:

$$y - 8751 = 453(x - 11) \qquad \text{Point–slope form}$$
$$y - 8751 = 453x - 4983 \qquad \text{Distributive property}$$
$$y = 453x + 3768. \qquad \text{Add 8751 to both sides.}$$

Figure 2.30 shows the derived equation.

Figure 2.30

✓**Checkpoint 9**

The average cost of tuition and fees at private four-year universities was $19,307 in 2000 and $34,805 in 2011.

(a) Let $x = 0$ correspond to 2000, and find a linear equation for the given data. (*Hint: Round the slope to the nearest integer.*)

(b) Assuming that your equation remains accurate, estimate the average cost in 2017.

(b) Use this equation to estimate the average cost of tuition and fees in the fall of 2009.

Solution Since 2009 corresponds to $x = 9$, let $x = 9$ in the equation part of (a). Then

$$y = 453(9) + 3768 = \$7845.$$

(c) Assuming the equation remains valid beyond the fall of 2011, estimate the average cost of tuition and fees in the fall of 2018.

Solution The year 2018 corresponds to $x = 18$, so the average cost is

$$y = 453(18) + 3768 = \$11,922. \; \boxed{\text{✓}_9}$$

2.2 Exercises

Find the slope of the given line, if it is defined. (See Examples 1–3.)

1. The line through $(2, 5)$ and $(0, 8)$

2. The line through $(9, 0)$ and $(12, 12)$

3. The line through $(-4, 14)$ and $(3, 0)$

4. The line through $(-5, -2)$ and $(-4, 11)$

5. The line through the origin and $(-4, 10)$

6. The line through the origin and $(8, -2)$

7. The line through $(-1, 4)$ and $(-1, 6)$

8. The line through $(-3, 5)$ and $(2, 5)$

Find an equation of the line with the given y-intercept and slope m. (See Examples 4 and 5.)

9. $5, m = 4$

10. $-3, m = -7$

11. $1.5, m = -2.3$

12. $-4.5, m = 2.5$

13. $4, m = -3/4$

14. $-3, m = 4/3$

Find the slope m and the y-intercept b of the line whose equation is given. (See Example 6.)

15. $2x - y = 9$

16. $x + 2y = 7$

17. $6x = 2y + 4$

18. $4x + 3y = 24$

19. $6x - 9y = 16$ **20.** $4x + 2y = 0$

21. $2x - 3y = 0$ **22.** $y = 7$

23. $x = y - 5$

24. On one graph, sketch six straight lines that meet at a single point and satisfy this condition: one line has slope 0, two lines have positive slope, two lines have negative slope, and one line has undefined slope.

25. For which of the line segments in the figure is the slope

   (a) largest?   **(b)** smallest?

   (c) largest in absolute value?   **(d)** closest to 0?

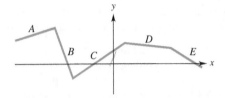

26. Match each equation with the line that most closely resembles its graph. (*Hint:* Consider the signs of m and b in the slope–intercept form.)

   (a) $y = 3x + 2$ **(b)** $y = -3x + 2$

   (c) $y = 3x - 2$ **(d)** $y = -3x - 2$

Sketch the graph of the given equation and label its intercepts. (See Example 7.)

27. $2x - y = -2$ **28.** $2y + x = 4$

29. $2x + 3y = 4$ **30.** $-5x + 4y = 3$

31. $4x - 5y = 2$ **32.** $3x + 2y = 8$

Determine whether each pair of lines is parallel, perpendicular, or neither. (See Example 8.)

33. $4x - 3y = 6$ and $3x + 4y = 8$

34. $2x - 5y = 7$ and $15y - 5 = 6x$

35. $3x + 2y = 8$ and $6y = 5 - 9x$

36. $x - 3y = 4$ and $y = 1 - 3x$

37. $4x = 2y + 3$ and $2y = 2x + 3$

38. $2x - y = 6$ and $x - 2y = 4$

39. **(a)** Find the slope of each side of the triangle with vertices $(9, 6)$, $(-1, 2)$, and $(1, -3)$.

   (b) Is this triangle a right triangle? (*Hint:* Are two sides perpendicular?)

40. **(a)** Find the slope of each side of the quadrilateral with vertices $(-5, -2)$, $(-3, 1)$, $(3, 0)$, and $(1, -3)$.

   (b) Is this quadrilateral a parallelogram? (*Hint:* Are opposite sides parallel?)

Find an equation of the line with slope m that passes through the given point. Put the answer in slope–intercept form. (See Example 10.)

41. $(-3, 2), m = -2/3$ **42.** $(-5, -2), m = 4/5$

43. $(2, 3), m = 3$ **44.** $(3, -4), m = -1/4$

45. $(10, 1), m = 0$ **46.** $(-3, -9), m = 0$

47. $(-2, 12)$, undefined slope   **48.** $(1, 1)$, undefined slope

Find an equation of the line that passes through the given points. (See Example 10.)

49. $(-1, 1)$ and $(2, 7)$ **50.** $(2, 5)$ and $(0, 6)$

51. $(1, 2)$ and $(3, 9)$ **52.** $(-1, -2)$ and $(2, -1)$

Find an equation of the line satisfying the given conditions.

53. Through the origin with slope 5

54. Through the origin and horizontal

55. Through $(6, 8)$ and vertical

56. Through $(7, 9)$ and parallel to $y = 6$

57. Through $(3, 4)$ and parallel to $4x - 2y = 5$

58. Through $(6, 8)$ and perpendicular to $y = 2x - 3$

59. x-intercept 6; y-intercept -6

60. Through $(-5, 2)$ and parallel to the line through $(1, 2)$ and $(4, 3)$

61. Through $(-1, 3)$ and perpendicular to the line through $(0, 1)$ and $(2, 3)$

62. y-intercept 3 and perpendicular to $2x - y + 6 = 0$

Business *The lost value of equipment over a period of time is called depreciation. The simplest method for calculating depreciation is straight-line depreciation. The annual straight-line depreciation D of an item that cost x dollars with a useful life of n years is $D = (1/n)x$. Find the depreciation for items with the given characteristics.*

63. Cost: $15,965; life 12 yr

64. Cost: $41,762; life 15 yr

65. Cost: $201,457; life 30 yr

66. Business Ral Corp. has an incentive compensation plan under which a branch manager receives 10% of the branch's income after deduction of the bonus, but before deduction of income tax. The income of a particular branch before the bonus and income tax was $165,000. The tax rate was 30%. The bonus amounted to

(a) $12,600   (b) $15,000

(c) $16,500   (d) $18,000

67. Business According to data from the U.S. Centers for Medicare and Medicaid Services, the sales (in billions of dollars) from drug prescriptions can be approximated by

$$y = 13.69x + 133.6,$$

where $x = 1$ corresponds to the year 2001. Find the approximate sales from prescription drugs in the following years.

(a) 2005

(b) 2010

(c) Assuming this model remains accurate, in what year will the prescriptions be $340 billion?

68. Business The total revenue generated from hospital care (in billions of dollars) can be approximated by

$$y = 40.89x + 405.3,$$

where $x = 1$ corresponds to the year 2001. (Data from: U.S. Centers for Medicare and Medicaid Services.)

(a) What was the approximate revenue generated from hospital stays in 2010?

(b) Assuming the model remains accurate, in what year will revenue be approximately $1 trillion?

69. Business The number of employees (in thousands) working in the motion picture and sound recording industries can be approximated by

$$y = -1.8x + 384.6,$$

where $x = 0$ corresponds to the year 2000. (Data from: U.S. Bureau of Labor Statistics.)

(a) What was the number of employees in the year 2000?

(b) What was the number of employees in the year 2010?

(c) Assuming the model remains accurate, in what year will the number of employees be 350,000?

70. Business The number of golf facilities in the United States has been declining and can be approximated with the equation

$$y = -42.1x + 16,288,$$

where $x = 5$ corresponds to the year 2005. (Data from: National Golf Association.)

(a) How many golf facilities were there in 2010?

(b) If the trend continues to hold, in what year will there be 15,500 golf facilities?

71. Business In the United States, total sales related to lawn care were approximately $35.1 billion in 2005 and $29.7 billion in 2011. (Data from: The National Gardening Association.)

(a) Let the x-axis denote time and the y-axis denote the sales related to lawn care (in billions of dollars). Let $x = 5$ correspond to 2005. Fill in the blanks. The given data is represented by the points (_____, $35.1) and (11, _____).

(b) Find the linear equation determined by the two points in part (a).

(c) Use the equation in part (b) to estimate the sales produced in 2009.

(d) If the model remains accurate, when will lawn care sales reach $25 billion?

72. Business According the Bureau of Labor Statistics, there were approximately 16.3 million union workers in the year 2000 and 14.9 million union workers in the year 2010.

(a) Consider the change in union workers to be linear and write an equation expressing the number y of union workers in terms of the number x of years since 2000.

(b) Assuming that the equation in part (a) remains accurate, use it to predict the number of union workers in 2015.

73. Business The demand for chicken legs in the chicken industry has increased. According to the U.S. Department of Agriculture, in the year 2002, the average price per pound of chicken legs was $.40 a pound, while in 2012, the price had risen to $.75 a pound.

(a) Write an equation assuming a linear trend expressing the price per pound of leg meat y in terms of the number x of years since 2002.

(b) Assuming the future accuracy of the equation you found in part (a), predict the price per pound of chicken legs in 2014.

74. Business Similar to Exercise 73, the price per pound of chicken thighs was $.60 a pound in the year 2002 and $1.25 in 2012.

(a) If the price of thigh meat is linear, express the price per pound of thigh meat y in terms of the number x of years since the year 2002.

(b) Use your expression from (a) to find the price of thigh meat in the year 2010.

75. Social Science According to data from the U.S. Drug Enforcement Administration, there were 36,845 federal drug arrests in the year 2000 and 27,200 in the year 2010.

(a) Write a linear equation expressing the number of federal drug arrests y in terms of the number x of years since 2000.

(b) Using the equation you found in (a), find the number of federal drug arrests in 2006.

76. Social Science According to data from the U.S. Drug Enforcement Administration, the total seizure of drugs (in millions of pounds) was 1.5 in the year 2000 and 4.5 in the year 2010.

(a) Write a linear equation expressing the weight in pounds from the seizure of drugs y in terms of the number x of years since 2000.

(b) How much was seized in 2007?

(c) If the trend continues, in what year will the total of seized drugs be 5.7 million pounds?

77. Physical Science The accompanying graph shows the winning time (in minutes) at the Olympic Games from 1952 to 2008 for the men's 5000-meter run, together with a linear approximation of the data. (Data from: *The World Almanac and Book of Facts*: 2009.)

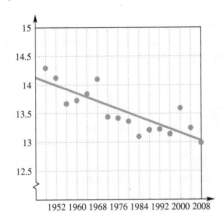

(a) The equation for the linear approximation is

$$y = -.01723x + 47.61.$$

What does the slope of this line represent? Why is the slope negative?

(b) Use the approximation to estimate the winning time in the 2012 Olympics. If possible, check this estimate against the actual time.

78. Business The accompanying graph shows the number of civilians in the U.S. labor force (in millions) in selected years (with the year 2020 projected). (Data from: U.S. Bureau of Labor Statistics.)

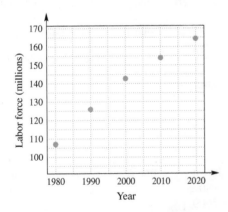

(a) Use the data points (1980, 106.9) and (2010, 153.9) to estimate the slope of the line shown. Interpret this number.

(b) Use part (a) and the point (2010, 153.9) to approximate the civilian labor force in 2015.

✓ **Checkpoint Answers**

1. **(a)** $6/5$ **(b)** $-9/2$

2. **(a)** $y = \dfrac{2}{3}x - 3$ **(b)** $y = -\dfrac{3}{2}x + \dfrac{1}{4}$

3. **(a)** Slope $-1/4$; y-intercept $3/2$
   (b) Slope $3/2$; y-intercept $-1/2$

4. **(a)** Slope of $E = -.3$; slope of $F = -1$; slope of $G = -2$; slope of $H = -5$.
   (b)

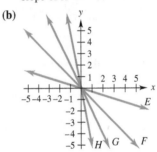

   (c) The larger the slope in absolute value, the more steeply the line falls from left to right.

5. **(a)**   **(b)**

6. **(a)** Perpendicular   **(b)** Neither   **(c)** Parallel

7. **(a)** $y + 2 = -\dfrac{3}{5}(x - 5)$; $y = -\dfrac{3}{5}x + 1$.

   (b) $y - 8 = \dfrac{1}{3}(x - 6)$; $y = \dfrac{1}{3}x + 6$.

8. **(a)** $2y = -x + 8$ **(b)** $11y = -8x - 42$

9. **(a)** $y = 1409x + 19,307$ **(b)** $\$43,260$

2.3 Linear Models

In business and science, it is often necessary to make judgments on the basis of data from the past. For instance, a stock analyst might use a company's profits in previous years to estimate the next year's profits. Or a life insurance company might look at life expectancies of people born in various years to predict how much money it should expect to pay out in the next year.

In such situations, the available data is used to construct a mathematical model, such as an equation or a graph, which is used to approximate the likely outcome in cases where complete data is not available. In this section, we consider applications in which the data can be modeled by a linear equation.

Figure 2.31

Figure 2.32

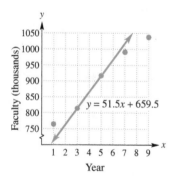

Figure 2.33

✓ **Checkpoint 1**

Use the points (5, 917) and
(9, 1038) to find another model for
the data in Example 1.

Figure 2.34

The simplest way to construct a linear model is to use the line determined by two of the data points, as illustrated in the following example.

> **Example 1**   **Social Science**   The number of full-time faculty at four-year colleges and universities (in thousands) in selected years is shown in the following table. (Data from: U.S. National Center for Education Statistics.)
>
> | Year | 2001 | 2003 | 2005 | 2007 | 2009 |
> |------|------|------|------|------|------|
> | **Number of Faculty** | 764 | 814 | 917 | 991 | 1038 |

(a) Let $x = 1$ correspond to 2001, and plot the points (x, y), where x is the year and y is the number of full-time faculty at four-year colleges and universities.

Solution The data points are $(1, 764)$, $(3, 814)$, $(5, 917)$, $(7, 991)$, and $(9, 1038)$, as shown in Figure 2.31.

(b) Use the data points $(5, 917)$ and $(9, 991)$ to find a line that models the data.

Solution The slope of the line through $(5, 917)$ and $(7, 991)$ is $\dfrac{991 - 917}{7 - 5} = \dfrac{74}{2} = 37$.

Using the point $(5, 917)$ and the slope 37, we find that the equation of this line is

$$y - 917 = 37(x - 5) \qquad \text{Point–slope form for the equation of a line}$$
$$y - 917 = 37x - 185 \qquad \text{Distributive property}$$
$$y = 37x + 732 \qquad \text{Slope–intercept form}$$

The line and the data points are shown in Figure 2.32. Although the line fits the two points we used to calculate the slope perfectly, it overestimates the remaining three data points.

(c) Use the points $(3, 814)$ and $(5, 917)$ to find another line that models the data.

The slope of the line is $\dfrac{917 - 814}{5 - 3} = \dfrac{103}{2} = 51.5$. Using the point $(3, 814)$ and the slope 51.5, we find that the equation of this line is

$$y - 814 = 51.5(x - 3) \qquad \text{Point–slope form for the equation of a line}$$
$$y - 814 = 51.5x - 154.5 \qquad \text{Distributive property}$$
$$y = 51.5x + 659.5 \qquad \text{Slope–intercept form}$$

The line and the data points are shown in Figure 2.33. This line passes through two data points, but significantly underestimates the number of faculty in 2001 and over-estimates the number of faculty in 2009. ✓₁

Opinions may vary as to which of the lines in Example 1 best fits the data. To make a decision, we might try to measure the amount of error in each model. One way to do this is to compute the difference between the number of faculty y and the amount $\hat{y}$ given by the model. If the data point is (x, y) and the corresponding point on the line is $(x, \hat{y})$, then the difference $y - \hat{y}$ measures the error in the model for that particular value of x. The number $y - \hat{y}$ is called a **residual**. As shown in Figure 2.34, the residual $y - \hat{y}$ is the vertical distance from the data point to the line (positive when the data point is above the line, negative when it is below the line, and 0 when it is on the line).

One way to determine how well a line fits the data points is to compute the sum of its residuals—that is, the sum of the individual errors. Unfortunately, however, the sum of the residuals of two different lines might be equal, thwarting our effort to decide which is the better fit. Furthermore, the residuals may sum to 0, which doesn't mean that there is no error, but only that the positive and negative errors (which might be quite large) cancel each other out. (See Exercise 11 at the end of this section for an example.)

To avoid this difficulty, mathematicians use the sum of the *squares* of the residuals to measure how well a line fits the data points. When the sum of the squares is used, a smaller sum means a smaller overall error and hence a better fit. The error is 0 only when all the data points lie on the line (a perfect fit).

Example 2   **Social Science**   Two linear models for the number of full-time faculty at four-year colleges and universities were constructed in Example 1:

$$y = 37x + 732 \quad \text{and} \quad y = 51.5x + 659.5.$$

For each model, determine the five residuals, square of each residual, and the sum of the squares of the residuals.

Solution The information for each model is summarized in the following tables:

$$y = 37x + 732$$

Data Point (x, y)	Model Point $(x, \hat{y})$	Residual $y - \hat{y}$	Squared Residual $(y - \hat{y})^2$
(1, 764)	(1, 769)	−5	25
(3, 814)	(3, 843)	−29	841
(5, 917)	(5, 917)	0	0
(7, 991)	(7, 991)	0	0
(9, 1038)	(9, 1065)	−27	729
			Sum = 1595

$$y = 51.5x + 659.5$$

Data Point (x, y)	Model Point $(x, \hat{y})$	Residual $y - \hat{y}$	Squared Residual $(y - \hat{y})^2$
(1, 764)	(1, 711)	53	2809
(3, 814)	(3, 814)	0	0
(5, 917)	(5, 917)	0	0
(7, 991)	(7, 1020)	−29	841
(9, 1038)	(9, 1123)	−85	7225
			Sum = 10,875

✓ Checkpoint 2

Another model for the data in Examples 1 and 2 is $y = 34.25x + 729.75$. Use this line to find

(a) the residuals and

(b) the sum of the squares of the residuals.

(c) Does this line fit the data better than the two lines in Example 2?

According to this measure of the error, the line $y = 37x + 732$ is a better fit for the data because the sum of the squares of its residuals is smaller than the sum of the squares of the residuals for $y = 51.5x + 659.5$. ✓ 2

✎ Linear Regression (Optional)*

Mathematical techniques from multivariable calculus can be used to prove the following result.

> For any set of data points, there is one, and only one, line for which the sum of the squares of the residuals is as small as possible.

---

*Examples 3–6 require either a graphing calculator or a spreadsheet program.

This *line of best fit* is called the **least-squares regression line,** and the computational process for finding its equation is called **linear regression.** Linear-regression formulas are quite complicated and require a large amount of computation. Fortunately, most graphing calculators and spreadsheet programs can do linear regression quickly and easily.

NOTE The process outlined here works for most TI graphing calculators. Other graphing calculators and spreadsheet programs operate similarly, but check your instruction manual or see the Graphing Calculator Appendix.

Example 3   Social Science   Recall the number of full-time faculty at four-year colleges and universities (in thousands) in selected years was as follows.

Year	2001	2003	2005	2007	2009
Number of Faculty	764	814	917	991	1038

Use a graphing calculator to do the following:

(a) Plot the data points with $x = 1$ corresponding to 2001.

Solution   The data points are (1, 764), (3, 814), (5, 917), (7, 991), and (9, 1038). Press STAT EDIT to bring up the statistics editor. Enter the x-coordinates as list L_1 and the corresponding y-coordinates as L_2, as shown in Figure 2.35. To plot the data points, go to the STAT PLOT menu, choose a plot (here it is Plot 1), choose ON, and enter the lists L_1 and L_2 as shown in Figure 2.36. Then set the viewing window as usual and press GRAPH to produce the plot in Figure 2.37.

Figure 2.35

Figure 2.36

Figure 2.37

(b) Find the least squares regression line for these data.

Solution   Go to the STAT CALC menu and choose LINREG, which returns you to the home screen. As shown in Figure 2.38, enter the list names and the place where the equation of the regression line should be stored (here, Y_1 is chosen; it is on the VARS Y-VARS FUNCTION menu); then press ENTER. Figure 2.39 shows that the equation of the regression line is

$$y = 36.25x + 723.55.$$

✓ Checkpoint 3

Use the least-squares regression line $y = 36.25x + 723.55$ and the data points of Example 3 to find

(a) the residuals and

(b) the sum of the squares of the residuals.

(c) How does this line compare with those in Example 1 and Checkpoint 2?

Figure 2.38

Figure 2.39

Figure 2.40

(c) Graph the data points and the regression line on the same screen.

Solution   Press GRAPH to see the line plotted with the data points (Figure 2.40).

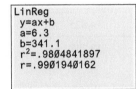

```
LinReg
  y=ax+b
  a=6.3
  b=341.1
  r²=.9804841897
  r=.9901940162
```

Figure 2.41

Figure 2.42

 Checkpoint 4

Using only the data from 2005 and later in Example 4, find the equation of the least-squares regression line. Round the coefficients to two decimal places.

Example 4 **Social Science** The following table gives the number (in thousands) of full-time faculty at two-year colleges. (Data from: U.S. National Center for Education Statistics.)

Year	2001	2003	2005	2007	2009
Number of Faculty	349	359	373	381	401

(a) Let $x = 1$ correspond to the year 2001. Use a graphing calculator or spreadsheet program to find the least-squares regression line that models the data in the table.

Solution The data points are (1, 349), (3, 359), (5, 373), (7, 381), and (9, 401). Enter the x-coordinates as list L_1 and the corresponding y-coordinates as list L_2 in a graphing calculator and then find the regression line as in Figure 2.41.

(b) Plot the data points and the regression line on the same screen.

Solution See Figure 2.42, which shows that the line is a reasonable model for the data.

(c) Assuming the trend continues, estimate the number of faculty in the year 2015.

Solution The year 2015 corresponds to $x = 15$. Substitute $x = 15$ into the regression-line equation:

$$y = 6.3(15) + 341.1 = 435.6.$$

This model estimates that the number of full-time faculty at two-year colleges will be approximately 435,600 in the year 2015.

Correlation

Although the "best fit" line can always be found by linear regression, it may not be a good model. For instance, if the data points are widely scattered, no straight line will model the data accurately. We calculate a value called the **correlation coefficient** to assess the fit of the regression line to the scatterplot. It measures how closely the data points fit the regression line and thus indicates how good the regression line is for predictive purposes.

The correlation coefficient r is always between -1 and 1. When $r = \pm 1$, the data points all lie on the regression line (a perfect fit). When the absolute value of r is close to 1, the line fits the data quite well, and when r is close to 0, the line is a poor fit for the data (but some other curve might be a good fit). Figure 2.43 shows how the value of r varies, depending on the pattern of the data points.

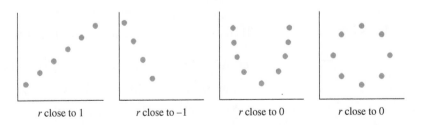

| r close to 1 | r close to -1 | r close to 0 | r close to 0 |

Figure 2.43

Example 5 **Business** The number of unemployed people in the U.S. labor force (in millions) in recent years is shown in the table. (Data from: U.S. Department of Labor, Bureau of Labor Statistics.)

Figure 2.44

Figure 2.45

✓**Checkpoint 5**

Using only the data from 2002 and later in Example 5, find

(a) the equation of the least-squares regression line and

(b) the correlation coefficient.

(c) How well does this line fit the data?

Year	Unemployed	Year	Unemployed	Year	Unemployed
1994	7.996	2000	5.692	2006	7.001
1995	7.404	2001	6.801	2007	7.078
1996	7.236	2002	8.378	2008	8.924
1997	6.739	2003	8.774	2009	14.265
1998	6.210	2004	8.149	2010	14.825
1999	5.880	2005	7.591	2011	13.747

Determine whether a linear equation is a good model for these data or not.

Solution   Let $x = 4$ correspond to 1994, and plot the data points (4, 7.996), etc., either by hand or with a graphing calculator, as in Figure 2.44. They do not form a linear pattern (because unemployment tends to rise and fall). Alternatively, you could compute the regression equation for the data, as in Figure 2.45. Figure 2.45 shows that the correlation coefficient is $r \approx .69$, which is a relatively high value. However, we can see that, even though the correlation is somewhat high, a straight line is not a good fit because of the peaks and valleys in Figure 2.44. ✓₅

Example 6   **Education**   Enrollment projections (in millions) for all U.S. colleges and universities in selected years are shown in the following table: (Data from: U.S. Center for Educational Statistics.)

Year	2005	2007	2008	2009	2010
Enrollment	17.5	18.2	19.1	20.4	21.0

(a) Let $x = 5$ correspond to the year 2005. Use a graphing calculator or spreadsheet program to find a linear model for the data and determine how well it fits the data points.

Solution   The least-squares regression line (with coefficients rounded) is

$$y = .74x + 13.5,$$

as shown in Figure 2.46. The correlation coefficient is $r \approx .97$, which is very close to 1, and Figure 2.47 shows a linear trend. Thus, the line fits the data well.

(b) Assuming the trend continues, predict the enrollment in 2015.

Solution   Let $x = 15$ (corresponding to 2015) in the regression equation:

$$y = .74(15) + 13.5 = 24.6.$$

Therefore, the enrollment in 2015 will be approximately 24.6 million students.

(c) According to this model, in what year will enrollment reach 30 million?

Solution   Let $y = 30$ and solve the regression equation for x:

$$y = .74x + 13.5$$
$$30 = .74x + 13.5 \qquad \text{Let } y = 30.$$
$$16.5 = .74x \qquad \text{Subtract 13.5 from both sides.}$$
$$x \approx 22.3. \qquad \text{Divide both sides by 0.74.}$$

Since these enrollment figures change once a year, use the nearest integer value for x, namely, 22. So enrollment will reach 30 million in 2022.

Figure 2.46

Figure 2.47

2.3 Exercises

1. **Physical Science** The following table shows equivalent Fahrenheit and Celsius temperatures:

Degrees Fahrenheit	32	68	104	140	176	212
Degrees Celsius	0	20	40	60	80	100

   (a) Choose any two data points and use them to construct a linear equation that models the data, with x being Fahrenheit and y being Celsius.

   (b) Use the model in part (a) to find the Celsius temperature corresponding to

   $$50° \text{ Fahrenheit and } 75° \text{ Fahrenheit.}$$

Physical Science *Use the linear equation derived in Exercise 1 to work the following problems.*

2. Convert each temperature.

   (a) 58°F to Celsius   (b) 50°C to Fahrenheit

   (c) −10°C to Fahrenheit   (d) −20°F to Celsius

3. According to the *World Almanac and Book of Facts*, 2008, Venus is the hottest planet, with a surface temperature of 867° Fahrenheit. What is this temperature in degrees Celsius?

4. Find the temperature at which Celsius and Fahrenheit temperatures are numerically equal.

In each of the next set of problems, assume that the data can be modeled by a straight line and that the trend continues indefinitely. Use two data points to find such a line and then answer the question. (See Example 1.)

5. **Business** The Consumer Price Index (CPI), which measures the cost of a typical package of consumer goods, was 201.6 in the year 2006 and 224.9 in the year 2011. Let $x = 6$ correspond to 2006, and estimate the CPI in 2008 and 2015. (Data from: U.S. Bureau of Labor Statistics.)

6. **Finance** The approximate number (in millions) of individual tax returns filed with the Internal Revenue Service in the year 2001 was 127.1 and in the year 2011 it was 140.8. Let $x = 1$ correspond to 2001, and estimate the number of returns filed in 2005 and 2012. (Data from: U.S. Internal Revenue Service.)

7. **Business** The number (in millions) of employees working in the finance and insurance industries was 6.0 in the year 2000 and 6.5 in the year 2008. Let $x = 0$ correspond to 2000, and estimate the number of employees in 2010. (Data from: U.S. Census Bureau.)

8. **Business** The number (in millions) of employees working in the health care and social assistance industries was 14.1 in the year 2000 and 17.2 in the year 2008. Let $x = 0$ correspond to 2000, and estimate the number of employees in 2014. (Data from: U.S. Census Bureau.)

9. **Physical Science** Suppose a baseball is thrown at 85 miles per hour. The ball will travel 320 feet when hit by a bat swung at 50 miles per hour and will travel 440 feet when hit by a bat swung at 80 miles per hour. Let y be the number of feet traveled by the ball when hit by a bat swung at x miles per hour. (*Note:* The preceding data are valid for $50 \le x \le 90$, where the bat is 35 inches long, weighs 32 ounces, and strikes a waist-high pitch so that the place of the swing lies at 10° from the diagonal). [Data from: Robert K. Adair, *The Physics of Baseball* (HarperCollins, 1990)]. How much farther will a ball travel for each mile-per-hour increase in the speed of the bat?

10. **Physical Science** Ski resorts require large amounts of water in order to make snow. Snowmass Ski Area in Colorado plans to pump at least 1120 gallons of water per minute for at least 12 hours a day from Snowmass Creek between mid-October and late December. Environmentalists are concerned about the effects on the ecosystem. Find the minimum amount of water pumped in 30 days. [*Hint:* Let y be the total number of gallons pumped x days after pumping begins. Note that $(0, 0)$ is on the graph of the equation.] (Data from: York Snow, Inc.)

In each of the next two problems, two linear models are given for the data. For each model,

(a) *find the residuals and their sum;*

(b) *find the sum of the squares of the residuals;*

(c) *decide which model is the better fit. (See Example 2.)*

11. **Finance** The following table shows the number of operating federal credit unions in the United States for several years.

Year	2007	2008	2009	2010	2011
Number of federal credit unions	5036	4847	4714	4589	4447

   Let $x = 7$ correspond to the year 2007. Two equations that model the data are $y = -143.6x + 6019$ and $y = -170.2x + 6250$. (Data from: National Credit Union Association.)

12. **Business** The percentage of households using direct deposit for selected years is shown in the following table. (Data from: Board of Governors of the Federal Reserve System.)

Year	1995	1998	2001	2004	2007
Percent of households	53	67	71	75	80

   Let $x = 5$ correspond to the year 1995. Two equations that model the data are $y = 2.1x + 47$ and $y = 2.8x + 44$.

In each of the following problems, determine whether a straight line is a good model for the data. Do this visually by plotting the data points and by finding the correlation coefficient for the least-squares regression line. (See Examples 5 and 6.)

13. **Business** The accompanying table gives the total sales (in billions of dollars) for the aerospace industry. Let $x = 6$

correspond to the year 2006. (Data from: ProQuest Statistical Abstract of the United States 2013.)

Year	2006	2007	2008	2009	2010	2011
Total Sales	177.3	192.0	194.7	203.0	203.6	210.0

14. Business   The accompanying table gives the number (in thousands) of new houses built for each of the years. Let $x = 6$ correspond to the year 2006. (Data from: U.S. Census Bureau.)

Year	2006	2007	2008	2009	2010	2011
Total Sales	1801	1355	906	554	587	609

In Exercises 15–18 find the required linear model using least-squares regression. (See Examples 3–6.)

15. Business   Use the data on sales of the aerospace industry in Exercise 13.

(a) Find a linear model for the data with $x = 6$ corresponding to the year 2006.

(b) Assuming the trend continues, estimate the total sales for the year 2015.

16. Health   The accompanying table shows the number of deaths per 100,000 people from heart disease in selected years. (Data from: U.S. National Center for Health Statistics.)

Year	1985	1990	1995	2000	2005	2010
Deaths	375.0	321.8	293.4	257.6	211.1	178.5

(a) Find a linear model for the data with $x = 5$ corresponding to the year 1985.

(b) Assuming the trend continues, estimate the number of deaths per 100,000 people for the year 2015.

17. Business   The accompanying table shows the revenue (in billions of dollars) from newspaper publishers. (Data from: U.S. Census Bureau.)

Year	2006	2007	2008	2009	2010
Revenue	48.9	47.6	43.9	36.4	34.7

(a) Find a linear model for the data with $x = 6$ corresponding to the year 2006.

(b) Assuming the trend continues, estimate the revenue in 2016.

18. Health   Researchers wish to determine if a relationship exists between age and systolic blood pressure (SBP). The accompanying table gives the age and systolic blood pressure for 10 adults.

Age (x)	35	37	42	46	53	57	61	65	69	74
SBP (y)	102	127	120	131	126	137	140	130	148	147

(a) Find a linear model for these data using age (x) to predict systolic blood pressure (y).

(b) Use the results from part (a) to predict the systolic blood pressure for a person who is 42-years-old, 53-years-old, and 69-years-old. How well do the actual data agree with the predicted values?

(c) Use the results from part (a) to predict the systolic blood pressure for a person who is 45-years-old and 70-years-old.

Work these problems.

19. Business   The estimated operating revenue (in billions of dollars) from Internet publishing and broadcasting is given in the accompanying table. (Data from: U.S. Census Bureau.)

Year	2006	2007	2008	2009	2010
Revenue	11.5	15.0	17.8	19.1	21.3

(a) Find the least squares regression line that models these data with $x = 6$ corresponding to the year 2006.

(b) Assuming the trend continues, estimate the operating revenue in the years 2012 and 2014.

20. Business   The number of basic cable television subscribers (in millions) is shown in the following table for various years. (Data from: ProQuest Statistical Abstract of the United States 2013.)

Year	2002	2004	2006	2008	2010
Subscribers	66.5	65.7	65.3	64.3	61.0

(a) Find the least-squares regression line that models these data with $x = 2$ corresponding to the year 2002.

(b) Find the number of subscribers for the year 2009.

(c) If the trend continues indefinitely, determine in what year there will be 55 million subscribers.

(d) Find the correlation coefficient.

21. Social Science   The number (in thousands) of traffic fatalities by year is displayed in the accompanying table. (Data from: U.S. National Highway Traffic Administration.)

Year	2005	2007	2008	2009	2010
Traffic Fatalities	43.5	41.3	37.4	33.9	32.9

(a) Find the least-squares regression line that models these data with $x = 5$ corresponding to the year 2005.

(b) Find the number of deaths for the year 2006.

(c) If the trend continues indefinitely, determine in what year there will be 28 thousand deaths.

(d) Find the correlation coefficient.

22. **Health** The following table shows men's and women's life expectancy at birth (in years) for selected birth years in the United States: (Data from: U.S. Center for National Health Statistics.)

Birth Year	Life Expectancy	
	Men	**Women**
1970	67.1	74.7
1975	68.8	76.6
1980	70.0	77.4
1985	71.1	78.2
1990	71.8	78.8
1995	72.5	78.9
1998	73.8	79.5
2000	74.3	79.7
2001	74.4	79.8
2004	75.2	80.4
2010	75.6	81.4

(a) Find the least-squares regression line for the men's data, with $x = 70$ corresponding to 1970.

(b) Find the least-squares regression line for the women's data, with $x = 70$ corresponding to 1970.

(c) Suppose life expectancy continues to increase as predicted by the equations in parts (a) and (b). Will men's life expectancy ever be the same as women's? If so, in what birth year will this occur?

✓**Checkpoint Answers**

1. $y = 30.25x + 765.75$

2. (a) $0, -18.5, 16, 21.5, 0$
   (b) 1060.5
   (c) Yes, because the sum of the squares of the residuals is lower.

3. (a) $4.2, -18.3, 12.2, 13.7, -11.8$
   (b) 828.30
   (c) It fits the data best because the sum of the squares of its residuals is smallest.

4. $y = 7x + 336$

5. (a) $y = .76x - 2.66$
   (b) $r \approx .74$
   (c) It fits reasonably well because $|r|$ is close to 1 and the pattern is linear.

2.4 Linear Inequalities

An **inequality** is a statement that one mathematical expression is greater than (or less than) another. Inequalities are very important in applications. For example, a company wants revenue to be *greater than* costs and must use *no more than* the total amount of capital or labor available.

Inequalities may be solved by algebraic or geometric methods. In this section, we shall concentrate on algebraic methods for solving **linear inequalities**, such as

$$4 - 3x \leq 7 + 2x \quad \text{and} \quad -2 < 5 + 3m < 20,$$

and absolute-value inequalities, such as $|x - 2| < 5$. The following properties are the basic algebraic tools for working with inequalities.

Properties of Inequality

For real numbers a, b, and c,

(a) if $a < b$, then $a + c < b + c$;

(b) if $a < b$, and if $c > 0$, then $ac < bc$;

(c) if $a < b$, and if $c < 0$, then $ac > bc$.

Throughout this section, definitions are given only for $<$, but they are equally valid for $>$, $\leq$, and $\geq$.

🛑 **CAUTION** Pay careful attention to part (c) in the previous box; if both sides of an inequality are multiplied by a negative number, the direction of the inequality symbol must be reversed. For example, starting with the true statement $-3 < 5$ and multiplying both sides by the positive number 2 gives

$$-3 \cdot 2 < 5 \cdot 2,$$

or

$$-6 < 10,$$

still a true statement. However, starting with $-3 < 5$ and multiplying both sides by the negative number -2 gives a true result only if the direction of the inequality symbol is reversed:

$$-3(-2) > 5(-2)$$
$$6 > -10. \quad \checkmark_1$$

✓**Checkpoint 1**

(a) First multiply both sides of $-6 < -1$ by 4, and then multiply both sides of $-6 < -1$ by -7.

(b) First multiply both sides of $9 \geq -4$ by 2, and then multiply both sides of $9 \geq -4$ by -5.

(c) First add 4 to both sides of $-3 < -1$, and then add -6 to both sides of $-3 < -1$.

Example 1   Solve $3x + 5 > 11$. Graph the solution.

Solution   First add -5 to both sides:

$$3x + 5 + (-5) > 11 + (-5)$$
$$3x > 6.$$

Now multiply both sides by $1/3$:

$$\frac{1}{3}(3x) > \frac{1}{3}(6)$$
$$x > 2.$$

(Why was the direction of the inequality symbol not changed?) In interval notation (introduced in Section 1.1), the solution is the interval $(2, \infty)$, which is graphed on the number line in Figure 2.48. The parenthesis at 2 shows that 2 is not included in the solution.

Figure 2.48

As a partial check, note that 0, which is not part of the solution, makes the inequality false, while 3, which is part of the solution, makes it true:

$$3(0) + 5 \overset{?}{>} 11 \qquad\qquad 3(3) + 5 \overset{?}{>} 11$$
$$5 > 11 \quad \text{False} \qquad\qquad 14 > 11. \quad \text{True} \;\checkmark_2$$

✓**Checkpoint 2**

Solve these inequalities. Graph each solution.

(a) $5z - 11 < 14$

(b) $-3k \leq -12$

(c) $-8y \geq 32$

Example 2   Solve $4 - 3x \leq 7 + 2x$.

Solution   Add -4 to both sides:

$$4 - 3x + (-4) \leq 7 + 2x + (-4)$$
$$-3x \leq 3 + 2x.$$

Add $-2x$ to both sides (remember that *adding* to both sides never changes the direction of the inequality symbol):

$$-3x + (-2x) \leq 3 + 2x + (-2x)$$
$$-5x \leq 3.$$

Multiply both sides by $-1/5$. Since $-1/5$ is negative, change the direction of the inequality symbol:

$$-\frac{1}{5}(-5x) \geq -\frac{1}{5}(3)$$

$$x \geq -\frac{3}{5}.$$

Figure 2.49 shows a graph of the solution, $[-3/5, \infty)$. The bracket in Figure 2.49 shows that $-3/5$ is included in the solution.

Checkpoint 3

Solve these inequalities. Graph each solution.

(a) $8 - 6t \geq 2t + 24$

(b) $-4r + 3(r + 1) < 2r$

Figure 2.49

Example 3   Solve $-2 < 5 + 3m < 20$. Graph the solution.

Solution   The inequality $-2 < 5 + 3m < 20$ says that $5 + 3m$ is between -2 and 20. We can solve this inequality with an extension of the properties given at the beginning of this section. Work as follows, first adding -5 to each part:

$$-2 + (-5) < 5 + 3m + (-5) < 20 + (-5)$$
$$-7 < 3m < 15.$$

Now multiply each part by $1/3$:

$$-\frac{7}{3} < m < 5.$$

Checkpoint 4

Solve each of the given inequalities. Graph each solution.

(a) $9 < k + 5 < 13$

(b) $-6 \leq 2z + 4 \leq 12$

A graph of the solution, $(-7/3, 5)$, is given in Figure 2.50.

Figure 2.50

Example 4   The formula for converting from Celsius to Fahrenheit temperature is

$$F = \frac{9}{5}C + 32.$$

What Celsius temperature range corresponds to the range from $32°F$ to $77°F$?

Solution   The Fahrenheit temperature range is $32 < F < 77$. Since $F = (9/5)C + 32$, we have

$$32 < \frac{9}{5}C + 32 < 77.$$

Solve the inequality for C:

$$32 < \frac{9}{5}C + 32 < 77$$

$$0 < \frac{9}{5}C < 45 \qquad \text{Subtract 32 from each part.}$$

$$\frac{5}{9} \cdot 0 < \frac{5}{9} \cdot \frac{9}{5}C < \frac{5}{9} \cdot 45 \qquad \text{Multiply each part by } \frac{5}{9}.$$

$$0 < C < 25.$$

Checkpoint 5

In Example 4, what Celsius temperatures correspond to the range from $5°F$ to $95°F$?

The corresponding Celsius temperature range is $0°C$ to $25°C$.

A product will break even or produce a profit only if the revenue R from selling the product at least equals the cost C of producing it—that is, if $R \geq C$.

Example 5   **Business**   A company analyst has determined that the cost to produce and sell x units of a certain product is $C = 20x + 1000$. The revenue for that product is $R = 70x$. Find the values of x for which the company will break even or make a profit on the product.

Solution   Solve the inequality $R \geq C$:

$$R \geq C$$
$$70x \geq 20x + 1000 \qquad \text{Let } R = 70x \text{ and } C = 20x + 1000.$$
$$50x \geq 1000 \qquad \text{Subtract } 20x \text{ from both sides.}$$
$$x \geq 20. \qquad \text{Divide both sides by 50.}$$

The company must produce and sell 20 items to break even and more than 20 to make a profit.

Example 6   **Business**   A pretzel manufacturer can sell a 6-ounce bag of pretzels to a wholesaler for $.35 a bag. The variable cost of producing each bag is $.25 per bag, and the fixed cost for the manufacturing operation is $110,000.* How many bags of pretzels need to be sold in order to break even or earn a profit?

Solution   Let x be the number of bags produced. Then the revenue equation is

$$R = .35x,$$

and the cost is given by

$$\text{Cost} = \text{Fixed Costs} + \text{Variable Costs}$$
$$C = 110,000 + .25x.$$

We now solve the inequality $R \geq C$:

$$R \geq C$$
$$.35x \geq 110,000 + .25x$$
$$.1x \geq 110,000$$
$$x \geq 1,110,000.$$

The manufacturer must produce and sell 1,110,000 bags of pretzels to break even and more than that to make a profit.

Absolute-Value Inequalities

You may wish to review the definition of absolute value in Section 1.1 before reading the following examples, which show how to solve inequalities involving absolute values.

Example 7   Solve each inequality.

(a) $|x| < 5$

Solution   Because absolute value gives the distance from a number to 0, the inequality $|x| < 5$ is true for all real numbers whose distance from 0 is less than 5. This includes all numbers between -5 and 5, or numbers in the interval $(-5, 5)$. A graph of the solution is shown in Figure 2.51 on the following page.

*Variable costs, fixed costs, and revenue were discussed on page 15.

Figure 2.51

(b) $|x| > 5$

Solution   The solution of $|x| > 5$ is given by all those numbers whose distance from 0 is *greater* than 5. This includes the numbers satisfying $x < -5$ or $x > 5$. A graph of the solution, all numbers in

$$(-\infty, -5) \quad \text{or} \quad (5, \infty),$$

is shown in Figure 2.52.

Figure 2.52

The preceding examples suggest the following generalizations.

> Assume that a and b are real numbers and that b is positive.
>
> **1.** Solve $|a| < b$ by solving $-b < a < b$.
> **2.** Solve $|a| > b$ by solving $a < -b$ or $a > b$.

Example 8   Solve $|x - 2| < 5$.

Solution   Replace a with $x - 2$ and b with 5 in property (1) in the box above. Now solve $|x - 2| < 5$ by solving the inequality

$$-5 < x - 2 < 5.$$

Add 2 to each part, getting the solution

$$-3 < x < 7,$$

which is graphed in Figure 2.53.

Example 9   Solve $|2 - 7m| - 1 > 4$.

Solution   First add 1 to both sides:

$$|2 - 7m| > 5$$

Now use property (2) from the preceding box to solve $|2 - 7m| > 5$ by solving the inequality

$$2 - 7m < -5 \quad \text{or} \quad 2 - 7m > 5.$$

Solve each part separately:

$$-7m < -7 \quad \text{or} \quad -7m > 3$$
$$m > 1 \quad \text{or} \quad m < -\frac{3}{7}.$$

The solution, all numbers in $\left(-\infty, -\frac{3}{7}\right)$ or $(1, \infty)$, is graphed in Figure 2.54.

Figure 2.54

✓ **Checkpoint 6**

Solve each inequality. Graph each solution.

(a) $|x| \leq 1$
(b) $|y| \geq 3$

Figure 2.53

✓ **Checkpoint 7**

Solve each inequality. Graph each solution.

(a) $|p + 3| < 4$
(b) $|2k - 1| \leq 7$

✓ **Checkpoint 8**

Solve each inequality. Graph each solution.

(a) $|y - 2| > 5$
(b) $|3k - 1| \geq 2$
(c) $|2 + 5r| - 4 \geq 1$

✓ **Checkpoint 9**

Solve each inequality.

(a) $|5m - 3| > -10$

(b) $|6 + 5a| < -9$

(c) $|8 + 2r| > 0$

Example 10   Solve $|3 - 7x| \geq -8$.

Solution The absolute value of a number is always nonnegative. Therefore, $|3 - 7x| \geq -8$ is always true, so the solution is the set of all real numbers. Note that the inequality $|3 - 7x| \leq -8$ has no solution, because the absolute value of a quantity can never be less than a negative number. ✓₉

2.4 Exercises

1. Explain how to determine whether a parenthesis or a bracket is used when graphing the solution of a linear inequality.

2. The three-part inequality $p < x < q$ means "p is less than x and x is less than q." Which one of the given inequalities is not satisfied by any real number x? Explain why.

   (a) $-3 < x < 5$ (b) $0 < x < 4$

   (c) $-7 < x < -10$ (d) $-3 < x < -2$

Solve each inequality and graph each solution. (See Examples 1–3.)

3. $-8k \leq 32$ 4. $-4a \leq 36$

5. $-2b > 0$ 6. $6 - 6z < 0$

7. $3x + 4 \leq 14$ 8. $2y - 7 < 9$

9. $-5 - p \geq 3$ 10. $5 - 3r \leq -4$

11. $7m - 5 < 2m + 10$ 12. $6x - 2 > 4x - 10$

13. $m - (4 + 2m) + 3 < 2m + 2$

14. $2p - (3 - p) \leq -7p - 2$

15. $-2(3y - 8) \geq 5(4y - 2)$

16. $5r - (r + 2) \geq 3(r - 1) + 6$

17. $3p - 1 < 6p + 2(p - 1)$

18. $x + 5(x + 1) > 4(2 - x) + x$

19. $-7 < y - 2 < 5$ 20. $-3 < m + 6 < 2$

21. $8 \leq 3r + 1 \leq 16$ 22. $-6 < 2p - 3 \leq 5$

23. $-4 \leq \dfrac{2k - 1}{3} \leq 2$ 24. $-1 \leq \dfrac{5y + 2}{3} \leq 4$

25. $\dfrac{3}{5}(2p + 3) \geq \dfrac{1}{10}(5p + 1)$

26. $\dfrac{8}{3}(z - 4) \leq \dfrac{2}{9}(3z + 2)$

In the following exercises, write a linear inequality that describes the given graph.

27.
   $$-6 \quad -4 \quad -2 \quad 0 \quad 2 \quad 4 \quad 6$$

28.
   $$-6 \quad -4 \quad -2 \quad 0 \quad 2 \quad 4 \quad 6$$

29.
   $$-6 \quad -4 \quad -2 \quad 0 \quad 2 \quad 4 \quad 6$$

30.
   $$-6 \quad -4 \quad -2 \quad 0 \quad 2 \quad 4 \quad 6$$

Business   *In Exercises 31–36, find all values of x for which the given products will at least break even. (See Examples 5 and 6.)*

31. The cost to produce x units of wire is $C = 50x + 6000$, while the revenue is $R = 65x$.

32. The cost to produce x units of squash is $C = 100x + 6000$, while the revenue is $R = 500x$.

33. $C = 85x + 1000$; $R = 105x$

34. $C = 70x + 500$; $R = 60x$

35. $C = 1000x + 5000$; $R = 900x$

36. $C = 25{,}000x + 21{,}700{,}000$; $R = 102{,}500x$

Solve each inequality. Graph each solution. (See Examples 7–10.)

37. $|p| > 7$ 38. $|m| < 2$

39. $|r| \leq 5$ 40. $|a| < -2$

41. $|b| > -5$ 42. $|2x + 5| < 1$

43. $\left|x - \dfrac{1}{2}\right| < 2$ 44. $|3z + 1| \geq 4$

45. $|8b + 5| \geq 7$ 46. $\left|5x + \dfrac{1}{2}\right| - 2 < 5$

Work these problems.

Physical Science   *The given inequality describes the monthly average high daily temperature T in degrees Fahrenheit in the given location. (Data from: Weatherbase.com.) What range of temperatures corresponds to the inequality?*

47. $|T - 83| \leq 7$; Miami, Florida

48. $|T - 63| \leq 27$; Boise, Idaho

49. $|T - 61| \leq 21$; Flagstaff, Arizona

50. $|T - 43| \leq 22$; Anchorage, Alaska

51. **Natural Science**   Human beings emit carbon dioxide when they breathe. In one study, the emission rates of carbon dioxide by college students were measured both during lectures and during exams. The average individual rate R_L (in grams per hour) during a lecture class satisfied the inequality $|R_L - 26.75| \leq 1.42$, whereas during an exam, the rate R_E satisfied the inequality $|R_E - 38.75| \leq 2.17$. (Data from: T.C. Wang, *ASHRAE Transactions* 81 [Part 1], 32 [1975].)

   (a) Find the range of values for R_L and R_E.

   (b) A class had 225 students. If T_L and T_E represent the total amounts of carbon dioxide (in grams) emitted during a one-hour lecture and one-hour exam, respectively, write inequalities that describe the ranges for T_L and T_E.

52. **Social Science** When administering a standard intelligence quotient (IQ) test, we expect about one-third of the scores to be more than 12 units above 100 or more than 12 units below 100. Describe this situation by writing an absolute value inequality.

53. **Social Science** A Gallup poll found that among Americans aged 18–34 years who consume alcohol, between 35% and 43% prefer beer. Let B represent the percentage of American alcohol consumers who prefer beer. Write the preceding information as an inequality. (Data from: Gallup.com.)

54. **Social Science** A Gallup poll in February 2013 found that between 17% and 19% of Americans considered themselves underemployed (working part-time or not working at all, but wanting to work full-time). Let U represent the percentage of underemployed workers. Write the preceding information as an inequality. (Data from: Gallup.com.)

55. **Finance** The following table shows the 2012 federal income tax for a single person. (Data from: Internal Revenue Service.)

If Taxable Income Is Over	But Not Over	Tax Rate
$0	$8700	10%
$8700	$35,350	15%
$35,350	$85,650	25%
$85,650	$178,650	28%
$178,650	$388,350	33%
$388,350	No limits	35%

Let x denote the taxable income. Write each of the six income ranges in the table as an inequality.

56. **Health** Federal guidelines require drinking water to have less than .050 milligrams per liter of lead. A test using 21 samples of water in a Midwestern city found that the average amount of lead in the samples was 0.040 milligrams per liter. All samples had lead content within 5% of the average.

    (a) Select a variable and write down what it represents.

    (b) Write an inequality to express the results obtained from the sample.

    (c) Did all the samples meet the federal requirement?

✓ **Checkpoint Answers**

1. (a) $-24 < -4$; $42 > 7$ (b) $18 \geq -8$; $-45 \leq 20$
   (c) $1 < 3$; $-9 < -7$

2. (a) $z < 5$ (b) $k \geq 4$

   (c) $y \leq -4$

3. (a) $t \leq -2$ (b) $r > 1$

4. (a) $4 < k < 8$ (b) $-5 \leq z \leq 4$

5. $-15°C$ to $35°C$

6. (a) $[-1, 1]$

   (b) All numbers in $(-\infty, -3]$ or $[3, \infty)$

7. (a) $(-7, 1)$ (b) $[-3, 4]$

8. (a) All numbers in $(-\infty, -3)$ or $(7, \infty)$

   (b) All numbers in $\left(-\infty, -\dfrac{1}{3}\right]$ or $[1, \infty)$

   (c) All numbers in $\left(-\infty, -\dfrac{7}{5}\right]$ or $\left[\dfrac{3}{5}, \infty\right)$

9. (a) All real numbers
   (b) No solution
   (c) All real numbers except -4

2.5 Polynomial and Rational Inequalities

This section deals with the solution of polynomial and rational inequalities, such as

$$r^2 + 3r - 4 \geq 0, \quad x^3 - x \leq 0, \quad \text{and} \quad \frac{2x - 1}{3x + 4} < 5.$$

We shall concentrate on algebraic solution methods, but to understand why these methods work, we must first look at such inequalities from a graphical point of view.

Figure 2.55

Example 1 Use the graph of $y = x^3 - 5x^2 + 2x + 8$ in Figure 2.55 to solve each of the given inequalities.

(a) $x^3 - 5x^2 + 2x + 8 > 0$

Solution Each point on the graph has coordinates of the form $(x, x^3 - 5x^2 + 2x + 8)$. The number x is a solution of the inequality exactly when the second coordinate of this point is positive—that is, when the point lies *above* the x-axis. So to solve the inequality, we need only find the first coordinates of points on the graph that are above the x-axis. This information can be read from Figure 2.55. The graph is above the x-axis when $-1 < x < 2$ and when $x > 4$. Therefore, the solutions of the inequality are all numbers x in the interval $(-1, 2)$ or the interval $(4, \infty)$.

(b) $x^3 - 5x^2 + 2x + 8 < 0$

Solution The number x is a solution of the inequality exactly when the second coordinate of the point $(x, x^3 - 5x^2 + 2x + 8)$ on the graph is negative—that is, when the point lies *below* the x-axis. Figure 2.55 shows that the graph is below the x-axis when $x < -1$ and when $2 < x < 4$. Hence, the solutions are all numbers x in the interval $(-\infty, -1)$ or the interval $(2, 4)$.

The solution process in Example 1 depends only on knowing the graph and its x-intercepts (that is, the points where the graph intersects the x-axis). This information can often be obtained algebraically, without doing any graphing.

Steps for Solving an Inequality Involving a Polynomial

1. Rewrite the inequality so that all the terms are on the left side and 0 is on the right side.
2. Find the x-intercepts by setting $y = 0$ and solving for x.
3. Divide the x-axis (number line) into regions using the solutions found in Step 2.
4. Test a point in each region by choosing a value for x and substituting it into the equation for y.
5. Determine which regions satisfy the original inequality and graph the solution.

Example 2 Solve each of the given quadratic inequalities.

(a) $x^2 - x < 12$

Solution

Step 1 Rewrite the inequality so that all the terms are on the left side and 0 is on the right side.
Hence we add -12 to each side and obtain $x^2 - x - 12 < 0$.

Step 2 Find the x-intercepts by setting $y = 0$ and solving for x.
We find the x-intercepts of $y = x^2 - x - 12$ by setting $y = 0$ and solving for x:

$$x^2 - x - 12 = 0$$
$$(x + 3)(x - 4) = 0$$
$$x + 3 = 0 \quad \text{or} \quad x - 4 = 0$$
$$x = -3 \qquad x = 4.$$

Step 3 Divide the x-axis (number line) into regions using the solutions found in Step 2.
These numbers divide the x-axis into three regions, as indicated in Figure 2.56.

Region A	Region B	Region C
$x < -3$	$-3 < x < 4$	$x > 4$

Figure 2.56

Step 4 Test a point in each region by choosing a value for x and substituting it in to the equation for y.

In each region, the graph of $y = x^2 - x - 12$ is an unbroken curve, so it will be entirely above or entirely below the axis. It can pass from above to below the x-axis only at the x-intercepts. To see whether the graph is above or below the x-axis when x is in region A, choose a value of x in region A, say, $x = -5$, and substitute it into the equation:

$$y = x^2 - x - 12 = (-5)^2 - (-5) - 12 = 18.$$

Therefore, the point $(-5, 18)$ is on the graph. Since its y-coordinate 18 is positive, this point lies above the x-axis; hence, the entire graph lies above the x-axis in region A.

Similarly, we can choose a value of x in region B, say, $x = 0$. Then

$$y = x^2 - x - 12 = 0^2 - 0 - 12 = -12,$$

so that $(0, -12)$ is on the graph. Since this point lies below the x-axis (why?), the entire graph in region B must be below the x-axis. Finally, in region C, let $x = 5$. Then $y = 5^2 - 5 - 12 = 8$, so that $(5, 8)$ is on the graph, and the entire graph in region C lies above the x-axis. We can summarize the results as follows:

Interval	$x < -3$	$-3 < x < 4$	$x > 4$
Test value in interval	-5	0	5
Value of $x^2 - x - 12$	18	-12	8
Graph	above x-axis	below x-axis	above x-axis
Conclusion	$x^2 - x - 12 > 0$	$x^2 - x - 12 < 0$	$x^2 - x - 12 > 0$

Step 5 Determine which regions satisfy the original inequality and graph the solution.

The last row shows that the only region where $x^2 - x - 12 < 0$ is region B, so the solutions of the inequality are all numbers x with $-3 < x < 4$—that is, the interval $(-3, 4)$, as shown in the number line graph in Figure 2.57.

Figure 2.57

(b) $x^2 - x - 12 > 0$

Solution Use the chart in part (a). The last row shows that $x^2 - x - 12 > 0$ only when x is in region A or region C. Hence, the solutions of the inequality are all numbers x with $x < -3$ or $x > 4$—that is, all numbers in the interval $(-\infty, -3)$ or the interval $(4, \infty)$. ✓

✓ **Checkpoint 1**

Solve each inequality. Graph the solution on the number line.

(a) $x^2 - 2x < 15$

(b) $2x^2 - 3x - 20 < 0$

Example 3 Solve the quadratic inequality $r^2 + 3r \geq 4$.

Solution

Step 1 First rewrite the inequality so that one side is 0:

$$r^2 + 3r \geq 4$$
$$r^2 + 3r - 4 \geq 0. \quad \text{Add } -4 \text{ to both sides.}$$

Step 2 Now solve the corresponding equation (which amounts to finding the x-intercepts of $y = r^3 + 3r - 4$):

$$r^2 + 3r - 4 = 0$$
$$(r - 1)(r + 4) = 0$$
$$r = 1 \quad \text{or} \quad r = -4.$$

Step 3 These numbers separate the number line into three regions, as shown in Figure 2.58. Test a number from each region:

Step 4 Let $r = -5$ from region A: $(-5)^2 + 3(-5) - 4 = 6 > 0$.

Let $r = 0$ from region B: $(0)^2 + 3(0) - 4 = -4 < 0$.

Let $r = 2$ from region C: $(2)^2 + 3(2) - 4 = 6 > 0$.

Step 5 We want the inequality to be positive or 0. The solution includes numbers in region A and in region C, as well as -4 and 1, the endpoints. The solution, which includes all numbers in the interval $(-\infty, -4]$ or the interval $[1, \infty)$, is graphed in Figure 2.58. ✓₂

✓ **Checkpoint 2**

Solve each inequality. Graph each solution.

(a) $k^2 + 2k - 15 \geq 0$

(b) $3m^2 + 7m \geq 6$

Figure 2.58

Example 4 Solve $q^3 - 4q > 0$.

Solution

Step 1 Step 1 is already complete in the statement of the problem.

Step 2 Solve the corresponding equation by factoring:

$$q^3 - 4q = 0$$
$$q(q^2 - 4) = 0$$
$$q(q + 2)(q - 2) = 0$$
$$q = 0 \quad \text{or} \quad q + 2 = 0 \quad \text{or} \quad q - 2 = 0$$
$$q = 0 \qquad\qquad q = -2 \qquad\qquad q = 2.$$

Step 3 These three numbers separate the number line into the four regions shown in Figure 2.59.

Step 4 Test a number from each region:

A: If $q = -3, (-3)^3 - 4(-3) = -15 < 0$.

B: If $q = -1, (-1)^3 - 4(-1) = 3 > 0$.

C: If $q = 1, (1)^3 - 4(1) = -3 < 0$.

D: If $q = 3, (3)^3 - 4(3) = 15 > 0$.

Step 5 The numbers that make the polynomial positive are in the interval $(-2, 0)$ or the interval $(2, \infty)$, as graphed in Figure 2.59. ✓₃

✓ **Checkpoint 3**

Solve each inequality. Graph each solution.

(a) $m^3 - 9m > 0$

(b) $2k^3 - 50k \leq 0$

Figure 2.59

−.9254   1.4481   4.4774

Figure 2.60

Checkpoint 4

Use graphical methods to find approximate solutions of these inequalities.

(a) $x^2 - 6x + 2 > 0$

(b) $x^2 - 6x + 2 < 0$

A graphing calculator can be used to solve inequalities without the need to evaluate at a test number in each interval. It is also useful for finding approximate solutions when the x-intercepts of the graph cannot be found algebraically.

Example 5   Use a graphing calculator to solve $x^3 - 5x^2 + x + 6 > 0$.

Solution   Begin by graphing $y = x^3 - 5x^2 + x + 6$ (Figure 2.60). Find the x-intercepts by solving $x^3 - 5x^2 + x + 6 = 0$. Since this cannot readily be done algebraically, use the graphical root finder to determine that the solutions (x-intercepts) are approximately −.9254, 1.4481, and 4.4774.

The graph is above the x-axis when $-.9254 < x < 1.4481$ and when $x > 4.4774$. Therefore, the approximate solutions of the inequality are all numbers in the interval $(-.9254, 1.4481)$ or the interval $(4.4774, \infty)$. ✓4

Example 6   **Business**   A company sells wholesale portable DVD players for $39 each. The variable cost of producing x thousand players is $5.5x - 4.9x^2$ (in thousands of dollars), and the fixed cost is $550 (in thousands). Find the values of x for which the company will break even or make a profit on the product.

Solution   If x thousand DVD players are sold at $39 each, then

$$R = 39 \times x = 39x.$$

The cost function (in thousands of dollars) is

$$\text{Cost} = \text{Fixed Costs} + \text{Variable Costs}$$
$$C = 550 + (5.5x - 4.9x^2).$$

Therefore, to break even or earn a profit, we need Revenue (R) greater than or equal to Cost (C).

$$R \geq C$$
$$39x \geq 550 + 5.5x - 4.9x^2$$
$$4.9x^2 + 33.5x - 550 \geq 0.$$

Figure 2.61

Now graph $4.9x^2 + 33.5x - 550$. Since x has to be positive in this situation (why?), we need only look at the graph in the right half of the plane. Here, and in other cases, you may have to try several viewing windows before you find one that shows what you need. Once you find a suitable window, such as in Figure 2.61, use the graphical root finder to determine the relevant x-intercept. Figure 2.61 shows the intercept is approximately $x \approx 7.71$. Hence, the company must manufacture at least $7.71 \times 1000 = 7710$ portable DVD players to make a profit.

Rational Inequalities

Inequalities with quotients of algebraic expressions are called **rational inequalities**. These inequalities can be solved in much the same way as polynomial inequalities can.

Steps for Solving Inequalities Involving Rational Expressions

1. Rewrite the inequality so that all the terms are on the left side and the 0 is on the right side.
2. Write the left side as a single fraction.
3. Set the numerator and the denominator equal to 0 and solve for x.
4. Divide the x-axis (number line) into regions using the solutions found in Step 3.
5. Test a point in each region by choosing a value for x and substituting it into the equation for y.
6. Determine which regions satisfy the original inequality and graph the solution.

Example 7   Solve the rational inequality

$$\frac{5}{x + 4} \geq 1.$$

Solution

Step 1   Write an equivalent inequality with one side equal to 0:

$$\frac{5}{x + 4} \geq 1$$

$$\frac{5}{x + 4} - 1 \geq 0.$$

Step 2   Write the left side as a single fraction:

$$\frac{5}{x + 4} - \frac{x + 4}{x + 4} \geq 0 \qquad \text{Obtain a common denominator.}$$

$$\frac{5 - (x + 4)}{x + 4} \geq 0 \qquad \text{Subtract fractions.}$$

$$\frac{5 - x - 4}{x + 4} \geq 0 \qquad \text{Distributive property}$$

$$\frac{1 - x}{x + 4} \geq 0.$$

Step 3   The quotient can change sign only at places where the denominator is 0 or the numerator is 0. (In graphical terms, these are the only places where the graph of $y = \dfrac{1 - x}{x + 4}$ can change from above the x-axis to below.) This happens when

$$1 - x = 0 \qquad \text{or} \qquad x + 4 = 0$$
$$x = 1 \qquad \text{or} \qquad x = -4.$$

Step 4   As in the earlier examples, the numbers -4 and 1 divide the x-axis into three regions:

$$x < -4, \quad -4 < x < 1, \quad x > 1.$$

Step 5   Test a number from each of these regions:

$$\text{Let } x = -5: \quad \frac{1 - (-5)}{-5 + 4} = -6 < 0.$$

$$\text{Let } x = 0: \quad \frac{1 - 0}{0 + 4} = \frac{1}{4} > 0.$$

$$\text{Let } x = 2: \quad \frac{1 - 2}{2 + 4} = -\frac{1}{6} < 0.$$

Step 6   The test shows that numbers in $(-4, 1)$ satisfy the inequality. With a quotient, the endpoints must be considered individually to make sure that no denominator is 0. In this inequality, -4 makes the denominator 0, while 1 satisfies the given inequality. Write the solution in interval notation as $(-4, 1]$ and graphically as in Figure 2.62.

Figure 2.62

✓ **Checkpoint 5**

Solve each inequality.

(a) $\dfrac{3}{x - 2} \geq 4$

(b) $\dfrac{p}{1 - p} < 3$

(c) Why is 2 excluded from the solution in part (a)?

 CAUTION   As suggested by Example 7, be very careful with the endpoints of the intervals in the solution of rational inequalities. ✓5

Example 8 Solve

$$\frac{2x - 1}{3x + 4} < 5.$$

Solution

Step 1 Write an equivalent inequality with 0 on one side by adding −5 to each side.

$$\frac{2x - 1}{3x + 4} - 5 < 0 \qquad \text{Get 0 on the right side.}$$

Step 2 Write the left side as a single fraction by using $3x + 4$ as a common denominator.

$$\frac{2x - 1 - 5(3x + 4)}{3x + 4} < 0 \qquad \text{Obtain a common denominator.}$$

$$\frac{-13x - 21}{3x + 4} < 0 \qquad \text{Distribute in the numerator and combine terms.}$$

Step 3 Set the numerator and denominator each equal to 0 and solve the two equations:

$$-13x - 21 = 0 \qquad \text{or} \qquad 3x + 4 = 0$$

$$x = -\frac{21}{13} \qquad \text{or} \qquad x = -\frac{4}{3}$$

Step 4 The values $-21/13$ and $-4/3$ divide the x-axis into three regions:

$$x < -\frac{21}{13}, \quad -\frac{21}{13} < x < -\frac{4}{3}, \quad x > -\frac{4}{3}.$$

Steps 5 and 6 Testing points from each interval yields that the quotient is negative for numbers in the interval $(-\infty, -21/13)$ or $(-4/3, \infty)$. Neither endpoint satisfies the given inequality.

Figure 2.63

✓ **Checkpoint 6**

Solve each rational inequality.

(a) $\dfrac{3y - 2}{2y + 5} < 1$

(b) $\dfrac{3c - 4}{2 - c} \geq -5$

✓ **Checkpoint 7**

(a) Solve the inequality

$$\frac{10}{x + 2} \geq 3$$

by first multiplying both sides by $x + 2$.

(b) Show that this method produces a wrong answer by testing $x = -3$.

⊘ **CAUTION** In problems like those in Examples 7 and 8, you should *not* begin by multiplying both sides by the denominator to simplify the inequality. Doing so will usually produce a wrong answer. For the reason, see Exercise 38. For an example, see Checkpoint 7. ✓

◤ **TECHNOLOGY TIP** Rational inequalities can also be solved graphically. In Example 7, for instance, after rewriting the original inequality in the form $\dfrac{1 - x}{x + 4} \geq 0$, determine the values of x that make the numerator and denominator 0 (namely, $x = 1$ and $x = -4$). Then graph $\dfrac{1 - x}{x + 4}$. Figure 2.64 shows that the graph is above the x-axis when it is between the vertical asymptote at $x = -4$ and the x-intercept at $x = 1$. So the solution of the inequality is the interval $(-4, 1]$. (When the values that make the numerator and denominator 0 cannot be found algebraically, as they were here, you can use the root finder to approximate them.)

Figure 2.64

2.5 Exercises

Solve each of these quadratic inequalities. Graph the solutions on the number line. (See Examples 2 and 3.)

1. $(x + 4)(2x - 3) \leq 0$ **2.** $(5y - 1)(y + 3) > 0$

3. $r^2 + 4r > -3$ **4.** $z^2 + 6z > -8$

5. $4m^2 + 7m - 2 \leq 0$ **6.** $6p^2 - 11p + 3 \leq 0$

7. $4x^2 + 3x - 1 > 0$ **8.** $3x^2 - 5x > 2$

9. $x^2 \leq 36$ **10.** $y^2 \geq 9$

11. $p^2 - 16p > 0$ **12.** $r^2 - 9r < 0$

Solve these inequalities. (See Example 4.)

13. $x^3 - 9x \geq 0$ **14.** $p^3 - 25p \leq 0$

15. $(x + 7)(x + 2)(x - 2) \geq 0$

16. $(2x + 4)(x^2 - 9) \leq 0$

17. $(x + 5)(x^2 - 2x - 3) < 0$

18. $x^3 - 2x^2 - 3x \leq 0$ **19.** $6k^3 - 5k^2 < 4k$

20. $2m^3 + 7m^2 > 4m$

21. A student solved the inequality $p^2 < 16$ by taking the square root of both sides to get $p < 4$. She wrote the solution as $(-\infty, 4)$. Is her solution correct?

⚹ *Use a graphing calculator to solve these inequalities. (See Example 5.)*

22. $6x + 7 < 2x^2$ **23.** $.5x^2 - 1.2x < .2$

24. $3.1x^2 - 7.4x + 3.2 > 0$

25. $x^3 - 2x^2 - 5x + 7 \geq 2x + 1$

26. $x^4 - 6x^3 + 2x^2 < 5x - 2$

27. $2x^4 + 3x^3 < 2x^2 + 4x - 2$

28. $x^5 + 5x^4 > 4x^3 - 3x^2 - 2$

Solve these rational inequalities. (See Examples 7 and 8.)

29. $\dfrac{r - 4}{r - 1} \geq 0$ **30.** $\dfrac{z + 6}{z + 4} > 1$

31. $\dfrac{a - 2}{a - 5} < -1$ **32.** $\dfrac{1}{3k - 5} < \dfrac{1}{3}$

33. $\dfrac{1}{p - 2} < \dfrac{1}{3}$ **34.** $\dfrac{7}{k + 2} \geq \dfrac{1}{k + 2}$

35. $\dfrac{5}{p + 1} > \dfrac{12}{p + 1}$ **36.** $\dfrac{x^2 - 4}{x} > 0$

37. $\dfrac{x^2 - x - 6}{x} < 0$

38. Determine whether $x + 4$ is positive or negative when
(a) $x > -4$; (b) $x < -4$.

(c) If you multiply both sides of the inequality $\dfrac{1 - x}{x + 4} \geq 0$ by $x + 4$, should you change the direction of the inequality sign? If so, when?

(d) Explain how you can use parts (a)–(c) to solve $\dfrac{1 - x}{x + 4} \geq 0$ correctly.

⚹ *Use a graphing calculator to solve these inequalities. You may have to approximate the roots of the numerators or denominators.*

39. $\dfrac{2x^2 + x - 1}{x^2 - 4x + 4} \leq 0$

40. $\dfrac{x^3 - 3x^2 + 5x - 29}{x^2 - 7} > 3$

41. **Business** An analyst has found that her company's profits, in hundreds of thousands of dollars, are given by $P = 2x^2 - 12x - 32$, where x is the amount, in hundreds of dollars, spent on advertising. For what values of x does the company make a profit?

42. **Business** The commodities market is highly unstable; money can be made or lost quickly on investments in soybeans, wheat, and so on. Suppose that an investor kept track of his total profit P at time t, in months, after he began investing, and he found that $P = 4t^2 - 30t + 14$. Find the time intervals during which he has been ahead.

43. **Business** The manager of a 200-unit apartment complex has found that the profit is given by

$$P = x^2 + 300x - 18,000,$$

where x is the number of apartments rented. For what values of x does the complex produce a profit?

⚹ *Use a graphing calculator or other technology to complete Exercises 44–48. You may need to find a larger viewing window for some of these problems.*

44. **Business** A door-to-door knife salesman finds that his weekly profit can be modeled by the equation

$$P = x^2 + 5x - 530$$

where x is the number of pitches he makes in a week. For what values of x does the salesman need to make in order to earn a profit?

45. **Business** The number of subscribers for cellular telecommunications (in millions) can be approximated by $.79x^2 + 5.4x + 178$ where $x = 7$ corresponds to the year 2007. Assuming the model to be valid indefinitely, in what years was the number of subscribers higher than 300 million? (Data from: ProQuest Statistical Abstract of the United States 2013.)

46. **Business** The percentage of delinquent real estate loans can be approximated by $-.65x^2 + 13.6x - 61.1$ where $x = 7$ corresponds to the year 2007. Assuming the model holds up to and including 2014, find the years in which the percentage of delinquent real estate loans was greater than 8%. (Data from: U.S. Federal Reserve.)

47. **Finance** The amount of outstanding mortgage debt (in trillions of dollars) can be approximated by $-.2x^2 + 3.44x + .16$ where $x = 4$ corresponds to the year 2004. Assuming the model holds up to and including 2014, find the years in which the amount of outstanding mortgage debt was higher than $13 trillion. (Data from: Board of Governors of the Federal Reserve.)

48. **Finance** Similar to Exercise 47, the amount of outstanding debt for home mortgages (in trillions of dollars) can be approximated by $-.15x^2 + 2.53x + .66$ where $x = 4$ corresponds to the year 2004. Assuming the model holds up to and including 2014, find the years in which the amount of outstanding home mortgage debt was higher than $9 trillion. (Data from: Board of Governors of the Federal Reserve.)

✓ Checkpoint Answers

1. **(a)** $(-3, 5)$

   (b) $(-5/2, 4)$

2. **(a)** All numbers in $(-\infty, -5]$ or $[3, \infty)$

   (b) All numbers in $(-\infty, -3]$ or $[2/3, \infty)$

3. **(a)** All numbers in $(-3, 0)$ or $(3, \infty)$

   (b) All numbers in $(-\infty, -5]$ or $[0, 5]$

4. **(a)** All numbers in $(-\infty, .3542)$ or $(5.6458, \infty)$

   (b) All numbers in $(.3542, 5.6458)$

5. **(a)** $(2, 11/4]$

   (b) All numbers in $(-\infty, 3/4)$ or $(1, \infty)$

   (c) When $x = 2$, the fraction is undefined.

6. **(a)** $(-5/2, 7)$

   (b) All numbers in $(-\infty, 2)$ or $[3, \infty)$

7. **(a)** $x \le \dfrac{4}{3}$

   (b) $x = -3$ is a solution of $x \le \dfrac{4}{3}$, but not of the original inequality $\dfrac{10}{x + 2} \ge 3$.

CHAPTER 2 Summary and Review

Key Terms and Symbols*

2.1 Cartesian coordinate system
x-axis
y-axis
origin
ordered pair
x-coordinate
y-coordinate
quadrant
solution of an equation
graph

x-intercept
y-intercept
[viewing window]
[trace]
[graphical root finder]
[maximum and minimum finder]
graph reading

2.2 change in x
change in y

slope
slope–intercept form
parallel and perpendicular lines
point–slope form
linear equations
general form

2.3 linear models
residual
[least-squares regression line]

[linear regression]
[correlation coefficient]

2.4 linear inequality
properties of inequality
absolute-value inequality

2.5 polynomial inequality
algebraic solution methods
[graphical solution methods]
rational inequality

Chapter 2 Key Concepts

Slope of a Line   The **slope** of the line through the points (x_1, y_1) and (x_2, y_2), where $x_1 \ne x_2$, is $m = \dfrac{y_2 - y_1}{x_2 - x_1}$.

Equation of a Line   The line with equation $y = mx + b$ has slope m and y-intercept b.

The line with equation $y - y_1 = m(x - x_1)$ has slope m and goes through (x_1, y_1).

The line with equation $ax + by = c$ (with $a \ne 0, b \ne 0$) has x-intercept c/a and y-intercept c/b.

*Terms in brackets deal with material in which a graphing calculator or other technology is used.

The line with equation $x = k$ is vertical, with x-intercept k, no y-intercept, and undefined slope.

The line with equation $y = k$ is horizontal, with y-intercept k, no x-intercept, and slope 0.

Parellel and Perpendicular Lines   Nonvertical **parallel lines** have the same slope, and **perpendicular lines,** if neither is vertical, have slopes with a product of -1.

Chapter 2 Review Exercises

Which of the ordered pairs $(-2, 3), (0, -5), (2, -3), (3, -2),$ *$(4, 3),$ and $(7, 2)$ are solutions of the given equation?*

1. $y = x^2 - 2x - 5$ 2. $x - y = 5$

Sketch the graph of each equation.

3. $5x - 3y = 15$ 4. $2x + 7y - 21 = 0$

5. $y + 3 = 0$ 6. $y - 2x = 0$

7. $y = .25x^2 + 1$ 8. $y = \sqrt{x + 4}$

9. The following temperature graph was recorded in Bratenahl, Ohio:

(a) At what times during the day was the temperature over 55°?

(b) When was the temperature below 40°?

10. Greenville, South Carolina, is 500 miles south of Bratenahl, Ohio, and its temperature is 7° higher all day long. (See the graph in Exercise 9.) At what time was the temperature in Greenville the same as the temperature at noon in Bratenahl?

11. In your own words, define the slope of a line.

In Exercises 12–21, find the slope of the line defined by the given conditions.

12. Through $(-1, 3)$ and $(2, 6)$

13. Through $(4, -5)$ and $(1, 4)$

14. Through $(8, -3)$ and the origin

15. Through $(8, 2)$ and $(0, 4)$

16. $3x + 5y = 25$ 17. $6x - 2y = 7$

18. $x - 2 = 0$ 19. $y = -4$

20. Parallel to $3x + 8y = 0$

21. Perpendicular to $x = 3y$

22. Graph the line through $(0, 5)$ with slope $m = -2/3$.

23. Graph the line through $(-4, 1)$ with $m = 3$.

24. What information is needed to determine the equation of a line?

Find an equation for each of the following lines.

25. Through $(5, -1)$, slope $2/3$

26. Through $(8, 0)$, slope $-1/4$

27. Through $(5, -2)$ and $(1, 3)$

28. Through $(2, -3)$ and $(-3, 4)$

29. Undefined slope, through $(-1, 4)$

30. Slope 0, through $(-2, 5)$

31. x-intercept -3, y-intercept 5

32. Here is a sample SAT question: Which of the following is an equation of the line that has a y-intercept of 2 and an x-intercept of 3?

(a) $-2x + 3y = 4$ (b) $-2x + 3y = 6$

(c) $2x + 3y = 4$ (d) $2x + 3y = 6$

(e) $3x + 2y = 6$

33. **Business**   According to the U.S. Department of Agriculture, in 2005, the United States exported 14.0 million hectoliters of fruit juices and wine. In 2011, that number was 17.3 million hectoliters.

(a) Assuming the increase in exports of fruit juice and wine is linear, write an equation that gives the amount exported in year x, with $x = 5$ corresponding to the year 2005.

(b) Is the slope of the line positive or negative? Why?

(c) Assuming the linear trend continues, estimate the amount exported in the year 2014.

34. **Business**   In the year 2005, the total domestic fish and shellfish catch was 9.7 billion pounds. In 2010, the total was 8.2 billion pounds. (Data from: U.S. National Oceanic and Atmospheric Administration.)

(a) Assuming the decline in fish and shellfish catch is linear, write an equation that gives the amount of the catch produced in year x, where $x = 5$ corresponds to the year 2005.

(b) Graph the equation for the years 2005 through 2010.

(c) Assuming the trend continues, estimate the total fish and shellfish catch in the year 2013.

35. **Business**   The following table gives the total compensation (in dollars) per full-time employee for various years. (Data from: U.S. Bureau of Economic Analysis.)

Year	2000	2005	2010	2011
Compensation	47,059	56,620	66,249	68,129

(a) Use the data from the years 2000 and 2010 to find a linear model for the data, with $x = 0$ corresponding to the year 2000.

(b) Find the least-squares regression line for the data.

(c) Use the models from part (a) and (b) to estimate the compensation for the year 2011. Compare the estimates to the actual compensation of $68,129 for the year 2011.

(d) Assume the trend continues and use the model for (b) to estimate the compensation per full-time employee in the year 2015.

36. **Business** If current trends continue, the median weekly earnings (in dollars) that a male can expect to earn is approximated by the equation $y = 17.4x + 639$, where $x = 0$ corresponds to the year 2000. The equation $y = 17.3x + 495$ approximates median weekly earnings for females. (Data from: U.S. Bureau of Labor Statistics.)

(a) In what year will males achieve median weekly earnings of $900?

(b) In what year will females achieve median weekly earnings of $900?

37. **Business** The following table shows the total private philanthropy donations (in billions of dollars) for various years. (Data from: Center on Philanthropy at Indiana University.)

Year	1990	1995	2000	2005	2010
Philanthropy	101	124	230	288	287

(a) Let $x = 0$ correspond to the year 1990, and find the least-squares regression line for the data.

(b) Graph the data from the years 1990 to 2010 with the least-squares regression line.

(c) Does the least-squares regression line form a good fit?

(d) What is the correlation coefficient?

38. **Economics** According to the U.S. Department of Education, the average financial aid award (in dollars) for a full-time student is given in the following table for various years:

Year	2000	2005	2008	2009	2010	2011
Amount	2925	3407	3791	4056	4232	4341

(a) Let $x = 0$ correspond to the year 2000, and find the least-squares regression line for the data.

(b) Graph the data from the years 2000 to 2011 with the least-squares regression line.

(c) Does the least-squares regression line form a good fit?

(d) What is the correlation coefficient?

Solve each inequality.

39. $-6x + 3 < 2x$

40. $12z \geq 5z - 7$

41. $2(3 - 2m) \geq 8m + 3$

42. $6p - 5 > -(2p + 3)$

43. $-3 \leq 4x - 1 \leq 7$

44. $0 \leq 3 - 2a \leq 15$

45. $|b| \leq 8$

46. $|a| > 7$

47. $|2x - 7| \geq 3$

48. $|4m + 9| \leq 16$

49. $|5k + 2| - 3 \leq 4$

50. $|3z - 5| + 2 \geq 10$

51. **Natural Science** Here is a sample SAT question: For pumpkin carving, Mr. Sephera will not use pumpkins that weigh less than 2 pounds or more than 10 pounds. If x represents the weight of a pumpkin (in pounds) that he will *not* use, which of the following inequalities represents all possible values of x?

(a) $|x - 2| > 10$ (b) $|x - 4| > 6$

(c) $|x - 5| > 5$ (d) $|x - 6| > 4$

(e) $|x - 10| > 4$

52. **Business** Prices at several retail outlets for a new 24-inch, 2-cycle snow thrower were all within $55 of $600. Write this information as an inequality, using absolute-value notation.

53. **Business** The amount of renewable energy consumed by the industrial sector of the U.S. economy (in trillion BTUs) was 1873 in the year 2005 and 2250 in the year 2010. Assume the amount of energy consumed is increasing linearly. (Data from: U.S. Energy Information Administration.)

(a) Find the linear equation that gives the number of BTUs consumed with $x = 5$ corresponding to the year 2005.

(b) Assume the linear equation that gives the amount of energy consumed continues indefinitely. Determine when the consumption will exceed 2500.

54. **Business** One car rental firm charges $125 for a weekend rental (Friday afternoon through Monday morning) and gives unlimited mileage. A second firm charges $95 plus $.20 a mile. For what range of miles driven is the second firm cheaper?

Solve each inequality.

55. $r^2 + r - 6 < 0$

56. $y^2 + 4y - 5 \geq 0$

57. $2z^2 + 7z \geq 15$

58. $3k^2 \leq k + 14$

59. $(x - 3)(x^2 + 7x + 10) \leq 0$

60. $(x + 4)(x^2 - 1) \geq 0$

61. $\dfrac{m + 2}{m} \leq 0$

62. $\dfrac{q - 4}{q + 3} > 0$

63. $\dfrac{5}{p + 1} > 2$

64. $\dfrac{6}{a - 2} \leq -3$

65. $\dfrac{2}{r + 5} \leq \dfrac{3}{r - 2}$

66. $\dfrac{1}{z - 1} > \dfrac{2}{z + 1}$

67. **Business** The net income (in millions of dollars) generated by the satellite radio company SiriusXM can be approximated by the equation $y = 340.1x^2 - 5360x + 18,834$, where $x = 6$ corresponds to the year 2006. In what years between 2006 and 2012 did SiriusXM have positive net income? (Data from: www.morningstar.com.)

68. **Business** The net income (in millions of dollars) generated by Xerox corporation can be approximated by the equation $y = 89.29x^2 - 1577x + 7505$, where $x = 6$ corresponds to the year 2006. In what years between 2006 and 2012 did Xerox have net income higher than $1000 million? (Data from: www.morningstar.com.)

Case Study 2 Using Extrapolation and Interpolation for Prediction

One reason for developing a mathematical model is to make predictions. If your model is a least-squares line, you can predict the y-value corresponding to some new x-value by substituting that x-value into an equation of the form $\hat{y} = mx + b$. (We use $\hat{y}$ to remind us that we're getting a predicted value rather than an actual data value.) Data analysts distinguish between two very different kinds of prediction: *interpolation* and *extrapolation*. An interpolation uses a new x inside the x-range of your original data. For example, if you have inflation data at five-year intervals from 1950 to 2010, estimating the rate of inflation in 1957 is an interpolation problem. But if you use the same data to estimate what the inflation rate was in 1920, or what it will be in 2020, you are extrapolating.

In general, interpolation is much safer than extrapolation, because data that are approximately linear over a short interval may be nonlinear over a larger interval. Let us examine a case of the dangers of extrapolation. Figure 1 shows the net income (in millions of dollars) for the Starbucks Corporation from the years 2001–2007. Also on Figure 1, we see the least-squares regression line. (Data from: www.morningstar.com.)

As we know, however, the year 2008 saw the start of a deep recession in the United States, and the net earnings for Starbucks were actually $316 million in the year 2008 and $391 million in the year 2009—substantially lower than the predictions.

Using the past to predict the future is generally a dangerous business because we often cannot foresee events with major impact such as recessions, natural disasters, etc. Predictions into the future are often made, however, because planning has to occur and we use the best data we have available. One merely needs to realize that predictions into the future are highly likely to be inaccurate.

One way to determine if a model is likely to be inaccurate in the future is to examine the residuals. In Section 2.3, we defined a residual to be the difference between the actual value y and its predicted value $\hat{y}$.

$$\text{Residual} = y - \hat{y}.$$

Graphing these residuals on the y-axis and the predictor variable on the x-axis can be illuminating. Let's look at another historical example. Figure 2 shows the total household debt (in trillions of dollars) from the years 2004 through 2010. (Data from: Federal Reserve Bank of New York.)

Figure 1

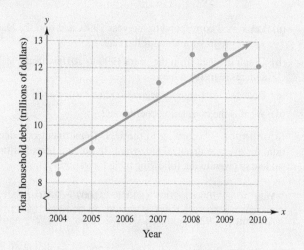

Figure 2

As we can see from graph, the fit is quite good and the linear trend seems quite clear. Additionally, the correlation coefficient is $r \approx .99$, which is quite high. The least-squares regression equation is

$$y = 85.7x + 55.3,$$

where $x = 1$ corresponds to 2001. If we extrapolate to the next two years, we predict the net earnings for Starbucks to be

2008: 85.7(8) + 55.3 = $740.9 million

2009: 85.7(9) + 55.3 = $826.6 million

The regression equation for the least-squares line in Figure 2 is

$$y = .7x + 5.9,$$

where $x = 4$ corresponds to the year 2004. Since the correlation coefficient r is approximately .93, our linear model appears to fit the data well. We notice, however, that the predictions overpredict, then underpredict, and then overpredict. We can get a better look at this pattern by plotting the residuals. To find them, we put each value of the independent variable into the regression equation, calculate the predicted value $\hat{y}$, and subtract it from the actual value of y as in the table.

Year	2004	2005	2006	2007	2008	2009	2010
x	4	5	6	7	8	9	10
y	8.3	9.2	10.4	11.5	12.5	12.5	12.1
$\hat{y}$	8.7	9.4	10.1	10.8	11.5	12.2	12.9
Residual $y - \hat{y}$	−.4	−.2	.3	.7	1.0	.3	−.8

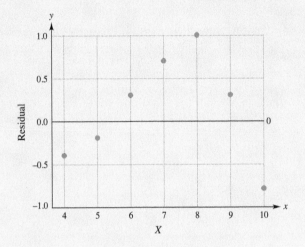

Figure 3

The residuals in Figure 3 indicate that our data have a nonlinear U-shaped component that is not captured by a linear model. When a residual plot shows a pattern such as this (or a similar pattern with an upside down U), extrapolating from the data is probably not a good idea. Our prediction for the year 2011, for example, would be

$$\hat{y} = .7(11) + 5.9 = \$13.6 \text{ trillion,}$$

which is far higher than the actual value of $11.8 trillion.

Exercises

Business   The following table gives the number of completed new single family homes (in thousands) from the years 2002 to 2012. (Data from: U.S. Census Bureau.)

Year	Housing Units	Year	Housing Units
2002	1648	2008	1120
2003	1679	2009	794
2004	1842	2010	652
2005	1931	2011	585
2006	1979	2012	650
2007	1503		

1. If you have access to the appropriate technology, verify that the least-squares regression line that models these data (with rounded coefficients) is $y = -146.1x + 2330$, where $x = 2$ corresponds to the year 2002.

2. Use the model from Exercise 1 to calculate the predicted values $\hat{y}$ for each year in the table.

3. Use your answers from Exercise 2 to calculate the residuals for each year in the table. Make a graph of the residuals similar to Figure 3.

4. Do you think the linear model of Exercise 1 is a good fit for these data? Why or why not?

Business   The following table gives the average hourly earnings (in dollars) of U.S. production workers from 1970 to 2010. (Data from: U.S. Bureau of Labor Statistics.)

Year	Average Hourly Wage (Dollars)
1970	3.40
1975	4.73
1980	6.85
1985	8.74
1990	10.20
1995	11.65
2000	14.02
2005	16.13
2010	16.26

5. If you have appropriate technology, verify that the least-squares regression line that models these data (with coefficients rounded) is $y = .343x - 20.65$, where y is the average hourly wage in year x and $x = 0$ corresponds to 1900.

6. Use the model from Exercise 5 to interpolate a prediction of the hourly wage in 2002. The actual value was $14.97. How close was your prediction?

7. Use the model from Exercise 5 to extrapolate to 1960 and predict the hourly average wage. Why is this prediction nonsensical?

8. Using the model from Exercise 5, find the average hourly wage for each year in the table, and subtract it from the actual value in the second column. This gives you a table of the residuals. Plot your residuals as points on a graph.

9. What will happen if you try linear regression on the *residuals*? If you're not sure, use technology such as a graphing calculator to find the regression equation for the residuals. Why does this result make sense?

Extended Project

Go the library or use the Internet to obtain the average amount of student loan debt for the most recent years available.

1. Create a scatterplot of the data with the amount on the *y*-axis and the year on the *x*-axis and assess the trend.
2. Fit a linear model to the data and predict the loan debt amount for each year.

3. Calculate the residuals from each year in the data set. Graph the residuals.
4. Do the residuals show a U-shape?
5. Find the correlation coefficient for your data.

Functions and Graphs

3

CHAPTER

The modern world is overwhelmed with data—from the cost of college to mortgage rates, health care expenditures, and hundreds of other pieces of information. Functions enable us to construct mathematical models that can sometimes be used to estimate outcomes. Graphs of functions allow us to visualize a situation and to detect trends more easily. See Example 11 on page 129 and Exercises 57 and 58 on page 179.

Functions are an extremely useful way of describing many real-world situations in which the value of one quantity varies with, depends on, or determines the value of another. In this chapter, you will be introduced to functions, learn how to use functional notation, develop skills in constructing and interpreting the graphs of functions, and, finally, learn to apply this knowledge in a variety of situations.

3.1   Functions

To understand the origin of the concept of a function, we consider some real-life situations in which one numerical quantity depends on, corresponds to, or determines another.

Example 1   The amount of the electric bill you pay depends on the amount of kilowatt hours (kWh) consumed. The way in which the usage determines the bill is given by the rate per kWh.

Example 2   Economics   The graph in Figure 3.1 shows the poverty rate from the years 1959 to 2011. The blue vertical bands indicate times of economic recession. The graph displays the percentage living in poverty that corresponds to each year. (Source: DeNavas-Walt, Carmen, Bernadette D. Proctor, and Jessica C. Smith, U.S. Census Bureau, Current Population Reports, P60-243, Income, Poverty, and Health Insurance Coverage in the United States: 2011, U.S. Government Printing Office, Washington, DC, 2012.)

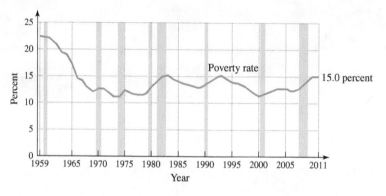

Figure 3.1

Example 3   Physical Science   Suppose a rock is dropped straight down from a high point. From physics, we know that the distance traveled by the rock in t seconds is $16t^2$ feet. So the distance depends on the time.

These examples share a couple of features. First, each involves two sets of numbers, which we can think of as inputs and outputs. Second, in each case, there is a rule by which each input determines an output, as summarized here:

	Set of Inputs	Set of Outputs	Rule
Example 1	All usages	All bill amounts	The rate per kWh
Example 2	Year	Poverty rate	Time-rate graph
Example 3	Seconds elapsed after dropping the rock	Distances the rock travels	Distance $= 16t^2$

Each of these examples may be mentally represented by an idealized calculator that has a single operation key: A number is entered [*input*], the rule key is pushed [*rule*], and an answer is displayed [*output*]. The formal definition of a function incorporates these same common features (input–rule–output), with a slight change in terminology.

> A **function** consists of a set of inputs called the **domain,** a set of outputs called the **range,** and a rule by which each input determines *exactly one* output.

✓**Checkpoint 1**

Find the domain and range of the function in Example 3, assuming (unrealistically) that the rock can fall forever.

Answers to Checkpoint exercises are found at the end of the section.

Example 4   Find the domains and ranges for the functions in Examples 1 and 2.

Solution   In Example 1, the domain consists of all possible usage amounts and the range consists of all possible bill amounts.

In Example 2, the domain is the set of years from 1959 to 2011, all real numbers in the interval [1959, 2011]. The range consists of the poverty rates that actually occur during those years. Figure 3.1 suggests that these are all numbers in the interval [11, 22]. ✓₁

Be sure that you understand the phrase "exactly one output" in the definition of the rule of a function. In Example 2, for instance, each year (input) determines exactly one poverty rate (output)—you can't have two different rates at the same time. However, it is quite possible to have the same rate (output) at two different times (inputs). In other words, we can say the following:

In a function, each input produces a single output, but different inputs may produce the same output.

Example 5   Which of the following rules describe functions?

(a) Use the optical reader at the checkout counter of the supermarket to convert codes to prices.

Solution   For each code, the reader produces exactly one price, so this is a function.

(b) Enter a number in a calculator and press the x^2 key.

Solution   This is a function, because the calculator produces just one number x^2 for each number x that is entered.

(c) Assign to each number x the number y given by this table:

x	1	1	2	2	3	3
y	3	−3	−5	−5	8	−8

Solution   Since $x = 1$ corresponds to more than one y-value (as does $x = 3$), this table does not define a function.

(d) Assign to each number x the number y given by the equation $y = 3x - 5$.

Solution   Because the equation determines a unique value of y for each value of x, it defines a function. ✓₂

The equation $y = 3x - 5$ in part (d) of Example 5 defines a function, with x as input and y as output, because each value of x determines a *unique* value of y. In such a case, the equation is said to **define y as a function of x.**

Example 6   Decide whether each of the following equations defines y as a function of x.

(a) $y = -4x + 11$

Solution   For a given value of x, calculating $-4x + 11$ produces exactly one value of y. (For example, if $x = -7$, then $y = -4(-7) + 11 = 39$). Because one value of the input variable leads to exactly one value of the output variable, $y = -4x + 11$ defines y as a function of x.

(b) $y^2 = x$

Solution   Suppose $x = 36$. Then $y^2 = x$ becomes $y^2 = 36$, from which $y = 6$ or $y = -6$. Since one value of x can lead to two values of y, $y^2 = x$ does *not* define y as a function of x. ✓₃

Almost all the functions in this text are defined by formulas or equations, as in part (a) of Example 6. The domain of such a function is determined by the following **agreement on domains.**

✓ **Checkpoint 2**

Do the following define functions?

(a) The correspondence defined by the rule $y = x^2 + 5$, where x is the input and y is the output.

(b) The correspondence defined by entering a nonzero number in a calculator and pressing the $1/x$ key.

(c) The correspondence between a computer, x, and several users of the computer, y.

✓ **Checkpoint 3**

Do the following define y as a function of x?

(a) $y = -6x + 1$

(b) $y = x^2$

(c) $x = y^2 - 1$

(d) $y < x + 2$

Unless otherwise stated, assume that the domain of any function defined by a formula or an equation is the largest set of real numbers (inputs) that each produces a real number as output.

Example 7 Each of the given equations defines y as a function of x. Find the domain of each function.

(a) $y = x^4$

Solution Any number can be raised to the fourth power, so the domain is the set of all real numbers, which is sometimes written as $(-\infty, \infty)$.

(b) $y = \sqrt{x - 6}$

Solution For y to be a real number, $x - 6$ must be nonnegative. This happens only when $x - 6 \geq 0$—that is, when $x \geq 6$. So the domain is the interval $[6, \infty)$.

(c) $y = \sqrt{4 - x}$

Solution For y to be a real number here, we must have $4 - x \geq 0$, which is equivalent to $x \leq 4$. So the domain is the interval $(-\infty, 4]$.

(d) $y = \dfrac{1}{x + 3}$

Solution Because the denominator cannot be 0, $x \neq -3$ and the domain consists of all numbers in the intervals,

$$(-\infty, -3) \quad \text{or} \quad (-3, \infty).$$

(e) $y = \dfrac{\sqrt{x}}{x^2 - 3x + 2}$

Solution The numerator is defined only when $x \geq 0$. The domain cannot contain any numbers that make the denominator 0—that is, the numbers that are solutions of

$$\begin{aligned}
x^2 - 3x + 2 &= 0. \\
(x - 1)(x - 2) &= 0 \qquad \text{Factor.} \\
x - 1 = 0 \quad &\text{or} \quad x - 2 = 0 \qquad \text{Zero-factor property} \\
x = 1 \quad &\text{or} \quad x = 2.
\end{aligned}$$

Therefore, the domain consists of all nonnegative real numbers except 1 and 2. ☑4

✓**Checkpoint 4**

Give the domain of each function.

(a) $y = 3x + 1$

(b) $y = x^2$

(c) $y = \sqrt{-x}$

(d) $y = \dfrac{3}{x^2 - 1}$

Functional Notation

In actual practice, functions are seldom presented in the style of domain–rule–range, as they have been here. Functions are usually denoted by a letter such as f. If x is an input, then $f(x)$ denotes the output number that the function f produces from the input x. The symbol $f(x)$ is read "f of x." The rule is usually given by a formula, such as $f(x) = \sqrt{x^2 + 1}$. This formula can be thought of as a set of directions:

Name of function   Input number

$$f(x) = \sqrt{x^2 + 1}$$

Output number   Directions that tell you what to do with input x in order to produce the corresponding output $f(x)$—namely, "square it, add 1, and take the square root of the result."

For example, to find $f(3)$ (the output number produced by the input 3), simply replace x by 3 in the formula:

$$f(3) = \sqrt{3^2 + 1}$$
$$= \sqrt{10}.$$

Similarly, replacing x respectively by -5 and 0 shows that

$$f(-5) = \sqrt{(-5)^2 + 1} \quad \text{and} \quad f(0) = \sqrt{0^2 + 1}$$
$$= \sqrt{26} \qquad\qquad\qquad = 1.$$

These directions can be applied to any quantities, such as $a + b$ or c^4 (where a, b, and c are real numbers). Thus, to compute $f(a + b)$, the output corresponding to input $a + b$, we square the input [obtaining $(a + b)^2$], add 1 [obtaining $(a + b)^2 + 1$], and take the square root of the result:

$$f(a + b) = \sqrt{(a + b)^2 + 1}$$
$$= \sqrt{a^2 + 2ab + b^2 + 1}.$$

Similarly, the output $f(c^4)$, corresponding to the input c^4, is computed by squaring the input $[(c^4)^2]$, adding 1 $[(c^4)^2 + 1]$, and taking the square root of the result:

$$f(c^4) = \sqrt{(c^4)^2 + 1}$$
$$= \sqrt{c^8 + 1}.$$

Example 8   Let $g(x) = -x^2 + 4x - 5$. Find each of the given outputs.

(a) $g(-2)$

Solution Replace x with -2:

$$g(-2) = -(-2)^2 + 4(-2) - 5$$
$$= -4 - 8 - 5$$
$$= -17.$$

(b) $g(x + h)$

Solution Replace x by the quantity $x + h$ in the rule of g:

$$g(x + h) = -(x + h)^2 + 4(x + h) - 5$$
$$= -(x^2 + 2xh + h^2) + (4x + 4h) - 5$$
$$= -x^2 - 2xh - h^2 + 4x + 4h - 5.$$

(c) $g(x + h) - g(x)$

Solution Use the result from part (b) and the rule for $g(x)$:

$$g(x + h) - g(x) = \overbrace{(-x^2 - 2xh - h^2 + 4x + 4h - 5)}^{g(x+h)} - \overbrace{(-x^2 + 4x - 5)}^{g(x)}$$
$$= -2xh - h^2 + 4h.$$

(d) $\dfrac{g(x + h) - g(x)}{h}$ (assuming that $h \neq 0$)

Solution The numerator was found in part (c). Divide it by h as follows:

$$\frac{g(x + h) - g(x)}{h} = \frac{-2xh - h^2 + 4h}{h}$$
$$= \frac{h(-2x - h + 4)}{h}$$
$$= -2x - h + 4.$$

The quotient found in Example 8(d),

$$\frac{g(x + h) - g(x)}{h},$$

is called the **difference quotient** of the function g. Difference quotients are important in calculus. ✓5

✓**Checkpoint 5**

Let $f(x) = 5x^2 - 2x + 1$. Find the
following.

(a) $f(1)$

(b) $f(3)$

(c) $f(1 + 3)$

(d) $f(1) + f(3)$

(e) $f(m)$

(f) $f(x + h) - f(x)$

(g) $\dfrac{f(x + h) - f(x)}{h} \ (h \neq 0)$

⊘ **CAUTION** Functional notation is *not* the same as ordinary algebraic notation. You cannot simplify an expression such as $f(x + h)$ by writing $f(x) + f(h)$. To see why, consider the answers to Checkpoints 5(c) and (d), which show that

$$f(1 + 3) \neq f(1) + f(3).$$

Applications

Example 9 **Finance** If you were a single person in Connecticut in 2013 with a taxable income of x dollars and $x \leq \$500,000$ then your state income tax T was determined by the rule

$$T(x) = \begin{cases} .03x & \text{if } 0 \leq x \leq 10,000 \\ 300 + .05(x - 10,000) & \text{if } 10,000 \leq x \leq 500,00 \end{cases}$$

Find the income tax paid by a single person with the given taxable income. (Data from: www.taxbrackets.org.)

(a) $9200

Solution We must find $T(9200)$. Since 9200 is less than 10,000, the first part of the rule applies:

$$T(x) = .03x$$
$$T(9200) = .03(9200) = \$276. \quad \text{Let } x = 9200.$$

(b) $30,000

Solution Now we must find $T(30,000)$. Since 30,000 is greater than $10,000, the second part of the rule applies:

$$T(x) = 300 + .05(x - 10,000)$$
$$T(30,000) = 300 + .05(30,000 - 10,000) \quad \text{Let } x = 30,000.$$
$$= 300 + .05(20,000) \quad \text{Simplify.}$$
$$= 300 + 1000 = \$1300. \ ✓6$$

✓**Checkpoint 6**

Use Example 9 to find the tax on
each of these incomes.

(a) $48,750

(b) $7345

A function with a multipart rule, as in Example 9, is called a **piecewise-defined function.**

Example 10 **Business** Suppose the projected sales (in thousands of dollars) of a small company over the next 10 years are approximated by the function

$$S(x) = .07x^4 - .05x^3 + 2x^2 + 7x + 62.$$

(a) What are the projected sales for the current year?

Solution The current year corresponds to $x = 0$, and the sales for this year are given by $S(0)$. Substituting 0 for x in the rule for S, we see that $S(0) = 62$. So the current projected sales are $62,000.

✓ **Checkpoint 7**

A developer estimates that the total cost of building x large apartment complexes in a year is approximated by

$$A(x) = x^2 + 80x + 60,$$

where $A(x)$ represents the cost in hundred thousands of dollars. Find the cost of building

(a) 4 complexes;

(b) 10 complexes.

(b) What will sales be in four years?

Solution The sales in four years from now are given by $S(4)$, which can be computed by hand or with a calculator:

$$S(x) = .07x^4 - .05x^3 + 2x^2 + 7x + 62$$
$$S(4) = .07(4)^4 - .05(4)^3 + 2(4)^2 + 7(4) + 62 \quad \text{Let } x = 4.$$
$$= 136.72.$$

Thus, sales are projected to be $136,720. ✓₇

X	Y1
5	184.5
6	255.92
7	359.92
8	507.12
9	709.82
10	982
11	1339.3

X=5

Figure 3.2

↗ **Example 11** **Business** Use the table feature of the graphing calculator to find the projected sales of the company in Example 10 for years 5 through 10.

Solution Enter the sales equation $y = .07x^4 - .05x^3 + 2x^2 + 7x + 62$ into the equation memory of the calculator (often called the Y = list). Check your instruction manual for how to set the table to start at $x = 5$ and go at least through $x = 10$. Then display the table, as in Figure 3.2. The figure shows that sales are projected to rise from $184,500 in year 5 to $982,000 in year 10.

3.1 Exercises

For each of the following rules, state whether it defines y as a function of x or not. (See Examples 5 and 6.)

1.

x	3	2	1	0	−1	−2	−3
y	9	4	1	0	1	4	9

2.

x	9	4	1	0	1	4	9
y	3	2	1	0	−1	−2	−3

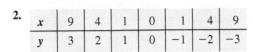

3. $y = x^3$

4. $y = \sqrt{x - 1}$

5. $x = |y + 2|$

6. $x = y^2 + 3$

7. $y = \dfrac{-1}{x - 1}$

8. $y = \dfrac{4}{2x + 3}$

State the domain of each function. (See Example 7.)

9. $f(x) = 4x - 1$

10. $f(x) = 2x + 7$

11. $f(x) = x^4 - 1$

12. $f(x) = (2x + 5)^2$

13. $f(x) = \sqrt{-x} + 3$

14. $f(x) = \sqrt{5 - x}$

15. $g(x) = \dfrac{1}{x - 2}$

16. $g(x) = \dfrac{x}{x^2 + x - 2}$

17. $g(x) = \dfrac{x^2 + 4}{x^2 - 4}$

18. $g(x) = \dfrac{x^2 - 1}{x^2 + 1}$

19. $h(x) = \dfrac{\sqrt{x + 4}}{x^2 + x - 12}$

20. $h(x) = |5 - 4x|$

21. $g(x) = \begin{cases} 1/x & \text{if } x < 0 \\ \sqrt{x^2 + 1} & \text{if } x \geq 0 \end{cases}$

22. $f(x) = \begin{cases} 2x + 3 & \text{if } x < 4 \\ x^2 - 1 & \text{if } 4 \leq x \leq 10 \end{cases}$

For each of the following functions, find

(a) $f(4)$; (b) $f(-3)$; (c) $f(2.7)$; (d) $f(-4.9)$.

(See Examples 8 and 9.)

23. $f(x) = 8$

24. $f(x) = 0$

25. $f(x) = 2x^2 + 4x$

26. $f(x) = x^2 - 2x$

27. $f(x) = \sqrt{x + 3}$

28. $f(x) = \sqrt{5 - x}$

29. $f(x) = |x^2 - 6x - 4|$

30. $f(x) = |x^3 - x^2 + x - 1|$

31. $f(x) = \dfrac{\sqrt{x - 1}}{x^2 - 1}$

32. $f(x) = \sqrt{-x} + \dfrac{2}{x + 1}$

33. $f(x) = \begin{cases} x^2 & \text{if } x < 2 \\ 5x - 7 & \text{if } x \geq 2 \end{cases}$

34. $f(x) = \begin{cases} -2x + 4 & \text{if } x \leq 1 \\ 3 & \text{if } 1 < x < 4 \\ x + 1 & \text{if } x \geq 4 \end{cases}$

For each of the following functions, find

(a) $f(p)$; (b) $f(-r)$; (c) $f(m + 3)$.

(See Example 8.)

35. $f(x) = 6 - x$

36. $f(x) = 3x + 5$

37. $f(x) = \sqrt{4 - x}$

38. $f(x) = \sqrt{-2x}$

39. $f(x) = x^3 + 1$

40. $f(x) = 3 - x^3$

41. $f(x) = \dfrac{3}{x - 1}$

42. $f(x) = \dfrac{-1}{5 + x}$

For each of the following functions, find the difference quotient

$$\frac{f(x + h) - f(x)}{h} \quad (h \neq 0).$$

(See Example 8.)

43. $f(x) = 2x - 4$

44. $f(x) = 2 + 4x$

45. $f(x) = x^2 + 1$

46. $f(x) = x^2 - x$

If you have a graphing calculator with table-making ability, display a table showing the (approximate) values of the given function at x = 3.5, 3.9, 4.3, 4.7, 5.1, and 5.5. (See Example 11.)

47. $g(x) = 3x^4 - x^3 + 2x$

48. $f(x) = \sqrt{x^2 - 2.4x + 8}$

Use a calculator to work these exercises. (See Examples 9 and 10.)

49. Finance The Minnesota state income tax for a single person in 2013 was determined by the rule

$$T(x) = \begin{cases} .0535x & \text{if } 0 \leq x \leq 23{,}100 \\ 1235.85 + .0705(x - 23{,}100) & \text{if } 23{,}100 < x \leq 75{,}891 \\ 4957.62 + .0785(x - 75{,}891) & \text{if } x > 75{,}891, \end{cases}$$

where x is the person's taxable income. Find the tax on each of these incomes. (Data from: www.taxbrackets.org.)

(a) \$20,000

(b) \$70,000

(c) \$120,000

50. Economics The gross domestic product (GDP) of the United States, which measures the overall size of the U.S. economy in trillions of dollars, is approximated by the function

$$f(x) = -.017x^2 + .68x + 9.6,$$

where $x = 0$ corresponds to the year 2000. Estimate the GDP in the given years. (Data from: U.S. Bureau of Economic Analysis.)

(a) 2005

(b) 2009

(c) 2011

51. Business The net revenue for Ford Motor Company (in billions of dollars) between the years 2006 and 2012 is approximated by

$$R(x) = -.722x^3 + 19.23x^2 - 161.2x + 421.8,$$

where $x = 6$ corresponds to the year 2006. (Data from: www.morningstar.com.)

(a) What was the net revenue in 2008?

(b) What was the net revenue in 2011?

52. Business The number of passengers enplaned (in millions) for the years 2000–2011 can be approximated by the function

$$f(x) = .377x^4 - 9.23x^3 + 71.4x^2 - 163x + 666,$$

where $x = 0$ corresponds to the year 2000. Find the number of enplaned passengers in the following years. (Data from: Airlines for America.)

(a) 2004

(b) 2009

(c) 2010

53. Business The value (in millions of dollars) of electric household ranges and ovens shipped in the United States can be approximated by the function

$$g(x) = -21.1x^2 + 205x + 2164,$$

where $x = 0$ corresponds to the year 2000. (Data from: U.S. Census Bureau.)

(a) What is the value of the ranges and ovens shipped in 2001?

(b) What is the value of the ranges and ovens shipped in 2009?

54. Natural Science High concentrations of zinc ions in water are lethal to rainbow trout. The function

$$f(x) = \left(\frac{x}{1960}\right)^{-.833}$$

gives the approximate average survival time (in minutes) for trout exposed to x milligrams per liter (mg/L) of zinc ions. Find the survival time (to the nearest minute) for the given concentrations of zinc ions.

(a) 110   **(b)** 525   **(c)** 1960   **(d)** 4500

55. Physical Science The distance from Chicago to Sacramento, California, is approximately 2050 miles. A plane flying directly to Sacramento passes over Chicago at noon. If the plane travels at 500 mph, find the rule of the function $f(t)$ that gives the distance of the plane from Sacramento at time t hours (with $t = 0$ corresponding to noon).

56. Physical Science The distance from Toronto, Ontario to Dallas, Texas is approximately 1200 miles. A plane flying directly to Dallas passes over Toronto at 2 p.m. If the plane travels at 550 mph, find the rule of the function $f(t)$ that gives the distance of the plane from Dallas at time t hours (with $t = 0$ corresponding to 2 pm).

57. Business A pretzel factory has daily fixed costs of \$1800. In addition, it costs 50 cents to produce each bag of pretzels. A bag of pretzels sells for \$1.20.

(a) Find the rule of the cost function $c(x)$ that gives the total daily cost of producing x bags of pretzels.

(b) Find the rule of the revenue function $r(x)$ that gives the daily revenue from selling x bags of pretzels.

(c) Find the rule of the profit function $p(x)$ that gives the daily profit from x bags of pretzels.

58. Business An aluminum can factory has daily fixed costs of \$120,000 per day. In addition, it costs \$.03 to produce each can. They can sell a can to a soda manufacturer for \$.05 a can.

(a) Find the rule of the cost function $c(x)$ that gives the total daily cost of producing x aluminum cans.

(b) Find the rule of the revenue function $r(x)$ that gives the daily revenue from selling x aluminum cans.

(c) Find the rule of the profit function $p(x)$ that gives the daily profit from x aluminum cans.

⚐ *Use the table feature of a graphing calculator to do these exercises. (See Example 11.)*

59. Business The value (in millions of dollars) of new orders for all manufacturing industries can be approximated by the function

$$h(x) = -4.83x^3 + 50.3x^2 + 25.5x + 4149,$$

where $x = 0$ corresponds to the year 2000. Create a table that gives the value of the sales for the years 2005–2010. (Data from: U.S. Census Bureau.)

60. Business The value added to the economy (in billions of dollars) for agricultural production can be approximated by the function

$$g(x) = -.35x^3 + 5.34x^2 - 5.17x + 217.3,$$

where $x = 0$ corresponds to 2000. Create a table that gives the value added to the economy for the years 2007–2010. (Data from: U.S. Department of Agriculture.)

✓**Checkpoint Answers**

1. The domain consists of all possible times—that is, all nonnegative real numbers. The range consists of all possible distances; thus, the range is also the set of all nonnegative real numbers.

2. **(a)** Yes   **(b)** Yes   **(c)** No

3. **(a)** Yes   **(b)** Yes   **(c)** No   **(d)** No

4. **(a)** $(-\infty, \infty)$ **(b)** $(-\infty, \infty)$ **(c)** $(-\infty, 0]$
   (d) All real numbers except 1 and -1

5. **(a)** 4   **(b)** 40   **(c)** 73   **(d)** 44
   (e) $5m^2 - 2m + 1$ **(f)** $10xh + 5h^2 - 2h$
   (g) $10x + 5h - 2$

6. **(a)** $2237.50   **(b)** $220.35

7. **(a)** $39,600,000   **(b)** $96,000,000

3.2 Graphs of Functions

The **graph** of a function $f(x)$ is defined to be the graph of the *equation* $y = f(x)$. It consists of all points $(x, f(x))$—that is, every point whose first coordinate is an input number from the domain of f and whose second coordinate is the corresponding output number.

> **Example 1** The graph of the function $g(x) = .5x - 3$ is the graph of the equation $y = .5x - 3$. So the graph is a straight line with slope .5 and y-intercept -3, as shown in Figure 3.3.
>
>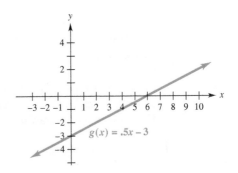
>
> $g(x) = .5x - 3$
>
> **Figure 3.3**

A function whose graph is a straight line, as in Example 1, is called a **linear function.** The rule of a linear function can always be put into the form

$$f(x) = ax + b$$

for some constants a and b.

Piecewise Linear Functions

We now consider functions whose graphs consist of straight-line segments. Such functions are called **piecewise linear functions** and are typically defined with different equations for different parts of the domain.

Example 2 Graph the following function:

$$f(x) = \begin{cases} x + 1 & \text{if } x \le 2 \\ -2x + 7 & \text{if } x > 2. \end{cases}$$

Solution Consider the two parts of the rule of f. The graphs of $y = x + 1$ and $y = -2x + 7$ are straight lines. The graph of f consists of

the part of the line $y = x + 1$ with $x \le 2$ and

the part of the line $y = -2x + 7$ with $x > 2$.

Each of these line segments can be graphed by plotting two points in the appropriate interval, as shown in Figure 3.4.

$x \le 2$		
x	0	2
$y = x + 1$	1	3

$x > 2$		
x	3	4
$y = -2x + 7$	1	-1

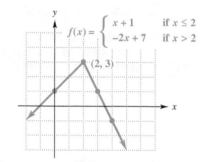

Figure 3.4

Note that the left and right parts of the graph each extend to the vertical line through $x = 2$, where the two halves of the graph meet at the point (2, 3).

✓**Checkpoint 1**

Graph

$$f(x) = \begin{cases} x + 2 & \text{if } x < 0 \\ 2 - x & \text{if } x \ge 0. \end{cases}$$

Example 3 Graph the function

$$f(x) = \begin{cases} x - 2 & \text{if } x \le 3 \\ -x + 8 & \text{if } x > 3. \end{cases}$$

Solution The graph consists of parts of two lines. To find the left side of the graph, choose two values of x with $x \le 3$, say, $x = 0$ and $x = 3$. Then find the corresponding points on $y = x - 2$, namely, $(0, -2)$ and $(3, 1)$. Use these points to draw the line segment to the left of $x = 3$, as in Figure 3.5. Next, choose two values of x with $x > 3$, say, $x = 4$ and $x = 6$, and find the corresponding points on $y = -x + 8$, namely, $(4, 4)$ and $(6, 2)$. Use these points to draw the line segment to the right of $x = 3$, as in Figure 3.5.

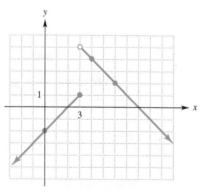

$$f(x) = \begin{cases} x - 2 & \text{if } x \le 3 \\ -x + 8 & \text{if } x > 3 \end{cases}$$

Figure 3.5

Note that both line segments of the graph of f extend to the vertical line through $x = 3$. The closed circle at (3, 1) indicates that this point is on the graph of f, whereas the open circle at (3, 5) indicates that this point is *not* on the graph of f (although it is on the graph of the line $y = -x + 8$). ✓₂

✓ **Checkpoint 2**

Graph

$$f(x) = \begin{cases} -2x - 3 & \text{if } x < 1 \\ x - 2 & \text{if } x \geq 1. \end{cases}$$

Example 4 Graph the **absolute-value function,** whose rule is $f(x) = |x|$.

Solution The definition of absolute value on page 8 shows that the rule of f can be written as

$$f(x) = \begin{cases} x & \text{if } x \geq 0 \\ -x & \text{if } x < 0. \end{cases}$$

So the right half of the graph (that is, where $x \geq 0$) will consist of a portion of the line $y = x$. It can be graphed by plotting two points, say, (0, 0) and (1, 1). The left half of the graph (where $x < 0$) will consist of a portion of the line $y = -x$, which can be graphed by plotting $(-2, 2)$ and $(-1, 1)$, as shown in Figure 3.6. ✓₃

✓ **Checkpoint 3**

Graph $f(x) = |3x - 4|$.

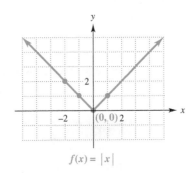

$$f(x) = |x|$$

Figure 3.6

⬛ **TECHNOLOGY TIP** To graph most piecewise linear functions on a graphing calculator, you must use a special syntax. For example, on TI calculators, the best way to obtain the graph in Example 3 is to graph two separate equations on the same screen:

$$y_1 = (x - 2)/(x \leq 3) \quad \text{and} \quad y_2 = (-x + 8)/(x > 3).$$

The inequality symbols are in the TEST (or CHAR) menu. However, most calculators will graph absolute-value functions directly. To graph $f(x) = |x + 2|$, for instance, graph the equation $y = abs(x + 2)$. "Abs" (for absolute value) is on the keyboard or in the MATH menu.

Step Functions

The **greatest-integer function,** usually written $f(x) = [x]$, is defined by saying that $[x]$ denotes the largest integer that is less than or equal to x. For example, $[8] = 8, [7.45] = 7, [\pi] = 3, [-1] = -1, [-2.6] = -3$, and so on.

Example 5 Graph the greatest-integer function $f(x) = [x]$.

Solution Consider the values of the function between each two consecutive integers—for instance,

x	$-2 \leq x < -1$	$-1 \leq x < 0$	$0 \leq x < 1$	$1 \leq x < 2$	$2 \leq x < 3$
$[x]$	-2	-1	0	1	2

Thus, between $x = -2$ and $x = -1$, the value of $f(x) = [x]$ is always -2, so the graph there is a horizontal line segment, all of whose points have second coordinate -2. The rest of the graph is obtained similarly (Figure 3.7). An open circle in that figure indicates that the endpoint of the segment is *not* on the graph, whereas a closed circle indicates that the endpoint *is* on the graph. ✓₄

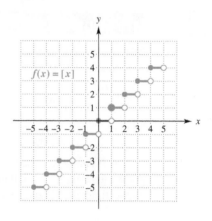

Figure 3.7

✓ **Checkpoint 4**

Graph $y = \left[\frac{1}{2}x + 1\right]$.

Functions whose graphs resemble the graph of the greatest-integer function are sometimes called **step functions.**

Example 6   **Business**   In 2013, the U.S. Post Office charged to ship a flat envelope first class to Eastern Europe, Europe, or Australia a fee of $2.05 for up to and including the first ounce, $.85 for each additional ounce or fraction of an ounce up to and including 8 ounces, and then $1.70 for each additional four ounces or less, up to a peak of 64 ounces. Let $D(x)$ represent the cost to send a flat envelope weighing x ounces. Graph $D(x)$ for x in the interval $(0, 20]$.

Solution   For x in the interval $(0, 1]$, $y = 2.05$. For x in $(1, 2]$, $y = 2.05 + .85 = 2.90$. For x in $(2, 3]$, $y = 2.90 + .85 = 3.75$, and so on up to x in $(7, 8]$, $y = 7.15 + .85 = 8.00$. Then for x in $(8, 12]$, $y = 8.00 + 1.70 = 9.70$. For x in $(12, 16]$, $y = 9.70 + 1.70 = 11.40$, and x in $(16, 20]$, $y = 11.40 + 1.70 = 13.10$. The graph, which is that of a step function, is shown in Figure 3.8. ✓₅

✓ **Checkpoint 5**

To mail a letter to the regions described in Example 6, the U.S. Post Office charges $1.10 for up to and including the first ounce, an additional $.95 for up to and including 2 ounces, an additional $.95 for up to and including 3 ounces, and then an additional $.95 to a maximum weight of 3.5 ounces. Let $L(x)$ represent the cost of sending a letter to those regions where x represents the weight of the letter in ounces. Graph $L(x)$ for x in the interval $(0, 3.5]$.

Figure 3.8

TECHNOLOGY TIP On most graphing calculators, the greatest-integer function is denoted INT or FLOOR. (Look on the MATH menu or its NUM submenu.) Casio calculators use INTG for the greatest-integer function and INT for a different function. When graphing these functions, put your calculator in "dot" graphing mode rather than the usual "connected" mode to avoid erroneous vertical line segments in the graph.

Other Functions

The graphs of many functions do not consist only of straight-line segments. As a general rule when graphing functions by hand, you should follow the procedure introduced in Section 2.1 and summarized here.

Graphing a Function by Plotting Points

1. Determine the domain of the function.
2. Select a few numbers in the domain of f (include both negative and positive ones when possible), and compute the corresponding values of $f(x)$.
3. Plot the points $(x, f(x))$ computed in Step 2. Use these points and any other information you may have about the function to make an educated guess about the shape of the entire graph.
4. Unless you have information to the contrary, assume that the graph is continuous (unbroken) wherever it is defined.

This method was used to find the graphs of the functions $f(x) = x^2 - 2x - 8$ and $g(x) = \sqrt{x + 2}$ in Examples 3 and 4 of Section 2.1. Here are some more examples.

✓ **Checkpoint 6**

Graph $f(x) = \sqrt{5 - 2x}$.

Example 7 Graph $g(x) = \sqrt{x - 1}$.

Solution Because the rule of the function is defined only when $x - 1 \geq 0$ (that is, when $x \geq 1$), the domain of g is the interval $[1, \infty)$. Use a calculator to make a table of values such as the one in Figure 3.9. Plot the corresponding points and connect them to get the graph in Figure 3.9. ✓6

x	$g(x) = \sqrt{x - 1}$
1	0
2	1
3	$\sqrt{2} \approx 1.414$
5	2
7	$\sqrt{6} \approx 2.449$
10	3

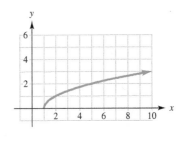

Figure 3.9

Example 8 Graph the function whose rule is

$$f(x) = 3 - \frac{x^3}{4}.$$

Solution Make a table of values and plot the corresponding points. They suggest the graph in Figure 3.10.

x	$f(x) = 3 - \dfrac{x^3}{4}$
−4	19.0
−3	9.8
−2	5.0
−1	3.3
0	3.0
1	2.8
2	1.0
3	−3.8
4	−13.0

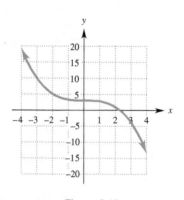

Figure 3.10

Example 9   Graph the piecewise defined function

$$f(x) = \begin{cases} x^2 & \text{if } x \le 2 \\ \sqrt{x - 1} & \text{if } x > 2. \end{cases}$$

Solution   When $x \le 2$, the rule of the function is $f(x) = x^2$. Make a table of values such as the one in Figure 3.11. Plot the corresponding points and connect them to get the left half of the graph in Figure 3.11. When $x > 2$, the rule of the function is $f(x) = \sqrt{x - 1}$, whose graph is shown in Figure 3.9. In Example 7, the entire graph was given, beginning at $x = 1$. Here we use only the part of the graph to the right of $x = 2$, as shown in Figure 3.11. The open circle at $(2, 1)$ indicates that this point is not part of the graph of f (why?).

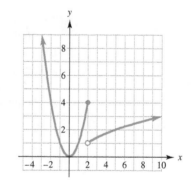

x	x^2
−2	4
−1	1
0	0
1	1
2	4

Figure 3.11

Graph Reading

Graphs are often used in business and the social sciences to present data. It is just as important to know how to *read* such graphs as it is to construct them.

Example 10   **Business**   Figure 3.12, on the following page, shows the median sales prices (in thousands of dollars) of new privately owned one-family houses by region of the United States (northeast, midwest, south, and west) from the years 2005 to 2011. (Data from: U.S. Census Bureau and U.S. Department of Housing and Urban Development.)

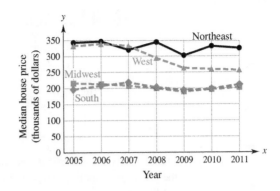

Figure 3.12

(a) How do prices in the west compare with those in the midwest over the period shown in the graph?

Solution The prices of the houses in the west started out approximately $100,000 higher than those in the midwest. In both regions prices declined until 2009 when prices in the midwest inched higher while those in the west continued to decline. In 2011, the gap between the two regions had shrunk to just over $50,000.

(b) Which region typically had the highest price?

Solution The northeast had the highest median price for all years except for 2007 when the west had the highest price.

Example 11 Figure 3.13 is the graph of the function f whose rule is $f(x)$ = average interest rate on a 30-year fixed-rate mortgage for a new home in year x. (Data from: www.fhfa.gov.)

Figure 3.13

(a) Find the function values of $f(1988)$ and $f(2009)$.

Solution The point (1988, 10) is on the graph, which means that $f(1988) = 10$. Similarly, $f(2009) = 5$, because the point (2009, 5) is on the graph. These values tell us the average mortgage rates were 10% in the year 1988 and 5% in the year 2009.

(b) During what period were mortgage rates at or above 7%?

Solution Look for points on the graph whose second coordinates are 7 or more—that is, points on or above the horizontal line through 7. These points represent the period from 1985 to 2001.

(c) During what period were mortgage rates at or below 5%?

Solution Look for points that are at or below the horizontal line through 5—that is, points with second coordinates less than or equal to 5. They occur from 2009 to 2011.

The Vertical-Line Test

The following fact distinguishes function graphs from other graphs.

Figure 3.14

Vertical-Line Test

No vertical line intersects the graph of a function $y = f(x)$ at more than one point.

In other words, if a vertical line intersects a graph at more than one point, the graph is not the graph of a function. To see why this is true, consider the graph in Figure 3.14. The vertical line $x = 3$ intersects the graph at two points. If this were the graph of a function f, it would mean that $f(3) = 2$ (because $(3, 2)$ is on the graph) and that $f(3) = -1$ (because $(3, -1)$ is on the graph). This is impossible, because a *function* can have only one value when $x = 3$ (because each input determines exactly one output). Therefore, the graph in Figure 3.14 cannot be the graph of a function. A similar argument works in the general case.

Example 12   Use the vertical-line test to determine which of the graphs in Figure 3.15 are the graphs of functions.

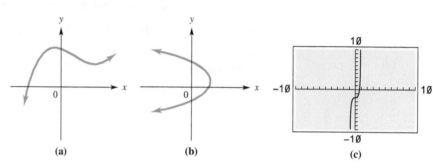

(a)   (b)   (c)

Figure 3.15

Solution   To use the vertical-line test, imagine dragging a ruler held vertically across the graph from left to right. If the graph is that of a function, the edge of the ruler would hit the graph only once for every x-value. If you do this for graph (a), every vertical line intersects the graph in at most one point, so this graph is the graph of a function. Many vertical lines (including the y-axis) intersect graph (b) twice, so it is not the graph of a function.

Graph (c) appears to fail the vertical-line test near $x = 1$ and $x = -1$, indicating that it is not the graph of a function. But this appearance is misleading because of the low resolution of the calculator screen. The table in Figure 3.16 and the very narrow segment of the graph in Figure 3.17 show that the graph actually rises as it moves to the right. The same thing happens near $x = -1$. So this graph *does* pass the vertical-line test and *is* the graph of a function. (Its rule is $f(x) = 15x^{11} - 2$). The moral of this story is that you can't always trust images produced by a graphing calculator. When in doubt, try other viewing windows or a table to see what is really going on. ✔7

✓ **Checkpoint 7**

Find a viewing window that indicates the actual shape of the graph of the function $f(x) = 15x^{11} - 2$ of Example 12 near the point $(-1, -17)$.

Figure 3.16

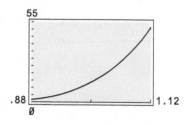

Figure 3.17

3.2 Exercises

Graph each function. (See Examples 1–4.)

1. $f(x) = -.5x + 2$ **2.** $g(x) = 3 - x$

3. $f(x) = \begin{cases} x + 3 & \text{if } x \leq 1 \\ 4 & \text{if } x > 1 \end{cases}$

4. $g(x) = \begin{cases} 2x - 1 & \text{if } x < 0 \\ -1 & \text{if } x \geq 0 \end{cases}$

5. $y = \begin{cases} 4 - x & \text{if } x \leq 0 \\ 3x + 4 & \text{if } x > 0 \end{cases}$

6. $y = \begin{cases} x + 5 & \text{if } x \leq 1 \\ 2 - 3x & \text{if } x > 1 \end{cases}$

7. $f(x) = \begin{cases} |x| & \text{if } x < 2 \\ -2x & \text{if } x \geq 2 \end{cases}$

8. $g(x) = \begin{cases} -|x| & \text{if } x \leq 1 \\ 2x & \text{if } x > 1 \end{cases}$

9. $f(x) = |x - 4|$ **10.** $g(x) = |4 - x|$

11. $f(x) = |3 - 3x|$ **12.** $g(x) = -|x|$

13. $y = -|x - 1|$ **14.** $f(x) = |x| - 2$

15. $y = |x - 2| + 3$

16. $|x| + |y| = 1$ (*Hint:* This is not the graph of a function, but is made up of four straight-line segments. Find them by using the definition of absolute value in these four cases: $x \geq 0$ and $y \geq 0$; $x \geq 0$ and $y < 0$; $x < 0$ and $y \geq 0$; $x < 0$ and $y < 0$).

Graph each function. (See Examples 5 and 6.)

17. $f(x) = [x - 3]$ **18.** $g(x) = [x + 3]$

19. $g(x) = [-x]$

20. $f(x) = [x] + [-x]$ (The graph contains horizontal segments, but is *not* a horizontal line.)

21. Business The accompanying table gives rates charged by the U.S. Postal Service for first-class letters in March 2013. Graph the function $f(x)$ that gives the price of mailing a first-class letter, where x represents the weight of the letter in ounces and $0 \leq x \leq 3.5$.

Weight Not Over	Price
1 ounce	$0.46
2 ounces	$0.66
3 ounces	$0.86
3.5 ounces	$1.06

22. Business The accompanying table gives rates charged by the U.S. Postal Service for first-class large flat envelopes in March, 2013. Graph the function $f(x)$ that gives the price of mailing a first-class large flat envelope, where x represents the weight of the envelope in ounces and $0 \leq x \leq 6$.

Weight Not Over	Price
1 ounce	$0.92
2 ounces	$1.12
3 ounces	$1.32
4 ounces	$1.53
5 ounces	$1.72
6 ounces	$1.92

Graph each function. (See Examples 7–9.)

23. $f(x) = 3 - 2x^2$

24. $g(x) = 2 - x^2$

25. $h(x) = x^3/10 + 2$

26. $f(x) = x^3/20 - 3$

27. $g(x) = \sqrt{-x}$

28. $h(x) = \sqrt{x} - 1$

29. $f(x) = \sqrt[3]{x}$

30. $g(x) = \sqrt[3]{x - 4}$

31. $f(x) = \begin{cases} x^2 & \text{if } x < 2 \\ -2x + 2 & \text{if } x \geq 2 \end{cases}$

32. $g(x) = \begin{cases} \sqrt{-x} & \text{if } x \leq -4 \\ \dfrac{x^2}{4} & \text{if } x > -4 \end{cases}$

Determine whether each graph is a graph of a function or not. (See Example 12.)

33.

34.

35.

36.

37.

38.

Use a graphing calculator or other technology to graph each of the given functions. If the graph has any endpoints, indicate whether they are part of the graph or not.

39. $f(x) = .2x^3 - .8x^2 - 4x + 9.6$

40. $g(x) = .1x^4 - .3x^3 - 1.3x^2 + 1.5x$

41. $g(x) = \begin{cases} 2x^2 + x & \text{if } x < 1 \\ x^3 - x - 1 & \text{if } x \geq 1 \end{cases}$ (*Hint:* See the Technology Tip on page 125)

42. $f(x) = \begin{cases} x|x| & \text{if } x \leq 0 \\ -x^2|x| + 2 & \text{if } x > 0 \end{cases}$

Use a graphical root finder to determine the x-intercepts of the graph of

43. f in Exercise 39;   **44.** g in Exercise 40.

Use a maximum–minimum finder to determine the location of the peaks and valleys in the graph of

45. g in Exercise 40;   **46.** f in Exercise 39.

See Examples 2, 3, 10, and 11 as you do Exercises 47–52.

47. Finance The Maine state income tax for a single person in 2013 was determined by the rule

$$T(x) = \begin{cases} .02x & \text{if } 0 \leq x \leq 5099 \\ 101.98 + .045(x - 5099) & \text{if } 5099 < x \leq 10,149 \\ 329.23 + .07(x - 10,149) & \text{if } 10,149 < x \leq 20,349 \\ 1043.23 + .085(x - 20,349) & \text{if } x > 20,349, \end{cases}$$

where x is the person's taxable income in dollars. Graph the function $T(x)$ for taxable incomes between 0 and $24,000.

48. Finance The Alabama state income tax for a single person in 2013 was determined by the rule

$$T(x) = \begin{cases} .02x & \text{if } 0 \leq x \leq 500 \\ 10 + .04(x - 500) & \text{if } 500 < x \leq 3000 \\ 110 + .05(x - 3000) & \text{if } x > 3000 \end{cases}$$

where x is the person's taxable income in dollars. Graph the function $T(x)$ for taxable incomes between 0 and $5000.

49. Finance The price of KeyCorp stock can be approximated by the function

$$f(x) = \begin{cases} 9.04 - .027x & \text{if } 0 < x \leq 43 \\ 7.879 + .032(x - 43) & \text{if } 43 < x \leq 113 \end{cases}$$

where x represents the number of trading days past September 14, 2012. (Data from: www.morningstar.com.)

(a) Graph $f(x)$.

(b) What is the lowest stock price during the period defined by $f(x)$?

50. Natural Science The number of minutes of daylight in Washington, DC, can be modeled by the function

$$g(x) = \begin{cases} .0106x^2 + 1.24x + 565 & \text{if } 1 \leq x < 84 \\ -.0202x^2 + 6.97x + 295 & \text{if } 84 \leq x < 263 \\ .0148x^2 - 11.1x + 2632 & \text{if } 263 \leq x \leq 365, \end{cases}$$

where x represents the number of days of the year, starting on January 1. Find the number of minutes of daylight on

(a) day 32.   (b) day 90.

(c) day 200.   (d) day 270.

(e) Graph $g(x)$.

(f) On what day is the number of minutes of daylight the greatest?

51. Health The following table shows the consumer price index (CPI) for medical care in selected years: (Data from: U.S. Bureau of Labor Statistics.)

Year	Medical-Care CPI
1950	15.1
1980	74.9
2010	388.4

(a) Let $x = 0$ correspond to 1950. Find the rule of a piecewise linear function that models these data—that is, a piecewise linear function f with $f(0) = 15.1$, $f(30) = 74.9$, and $f(60) = 388.4$. Round all coefficients in your final answer to one decimal place.

(b) Graph the function f for $0 \leq x \leq 65$.

(c) Use the function to estimate the medical-care CPI in 2004.

(d) Assuming that this model remains accurate after 2010, estimate the medical-care CPI for 2015.

52. Business The graph on the following page from the U.S. Office of Management and Budget shows the federal debt from the year 2007 to the year 2012 (in billions of dollars), with $x = 7$ corresponding to the year 2007. Find the rule of a linear function g that passes through the two points corresponding to 2007 and 2012. Draw the graph of g.

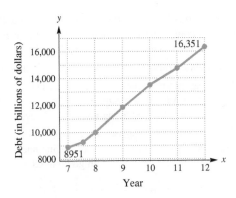

Year

Finance *Use the accompanying graph to answer Exercises 53 and 54. The graph shows the annual percent change in various consumer price indexes (CPIs). (See Examples 10 and 11.) (Data from: U.S. Census Bureau.)*

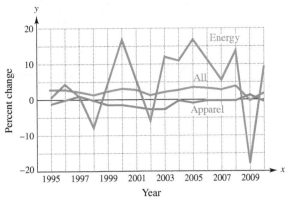

Year

53. (a) Was there any period between 1995 and 2010 when all three indexes showed a decrease?

(b) During what years did the CPI for energy show a decrease?

(c) When was the CPI for energy decreasing at the fastest rate?

54. (a) During what years did the CPI for apparel show an increase?

(b) When was the CPI for apparel increasing at the greatest rate?

55. Finance The following graph shows the number of FDIC-insured financial institutions in the United States for the year 1990 through the year 2010. (Data from: U.S. Federal Deposit Insurance Corporation.)

Year

(a) Is this the graph of a function?

(b) What does the domain represent?

(c) Estimate the range.

56. Finance The following graph shows the percent-per-year yield of the 10-year U.S. Treasury Bond from the year 2000 to the year 2010. (Data from: Board of Governors of the Federal Reserve System.)

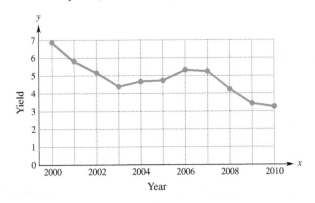

Year

(a) Is this the graph of a function?

(b) What does the domain represent?

(c) Estimate the range.

57. Business Whenever postage rates change, some newspaper publishes a graph like this one, which shows the price of a first-class stamp from 1982 to 2008:

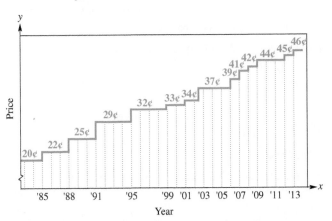

Year

(a) Let f be the function whose rule is

$$f(x) = \text{cost of a first-class stamp in year } x.$$

Find $f(2000)$ and $f(2011)$.

(b) Explain why the graph in the figure is not the graph of the *function f.* What must be done to the figure to make it an accurate graph of the function f?

58. Business A chain-saw rental firm charges $20 per day or fraction of a day to rent a saw, plus a fixed fee of $7 for resharpening the blade. Let $S(x)$ represent the cost of renting a saw for x days. Find each of the following.

(a) $S\left(\dfrac{1}{2}\right)$ **(b)** $S(1)$ **(c)** $S\left(1\dfrac{2}{3}\right)$ **(d)** $S\left(4\dfrac{3}{4}\right)$

(e) What does it cost to rent for $5\dfrac{7}{8}$ days?

(f) A portion of the graph of $y = S(x)$ is shown on the following page. Explain how the graph could be continued.

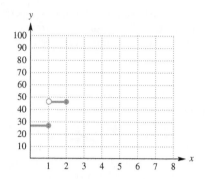

with $t = 0$ corresponding to the 4 p.m. takeoff. In each part of this exercise, draw a plausible graph of f under the given circumstances. (There are many correct answers for each part.)

(a)   The flight is nonstop and takes between 3.5 and 4 hours.

(b)   Bad weather forces the plane to land in Dallas (about 200 miles from Austin) at 5 p.m., remain overnight, and leave at 8 a.m. the next day, flying nonstop to Cleveland.

(c)   The plane flies nonstop, but due to heavy traffic it must fly in a holding pattern for an hour over Cincinnati (about 200 miles from Cleveland) and then go on to Cleveland.

(g)   What is the domain variable?

(h)   What is the range variable?

(i)   Write a sentence or two explaining what (c) and its answer represent.

(j)   We have left $x = 0$ out of the graph. Discuss why it should or should not be included. If it were included, how would you define $S(0)$?

59.   Business   Sarah Hendrickson needs to rent a van to pick up a new couch she has purchased. The cost of the van is $19.99 for the first 75 minutes and then an additional $5 for each block of 15 minutes beyond 75. Find the cost to rent a van for

(a)   2 hours;   **(b)**   1.5 hours;

(c)   3.5 hours;   **(d)**   4 hours.

(e)   Graph the ordered pairs (hours, cost).

60.   Business   A delivery company charges $25 plus 60¢ per mile or part of a mile. Find the cost for a trip of

(a)   3 miles;   **(b)**   4.2 miles;

(c)   5.9 miles;   **(d)**   8 miles.

(e)   Graph the ordered pairs (miles, cost).

(f)   Is this a function?

Work these problems.

61.   Natural Science   A laboratory culture contains about 1 million bacteria at midnight. The culture grows very rapidly until noon, when a bactericide is introduced and the bacteria population plunges. By 4 p.m., the bacteria have adapted to the bactericide and the culture slowly increases in population until 9 p.m., when the culture is accidentally destroyed by the cleanup crew. Let $g(t)$ denote the bacteria population at time t (with $t = 0$ corresponding to midnight). Draw a plausible graph of the function g. (Many correct answers are possible.)

62.   Physical Science   A plane flies from Austin, Texas, to Cleveland, Ohio, a distance of 1200 miles. Let f be the function whose rule is

$f(t) = $ distance (in miles) from Austin at time t hours,

✓ Checkpoint Answers

1.

2.

3.

4.

5.

6.

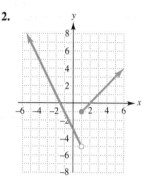

7.   There are many correct answers, including, $-1.4 \le x \le -.6$ and $-30 \le y \le 0$.

3.3   Applications of Linear Functions

Most of this section deals with the basic business relationships that were introduced in Section 1.2:

Revenue = (Price per item) × (Number of items);

Cost = Fixed Costs + Variable Costs;

Profit = Revenue − Cost.

The examples will use only linear functions, but the methods presented here also apply to more complicated functions.

Cost Analysis

Recall that fixed costs are for such things as buildings, machinery, real-estate taxes, and product design. Within broad limits, the fixed cost is constant for a particular product and does not change as more items are made. Variable costs are for labor, materials, shipping, and so on, and depend on the number of items made.

If $C(x)$ is the cost of making x items, then the fixed cost (the cost that occurs even when no items are produced) can be found by letting $x = 0$. For example, for the cost function $C(x) = 45x + 250,000$, the fixed cost is

$$C(0) = 45(0) + 250,000 = \$250,000.$$

In this case, the variable cost of making x items is $45x$—that is, $45 per item manufactured.

Example 1   **Business**   An anticlot drug can be made for $10 per unit. The total cost to produce 100 units is $1500.

(a)   Assuming that the cost function is linear, find its rule.

Solution   Since the cost function $C(x)$ is linear, its rule is of the form $C(x) = mx + b$. We are given that m (the cost per item) is 10, so the rule is $C(x) = 10x + b$. To find b, use the fact that it costs $1500 to produce 100 units, which means that

$$C(100) = 1500$$
$$10(100) + b = 1500 \qquad C(x) = 10x + b.$$
$$1000 + b = 1500$$
$$b = 500.$$

So the rule of the cost function is $C(x) = 10x + 500$.

(b)   What are the fixed costs?

✓ **Checkpoint 1**

The total cost of producing 10 calculators is $100. The variable costs per calculator are $4. Find the rule of the linear cost function.

Solution   The fixed costs are $C(0) = 10(0) + 500 = \$500.$ ✓₁

If $C(x)$ is the total cost to produce x items, then the **average cost** per item is given by

$$\overline{C}(x) = \frac{C(x)}{x}.$$

As more and more items are produced, the average cost per item typically decreases.

Example 2   **Business**   Find the average cost of producing 100 and 1000 units of the anticlot drug in Example 1.

Solution   The cost function is $C(x) = 10x + 500$, so the average cost of producing 100 units is

$$\overline{C}(100) = \frac{C(100)}{100} = \frac{10(100) + 500}{100} = \frac{1500}{100} = \$15.00 \text{ per unit.}$$

✓ **Checkpoint 2**

In Checkpoint 1, find the average cost per calculator when 100 are produced.

The average cost of producing 1000 units is

$$\overline{C}(1000) = \frac{C(1000)}{1000} = \frac{10(1000) + 500}{1000} = \frac{10,500}{1000} = \$10.50 \text{ per unit.} \checkmark_2$$

Rates of Change

The rate at which a quantity (such as revenue or profit) is changing can be quite important. For instance, if a company determines that the rate of change of its revenue is decreasing, then sales growth is slowing down, a trend that may require a response.

The rate of change of a linear function is easily determined. For example, suppose $f(x) = 3x + 5$ and consider the table of values in the margin. The table shows that each time x changes by 1, the corresponding value of $f(x)$ changes by 3. Thus, the rate of change of $f(x) = 3x + 5$ with respect to x is 3, which is the slope of the line $y = 3x + 5$. The same thing happens for any linear function:

x	$f(x) = 3x + 5$
1	8
2	11
3	14
4	17
5	20

> **The rate of change of a linear function $f(x) = mx + b$ is the slope m.**

In particular, the rate of change of a linear function is constant.

The value of a computer, or an automobile, or a machine *depreciates* (decreases) over time. **Linear depreciation** means that the value of the item at time x is given by a linear function $f(x) = mx + b$. The slope m of this line gives the rate of depreciation.

Example 3   **Business**   According to the *Kelley Blue Book*, a Ford Mustang two-door convertible that is worth $14,776 today will be worth $10,600 in two years (if it is in excellent condition with average mileage).

(a) Assuming linear depreciation, find the depreciation function for this car.

Solution   We know the car is worth $14,776 now ($x = 0$) and will be worth $10,600 in two years ($x = 2$). So the points $(0, 14,776)$ and $(2, 10,600)$ are on the graph of the linear-depreciation function and can be used to determine its slope:

$$m = \frac{10,600 - 14,776}{2} = \frac{-4176}{2} = -2088.$$

Using the point $(0, 14,776)$, we find that the equation of the line is

$$y - 14,776 = -2088(x - 0) \qquad \text{Point–slope form}$$
$$y = -2088x + 14,776. \qquad \text{Slope–intercept form}$$

Therefore, the rule of the depreciation function is $f(x) = -2088x + 14,776$.

(b) What will the car be worth in 4 years?

Solution   Evaluate f when $x = 4$:

$$f(x) = -2088x + 14,776$$
$$f(4) = -2088(4) + 14,776 = \$6424.$$

(c) At what rate is the car depreciating?

Solution   The depreciation rate is given by the slope of $f(x) = -2088x + 14,776$, namely, -2088. This negative slope means that the car is decreasing in value an average of $2088 a year. ✓ 3

✓ **Checkpoint 3**

Using the information from Example 3, determine what the car will be worth in 6 years.

In economics, the rate of change of the cost function is called the **marginal cost.** Marginal cost is important to management in making decisions in such areas as cost control, pricing, and production planning. When the cost function is linear, say, $C(x) = mx + b$, the marginal cost is the number m (the slope of the graph of C). Marginal cost can also be thought of as the cost of producing one more item, as the next example demonstrates.

Example 4   **Business**   An electronics company manufactures handheld PCs. The cost function for one of its models is $C(x) = 160x + 750,000$.

(a) What are the fixed costs for this product?

Solution   The fixed costs are $C(0) = 160(0) + 750,000 = \$750,000$.

(b) What is the marginal cost?

Solution   The slope of $C(x) = 160x + 750,000$ is 160, so the marginal cost is $160 per item.

(c) After 50,000 units have been produced, what is the cost of producing one more?

Solution   The cost of producing 50,000 is

$$C(50,000) = 160(50,000) + 750,000 = \$8,750,000.$$

The cost of 50,001 units is

$$C(50,001) = 160(50,001) + 750,000 = \$8,750,160.$$

The cost of the additional unit is the difference

$$C(50,001) - C(50,000) = 8,750,160 - 8,750,000 = \$160.$$

Thus, the cost of one more item is the marginal cost. ✓4

Similarly, the rate of change of a revenue function is called the **marginal revenue**. When the revenue function is linear, the marginal revenue is the slope of the line, as well as the revenue from producing one more item.

Example 5   **Business**   The energy company New York State Electric and Gas charges each residential customer a basic fee for electricity of $15.11, plus $.0333 per kilowatt hour (kWh).

(a) Assuming there are 700,000 residential customers, find the company's revenue function.

Solution   The monthly revenue from the basic fee is

$$15.11(700,000) = \$10,577,000.$$

If x is the total number of kilowatt hours used by all customers, then the revenue from electricity use is $.0333x$. So the monthly revenue function is given by

$$R(x) = .0333x + 10,577,000.$$

(b) What is the marginal revenue?

Solution   The marginal revenue (the rate at which revenue is changing) is given by the slope of the rate function: $0.0333 per kWh. ✓5

Examples 4 and 5 are typical of the general case, as summarized here.

In a **linear cost function** $C(x) = mx + b$, the marginal cost is m (the slope of the cost line) and the fixed cost is b (the y-intercept of the cost line). The marginal cost is the cost of producing one more item.

Similarly, in a **linear revenue function** $R(x) = kx + d$, the marginal revenue is k (the slope of the revenue line), which is the revenue from selling one more item.

✓ **Checkpoint 4**

The cost in dollars to produce x kilograms of chocolate candy is given by $C(x) = 3.5x + 800$. Find each of the following.

(a) The fixed cost

(b) The total cost for 12 kilograms

(c) The marginal cost of the 40th kilogram

(d) The marginal cost per kilogram

✓ **Checkpoint 5**

Assume that the average customer in Example 5 uses 1600 kWh in a month.

(a) What is the total number of kWh used by all customers?

(b) What is the company's monthly revenue?

Break-Even Analysis

A typical company must analyze its costs and the potential market for its product to determine when (or even whether) it will make a profit.

Example 6   **Business**   A company manufactures a 42-inch plasma HDTV that sells to retailers for $550. The cost of making x of these TVs for a month is given by the cost function $C(x) = 250x + 213{,}000$.

(a) Find the function R that gives the revenue from selling x TVs.

Solution   Since revenue is the product of the price per item and the number of items, $R(x) = 550x$.

(b) What is the revenue from selling 600 TVs?

Solution   Evaluate the revenue function R at 600:

$$R(600) = 550(600) = \$330{,}000.$$

(c) Find the profit function P.

Solution   Since Profit = Revenue − Cost,

$$P(x) = R(x) - C(x) = 550x - (250x + 213{,}000) = 300x - 213{,}000.$$

(d) What is the profit from selling 500 TVs?

Solution   Evaluate the profit function at 500 to obtain

$$P(500) = 300(500) - 213{,}000 = -63{,}000,$$

that is, a loss of $63,000.

A company can make a profit only if the revenue on a product exceeds the cost of manufacturing it. The number of units at which revenue equals cost (that is, profit is 0) is the **break-even point.**

Example 7   **Business**   Find the break-even point for the company in Example 6.

Solution   The company will break even when revenue equals cost—that is, when

$$R(x) = C(x)$$
$$550x = 250x + 213{,}000$$
$$300x = 213{,}000$$
$$x = 710.$$

The company breaks even by selling 710 TVs. The graphs of the revenue and cost functions and the break-even point (where $x = 710$) are shown in the Figure 3.18. The company must sell more than 710 TVs ($x > 710$) in order to make a profit. ✓6

✓ Checkpoint 6

For a certain newsletter, the cost equation is $C(x) = 0.90x + 1500$, where x is the number of newsletters sold. The newsletter sells for $1.25 per copy. Find the break-even point.

Figure 3.18

Intersection
X=710   Y=390500

Figure 3.19

TECHNOLOGY TIP The break-even point in Example 7 can be found on a graphing calculator by graphing the cost and revenue functions on the same screen and using the calculator's intersection finder, as shown in Figure 3.19. Depending on the calculator, the intersection finder is in the CALC or G-SOLVE menu or in the MATH or FCN submenu of the GRAPH menu.

Supply and Demand

The supply of and demand for an item are usually related to its price. Producers will supply large numbers of the item at a high price, but consumer demand will be low. As the price of the item decreases, consumer demand increases, but producers are less willing to supply large numbers of the item. The curves showing the quantity that will be supplied at a given price and the quantity that will be demanded at a given price are called **supply and demand curves,** respectively. In supply-and-demand problems, we use p for price and q for quantity. We will discuss the economic concepts of supply and demand in more detail in later chapters.

Example 8 **Economics** Joseph Nolan has studied the supply and demand for aluminum siding and has determined that the price per unit,[*] p, and the quantity demanded, q, are related by the linear equation

$$p = 60 - \frac{3}{4}q.$$

(a) Find the demand at a price of $40 per unit.

Solution Let $p = 40$. Then we have

$$p = 60 - \frac{3}{4}q$$

$$40 = 60 - \frac{3}{4}q \qquad \textit{Let p = 40.}$$

$$-20 = -\frac{3}{4}q \qquad \textit{Add −60 to both sides.}$$

$$\frac{80}{3} = q. \qquad \textit{Multiply both sides by } -\frac{4}{3}.$$

At a price of $40 per unit, $80/3$ (or $26\frac{2}{3}$) units will be demanded.

(b) Find the price if the demand is 32 units.

Solution Let $q = 32$. Then we have

$$p = 60 - \frac{3}{4}q$$

$$p = 60 - \frac{3}{4}(32) \qquad \textit{Let q = 32.}$$

$$p = 60 - 24$$

$$p = 36.$$

With a demand of 32 units, the price is $36.

(c) Graph $p = 60 - \frac{3}{4}q$.

Solution It is customary to use the horizontal axis for the quantity q and the vertical axis for the price p. In part (a), we saw that $80/3$ units would be demanded at a price of

[*]An appropriate unit here might be, for example, one thousand square feet of siding.

$40 per unit; this gives the ordered pair (80/3, 40). Part (b) shows that with a demand of 32 units, the price is $36, which gives the ordered pair (32, 36). Using the points (80/3, 40) and (32, 36) yields the demand graph depicted in Figure 3.20. Only the portion of the graph in Quadrant I is shown, because supply and demand are meaningful only for positive values of p and q. ✓7

Checkpoint 7

Suppose price and quantity demanded are related by
$p = 100 - 4q$.

(a) Find the price if the quantity demanded is 10 units.

(b) Find the quantity demanded if the price is $80.

(c) Write the corresponding ordered pairs.

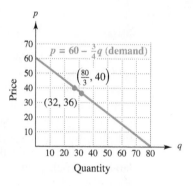

Figure 3.20

(d) From Figure 3.20, at a price of $30, what quantity is demanded?

Solution Price is located on the vertical axis. Look for 30 on the p-axis, and read across to where the line $p = 30$ crosses the demand graph. As the graph shows, this occurs where the quantity demanded is 40.

(e) At what price will 60 units be demanded?

Solution Quantity is located on the horizontal axis. Find 60 on the q-axis, and read up to where the vertical line $q = 60$ crosses the demand graph. This occurs where the price is about $15 per unit.

(f) What quantity is demanded at a price of $60 per unit?

Solution The point (0, 60) on the demand graph shows that the demand is 0 at a price of $60 (that is, there is no demand at such a high price).

Example 9 **Economics** Suppose the economist in Example 8 concludes that the supply q of siding is related to its price p by the equation

$$p = .85q.$$

(a) Find the supply if the price is $51 per unit.

Solution
$$51 = .85q \qquad \text{Let } p = 51.$$
$$60 = q. \qquad \text{Divide both sides by .85}$$

If the price is $51 per unit, then 60 units will be supplied to the marketplace.

(b) Find the price per unit if the supply is 20 units.

Solution
$$p = .85(20) = 17. \qquad \text{Let } q = 20.$$

If the supply is 20 units, then the price is $17 per unit.

(c) Graph the supply equation $p = .85q$.

Solution As with demand, each point on the graph has quantity q as its first coordinate and the corresponding price p as its second coordinate. Part (a) shows that the ordered pair (60, 51) is on the graph of the supply equation, and part (b) shows that (20, 17) is on the graph. Using these points, we obtain the supply graph in Figure 3.21.

Figure 3.21

(d) Use the graph in Figure 3.21 to find the approximate price at which 35 units will be supplied. Then use algebra to find the exact price.

Solution The point on the graph with first coordinate $q = 35$ is approximately $(35, 30)$. Therefore, 35 units will be supplied when the price is approximately \$30. To determine the exact price algebraically, substitute $q = 35$ into the supply equation:

$$p = .85q = .85(35) = \$29.75.$$

Figure 3.22

Example 10   **Economics**   The supply and demand curves of Examples 8 and 9 are shown in Figure 3.22. Determine graphically whether there is a surplus or a shortage of supply at a price of \$40 per unit.

Solution Find 40 on the vertical axis in Figure 3.22 and read across to the point where the horizontal line $p = 40$ crosses the supply graph (that is, the point corresponding to a price of \$40). This point lies above the demand graph, so supply is greater than demand at a price of \$40, and there is a surplus of supply.

Supply and demand are equal at the point where the supply curve intersects the demand curve. This is the **equilibrium point.** Its second coordinate is the **equilibrium price,** the price at which the same quantity will be supplied as is demanded. Its first coordinate is the quantity that will be demanded and supplied at the equilibrium price; this number is called the **equilibrium quantity.**

Example 11   **Economics**   In the situation described in Examples 8–10, what is the equilibrium quantity? What is the equilibrium price?

Solution The equilibrium point is where the supply and demand curves in Figure 3.22 intersect. To find the quantity q at which the price given by the demand equation $p = 60 - .75q$ (Example 8) is the same as that given by the supply equation $p = .85q$ (Example 9), set these two expressions for p equal to each other and solve the resulting equation:

$$60 - .75q = .85q$$
$$60 = 1.6q$$
$$37.5 = q.$$

Therefore, the equilibrium quantity is 37.5 units, the number of units for which supply will equal demand. Substituting $q = 37.5$ into either the demand or supply equation shows that

$$p = 60 - .75(37.5) = 31.875 \quad \text{or} \quad p = .85(37.5) = 31.875.$$

✓ **Checkpoint 8**

The demand for a certain commodity is related to the price by $p = 80 - (2/3)q$. The supply is related to the price by $p = (4/3)q$. Find

(a) the equilibrium quantity;

(b) the equilibrium price.

So the equilibrium price is $31.875 (or $31.88, rounded). (To avoid error, it is a good idea to substitute into both equations, as we did here, to be sure that the same value of p results; if it does not, a mistake has been made.) In this case, the equilibrium point—the point whose coordinates are the equilibrium quantity and price—is (37.5, 31.875).

⬆ **TECHNOLOGY TIP** The equilibrium point (37.5, 31.875) can be found on a graphing calculator by graphing the supply and demand curves on the same screen and using the calculator's intersection finder to locate their point of intersection.

3.3 Exercises

Business   *Write a cost function for each of the given scenarios. Identify all variables used. (See Example 1.)*

1. A chain-saw rental firm charges $25, plus $5 per hour.

2. A trailer-hauling service charges $95, plus $8 per mile.

3. A parking garage charges $8.00, plus $2.50 per half hour.

4. For a 1-day rental, a car rental firm charges $65, plus 45¢ per mile.

Business   *Assume that each of the given situations can be expressed as a linear cost function. Find the appropriate cost function in each case. (See Examples 1 and 4.)*

5. Fixed cost, $200; 50 items cost $2000 to produce.

6. Fixed cost, $2000; 40 items cost $5000 to produce.

7. Marginal cost, $120; 100 items cost $15,800 to produce.

8. Marginal cost, $90; 150 items cost $16,000 to produce.

Business   *In Exercises 9–12, a cost function is given. Find the average cost per item when the required numbers of items are produced. (See Example 2.)*

9. $C(x) = 12x + 1800$; 50 items, 500 items, 1000 items

10. $C(x) = 80x + 12,000$; 100 items, 1000 items, 10,000 items

11. $C(x) = 6.5x + 9800$; 200 items, 2000 items, 5000 items

12. $C(x) = 8.75x + 16,500$; 1000 items, 10,000 items, 75,000 items

Business   *Work these exercises. (See Example 3.)*

13. A Volkswagen Beetle convertible sedan is worth $16,615 now and is expected to be worth $8950 in 4 years.

(a) Find a linear depreciation function for this car.

(b) Estimate the value of the car 5 years from now.

(c) At what rate is the car depreciating?

14. A computer that cost $1250 new is expected to depreciate linearly at a rate of $250 per year.

(a) Find the depreciation function f.

(b) Explain why the domain of f is [0, 5].

15. A machine is now worth $120,000 and will be depreciated linearly over an 8-year period, at which time it will be worth $25,000 as scrap.

(a) Find the rule of the depreciation function f.

(b) What is the domain of f?

(c) What will the machine be worth in 6 years?

16. A house increases in value in an approximately linear fashion from $222,000 to $300,000 in 6 years.

(a) Find the *appreciation function* that gives the value of the house in year x.

(b) If the house continues to appreciate at this rate, what will it be worth 12 years from now?

Business   *Work these problems. (See Example 4.)*

17. The total cost (in dollars) of producing x college algebra books is $C(x) = 42.5x + 80,000$.

(a) What are the fixed costs?

(b) What is the marginal cost per book?

(c) What is the total cost of producing 1000 books? 32,000 books?

(d) What is the average cost when 1000 are produced? when 32,000 are produced?

18. The total cost (in dollars) of producing x DVDs is $C(x) = 6.80x + 450,000$.

(a) What are the fixed costs?

(b) What is the marginal cost per DVD?

(c) What is the total cost of producing 50,000 DVDs? 600,000 DVDs?

(d) What is the average cost per DVD when 50,000 are produced? when 500,000 are produced?

19. The manager of a restaurant found that the cost of producing 100 cups of coffee is $11.02, while the cost of producing 400 cups is $40.12. Assume that the cost $C(x)$ is a linear function of x, the number of cups produced.

(a) Find a formula for $C(x)$.

(b) Find the total cost of producing 1000 cups.

(c) Find the total cost of producing 1001 cups.

(d) Find the marginal cost of producing the 1000th cup.

(e) What is the marginal cost of producing *any* cup?

20. In deciding whether to set up a new manufacturing plant, company analysts have determined that a linear function is a reasonable estimation for the total cost $C(x)$ in dollars of producing x items. They estimate the cost of producing 10,000 items as $547,500 and the cost of producing 50,000 items as $737,500.

(a) Find a formula for $C(x)$.

(b) Find the total cost of producing 100,000 items.

(c) Find the marginal cost of the items to be produced in this plant.

Business *Work these problems. (See Example 5.)*

21. For the year 2013, a resident of the city of Dallas, Texas with a 5/8 inch water meter pays $4.20 per month plus $1.77 per 1000 gallons of water used (up to 4000 gallons). If the city of Dallas has 550,000 customers that use less than 4000 gallons a month, find its monthly revenue function $R(x)$, where the total number of gallons x is measured in thousands.

22. The Lacledge Gas Company in St. Louis, Missouri in the winter of 2012–2013 charged customers $21.32 per month plus $1.19071 per therm for the first 30 therms of gas used and $.57903 for each therm above 30.

(a) How much revenue does the company get from a customer who uses exactly 30 therms of gas in a month?

(b) Find the rule of the function $R(x)$ that gives the company's monthly revenue from one customer, where x is the number of therms of gas used. (*Hint:* $R(x)$ is a piecewise-defined function that has a two-part rule, one part for $x \le 30$ and the other for $x > 30$.)

Business *Assume that each row of the accompanying table has a linear cost function. Find (a) the cost function; (b) the revenue function; (c) the profit function; (d) the profit on 100 items. (See Example 6.)*

	Fixed Cost	Marginal Cost per Item	Item Sells For
23.	$750	$10	$35
24.	$150	$11	$20
25.	$300	$18	$28
26.	$17,000	$30	$80
27.	$20,000	$12.50	$30

28. Business In the following profit–volume chart, *EF* and *GH* represent the profit–volume graphs of a single-product company for, 2012 and 2013, respectively. (Adapted from: Uniform CPA Examination, American Institute of Certified Public Accountants.)

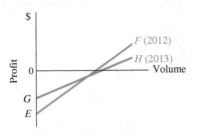

If the 2012 and 2013 unit sales prices are identical, how did the total fixed costs and unit variable costs of 2013 change compared with their values in 2012? Choose one:

	2012 Total Fixed Costs	2013 Unit Variable Costs
(a)	Decreased	Increased
(b)	Decreased	Decreased
(c)	Increased	Increased
(d)	Increased	Decreased

Use algebra to find the intersection points of the graphs of the given equations. (See Examples 7 and 11.)

29. $2x - y = 7$ and $y = 8 - 3x$

30. $6x - y = 2$ and $y = 4x + 7$

31. $y = 3x - 7$ and $y = 7x + 4$

32. $y = 3x + 5$ and $y = 12 - 2x$

Business *Work the following problems. (See Example 7.)*

33. An insurance company claims that for x thousand policies, its monthly revenue in dollars is given by $R(x) = 125x$ and its monthly cost in dollars is given by $C(x) = 100x + 5000$.

(a) Find the break-even point.

(b) Graph the revenue and cost equations on the same axes.

(c) From the graph, estimate the revenue and cost when $x = 100$ (100,000 policies).

34. The owners of a parking lot have determined that their weekly revenue and cost in dollars are given by $R(x) = 80x$ and $C(x) = 50x + 2400$, where x is the number of long-term parkers.

(a) Find the break-even point.

(b) Graph $R(x)$ and $C(x)$ on the same axes.

(c) From the graph, estimate the revenue and cost when there are 60 long-term parkers.

35. The revenue (in millions of dollars) from the sale of x units at a home supply outlet is given by $R(x) = .21x$. The profit (in millions of dollars) from the sale of x units is given by $P(x) = .084x - 1.5$.

(a) Find the cost equation.

(b) What is the cost of producing 7 units?

(c) What is the break-even point?

36. The profit (in millions of dollars) from the sale of x million units of Blue Glue is given by $P(x) = .7x - 25.5$. The cost is given by $C(x) = .9x + 25.5$.

(a) Find the revenue equation.

(b) What is the revenue from selling 10 million units?

(c) What is the break-even point?

Business *Suppose you are the manager of a firm. The accounting department has provided cost estimates, and the sales department sales estimates, on a new product. You must analyze the data they give you, determine what it will take to break even, and decide whether to go ahead with production of the new product. (See Example 7.)*

37. Cost is estimated by $C(x) = 80x + 7000$ and revenue is estimated by $R(x) = 95x$; no more than 400 units can be sold.

38. Cost is $C(x) = 140x + 3000$ and revenue is $R(x) = 125x$.

39. Cost is $C(x) = 125x + 42,000$ and revenue is $R(x) = 165.5x$; no more than 2000 units can be sold.

40. Cost is $C(x) = 1750x + 95,000$ and revenue is $R(x) = 1975x$; no more than 600 units can be sold.

41. Business The accompanying graph shows the percentage of females in the workforce for Ireland and South Korea for the years 1980 through 2010. Estimate the break-even point (the point at which the two countries had the same percentage of females in the workforce.) (Data from: Organisation for Economic Co-operation and Development.)

42. Social Science Gallup conducts an annual poll of residents of 130 countries around the world to ask about approval of world leadership. The graph below shows the percentage of respondents who approve of the job performance of the leadership of the United States and Great Britain from the years 2007 to 2012. Estimate the year in which the break-even point (the year in which the opinion on leadership was the same) occurred.

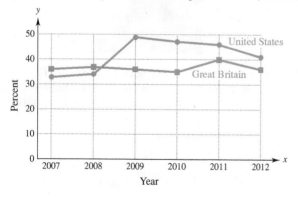

43. Social Science The population (in millions of people) of Florida from the year 2000 to the year 2010 can be approximated by the function $f(x) = .292x + 16.17$. Similarly, the population of (in millions of people) of New York can be approximated by the function $g(x) = .026x + 19.04$. For both of these models, let $x = 0$ correspond to the year 2000. (Data from: U.S. Census Bureau.)

(a) Graph both functions on the same coordinate axes for $x = 0$ to $x = 10$.

(b) Do the graphs intersect in this window?

(c) If trends continue at the same rate, will Florida overtake New York in population? If so, estimate what year that will occur.

44. Social Science The population (in millions of people) of Massachusetts from the year 2000 to the year 2010 can be approximated by the function $f(x) = .019x + 6.36$. Similarly, the population (in millions of people) of Arizona can be approximated by the function $g(x) = .130x + 5.15$. For both of these models, let $x = 0$ correspond to the year 2000. (Data from: U.S. Census Bureau.)

(a) Graph both functions on the same coordinate axes for $x = 0$ to $x = 10$.

(b) Do the graphs intersect in this window?

(c) If trends continue at the same rate, will Arizona overtake Massachusetts in population? If so, estimate what year that will occur.

Business *Use the supply and demand curves in the accompanying graph to answer Exercises 45–48. (See Examples 8–11.)*

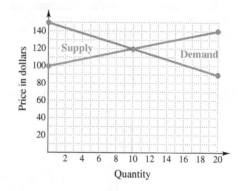

45. At what price are 20 items supplied?

46. At what price are 20 items demanded?

47. Find the equilibrium quantity.

48. Find the equilibrium price.

Economics *Work the following exercises. (See Examples 8–11.)*

49. Suppose that the demand and price for a certain brand of shampoo are related by

$$p = 16 - \frac{5}{4}q,$$

where p is price in dollars and q is demand. Find the price for a demand of

(a) 0 units;   (b) 4 units;   (c) 8 units.

Find the demand for the shampoo at a price of

(d) $6; **(e)** $11; **(f)** $16.

(g) Graph $p = 16 - (5/4)q$.

Suppose the price and supply of the shampoo are related by

$$p = \frac{3}{4}q,$$

where q represents the supply and p the price. Find the supply when the price is

(h) $0; **(i)** $10; **(j)** $20.

(k) Graph $p = (3/4)q$ on the same axes used for part (g).

(l) Find the equilibrium quantity.

(m) Find the equilibrium price.

50. Let the supply and demand for radial tires in dollars be given by

$$\text{supply: } p = \frac{3}{2}q; \quad \text{demand: } p = 81 - \frac{3}{4}q.$$

(a) Graph these equations on the same axes.

(b) Find the equilibrium quantity.

(c) Find the equilibrium price.

51. Let the supply and demand for bananas in cents per pound be given by

$$\text{supply: } p = \frac{2}{5}q; \quad \text{demand: } p = 100 - \frac{2}{5}q.$$

(a) Graph these equations on the same axes.

(b) Find the equilibrium quantity.

(c) Find the equilibrium price.

(d) On what interval does demand exceed supply?

52. Let the supply and demand for sugar be given by

$$\text{supply: } p = 1.4q - .6$$

and

$$\text{demand: } p = -2q + 3.2,$$

where p is in dollars.

(a) Graph these on the same axes.

(b) Find the equilibrium quantity.

(c) Find the equilibrium price.

(d) On what interval does supply exceed demand?

53. Explain why the graph of the (total) cost function is always above the x-axis and can never move downward as you go from left to right. Is the same thing true of the graph of the average cost function?

54. Explain why the graph of the profit function can rise or fall (as you go from left to right) and can be below the x-axis.

✓**Checkpoint Answers**

1. $C(x) = 4x + 60$. **2.** $4.60 **3.** $2248

4. **(a)** $800 **(b)** $842 **(c)** $3.50 **(d)** $3.50

5. **(a)** 1,120,000,000 **(b)** $47,873,000

6. 4286 newsletters

7. **(a)** $60 **(b)** 5 units **(c)** (10, 60); (5, 80)

8. **(a)** 40 **(b)** $160/3 \approx $53.33

3.4 Quadratic Functions and Applications

A **quadratic function** is a function whose rule is given by a quadratic polynomial, such as

$$f(x) = x^2, \quad g(x) = 3x^2 + 30x + 67, \quad \text{and} \quad h(x) = -x^2 + 4x.$$

Thus, a quadratic function is a function whose rule can be written in the form

$$f(x) = ax^2 + bx + c$$

for some constants a, b, and c, with $a \neq 0$.

Example 1 Graph each of these quadratic functions:

$$f(x) = x^2; \quad g(x) = 4x^2; \quad h(x) = -.2x^2.$$

Solution In each case, choose several numbers (negative, positive, and 0) for x, find the values of the function at these numbers, and plot the corresponding points. Then connect the points with a smooth curve to obtain Figure 3.23, on the next page.

$f(x) = x^2$					
x	-2	-1	0	1	2
x^2	4	1	0	1	4

$g(x) = 4x^2$					
x	-2	-1	0	1	2
$4x^2$	16	4	0	4	16

$h(x) = -.2x^2$					
x	-5	-3	-1	0	2	4
$-.2x^2$	-5	-1.8	-.2	0	-.8	-3.2

(a)

(b)

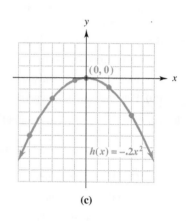

(c)

Figure 3.23

Each of the curves in Figure 3.23 is a **parabola.** It can be shown that the graph of every quadratic function is a parabola. Parabolas have many useful properties. Cross sections of radar dishes and spotlights form parabolas. Disks often visible on the sidelines of televised football games are microphones having reflectors with parabolic cross sections. These microphones are used by the television networks to pick up the signals shouted by the quarterbacks.

All parabolas have the same basic "cup" shape, although the cup may be broad or narrow and open upward or downward. The general shape of a parabola is determined by the coefficient of x^2 in its rule, as summarized here and illustrated in Example 1. ✓1

✓ **Checkpoint 1**

Graph each quadratic function.

(a) $f(x) = x^2 - 4$

(b) $g(x) = -x^2 + 4$

The graph of a quadratic function $f(x) = ax^2 + bx + c$ is a parabola.

If $a > 0$, the parabola opens upward.   [*Figure 3.23(a) and 3.23(b)*]

If $a < 0$, the parabola opens downward.   [*Figure 3.23(c)*]

If $|a| < 1$, the parabola appears wider than the graph of $y = x^2$. [*Figure 3.23(c)*]

If $|a| > 1$, the parabola appears narrower than the graph of $y = x^2$.
   [*Figure 3.23(b)*]

When a parabola opens upward [as in Figure 3.23(a), (b)], its lowest point is called the **vertex.** When a parabola opens downward [as in Figure 3.23(c)], its highest point is called the **vertex.** The vertical line through the vertex of a parabola is called the **axis of the parabola.** For example, (0, 0) is the vertex of each of the parabolas in Figure 3.23, and the axis of each parabola is the y-axis. If you were to fold the graph of a parabola along its axis, the two halves of the parabola would match exactly. This means that a parabola is *symmetric* about its axis.

Although the vertex of a parabola can be approximated by a graphing calculator's maximum or minimum finder, its exact coordinates can be found algebraically, as in the following examples.

Example 2   Consider the function $g(x) = 2(x - 3)^2 + 1$.

(a) Show that g is a quadratic function.

Solution   Multiply out the rule of g to show that it has the required form:

$$g(x) = 2(x - 3)^2 + 1$$
$$= 2(x^2 - 6x + 9) + 1$$
$$= 2x^2 - 12x + 18 + 1$$
$$g(x) = 2x^2 - 12x + 19.$$

According to the preceding box, the graph of g is a somewhat narrow, upward-opening parabola.

(b) Show that the vertex of the graph of $g(x) = 2(x - 3)^2 + 1$ is $(3, 1)$.

Solution   Since $g(3) = 2(3 - 3)^2 + 1 = 0 + 1 = 1$, the point $(3, 1)$ is on the graph. The vertex of an upward-opening parabola is the lowest point on the graph, so we must show that $(3, 1)$ is the lowest point. Let x be any number except 3 (so that $x - 3 \neq 0$). Then the quantity $2(x - 3)^2$ is positive, and hence

$$g(x) = 2(x - 3)^2 + 1 = (\text{a positive number}) + 1,$$

which means that $g(x) > 1$. Therefore, every point $(x, g(x))$ on the graph, where $x \neq 3$, has second coordinate $g(x)$ greater than 1. Hence $(x, g(x))$ lies *above* $(3, 1)$. In other words, $(3, 1)$ is the lowest point on the graph—the vertex of the parabola.

(c) Graph $g(x) = 2(x - 3)^2 + 1$.

Solution   Plot some points on both sides of the vertex $(3, 1)$ to obtain the graph in Figure 3.24. The vertical line $x = 3$ through the vertex is the axis of the parabola.

x	y
1	9
2	3
3	1
4	3
5	9

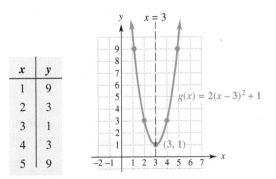

Figure 3.24

In Example 2, notice how the rule of the function g is related to the coordinates of the vertex:

$$g(x) = 2(x - 3)^2 + 1. \qquad (3, 1).$$

Arguments similar to those in Example 2 lead to the following fact.

> The graph of the quadratic function $f(x) = a(x - h)^2 + k$ is a parabola with vertex (h, k). It opens upward when $a > 0$ and downward when $a < 0$.

Example 3   Determine algebraically whether the given parabola opens upward or downward, and find its vertex.

(a) $f(x) = -3(x - 4)^2 - 7$

Solution The rule of the function is in the form $f(x) = a(x - h)^2 + k$ (with $a = -3$, $h = 4$, and $k = -7$). The parabola opens downward ($a < 0$), and its vertex is $(h, k) = (4, -7)$.

(b) $g(x) = 2(x + 3)^2 + 5$

Solution Be careful here: The vertex is *not* (3, 5). To put the rule of $g(x)$ in the form $a(x - h)^2 + k$, we must rewrite it so that there is a minus sign inside the parentheses:

$$g(x) = 2(x + 3)^2 + 5$$
$$= 2(x - (-3))^2 + 5.$$

This is the required form, with $a = 2$, $h = -3$, and $k = 5$. The parabola opens upward, and its vertex is $(-3, 5)$. ✓₂

✓ **Checkpoint 2**

Determine the vertex of each parabola, and graph the parabola.

(a) $f(x) = (x + 4)^2 - 3$

(b) $f(x) = -2(x - 3)^2 + 1$

Example 4 Find the rule of a quadratic function whose graph has vertex (3, 4) and passes through the point (6, 22).

Solution The graph of $f(x) = a(x - h)^2 + k$ has vertex (h, k). We want $h = 3$ and $k = 4$, so that $f(x) = a(x - 3)^2 + 4$. Since (6, 22) is on the graph, we must have $f(6) = 22$. Therefore,

$$f(x) = a(x - 3)^2 + 4$$
$$f(6) = a(6 - 3)^2 + 4$$
$$22 = a(3)^2 + 4$$
$$9a = 18$$
$$a = 2.$$

Thus, the graph of $f(x) = 2(x - 3)^2 + 4$ is a parabola with vertex (3, 4) that passes through (6, 22).

The vertex of each parabola in Examples 2 and 3 was easily determined because the rule of the function had the form

$$f(x) = a(x - h)^2 + k.$$

The rule of *any* quadratic function can be put in this form by using the technique of **completing the square**, which is illustrated in the next example.

Example 5 Determine the vertex of the graph of $f(x) = x^2 - 4x + 2$. Then graph the parabola.

Solution In order to get $f(x)$ in the form $a(x - h)^2 + k$, take half the coefficient of x, namely $\frac{1}{2}(-4) = -2$, and *square it:* $(-2)^2 = 4$. Then proceed as follows.

✓ **Checkpoint 3**

Rewrite the rule of each function by completing the square, and use this form to find the vertex of the graph.

(a) $f(x) = x^2 + 6x + 5$

(*Hint:* add and subtract the square of half the coefficient of *x*.)

(b) $g(x) = x^2 - 12x + 33$

$$f(x) = x^2 - 4x + 2$$
$$= x^2 - 4x + \underline{\quad} + 2 \qquad \text{Leave space for the squared term and its negative.}$$
$$= x^2 - 4x + 4 - 4 + 2 \qquad \text{Add and subtract 4.}$$
$$= (x^2 - 4x + 4) - 4 + 2 \qquad \text{Insert parentheses.}$$
$$= (x - 2)^2 - 2 \qquad \text{Factor expression in parentheses and add.}$$

Adding and subtracting 4 did not change the rule of $f(x)$, but did make it possible to have a perfect square as part of its rule: $f(x) = (x - 2)^2 - 2$. Now we can see that the graph is an upward-opening parabola, as shown in Figure 3.25, on the following page. ✓₃

Figure 3.25

⚠️ **CAUTION** The technique of completing the square only works when the coefficient of x^2 is 1. To find the vertex of a quadratic function such as

$$f(x) = 2x^2 + 12x - 19,$$

you must first factor out the coefficient of x^2 and write the rule as

$$f(x) = 2(x^2 + 6x - \tfrac{19}{2}).$$

Now complete the square on the expression in parentheses by adding and subtracting 9 (the square of half the coefficient of x), and proceed as in Example 5.

The technique of completing the square can be used to rewrite the general equation $f(x) = ax^2 + bx + c$ in the form $f(x) = a(x - h)^2 + k$. When this is done, we obtain a formula for the coordinates of the vertex.

> The graph of $f(x) = ax^2 + bx + c$ is a parabola with vertex (h, k), where
>
> $$h = \frac{-b}{2a} \quad \text{and} \quad k = f(h).$$

Additionally, the fact that the vertex of a parabola is the highest or lowest point on the graph can be used in applications to find a maximum or minimum value.

Example 6   **Business** Lynn Wolf owns and operates Wolf's microbrewery. She has hired a consultant to analyze her business operations. The consultant tells her that her daily profits from the sale of x cases of beer are given by

$$P(x) = -x^2 + 120x.$$

Find the vertex, determine if it is a maximum or minimum, write the equation of the axis of the parabola, and compute the x- and y-intercepts of the profit function $P(x)$.

Solution Since $a = -1$ and $b = 120$, the x-value of the vertex is

$$\frac{-b}{2a} = \frac{-120}{2(-1)} = 60.$$

The y-value of the vertex is

$$P(60) = -(60)^2 + 120(60) = 3600.$$

The vertex is (60, 3600) and since a is negative, it is a maximum because the parabola opens downward. The axis of the parabola is $x = 60$. The intercepts are found by setting x and y equal to 0.

x-intercepts	**y-intercept**
Set $P(x) = y = 0$, so that	Set $x = 0$ to obtain
$0 = -x^2 + 120x$	$P(0) = 0^2 + 120(0) = 0$
$0 = x(-x + 120)$	The y-intercept is 0.
$x = 0$ or $-x + 120 = 0$	
$-x = -120$	
$x = 120$	

The x-intercepts are 0 and 120.

 Checkpoint 4

When a company sells x units of a product, its profit is
$P(x) = -2x^2 + 40x + 280$. Find

(a) the number of units which should be sold so that maximum profit is received;

(b) the maximum profit.

Figure 3.26 shows the profit function $P(x)$.

Figure 3.26

TECHNOLOGY TIP The maximum or minimum finder on a graphing calculator can approximate the vertex of a parabola with a high degree of accuracy. The max–min finder is in the CALC menu or in the MATH or FCN submenu of the GRAPH menu. Similarly, the calculator's graphical root finder can approximate the x-intercepts of a parabola.

Supply and demand curves were introduced in Section 3.3. Here is a quadratic example.

Example 7   **Economics**   Suppose that the price of and demand for an item are related by

$$p = 150 - 6q^2,$$ Demand function

where p is the price (in dollars) and q is the number of items demanded (in hundreds). Suppose also that the price and supply are related by

$$p = 10q^2 + 2q,$$ Supply function

where q is the number of items supplied (in hundreds). Find the equilibrium quantity and the equilibrium price.

Solution   The graphs of both of these equations are parabolas (Figure 3.27), as seen on the following page. Only those portions of the graphs which lie in the first quadrant are included, because none of supply, demand, or price can be negative.

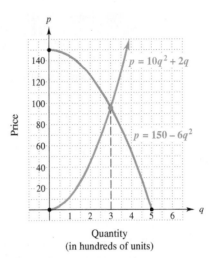

Figure 3.27

The point where the demand and supply curves intersect is the equilibrium point. Its first coordinate is the equilibrium quantity, and its second coordinate is the equilibrium price. These coordinates may be found in two ways.

Algebraic Method At the equilibrium point, the second coordinate of the demand curve must be the same as the second coordinate of the supply curve, so that

$$150 - 6q^2 = 10q^2 + 2q.$$

Write this quadratic equation in standard form as follows:

$$0 = 16q^2 + 2q - 150 \qquad \text{Add } -150 \text{ and } 6q^2 \text{ to both sides.}$$
$$0 = 8q^2 + q - 75. \qquad \text{Multiply both sides by } \frac{1}{2}.$$

This equation can be solved by the quadratic formula, given in Section 1.7. Here, $a = 8$, $b = 1$, and $c = -75$:

$$q = \frac{-1 \pm \sqrt{1 - 4(8)(-75)}}{2(8)}$$

$$= \frac{-1 \pm \sqrt{1 + 2400}}{16} \qquad -4(8)(-75) = 2400$$

$$= \frac{-1 \pm 49}{16} \qquad \sqrt{1 + 2400} = \sqrt{2401} = 49$$

$$q = \frac{-1 + 49}{16} = \frac{48}{16} = 3 \quad \text{or} \quad q = \frac{-1 - 49}{16} = -\frac{50}{16} = -\frac{25}{8}.$$

It is not possible to make $-25/8$ units, so discard that answer and use only $q = 3$. Hence, the equilibrium quantity is 300. Find the equilibrium price by substituting 3 for q in either the supply or the demand function (and check your answer by using the other one). Using the supply function gives

$$p = 10q^2 + 2q$$
$$p = 10 \cdot 3^2 + 2 \cdot 3 \qquad \text{Let } q = 3.$$
$$= 10 \cdot 9 + 6$$
$$p = \$96.$$

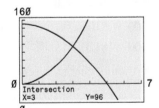

Figure 3.28

✓ **Checkpoint 5**

The price and demand for an item are related by $p = 32 - x^2$, while price and supply are related by $p = x^2$. Find

(a) the equilibrium quantity;

(b) the equilibrium price.

Graphical Method Graph the two functions on a graphing calculator, and use the intersection finder to determine that the equilibrium point is (3, 96), as in Figure 3.28. ✓₅

Example 8 **Business** The rental manager of a small apartment complex with 16 units has found from experience that each $40 increase in the monthly rent results in an empty apartment. All 16 apartments will be rented at a monthly rent of $500. How many $40 increases will produce maximum monthly income for the complex?

Solution Let x represent the number of $40 increases. Then the number of apartments rented will be $16 - x$. Also, the monthly rent per apartment will be $500 + 40x$. (There are x increases of $40, for a total increase of $40x$.) The monthly income, $I(x)$, is given by the number of apartments rented times the rent per apartment, so

$$I(x) = (16 - x)(500 + 40x)$$
$$= 8000 + 640x - 500x - 40x^2$$
$$= 8000 + 140x - 40x^2.$$

Since x represents the number of $40 increases and each $40 increase causes one empty apartment, x must be a whole number. Because there are only 16 apartments, $0 \le x \le 16$. Since there is a small number of possibilities, the value of x that produces maximum income may be found in several ways.

Brute Force Method Use a scientific calculator or the table feature of a graphing calculator (as in Figure 3.29) to evaluate $I(x)$ when $x = 1, 2, \ldots, 16$ and find the largest value.

X	Y1
0	8000
1	8100
2	8120
3	8060
4	7920
5	7700
6	7400
X=0	

X	Y1
7	7020
8	6560
9	6020
10	5400
11	4700
12	3920
13	3060
X=7	

X	Y1
14	2120
15	1100
16	0
17	-1180
18	-2440
19	-3780
20	-5200
X=14	

Figure 3.29

The tables show that a maximum income of $8120 occurs when $x = 2$. So the manager should charge rent of $500 + 2(40) = \$580$, leaving two apartments vacant.

Algebraic Method The graph of $I(x) = 8000 + 140x - 40x^2$ is a downward-opening parabola (why?), and the value of x that produces maximum income occurs at the vertex. The methods of Section 3.4 show that the vertex is $(1.75, 8122.50)$. Since x must be a whole number, evaluate $I(x)$ at $x = 1$ and $x = 2$ to see which one gives the best result:

$$\text{If } x = 1, \text{ then } I(1) = -40(1)^2 + 140(1) + 8000 = 8100.$$
$$\text{If } x = 2, \text{ then } I(2) = -40(2)^2 + 140(2) + 8000 = 8120.$$

So maximum income occurs when $x = 2$. The manager should charge a rent of $500 + 2(40) = \$580$, leaving two apartments vacant.

Quadratic Models

Real-world data can sometimes be used to construct a quadratic function that approximates the data. Such **quadratic models** can then be used (subject to limitations) to predict future behavior.

Example 9 **Business** The number of physical compact disks (CDs, in millions of units) shipped are given in the following table for the years 1997 through 2011. (Data from: Recording Industry Association of America.)

Year	1997	1998	1999	2000	2001	2002	2003	2004
CDs shipped	753	847	939	943	882	803	746	767
Year	2005	2006	2007	2008	2009	2010	2011	
CDs shipped	705	620	511	369	293	253	241	

(a) Let $x = 7$ correspond to the year 1997. Display the information graphically.

Solution   Plot the points (7, 753), (8, 847), and so on—as in Figure 3.30.

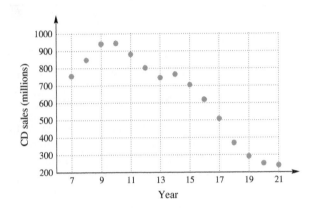

Figure 3.30

(b) The shape of the data points in Figure 3.31 resembles a downward-opening parabola. Using the year 2000 as the maximum, find a quadratic model $f(x) = a(x - h)^2 + k$ for these data.

Solution   Recall that when a quadratic function is written in the form $f(x) = a(x - h)^2 + k$, the vertex of its graph is (h, k). On the basis of Figure 3.30, let (10, 943) be the vertex, so that

$$f(x) = a(x - 10)^2 + 943.$$

To find a, choose another data point (15, 705). Assume this point lies on the parabola so that

$$f(x) = a(x - 10)^2 + 943$$
$$705 = a(15 - 10)^2 + 943 \quad \text{Substitute 15 for } x \text{ and 705 for } f(x).$$
$$705 = 25a + 943 \quad \text{Subtract inside the parentheses and then square.}$$
$$-238 = 25a \quad \text{Subtract 943 from both sides.}$$
$$a = -9.52. \quad \text{Divide both sides by 25.}$$

Therefore, $f(x) = -9.52(x - 10)^2 + 943$ is a quadratic model for these data. If we expand the form into $f(x) = ax^2 + bx + c$, we obtain

$$f(x) = -9.52(x - 10)^2 + 943$$
$$= -9.52(x^2 - 20x + 100) + 943 \quad \text{Expand inside the parentheses.}$$
$$= -9.52x^2 + 190.4x - 952 + 943 \quad \text{Distribute the } -9.52.$$
$$= -9.52x^2 + 190.4x - 9. \quad \text{Add the last two terms together.}$$

✓ **Checkpoint 6**

Find another quadratic model in Example 9(b) by using (10, 943) as the vertex and (19, 293) as the other point.

Figure 3.31, on the following page, shows the original data with the graph of $f(x)$. It appears to fit the data rather well except for the last two points. (We find a better fitting model in Example 10.) ✓6

Figure 3.31

Quadratic Regression

Linear regression was used in Section 2.3 to construct a linear function that modeled a set of data points. When the data points appear to lie on a parabola rather than on a straight line (as in Example 9), a similar least-squares regression procedure is available on most graphing calculators and spreadsheet programs to construct a quadratic model for the data. Simply follow the same steps as in linear regression, with one exception: Choose quadratic, rather than linear, regression. (Both options are on the same menu.)

Example 10 Use a graphing calculator to find a quadratic-regression model for the data in Example 9.

Solution Enter the first coordinates of the data points as list L_1 and the second coordinates as list L_2. Performing the quadratic regression, as in Figure 3.32, leads to the model

$$g(x) = -5.034x^2 + 90.25x + 461.8.$$

The number R^2 in Figure 3.32 is fairly close to 1, which indicates that this model fits the data fairly well. Figure 3.33 shows the data with the quadratic regression curve.

```
QuadReg
 y=ax²+bx+c
 a=-5.033775048
 b=90.25284421
 c=461.8438914
 R²=.9438752733
```

Figure 3.32

Figure 3.33

3.4 Exercises

The graph of each of the functions in Exercises 1–4 is a parabola. Without graphing, determine whether the parabola opens upward or downward. (See Example 1.)

1. $f(x) = x^2 - 3x - 12$ **2.** $g(x) = -x^2 + 5x + 15$

3. $h(x) = -3x^2 + 14x + 1$ **4.** $f(x) = 6.5x^2 - 7.2x + 4$

Without graphing, determine the vertex of the parabola that is the graph of the given function. State whether the parabola opens upward or downward. (See Examples 2 and 3.)

5. $f(x) = -2(x - 5)^2 + 7$ **6.** $g(x) = -7(x - 8)^2 - 3$

7. $h(x) = 4(x + 1)^2 - 9$ **8.** $f(x) = -8(x + 12)^2 + 9$

Match each function with its graph, which is one of those shown.
(See Examples 1–3.)

9. $f(x) = x^2 + 2$

10. $g(x) = x^2 - 2$

11. $g(x) = (x - 2)^2$

12. $f(x) = -(x + 2)^2$

13. $f(x) = 2(x - 2)^2 + 2$

14. $g(x) = -2(x - 2)^2 - 2$

15. $g(x) = -2(x + 2)^2 + 2$

16. $f(x) = 2(x + 2)^2 - 2$

(a)

(b)

(c)

(d)

(e)

(f)

(g)

(h)

(i)

(j)

(k)

(l)

Find the rule of a quadratic function whose graph has the given
vertex and passes through the given point. (See Example 4.)

17. Vertex (1, 2); point (5, 6)

18. Vertex (−3, 2); point (2, 1)

19. Vertex (−1, −2); point (1, 2)

20. Vertex (2, −4); point (5, 2)

Without graphing, find the vertex of the parabola that is the graph
of the given function. (See Examples 5 and 6.)

21. $f(x) = -x^2 - 6x + 3$ **22.** $g(x) = x^2 + 10x + 9$

23. $f(x) = 3x^2 - 12x + 5$ **24.** $g(x) = -4x^2 - 16x + 9$

Without graphing, determine the x- and y-intercepts of each of the
given parabolas. (See Example 6.)

25. $f(x) = 3(x - 2)^2 - 3$ **26.** $f(x) = x^2 - 4x - 1$

27. $g(x) = 2x^2 + 8x + 6$ **28.** $g(x) = x^2 - 10x + 20$

Graph each parabola and find its vertex and axis of symmetry. (See
Examples 1–6.)

29. $f(x) = (x + 2)^2$

30. $f(x) = -(x + 5)^2$

31. $f(x) = x^2 - 4x + 6$

32. $f(x) = x^2 + 6x + 3$

Use a calculator to work these problems.

33. Social Science　According to data from the National Safety Council, the fatal-accident rate per 100,000 licensed drivers can be approximated by the function $f(x) = .0328x^2 - 3.55x + 115$, where x is the age of the driver ($16 \leq x \leq 88$). At what age is the rate the lowest?

34. Social Science　Using data from the U.S. Census Bureau, the population (in thousands) of Detroit, Michigan can be approximated by $g(x) = -.422x^2 + 48.84x + 248$, where $x = 0$ corresponds to the year 1900. In what year, according to the given model, did Detroit have its highest population?

35. Natural Science　A researcher in physiology has decided that a good mathematical model for the number of impulses fired after a nerve has been stimulated is given by $y = -x^2 + 20x - 60$, where y is the number of responses per millisecond and x is the number of milliseconds since the nerve was stimulated.

(a)　When will the maximum firing rate be reached?

(b)　What is the maximum firing rate?

36. Physical Science　A bullet is fired upward from ground level. Its height above the ground (in feet) at time t seconds is given by

$$H = -16t^2 + 1000t.$$

Find the maximum height of the bullet and the time at which it hits the ground.

37. Business　Pat Kan owns a factory that manufactures souvenir key chains. Her weekly profit (in hundreds of dollars) is given by $P(x) = -2x^2 + 60x - 120$, where x is the number of cases of key chains sold.

(a)　What is the largest number of cases she can sell and still make a profit?

(b)　Explain how it is possible for her to lose money if she sells more cases than your answer in part (a).

(c)　How many cases should she make and sell in order to maximize her profits?

38. Business　The manager of a bicycle shop has found that, at a price (in dollars) of $p(x) = 150 - \dfrac{x}{4}$ per bicycle, x bicycles will be sold.

(a)　Find an expression for the total revenue from the sale of x bicycles. (*Hint:* Revenue = Demand × Price.)

(b)　Find the number of bicycle sales that leads to maximum revenue.

(c)　Find the maximum revenue.

Work the following problems. (See Example 7.)

39. Business　Suppose the supply of and demand for a certain textbook are given by

$$\text{supply: } p = \frac{1}{5}q^2 \quad \text{and} \quad \text{demand: } p = -\frac{1}{5}q^2 + 40,$$

where p is price and q is quantity. How many books are demanded at a price of

(a)　10?　　(b)　20?　　(c)　30?　　(d)　40?

How many books are supplied at a price of

(e)　5?　　(f)　10?　　(g)　20?　　(h)　30?

(i)　Graph the supply and demand functions on the same axes.

40. Business　Find the equilibrium quantity and the equilibrium price in Exercise 39.

41. Business　Suppose the price p of widgets is related to the quantity q that is demanded by

$$p = 640 - 5q^2,$$

where q is measured in hundreds of widgets. Find the price when the number of widgets demanded is

(a)　0;　　　　(b)　5;　　　　(c)　10.

Suppose the supply function for widgets is given by $p = 5q^2$, where q is the number of widgets (in hundreds) that are supplied at price p.

(d)　Graph the demand function $p = 640 - 5q^2$ and the supply function $p = 5q^2$ on the same axes.

(e)　Find the equilibrium quantity.

(f)　Find the equilibrium price.

42. Business　The supply function for a commodity is given by $p = q^2 + 200$, and the demand function is given by $p = -10q + 3200$

(a)　Graph the supply and demand functions on the same axes.

(b)　Find the equilibrium point.

(c)　What is the equilibrium quantity? the equilibrium price?

Business　*Find the equilibrium quantity and equilibrium price for the commodity whose supply and demand functions are given.*

43.　Supply: $p = 45q$; demand: $p = -q^2 + 10,000$.

44.　Supply: $p = q^2 + q + 10$; demand: $p = -10q + 3060$.

45.　Supply: $p = q^2 + 20q$; demand: $p = -2q^2 + 10q + 3000$.

46.　Supply: $p = .2q + 51$; demand: $p = \dfrac{3000}{q + 5}$.

Business　*The revenue function R(x) and the cost function C(x) for a particular product are given. These functions are valid only for the specified domain of values. Find the number of units that must be produced to break even.*

47.　$R(x) = 200x - x^2$; $C(x) = 70x + 2200$; $0 \leq x \leq 100$

48.　$R(x) = 300x - x^2$; $C(x) = 65x + 7000$; $0 \leq x \leq 150$

49.　$R(x) = 400x - 2x^2$; $C(x) = -x^2 + 200x + 1900$; $0 \leq x \leq 100$

50.　$R(x) = 500x - 2x^2$; $C(x) = -x^2 + 270x + 5125$; $0 \leq x \leq 125$

Business　*Work each problem. (See Example 8.)*

51.　A charter flight charges a fare of $200 per person, plus $4 per person for each unsold seat on the plane. If the plane holds 100 passengers and if x represents the number of unsold seats, find the following:

(a)　an expression for the total revenue received for the flight. (*Hint:* Multiply the number of people flying, $100 - x$, by the price per ticket);

(b)　the graph for the expression in part (a);

(c) the number of unsold seats that will produce the maximum revenue;

(d) the maximum revenue.

52. The revenue of a charter bus company depends on the number of unsold seats. If 100 seats are sold, the price is $50 per seat. Each unsold seat increases the price per seat by $1. Let x represent the number of unsold seats.

(a) Write an expression for the number of seats that are sold.

(b) Write an expression for the price per seat.

(c) Write an expression for the revenue.

(d) Find the number of unsold seats that will produce the maximum revenue.

(e) Find the maximum revenue.

53. A hog farmer wants to find the best time to take her hogs to market. The current price is 88 cents per pound, and her hogs weigh an average of 90 pounds. The hogs gain 5 pounds per week, and the market price for hogs is falling each week by 2 cents per pound. How many weeks should the farmer wait before taking her hogs to market in order to receive as much money as possible? At that time, how much money (per hog) will she get?

54. The manager of a peach orchard is trying to decide when to arrange for picking the peaches. If they are picked now, the average yield per tree will be 100 pounds, which can be sold for 40¢ per pound. Past experience shows that the yield per tree will increase about 5 pounds per week, while the price will decrease about 2¢ per pound per week.

(a) Let x represent the number of weeks that the manager should wait. Find the price per pound.

(b) Find the number of pounds per tree.

(c) Find the total revenue from a tree.

(d) When should the peaches be picked in order to produce the maximum revenue?

(e) What is the maximum revenue?

Work these exercises. (See Example 9.)

55. Health The National Center for Catastrophic Sport Injury Research keeps data on the number of fatalities directly related to football each year. These deaths occur in sandlot, pro and semipro, high school, and college-level playing. The following table gives selected years and the number of deaths. (Data from: www.unc.edu/depts/nccsi/FootballAnnual.pdf.)

Year	Deaths
1970	29
1975	15
1980	9
1985	7
1990	0
1995	4
2000	3
2005	3
2010	5

(a) Let $x = 0$ correspond to 1970. Use (20, 0) as the vertex and the data from 2005 to find a quadratic function $g(x) = a(x - h)^2 + k$ that models the data.

(b) Use the model to estimate the number of deaths in 2008.

56. Natural Science The acreage (in millions) consumed by forest fires in the United States is given in the following table. (Data from: National Interagency Fire Center.)

Year	Acres
1985	2.9
1988	5.0
1991	3.0
1994	4.1
1997	2.9
2000	7.4
2003	4.0
2006	9.9
2009	5.9
2012	9.2

(a) Let $x = 5$ correspond to the year 1985. Use (5, 2.9) as the vertex and the data for the year 1994 to find a quadratic function $f(x) = a(x - h)^2 + k$ that models the data.

(b) Use the model to estimate the acreage destroyed by forest fires in the year 2009.

57. Business The following table shows China's gross domestic expenditures on research and development (in billions of U.S. dollars) for the years 2004 through 2010. (Data from: National Science Foundation, *National Patterns of R & D Resources* [annual series].)

Year	Acres
2004	57.8
2005	71.1
2006	86.7
2007	102.4
2008	120.8
2009	154.1
2010	179.0

(a) Let $x = 4$ correspond to the year 2004. Use (4, 57.8) as the vertex and the data from 2008 to find a quadratic function $f(x) = a(x - h)^2 + k$ that models these data.

(b) Use the model to estimate the expenditures in the year 2012.

58. Economics The amount (in billions of dollars) of personal health care expenditures for hospital care for various years is given in the table on the following page. (Data from: U.S. Centers for Medicare and Medicaid Services.)

Year	Expenditures
1990	250
1995	339
2000	416
2005	609
2006	652
2007	693
2008	729
2009	776
2010	814

(a) Let $x = 0$ correspond to the year 1990. Use (0, 250) as the vertex and the data from the year 2007 to find a quadratic function $f(x) = a(x - h)^2 + k$ that models these data.

(b) Use the model to estimate the expenditures in 1997 and 2012.

📈 *In Exercises 59–62, plot the data points and use quadratic regression to find a function that models the data. (See Example 10.)*

59. Health Use the data in Exercise 55, with $x = 0$ corresponding to 1970. What number of injuries does this model estimate for 2008? Compare your answer with that for Exercise 55.

60. Natural Science Use the data from Exercise 56, with $x = 5$ corresponding to the year 1985. How much acreage does this model estimate for the year 2009? Compare your answer with that for Exercise 56.

61. Business Use the data from Exercise 57, with $x = 4$ corresponding to the year 2004. What is the estimate of the amount of R&D expenditures for China in the year 2012? Compare your answer with that for Exercise 57.

62. Economics Use the data from Exercise 58, with $x = 0$ corresponding to the year 1990. What is the amount of expenditures for hospital care estimated by this model for the years 1997 and 2012? Compare your answers with those for Exercise 58.

Business *Recall that profit equals revenue minus cost. In Exercises 63 and 64, find the following:*

(a) *The break-even point (to the nearest tenth)*

(b) *The x-value that makes profit a maximum*

(c) *The maximum profit*

(d) *For what x-values will a loss occur?*

(e) *For what x-values will a profit occur?*

63. $R(x) = 400x - 2x^2$ and $C(x) = 200x + 2000$, with $0 \le x \le 100$

64. $R(x) = 900x - 3x^2$ and $C(x) = 450x + 5000$, with $20 \le x \le 150$

✓ **Checkpoint Answers**

1. **(a)**

(b)

2. **(a)**

(b)

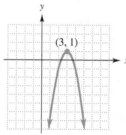

3. **(a)** $f(x) = (x + 3)^2 - 4; (-3, -4)$

  (b) $g(x) = (x - 6)^2 - 3; (6, -3)$

4. **(a)** 10 units   **(b)** \$480

5. **(a)** 4   **(b)** 16

6. $f(x) = -8.02x^2 + 160.4x + 141$

3.5 Polynomial Functions

A **polynomial function of degree** n is a function whose rule is given by a polynomial of degree n.[*] For example

$$f(x) = 3x - 2$$ polynomial function of degree 1;

$$g(x) = 3x^2 + 4x - 6$$ polynomial function of degree 2;

$$h(x) = x^4 + 5x^3 - 6x^2 + x - 3$$ polynomial function of degree 4.

[*]The degree of a polynomial was defined on page 13.

Basic Graphs

The simplest polynomial functions are those whose rules are of the form $f(x) = ax^n$ (where a is a constant).

Checkpoint 1

Graph $f(x) = -\dfrac{1}{2}x^3$

Example 1   Graph $f(x) = x^3$.

Solution   First, find several ordered pairs belonging to the graph. Be sure to choose some negative x-values, $x = 0$, and some positive x-values in order to get representative ordered pairs. Find as many ordered pairs as you need in order to see the shape of the graph. Then plot the ordered pairs and draw a smooth curve through them to obtain the graph in Figure 3.34.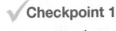

x	y
2	8
1	1
0	0
−1	−1
−2	−8

Figure 3.34

Checkpoint 2

Graph $g(x) = -2x^4$

Example 2   Graph

$$f(x) = \frac{3}{2}x^4.$$

Solution   The following table gives some typical ordered pairs and leads to the graph in Figure 3.35.

x	$f(x)$
−2	24
−1	3/2
0	0
1	3/2
2	24

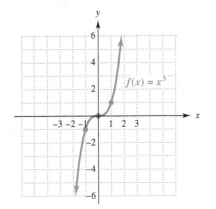

Figure 3.35

The graph of $f(x) = ax^n$ has one of the four basic shapes illustrated in Examples 1 and 2 and in Checkpoints 1 and 2. The basic shapes are summarized on the next page.

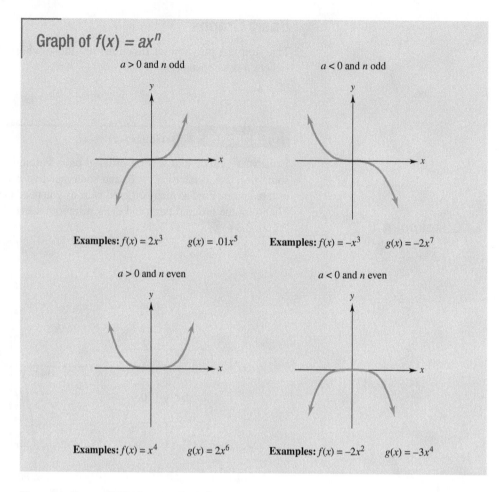

Graph of $f(x) = ax^n$

$a > 0$ and n odd

Examples: $f(x) = 2x^3$ $g(x) = .01x^5$

$a < 0$ and n odd

Examples: $f(x) = -x^3$ $g(x) = -2x^7$

$a > 0$ and n even

Examples: $f(x) = x^4$ $g(x) = 2x^6$

$a < 0$ and n even

Examples: $f(x) = -2x^2$ $g(x) = -3x^4$

Properties of Polynomial Graphs

Unlike the graphs in the preceding figures, the graphs of more complicated polynomial functions may have several "peaks" and "valleys," as illustrated in Figure 3.36, on the following page. The locations of the peaks and valleys can be accurately approximated by a maximum or minimum finder on a graphing calculator. Calculus is needed to determine their exact location.

The total number of peaks and valleys in a polynomial graph, as well as the number of the graph's x-intercepts, depends on the degree of the polynomial, as shown in Figure 3.36 and summarized here.

Polynomial	Degree	Number of peaks & valleys	Number of x-intercepts
$f(x) = x^3 - 4x + 2$	3	2	3
$f(x) = x^5 - 5x^3 + 4x$	5	4	5
$f(x) = 1.5x^4 + x^3 - 4x^2 - 3x + 4$	4	3	2
$f(x) = -x^6 + x^5 + 2x^4 + 1$	6	3	2

In each case, the number of x-intercepts is *at most* the degree of the polynomial. The total number of peaks and valleys is at most *one less than* the degree of the polynomial. The same thing is true in every case.

1. The total number of peaks and valleys on the graph of a polynomial function of degree n is at most $n - 1$.

2. The number of x-intercepts on the graph of a polynomial function of degree n is at most n.

(a) $f(x) = x^3 - 4x + 2$
1 peak
1 valley $\Big\}$ total 2
3 x-intercepts

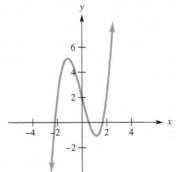

(b) $f(x) = x^5 - 5x^3 + 4x$
2 peaks
2 valleys $\Big\}$ total 4
5 x-intercepts

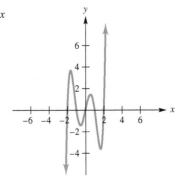

(c) $f(x) = 1.5x^4 + x^3 - 4x^2 - 3x + 4$
1 peak
2 valleys $\Big\}$ total 3
2 x-intercepts

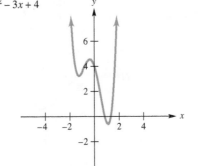

(d) $f(x) = -x^6 + x^5 + 2x^4 + 1$
2 peaks
1 (shallow) valley $\Big\}$ total 3
2 x-intercepts

Figure 3.36

The domain of every polynomial function is the set of all real numbers, which means that its graph extends forever to the left and right. We indicate this by the arrows on the ends of polynomial graphs.

Although there may be peaks, valleys, and bends in a polynomial graph, the far ends of the graph are easy to describe: *they look like the graph of the highest-degree term of the polynomial.* Consider, for example, $f(x) = 1.5x^4 + x^3 - 4x^2 - 3x + 4$, whose highest-degree term is $1.5x^4$ and whose graph is shown in Figure 3.36(c). The ends of the graph shoot upward, just as the graph of $y = 1.5x^4$ does in Figure 3.35. When $f(x)$ and $y = 1.5x^4$ are graphed in the same large viewing window of a graphing calculator (Figure 3.37), the graphs look almost identical, except near the origin. This is an illustration of the following facts.

Figure 3.37

The graph of a polynomial function is a smooth, unbroken curve that extends forever to the left and right. When $|x|$ is large, the graph resembles the graph of its highest-degree term and moves sharply away from the x-axis.

Example 3 Let $g(x) = x^3 - 11x^2 - 32x + 24$, and consider the graph in Figure 3.38.

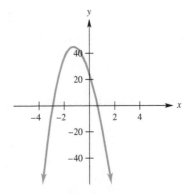

Figure 3.38

(a) Is Figure 3.38, on the previous page, a complete graph of $g(x)$; that is, does it show all the important features of the graph?

Solution The far ends of the graph of $g(x)$ should resemble the graph of its highest-degree term x^3. The graph of $f(x) = x^3$ in Figure 3.34 moves upward at the far right, but the graph in Figure 3.38 does not. So Figure 3.38 is *not* a complete graph.

 (b) Use a graphing calculator to find a complete graph of $g(x)$.

Solution Since the graph of $g(x)$ must eventually start rising on the right side (as does the graph of x^3), a viewing window that shows a complete graph must extend beyond $x = 4$. By experimenting with various windows, we obtain Figure 3.39. This graph shows a total of two peaks and valleys and three x-intercepts (the maximum possible for a polynomial of degree 3). At the far ends, the graph of $g(x)$ resembles the graph of $f(x) = x^3$. Therefore, Figure 3.39 is a complete graph of $g(x)$.

Figure 3.39

✓ Checkpoint 3

Find a viewing window on a graphing calculator that shows a complete graph of
$f(x) = -.7x^4 + 119x^2 + 400$.
(*Hint*: The graph has two x-intercepts and the maximum possible number of peaks and valleys.)

Graphing Techniques

 Accurate graphs of first- and second-degree polynomial functions (lines and parabolas) are easily found algebraically, as we saw in Sections 2.2 and 3.4. All polynomial functions of degree 3, and some of higher degree, can be accurately graphed by hand by using calculus and algebra to locate the peaks and valleys. When a polynomial can be completely factored, the general shape of its graph can be determined algebraically by using the basic properties of polynomial graphs, as illustrated in Example 4. Obtaining accurate graphs of other polynomial functions generally requires the use of technology.

✓ Checkpoint 4

Multiply out the expression for $f(x)$ in Example 4 and determine its degree.

Example 4 Graph $f(x) = (2x + 3)(x - 1)(x + 2)$.

Solution Note that $f(x)$ is a polynomial of degree 3. (If you don't see why, do Checkpoint 4.) Begin by finding any x-intercepts. Set $f(x) = 0$ and solve for x: ✓ 4

$$f(x) = 0$$
$$(2x + 3)(x - 1)(x + 2) = 0.$$

Solve this equation by setting each of the three factors equal to 0:

$$2x + 3 = 0 \quad \text{or} \quad x - 1 = 0 \quad \text{or} \quad x + 2 = 0$$
$$x = -\frac{3}{2} \qquad\qquad x = 1 \qquad\qquad x = -2.$$

The three numbers $-3/2$, 1, and -2 divide the x-axis into four intervals:

$$x < -2, \quad -2 < x < -\frac{3}{2}, \quad -\frac{3}{2} < x < 1, \quad \text{and} \quad 1 < x.$$

These intervals are shown in Figure 3.40.

Figure 3.40

Since the graph is an unbroken curve, it can change from above the x-axis to below it only by passing through the x-axis. As we have seen, this occurs only at the x-intercepts: $x = -2, -3/2$, and 1. Consequently, in the interval between two intercepts (or to the left of $x = -2$ or to the right of $x = 1$), the graph of $f(x)$ must lie entirely above or entirely below the x-axis.

We can determine where the graph lies over an interval by evaluating $f(x) = (2x + 3)(x - 1)(x + 2)$ at a number in that interval. For example, $x = -3$ is in the interval where $x < -2$, and

$$f(-3) = (2(-3) + 3)(-3 - 1)(-3 + 2)$$
$$= -12.$$

Therefore, $(-3, -12)$ is on the graph. Since this point lies below the x-axis, all points in this interval (that is, all points with $x < -2$) must lie below the x-axis. By testing numbers in the other intervals, we obtain the following table.

Interval	$x < -2$	$-2 < x < -3/2$	$-3/2 < x < 1$	$x > 1$
Test Number	-3	$-7/4$	0	2
Value of $f(x)$	-12	$11/32$	-6	28
Sign of $f(x)$	Negative	Positive	Negative	Positive
Graph	Below x-axis	Above x-axis	Below x-axis	Above x-axis

Since the graph intersects the x-axis at the intercepts and is above the x-axis between these intercepts, there must be at least one peak there. Similarly, there must be at least one valley between $x = -3/2$ and $x = 1$, because the graph is below the x-axis there. However, a polynomial function of degree 3 can have a total of at most $3 - 1 = 2$ peaks and valleys. So there must be exactly one peak and exactly one valley on this graph.

Furthermore, when $|x|$ is large, the graph must resemble the graph of $y = 2x^3$ (the highest-degree term). The graph of $y = 2x^3$, like the graph of $y = x^3$ in Figure 3.34, moves upward to the right and downward to the left. Using these facts and plotting the x-intercepts shows that the graph must have the general shape shown in Figure 3.41. Plotting additional points leads to the reasonably accurate graph in Figure 3.42. We say "reasonably accurate" because we cannot be sure of the exact locations of the peaks and valleys on the graph without using calculus. ✓5

✓ Checkpoint 5

Graph $f(x) = .4(x - 2)(x + 3)(x - 4)$.

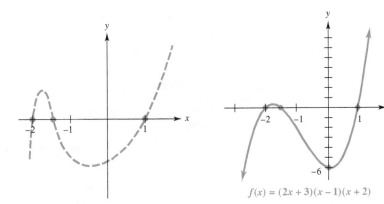

Figure 3.41   **Figure 3.42**

$$f(x) = (2x + 3)(x - 1)(x + 2)$$

◑ ✈ Polynomial Models

Regression procedures similar to those presented for linear regression in Section 2.3 and quadratic regression in Section 3.5 can be used to find cubic and quartic (degree 4) polynomial models for appropriate data.

Example 5   **Social Science**   The following table shows the population of the city of San Francisco, California in selected years.

Year	1950	1960	1970	1980	1990	2000	2010
Population	775,357	740,316	715,674	678,974	723,959	776,733	805,863

(a) Plot the data on a graphing calculator, with $x = 0$ corresponding to the year 1950.

Solution   The points in Figure 3.43 suggest the general shape of a fourth-degree (quartic) polynomial.

Figure 3.43

(b) Use quartic regression to obtain a model for these data.

Solution   The procedure is the same as for linear regression; just choose "quartic" in place of "linear." It produces the function

$$f(x) = -.137x^4 + 16.07x^3 - 470.34x^2 + 542.65x + 773,944.$$

Its graph, shown in Figure 3.44, appears to fit the data well.

Figure 3.44

(c) Use the model to estimate the population of San Francisco in the years 1985 and 2005.

Solution   The years 1985 and 2005 correspond to $x = 35$ and $x = 55$, respectively. Verify that

$$f(35) \approx 700,186 \quad \text{and} \quad f(55) \approx 801,022.$$

Example 6   **Business**   The following table shows the revenue and costs (in millions of dollars) for Ford Motor Company for the years 2004–2012. (Data from: www.morningstar.com.)

Year	Revenue	Costs
2004	171,652	168,165
2005	177,089	175,065
2006	160,123	172,736
2007	172,455	175,178
2008	146,277	160,949
2009	118,308	115,346
2010	128,954	122,397
2011	136,264	116,042
2012	134,252	128,588

(a) Let $x = 4$ correspond to the year 2004. Use cubic regression to obtain models for the revenue data $R(x)$ and the costs $C(x)$.

Solution The functions obtained using cubic regression from a calculator or software are

$$R(x) = 551.1x^3 - 12,601x^2 + 82,828x + 7002;$$
$$C(x) = 885.5x^3 - 21,438x^2 + 154,283x - 166,074.$$

(b) Graph $R(x)$ and $C(x)$ on the same set of axes. Did costs ever exceed revenues?

Solution The graph is shown in Figure 3.45. Since the lines cross twice, we can say that costs exceeded revenues in various periods.

(c) Find the profit function $P(x)$ and show its graph.

Solution The profit function is the difference between the revenue function and the cost function. We subtract the coefficients of the cost function from the respective coefficients of the revenue function.

$$\begin{aligned} P(x) &= R(x) - C(x) \\ &= (551.1 - 885.5)x^3 + (-12,601 + 21,438)x^2 \\ &\quad + (82,828 - 154,283)x + (7002 + 166,074) \quad \text{Subtract like terms.} \\ &= -334.4x^3 + 8837x^2 - 71,455x + 173,076. \end{aligned}$$

The graph of $P(x)$ appears in Figure 3.46.

(d) According to the model of the profit function $P(x)$, in what years was Ford Motor Company profitable?

Solution The motor company was profitable in 2004, 2009, 2010, 2011, and 2012 because that is where the graph is positive.

Figure 3.45

Figure 3.46

3.5 Exercises

Graph each of the given polynomial functions. (See Examples 1 and 2.)

1. $f(x) = x^4$

2. $g(x) = -.5x^6$

3. $h(x) = -.2x^5$

4. $f(x) = x^7$

In Exercises 5–8, state whether the graph could possibly be the graph of (a) some polynomial function; (b) a polynomial function of degree 3; (c) a polynomial function of degree 4; (d) a polynomial function of degree 5. (See Example 3.)

5.

6.

7.

8.

In Exercises 9–14, match the given polynomial function to its graph [(a)–(f)], without using a graphing calculator. (See Example 3 and the two boxes preceding it.)

(a)

(b)

(c)

(d)

(e)

(f)

9. $f(x) = x^3 - 7x - 9$

10. $f(x) = -x^3 + 4x^2 + 3x - 8$

11. $f(x) = x^4 - 5x^2 + 7$

12. $f(x) = x^4 + 4x^3 - 20$

13. $f(x) = .7x^5 - 2.5x^4 - x^3 + 8x^2 + x + 2$

14. $f(x) = -x^5 + 4x^4 + x^3 - 16x^2 + 12x + 5$

Graph each of the given polynomial functions. (See Example 4.)

15. $f(x) = (x + 3)(x - 4)(x + 1)$

16. $f(x) = (x - 5)(x - 1)(x + 1)$

17. $f(x) = x^2(x + 3)(x - 1)$

18. $f(x) = x^2(x + 2)(x - 2)$

19. $f(x) = x^3 - x^2 - 20x$

20. $f(x) = x^3 + 2x^2 - 10x$

21. $f(x) = x^3 + 4x^2 - 7x$

22. $f(x) = x^4 - 6x^2$

Exercises 23–26 require a graphing calculator. Find a viewing window that shows a complete graph of the polynomial function (that is, a graph that includes all the peaks and valleys and that indicates how the curve moves away from the x-axis at the far left and far right). There are many correct answers. Consider your answer correct if it shows all the features that appear in the window given in the answers. (See Example 3.)

23. $g(x) = x^3 - 3x^2 - 4x - 5$

24. $f(x) = x^4 - 10x^3 + 35x^2 - 50x + 24$

25. $f(x) = 2x^5 - 3.5x^4 - 10x^3 + 5x^2 + 12x + 6$

26. $g(x) = x^5 + 8x^4 + 20x^3 + 9x^2 - 27x - 7$

In Exercises 27–31, use a calculator to evaluate the functions. Generate the graph by plotting points or by using a graphing calculator.

27. Finance An idealized version of the Laffer curve (originated by economist Arthur Laffer) is shown in the accompanying graph. According to this theory, decreasing the tax rate, say, from x_2 to x_1, may actually increase the total revenue to the government. The theory is that people will work harder and earn more if they are taxed at a lower rate, which means higher total tax revenues than would be the case at a higher rate. Suppose that the Laffer curve is given by the function

$$f(x) = \frac{x(x - 100)(x - 160)}{240} \quad (0 \le x \le 100),$$

where $f(x)$ is government revenue (in billions of dollars) from a tax rate of x percent. Find the revenue from the given tax rates.

(a) 20%   **(b)** 40%   **(c)** 50%   **(d)** 70%

(e) Graph $f(x)$.

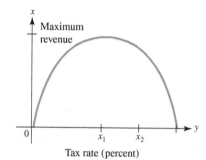

Tax rate (percent)

28. Health A technique for measuring cardiac output depends on the concentration of a dye after a known amount is injected into a vein near the heart. In a normal heart, the concentration of the dye at time x (in seconds) is given by the function defined by

$$g(x) = -.006x^4 + .140x^3 - .053x^2 + 1.79x.$$

(a) Find the following: $g(0)$; $g(1)$; $g(2)$; $g(3)$.

(b) Graph $g(x)$ for $x \ge 0$.

29. Business The revenue for Costco Wholesale Corporation (in millions of dollars) can be approximated by the function

$$R(x) = .141x^3 - 3.11x^2 + 26.98x - 19.99,$$

where $x = 4$ corresponds to the year 2004. (Data from: www.morningstar.com.)

(a) Find the following: $R(5)$; $R(7)$; $R(12)$.

(b) Graph $R(x)$.

(c) Is revenue always increasing in this model?

30. Business The revenue for Target Corporation (in billions of dollars) can be approximated by the function

$$R(x) = .0600x^4 - 1.9766x^3 + 23.155x^2 - 110.22x + 229.42,$$

where $x = 4$ corresponds to the year 2004. (Data from: www.morningstar.com.)

(a) Find the following: $R(6)$; $R(9)$; $R(11)$.

(b) Graph $R(x)$.

31. Business The cost function for Costco Wholesale Corporation (in millions of dollars) can be approximated by the function

$$C(x) = .135x^3 - 2.98x^2 + 25.99x - 18.71,$$

where $x = 4$ corresponds to the year 2004. (Data from: www.morningstar.com.)

(a) Find the following: $C(5)$; $C(7)$; $C(12)$.

(b) Graph $C(x)$.

(c) Are costs always increasing in this model?

32. Business The cost function for Target Corporation (in billions of dollars) can be approximated by the function

$$C(x) = .0697x^4 - 2.296x^3 + 26.947x^2 - 129.49x + 261.86,$$

where $x = 4$ corresponds to the year 2004. (Data from: www.morningstar.com.)

(a) Find the following: $C(6)$; $C(9)$; $C(11)$.

(b) Graph $C(x)$.

33. Business Use the revenue function $R(x)$ from Exercise 29 and the cost function $C(x)$ from Exercise 31 to write the profit function $P(x)$ for Costco Wholesale Corporation. Use your function to find the profit for the year 2012.

34. Business Use the revenue function $R(x)$ from Exercise 30 and the cost function $C(x)$ from Exercise 32 to write the profit function $P(x)$ for Target Corporation. Use your function to find the profit for the year 2011.

✈ *Use a graphing calculator to do the following problems. (See Example 5.)*

35. Social Science The following table shows the public school enrollment (in millions) in selected years. (Data from: U.S. National Center for Education Statistics.)

Year	Enrollment
1980	50.3
1985	48.9
1990	52.1
1995	55.9
2000	60.0
2005	62.1
2010	64.4

(a) Plot the data with $x = 0$ corresponding to the year 1980.

(b) Use cubic regression to find a third-order polynomial function $g(x)$ that models these data.

(c) Graph $g(x)$ on the same screen as the data points. Does the graph appear to fit the data well?

(d) According to the model, what was the enrollment in the year 2008?

36. Business The following table shows the profit (in billions of dollars) for Intel Corporation. (Data from: www.morningstar.com.)

Year	Profit
2004	7.5
2005	8.7
2006	5.0
2007	7.0
2008	5.3
2009	4.4
2010	11.5
2011	12.9
2012	11.0

(a) Plot the data with $x = 4$ corresponding to the year 2004.

(b) Use quartic regression to find a fourth-order polynomial function $h(x)$ that models these data.

(c) Graph $h(x)$ on the same screen as the data points. Does the graph appear to fit the data well?

(d) According to the model, what were Intel's profits in 2010?

37. Business The accompanying table gives the annual revenue for International Business Machines Corp. (IBM) in billions of dollars for the years 2004–2012. (Data from www.morningstar.com.)

Year	Revenue
2004	96.3
2005	91.1
2006	91.4
2007	98.8
2008	103.6
2009	95.8
2010	99.9
2011	106.9
2012	104.5

(a) Let $x = 4$ correspond to the year 2004. Use cubic regression to find a polynomial function $R(x)$ that models these data.

(b) Graph $R(x)$ on the same screen as the data points. Does the graph appear to fit the data well?

38. Business The accompanying table gives the annual costs for International Business Machines Corp. (IBM) in billions of dollars for the years 2004–2012. (Data from www.morningstar.com.)

Year	Costs
2004	87.9
2005	83.2
2006	81.9
2007	88.4
2008	91.3
2009	82.4
2010	85.1
2011	91.0
2012	87.9

(a) Let $x = 4$ correspond to the year 2004. Use cubic regression to find a polynomial function $C(x)$ that models these data.

(b) Graph $C(x)$ on the screen as the data points. Does the graph appear to fit the data well?

Business *For Exercises 39 and 40, use the functions R(x) and C(x) from the answers to Exercises 37(a) and 38(a).*

39. Find the profit function $P(x)$ for IBM for the years 2004–2012.

40. Find the profits for the year 2008.

✓ **Checkpoint Answers**

1.

2.

3. Many correct answers, including $-15 \le x \le 15$ and $-2000 \le y \le 6000$.

4. $f(x) = 2x^3 + 5x^2 - x - 6$; degree 3.

5.

3.6 Rational Functions

A **rational function** is a function whose rule is the quotient of two polynomials, such as

$$f(x) = \frac{2}{1 + x}, \qquad g(x) = \frac{3x + 2}{2x + 4}, \qquad \text{and} \qquad h(x) = \frac{x^2 - 2x - 4}{x^3 - 2x^2 + x}.$$

Thus, a rational function is a function whose rule can be written in the form

$$f(x) = \frac{P(x)}{Q(x)},$$

where $P(x)$ and $Q(x)$ are polynomials, with $Q(x) \ne 0$. The function is undefined for any values of x that make $Q(x) = 0$, so there are breaks in the graph at these numbers.

Linear Rational Functions

We begin with rational functions in which both numerator and denominator are first-degree or constant polynomials. Such functions are sometimes called **linear rational functions.**

Example 1   Graph the rational function defined by

$$y = \frac{2}{1 + x}.$$

Solution   This function is undefined for $x = -1$, since -1 leads to a 0 denominator. For that reason, the graph of this function will not intersect the vertical line $x = -1$. Since x can take on any value except -1, the values of x can approach -1 as closely as desired from either side of -1, as shown in the following table of values.

x approaches −1

x	−1.5	−1.2	−1.1	−1.01	−.99	−.9	−.8	−.5
$1 + x$	−.5	−.2	−.1	−.01	.01	.1	.2	.5
$\dfrac{2}{1 + x}$	−4	−10	−20	−200	200	20	10	4

$|f(x)|$ gets larger and larger

The preceding table suggests that as x gets closer and closer to −1 from either side, $|f(x)|$ gets larger and larger. The part of the graph near $x = -1$ in Figure 3.47 shows this behavior. The vertical line $x = -1$ that is approached by the curve is called a *vertical asymptote*. For convenience, the vertical asymptote is indicated by a dashed line in Figure 3.47, but this line is *not* part of the graph of the function.

As $|x|$ gets larger and larger, so does the absolute value of the denominator $1 + x$. Hence, $y = 2/(1 + x)$ gets closer and closer to 0, as shown in the following table.

x	−101	−11	−2	0	9	99
$1 + x$	−100	−10	−1	1	10	100
$\dfrac{2}{1 + x}$	−.02	−.2	−2	2	.2	.02

The horizontal line $y = 0$ is called a *horizontal asymptote* for this graph. Using the asymptotes and plotting the intercept and other points gives the graph of Figure 3.47. ✔1

✓ **Checkpoint 1**

Graph the following.

(a) $f(x) = \dfrac{3}{5 - x}$

(b) $f(x) = \dfrac{-4}{x + 4}$

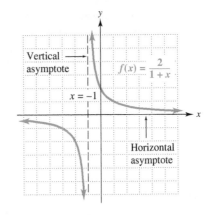

Vertical asymptote

$f(x) = \dfrac{2}{1 + x}$

$x = -1$

Horizontal asymptote

Figure 3.47

Example 1 suggests the following conclusion, which applies to all rational functions.

If a number c makes the denominator zero, but the numerator nonzero, in the expression defining a rational function, then the line $x = c$ is a **vertical asymptote** for the graph of the function.

If the graph of a function approaches a horizontal line very closely when x is very large or very small, we say that this line is a **horizontal asymptote** of the graph.

In Example 1, the horizontal asymptote was the *x*-axis. This is not always the case, however, as the next example illustrates.

Example 2 Graph

$$f(x) = \frac{3x + 2}{2x + 4}.$$

Solution Find the vertical asymptote by setting the denominator equal to 0 and then solving for *x*:

$$2x + 4 = 0$$
$$x = -2.$$

In order to see what the graph looks like when $|x|$ is very large, we rewrite the rule of the function. When $x \neq 0$, dividing both numerator and denominator by *x* does not change the value of the function:

$$f(x) = \frac{3x + 2}{2x + 4} = \frac{\dfrac{3x + 2}{x}}{\dfrac{2x + 4}{x}}$$

$$= \frac{\dfrac{3x}{x} + \dfrac{2}{x}}{\dfrac{2x}{x} + \dfrac{4}{x}} = \frac{3 + \dfrac{2}{x}}{2 + \dfrac{4}{x}}.$$

Now, when $|x|$ is very large, the fractions $2/x$ and $4/x$ are very close to 0. (For instance, when $x = 200, 4/x = 4/200 = .02$.) Therefore, the numerator of $f(x)$ is very close to $3 + 0 = 3$ and the denominator is very close to $2 + 0 = 2$. Hence, $f(x)$ is very close to $3/2$ when $|x|$ is large, so the line $y = 3/2$ is the horizontal asymptote of the graph, as shown in Figure 3.48. ✓₂

✓ Checkpoint 2

Graph the following.

(a) $f(x) = \dfrac{2x - 5}{x - 2}$

(b) $f(x) = \dfrac{3 - x}{x + 1}$

Figure 3.49

Figure 3.50

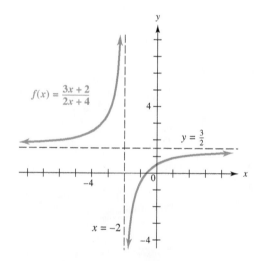

$$f(x) = \frac{3x + 2}{2x + 4}$$

$$y = \frac{3}{2}$$

$$x = -2$$

Figure 3.48

🔺 **TECHNOLOGY TIP** Depending on the viewing window, a graphing calculator may not accurately represent the graph of a rational function. For example, the graph of $f(x) = \dfrac{3x + 2}{2x + 4}$ in Figure 3.49, which should look like Figure 3.48, has an erroneous vertical line at the place where the graph has a vertical asymptote. This problem can usually be avoided by using a window that has the vertical asymptote at the center of the *x*-axis, as in Figure 3.50.

The horizontal asymptotes of a linear rational function are closely related to the coefficients of the x-terms of the numerator and denominator, as illustrated in Examples 1 and 2:

	Function	**Horizontal Asymptote**
Example 2:	$f(x) = \dfrac{3x + 2}{2x + 4}$	$y = \dfrac{3}{2}$
Example 1:	$f(x) = \dfrac{2}{1 + x} = \dfrac{0x + 2}{1x + 1}$	$y = \dfrac{0}{1} = 0$ (the x-axis)

The same pattern holds in the general case.

The graph of $f(x) = \dfrac{ax + b}{cx + d}$ (where $c \neq 0$ and $ad \neq bc$) has a vertical asymptote at the root of the denominator and has horizontal asymptote $y = \dfrac{a}{c}$.

Other Rational Functions

When the numerator or denominator of a rational function has degree greater than 1, the graph of the function can be more complicated than those in Examples 1 and 2. The graph may have several vertical asymptotes, as well as peaks and valleys.

Example 3 Graph

$$f(x) = \frac{2x^2}{x^2 - 4}.$$

Solution Find the vertical asymptotes by setting the denominator equal to 0 and solving for x:

$$x^2 - 4 = 0$$
$$(x + 2)(x - 2) = 0 \qquad \text{Factor.}$$
$$x + 2 = 0 \quad \text{or} \quad x - 2 = 0 \qquad \text{Set each term equal to 0.}$$
$$x = -2 \quad \text{or} \quad x = 2. \qquad \text{Solve for } x.$$

Since neither of these numbers makes the numerator 0, the lines $x = -2$ and $x = 2$ are vertical asymptotes of the graph. The horizontal asymptote can be determined by dividing both the numerator and denominator of $f(x)$ by x^2 (the highest power of x that appears in either one):

$$f(x) = \frac{2x^2}{x^2 - 4}$$

$$= \frac{\dfrac{2x^2}{x^2}}{\dfrac{x^2 - 4}{x^2}}$$

$$= \frac{\dfrac{2x^2}{x^2}}{\dfrac{x^2}{x^2} - \dfrac{4}{x^2}}$$

$$= \frac{2}{1 - \dfrac{4}{x^2}}.$$

When $|x|$ is very large, the fraction $4/x^2$ is very close to 0, so the denominator is very close to 1 and $f(x)$ is very close to 2. Hence, the line $y = 2$ is the horizontal asymptote of the graph. Using this information and plotting several points in each of the three regions determined by the vertical asymptotes, we obtain Figure 3.51. ✓₃

✓ Checkpoint 3

List the vertical and horizontal asymptotes of the given function.

(a) $f(x) = \dfrac{3x + 5}{x + 5}$

(b) $g(x) = \dfrac{2 - x^2}{x^2 - 4}$

Figure 3.51

Figure 3.52

⬈ **TECHNOLOGY TIP** When a function whose graph has more than one vertical asymptote (as in Example 3) is graphed on a graphing calculator, erroneous vertical lines can sometimes be avoided by using a *decimal window* (with the y-range adjusted to show the graph). On TI, use (Z)DECIMAL in the ZOOM or VIEWS menu. On Casio, use INIT in the V-WINDOW menu. Figure 3.52 shows the function of Example 3 graphed in a decimal window on a TI-84+. (The x-range may be different on other calculators.)

The arguments used to find the horizontal asymptotes in Examples 1–3 work in the general case and lead to the following conclusion.

> If the numerator of a rational function $f(x)$ is of *smaller* degree than the denominator, then the x-axis (the line $y = 0$) is the horizontal asymptote of the graph. If the numerator and denominator are of the *same* degree, say, $f(x) = \dfrac{ax^n + \cdots}{cx^n + \cdots}$, then the line $y = \dfrac{a}{c}$ is the horizontal asymptote.*

Applications

Rational functions have a variety of applications, some of which are explored next.

Example 4   **Natural Science**   In many situations involving environmental pollution, much of the pollutant can be removed from the air or water at a fairly reasonable cost, but the minute amounts of the pollutant that remain can be very expensive to remove.

Cost as a function of the percentage of pollutant removed from the environment can be calculated for various percentages of removal, with a curve fitted through the resulting data points. This curve then leads to a function that approximates the situation. Rational functions often are a good choice for these **cost–benefit functions.**

---

*When the numerator is of larger degree than the denominator, the graph has no horizontal asymptote, but may have nonhorizontal lines or other curves as asymptotes; see Exercises 32 and 33 at the end of this section for examples.

For example, suppose a cost–benefit function is given by

$$f(x) = \frac{18x}{106 - x},$$

where $f(x)$, or y, is the cost (in thousands of dollars) of removing x percent of a certain pollutant. The domain of x is the set of all numbers from 0 to 100, inclusive; any amount of pollutant from 0% to 100% can be removed. To remove 100% of the pollutant here would cost

$$y = \frac{18(100)}{106 - 100} = 300,$$

or \$300,000. Check that 95% of the pollutant can be removed for about \$155,000, 90% for about \$101,000, and 80% for about \$55,000, as shown in Figure 3.53 (in which the displayed y-coordinates are rounded to the nearest integer).

✓ **Checkpoint 4**

Using the function in Example 4, find the cost to remove the following percentages of pollutants.

(a) 70%

(b) 85%

(c) 98%

Figure 3.53

In management, **product-exchange functions** give the relationship between quantities of two items that can be produced by the same machine or factory. For example, an oil refinery can produce gasoline, heating oil, or a combination of the two; a winery can produce red wine, white wine, or a combination of the two. The next example discusses a product-exchange function.

Example 5   Business   The product-exchange function for the Fruits of the Earth Winery for red wine x and white wine y, in number of cases, is

$$y = \frac{150{,}000 - 75x}{1200 + x}.$$

Graph the function and find the maximum quantity of each kind of wine that can be produced.

Solution   Only nonnegative values of x and y make sense in this situation, so we graph the function in the first quadrant (Figure 3.54, on the following page). Note that the y-intercept of the graph (found by setting $x = 0$) is 125 and the x-intercept (found by setting $y = 0$ and solving for x) is 2000. Since we are interested only in the portion of the graph in Quadrant I, we can find a few more points in that quadrant and complete the graph as shown in Figure 3.54.

The maximum value of y occurs when $x = 0$, so the maximum amount of white wine that can be produced is 125 cases, as given by the y-intercept. The x-intercept gives the maximum amount of red wine that can be produced: 2000 cases. ✓5

✓ **Checkpoint 5**

Rework Example 5 with the product-exchange function

$$y = \frac{70{,}000 - 10x}{70 + x}$$

to find the maximum amount of each wine that can be produced.

◢ **Example 6   Business**   A retailer buys 2500 specialty lightbulbs from a distributor each year. In addition to the cost of each bulb, there is a fee for each order, so she wants to order as few times as possible. However, storage costs are higher when there are fewer orders (and hence more bulbs per order to store). Past experience shows that the total annual cost (for the bulbs, ordering fees, and storage costs) is given by the rational function.

$$C(x) = \frac{.98x^2 + 1200x + 22{,}000}{x},$$

where x is the number of bulbs ordered each time. How many bulbs should be ordered each time in order to have the smallest possible cost?

Solution   Graph the cost function $C(x)$ in a window with $0 \le x \le 2500$ (because the retailer cannot order a negative number of bulbs and needs only 2500 for the year).

Figure 3.55

Figure 3.56

For each point on the graph in Figure 3.55,

the x-coordinate is the number of bulbs ordered each time;
the y-coordinate is the annual cost when x bulbs are ordered each time.

Use the minimum finder on a graphing calculator to find the point with the smallest y-coordinate, which is approximately (149.83, 1493.67), as shown in Figure 3.56. Since the retailer cannot order part of a lightbulb, she should order 150 bulbs each time, for an approximate annual cost of $1494.

3.6 Exercises

Graph each function. Give the equations of the vertical and horizontal asymptotes. (See Examples 1–3.)

1. $f(x) = \dfrac{1}{x+5}$

2. $g(x) = \dfrac{-7}{x-6}$

3. $f(x) = \dfrac{-3}{2x+5}$

4. $h(x) = \dfrac{-4}{2-x}$

5. $f(x) = \dfrac{3x}{x-1}$

6. $g(x) = \dfrac{x-2}{x}$

7. $f(x) = \dfrac{x+1}{x-4}$

8. $f(x) = \dfrac{x-3}{x+5}$

9. $f(x) = \dfrac{2-x}{x-3}$

10. $g(x) = \dfrac{3x-2}{x+3}$

11. $f(x) = \dfrac{3x+2}{2x+4}$

12. $f(x) = \dfrac{4x-8}{8x+1}$

13. $h(x) = \dfrac{x+1}{x^2+2x-8}$

14. $g(x) = \dfrac{1}{x(x+2)^2}$

15. $f(x) = \dfrac{x^2+4}{x^2-4}$

16. $f(x) = \dfrac{x-1}{x^2-2x-3}$

Find the equations of the vertical asymptotes of each of the given rational functions.

17. $f(x) = \dfrac{x-3}{x^2+x-2}$

18. $g(x) = \dfrac{x+2}{x^2-1}$

19. $g(x) = \dfrac{x^2+2x}{x^2-4x-5}$

20. $f(x) = \dfrac{x^2-2x-4}{x^3-2x^2+x}$

Work these problems. (See Example 4.)

21. Natural Science Suppose a cost–benefit model is given by

$$f(x) = \frac{4.3x}{100-x},$$

where $f(x)$ is the cost, in thousands of dollars, of removing x percent of a given pollutant. Find the cost of removing each of the given percentages of pollutants.

(a) 50%   (b) 70%   (c) 80%

(d) 90%   (e) 95%   (f) 98%

(g) 99%

(h) Is it possible, according to this model, to remove *all* the pollutant?

(i) Graph the function.

22. Business Suppose a cost–benefit model is given by

$$f(x) = \frac{6.2x}{112-x},$$

where $f(x)$ is the cost, in thousands of dollars, of removing x percent of a certain pollutant. Find the cost of removing the given percentages of pollutants.

(a) 0%   (b) 50%

(c) 80%   (d) 90%

(e) 95%   (f) 99%

(g) 100%   (h) Graph the function.

23. Natural Science The function

$$f(x) = \frac{\lambda x}{1+(ax)^b}$$

is used in population models to give the size of the next generation $f(x)$ in terms of the current generation x. (See J. Maynard Smith, *Models in Ecology* [Cambridge University Press, 1974].)

(a) What is a reasonable domain for this function, considering what x represents?

(b) Graph the function for $\lambda = a = b = 1$ and $x \geq 0$.

(c) Graph the function for $\lambda = a = 1$ and $b = 2$ and $x \geq 0$.

(d) What is the effect of making b larger?

24. Natural Science The function

$$f(x) = \frac{Kx}{A+x}$$

is used in biology to give the growth rate of a population in the presence of a quantity x of food. This concept is called Michaelis–Menten kinetics. (See Leah Edelstein-Keshet, *Mathematical Models in Biology* [Random House, 1988].)

(a) What is a reasonable domain for this function, considering what x represents?

(b) Graph the function for $K = 5$, $A = 2$, and $x \geq 0$.

(c) Show that $y = K$ is a horizontal asymptote.

(d) What do you think K represents?

(e) Show that A represents the quantity of food for which the growth rate is half of its maximum.

25. Social Science The average waiting time in a line (or queue) before getting served is given by

$$W = \frac{S(S-A)}{A},$$

where A is the average rate at which people arrive at the line and S is the average service time. At a certain fast-food restaurant, the average service time is 3 minutes. Find W for each of the given average arrival times.

(a) 1 minute

(b) 2 minutes

(c) 2.5 minutes

(d) What is the vertical asymptote?

(e) Graph the equation on the interval (0, 3).

(f) What happens to W when $A > 3$? What does this mean?

Business *Sketch the portion of the graph in Quadrant I of each of the functions defined in Exercises 26 and 27, and then estimate the maximum quantities of each product that can be produced. (See Example 5.)*

26. The product-exchange function for gasoline x and heating oil y, in hundreds of gallons per day, is

$$y = \frac{125,000 - 25x}{125 + 2x}.$$

27. A drug factory found that the product-exchange function for a red tranquilizer x and a blue tranquilizer y is

$$y = \frac{900,000,000 - 30,000x}{x + 90,000}.$$

28. **Physical Science** The failure of several O-rings in field joints was the cause of the fatal crash of the *Challenger* space shuttle in 1986. NASA data from 24 successful launches prior to *Challenger* suggested that O-ring failure was related to launch temperature by a function similar to

$$N(t) = \frac{600 - 7t}{4t - 100} \quad (50 \leq t \leq 85),$$

where t is the temperature (in °F) at launch and N is the approximate number of O-rings that fail. Assume that this function accurately models the number of O-ring failures that would occur at lower launch temperatures (an assumption NASA did not make).

(a) Does $N(t)$ have a vertical asymptote? At what value of t does it occur?

(b) Without actually graphing the function, what would you conjecture that the graph would look like just to the right of the vertical asymptote? What does this suggest about the number of O-ring failures that might be expected near that temperature? (The temperature at the *Challenger* launching was 31°.)

(c) Confirm your conjecture by graphing $N(t)$ between the vertical asymptote and $t = 85$.

29. **Business** A company has fixed costs of $40,000 and a marginal cost of $2.60 per unit.

(a) Find the linear cost function.

(b) Find the average cost function. (Average cost was defined in Section 3.3.)

(c) Find the horizontal asymptote of the graph of the average cost function. Explain what the asymptote means in this situation. (How low can the average cost be?)

Use a graphing calculator to do Exercises 30–33. (See Example 6.)

30. **Finance** Another model of a Laffer curve (see Exercise 27 of Section 3.5) is given by

$$f(x) = \frac{300x - 3x^2}{10x + 200},$$

where $f(x)$ is government revenue (in billions of dollars) from a tax rate of x percent. Find the revenue from the given tax rates.

(a) 16%

(b) 25%

(c) 40%

(d) 55%

(e) Graph $f(x)$.

(f) What tax rate produces maximum revenue? What is the maximum revenue?

31. **Business** When no more than 110 units are produced, the cost of producing x units is given by

$$C(x) = .2x^3 - 25x^2 + 1531x + 25,000.$$

How many units should be produced in order to have the lowest possible average cost?

32. (a) Graph $f(x) = \dfrac{x^3 + 3x^2 + x + 1}{x^2 + 2x + 1}$.

(b) Does the graph appear to have a horizontal asymptote? Does the graph appear to have some nonhorizontal straight line as an asymptote?

(c) Graph $f(x)$ and the line $y = x + 1$ on the same screen. Does this line appear to be an asymptote of the graph of $f(x)$?

33. (a) Graph $g(x) = \dfrac{x^3 - 2}{x - 1}$ in the window with $-5 \leq x \leq 5$ and $-6 \leq y \leq 12$.

(b) Graph $g(x)$ and the parabola $y = x^2 + x + 1$ on the same screen. How do the two graphs compare when $|x| \geq 2$?

✓ **Checkpoint Answers**

1. (a)

$$f(x) = \frac{3}{5 - x}$$

(b)

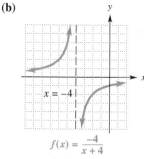

$$f(x) = \frac{-4}{x + 4}$$

2. (a)

(b)

3. (a) Vertical, $x = -5$; horizontal, $y = 3$

(b) Vertical, $x = -2$ and $x = 2$; horizontal, $y = -1$

4. (a) $35,000

(b) About $73,000

(c) About $221,000

5. 7000 cases of red, 1000 cases of white

CHAPTER 3 Summary and Review

Key Terms and Symbols

3.1 function
domain
range
functional notation
piecewise-defined function

3.2 graph
linear function
piecewise linear function
absolute-value function
greatest-integer function
step function

graph reading
vertical-line test

3.3 fixed costs
variable cost
average cost
linear depreciation
rate of change
marginal cost
linear cost function
linear revenue function
break-even point

supply and demand curves
equilibrium point
equilibrium price
equilibrium quantity

3.4 quadratic function
parabola
vertex
axis
quadratic model

3.5 polynomial function
graph of $f(x) = ax^n$

properties of polynomial
graphs
polynomial models

3.6 rational function
linear rational function
vertical asymptote
horizontal asymptote

Chapter 3 Key Concepts

Functions

A **function** consists of a set of inputs called the **domain,** a set of outputs called the **range,** and a rule by which each input determines exactly one output.

If a vertical line intersects a graph in more than one point, the graph is not that of a function.

Linear Functions

A **linear cost function** has equation $C(x) = mx + b$, where m is the **marginal cost** (the cost of producing one more item) and b is the **fixed cost.**

If $p = f(q)$ gives the price per unit when q units can be supplied and $p = g(q)$ gives the price per unit when q units are demanded, then the **equilibrium price** and **equilibrium quantity** occur at the q-value such that $f(q) = g(q)$.

Quadratic Functions

The **quadratic function** defined by $f(x) = a(x - h)^2 + k$ has a graph that is a **parabola** with vertex (h, k) and axis of symmetry $x = h$. The parabola opens upward if $a > 0$ and downward if $a < 0$.

If the equation is in the form $f(x) = ax^2 + bx + c$, the vertex is $\left(-\dfrac{b}{2a}, f\left(-\dfrac{b}{2a}\right)\right)$.

Polynomial Functions

When $|x|$ is large, the graph of a **polynomial function** resembles the graph of its highest-degree term ax^n. The graph of $f(x) = ax^n$ is described on page 160.

On the graph of a polynomial function of degree n,

the total number of peaks and valleys is at most $n - 1$;

the total number of x-intercepts is at most n.

Rational Functions

If a number c makes the denominator of a **rational function** 0, but the numerator nonzero, then the line $x = c$ is a **vertical asymptote** of the graph.

Whenever the values of y approach, but do not equal, some number k as $|x|$ gets larger and larger, the line $y = k$ is a **horizontal asymptote** of the graph.

If the numerator of a rational function is of *smaller* degree than the denominator, then the x-axis is the horizontal asymptote of the graph.

If the numerator and denominator of a rational function are of the *same* degree, say,

$$f(x) = \frac{ax^n + \cdots}{cx^n + \cdots},$$ then the line $y = \dfrac{a}{c}$ is the horizontal asymptote of the graph.

Chapter 3 Review Exercises

In Exercises 1–6, state whether the given rule defines a function or not.

1.

x	3	2	1	0	1	2
y	8	5	2	0	-2	-5

2.

x	2	1	0	-1	-2
y	5	3	1	-1	-3

3. $y = \sqrt{x}$

4. $x = |y|$

5. $x = y^2 + 1$

6. $y = 5x - 2$

For the functions in Exercises 7–10, find

(a) $f(6)$; (b) $f(-2)$; (c) $f(p)$; (d) $f(r + 1)$.

7. $f(x) = 4x - 1$ **8.** $f(x) = 3 - 4x$

9. $f(x) = -x^2 + 2x - 4$ **10.** $f(x) = 8 - x - x^2$

11. Let $f(x) = 5x - 3$ and $g(x) = -x^2 + 4x$. Find each of the following:

(a) $f(-2)$ (b) $g(3)$ (c) $g(-k)$

(d) $g(3m)$ (e) $g(k - 5)$ (f) $f(3 - p)$

12. Let $f(x) = x^2 + x + 1$. Find each of the following:

(a) $f(3)$ (b) $f(1)$ (c) $f(4)$

(d) Based on your answers in parts (a)–(c), is it true that $f(a + b) = f(a) + f(b)$ for all real numbers a and b?

Graph the functions in Exercises 13–24.

13. $f(x) = |x| - 3$ **14.** $f(x) = -|x| - 2$

15. $f(x) = -|x + 1| + 3$ **16.** $f(x) = 2|x - 3| - 4$

17. $f(x) = [x - 3]$ **18.** $f(x) = \left[\frac{1}{2}x - 2\right]$

19. $f(x) = \begin{cases} -4x + 2 & \text{if } x \leq 1 \\ 3x - 5 & \text{If } x > 1 \end{cases}$

20. $f(x) = \begin{cases} 3x + 1 & \text{if } x < 2 \\ -x + 4 & \text{if } x \geq 2 \end{cases}$

21. $f(x) = \begin{cases} |x| & \text{if } x < 3 \\ 6 - x & \text{if } x \geq 3 \end{cases}$

22. $f(x) = \sqrt{x^2}$

23. $g(x) = x^2/8 - 3$

24. $h(x) = \sqrt{x} + 2$

25. **Business** Let f be a function that gives the cost to rent a power washer for x hours. The cost is a flat \$45 for renting the washer, plus \$20 per day or fraction of a day for using the washer.

(a) Graph f.

(b) Give the domain and range of f.

(c) John McDonough wants to rent the washer, but he can spend no more than \$90. What is the maximum number of days he can use it?

26. **Business** A tree removal service assesses a \$400 fee and then charges \$80 per hour for the time on an owner's property.

(a) Is \$750 enough for 5 hours work?

(b) Graph the ordered pairs (hours, cost).

(c) Give the domain and range.

27. **Health** The following graph, which tracks the percentage of the female population of the United States who smoke cigarettes, appeared in a report from the Centers for Disease Control and Prevention.

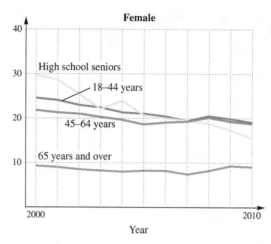

(a) What is the general trend for female high school seniors? What is the general trend for females 65 years and over?

(b) Let $x = 0$ correspond to the year 2000. Approximate a linear function for female high school seniors using the points (0, 30) and (10, 16).

(c) If the trend continues, estimate the percentage of female high school seniors who smoke cigarettes in 2012.

28. **Health** The following graph, which tracks the rate of traumatic brain injury-related deaths per 100,000 people, appeared on a website for the Centers for Disease Control and Prevention.

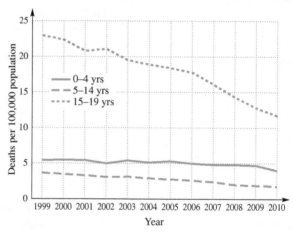

(a) What is the general trend for youth age 15–19 years?

(b) Let $x = 9$ correspond to the year 1999. Approximate a linear function to fit the data using 22 as the number of deaths in 2000 and 11 for 2010.

(c) If the trend continues, estimate the deaths per 100,000 people in the year 2012.

Business *In Exercises 29–32, find the following:*

(a) *the linear cost function;*

(b) *the marginal cost;*

(c) *the average cost per unit to produce 100 units.*

29. Eight units cost \$300; fixed cost is \$60.

30. Fixed cost is \$2000; 36 units cost \$8480.

31. Twelve units cost \$445; 50 units cost \$1585.

32. Thirty units cost \$1500; 120 units cost \$5640.

33. Business The cost of producing x ink cartridges for a printer is given by $C(x) = 24x + 18{,}000$. Each cartridge can be sold for $28.

(a) What are the fixed costs?

(b) Find the revenue function.

(c) Find the break-even point.

(d) If the company sells exactly the number of cartridges needed to break even, what is its revenue?

34. Business The cost of producing x laser printers is given by $C(x) = 325x + 2{,}300{,}000$. Each printer can be sold for $450.

(a) What are the fixed costs?

(b) Find the revenue function.

(c) Find the break-even point.

(d) If the company sells exactly the number of printers needed to break even, what is its revenue?

35. Business Suppose the demand and price for the HBO cable channel are related by $p = -.5q + 30.95$, where p is the monthly price in dollars and q is measured in millions of subscribers. If the price and supply are related by $p = .3q + 2.15$, what are the equilibrium quantity and price?

36. Business Suppose the supply and price for prescription-strength Tylenol are related by $p = .0015q + 1$, where p is the price (in dollars) of a 30-day prescription. If the demand is related to price by $p = -.0025q + 64.36$, what are the equilibrium quantity and price?

Without graphing, determine whether each of the following parabolas opens upward or downward, and find its vertex.

37. $f(x) = 3(x - 2)^2 + 6$ **38.** $f(x) = 2(x + 3)^2 - 5$

39. $g(x) = -4(x + 1)^2 + 8$ **40.** $g(x) = -5(x - 4)^2 - 6$

Graph each of the following quadratic functions, and label its vertex.

41. $f(x) = x^2 - 9$ **42.** $f(x) = 5 - 2x^2$

43. $f(x) = x^2 + 2x - 6$ **44.** $f(x) = -x^2 + 8x - 1$

45. $f(x) = -x^2 - 6x + 5$ **46.** $f(x) = 5x^2 + 20x - 2$

47. $f(x) = 2x^2 - 12x + 10$ **48.** $f(x) = -3x^2 - 12x - 2$

Determine whether the functions in Exercises 49–52 have a minimum or a maximum value, and find that value.

49. $f(x) = x^2 + 6x - 2$ **50.** $f(x) = x^2 + 4x + 5$

51. $g(x) = -4x^2 + 8x + 3$ **52.** $g(x) = -3x^2 - 6x + 3$

Solve each problem.

53. Business The weekly future price for a barrel of oil can be approximated by the function $f(x) = -.002x^2 + .644x + 45.32$, where x is the number of weeks since the beginning of the year 2009. How many weeks from the beginning of the year 2009 until the peak oil futures price occurs? What is the peak oil futures price with this model? (Data from: U.S. Energy Information Administration.)

54. Social Science The percent of children living below the poverty line can be approximated by the function $f(x) = .096x^2 - 2.40x + 31.7$, where $x = 6$ corresponds to the year 1996. What year saw the lowest percent living in poverty? What was the lowest percent?

55. Social Science The declining birth rate in China has demographers believing that the population of China will soon peak. A model for the population (in millions) for China is $g(x) = -.173x^2 + 12.86x + 1152$, where $x = 0$ corresponds to the year 1990. According to this model, what year will China reach its peak population? What is the estimate of the peak population? (Data from: U.S. Census Bureau.)

56. Business The amount of energy (in kilowatt hours) a new refrigerator typically used for a year of operation can be approximated by the function $h(x) = -1.44x^2 + 220x - 6953$, where $x = 50$ corresponds to the year 1950. According to this model, what year did peak electrical use occur? What was that amount? (Data from: U.S. Energy Information Administration.)

57. Business The following table shows the average cost of tuition and fees at private colleges in various years. (Data from: U.S. Center for Educational Statistics.)

Year	Cost
1975	3672
1980	5470
1985	8885
1990	12,910
1995	17,208
2000	21,373
2005	26,908
2010	32,026

(a) Let $x = 5$ correspond to the year 1975. Find a quadratic function $f(x) = a(x - h)^2 + k$ that models these data using $(5, 3672)$ as the vertex and the data for 2005.

(b) Estimate the average tuition and fees at private colleges in 2015.

58. Social Science According the U.S. Department of Justice, the following table gives the number (in thousands) of violent crimes committed in the given years.

Year	Crimes
2004	1360
2005	1391
2006	1418
2007	1408
2008	1393
2009	1326
2010	1246

(a) Let $x = 4$ correspond to the year 2004. Find a quadratic function $f(x) = a(x - h)^2 + k$ that models these data using $(6, 1418)$ as the vertex and the data for 2009.

(b) Estimate the number of violent crimes in 2012.

59. Business Use the data from Exercise 57 and use quadratic regression to find a function g that models these data.

(a) Give the function.

(b) Graph the function with the data points.

(c) Find the estimated tuition with this model for the year 2015.

60. Business Use the data from Exercise 58 and use quadratic regression to find a function g that models these data.

(a) Give the function.

(b) Graph the function with the data points.

(c) Find the estimated number of violent crimes with this model for the year 2012.

Graph each of the following polynomial functions.

61. $f(x) = x^4 - 5$ **62.** $g(x) = x^3 - 4x$

63. $f(x) = x(x - 4)(x + 1)$

64. $f(x) = (x - 1)(x + 2)(x - 3)$

65. $f(x) = x^4 - 5x^2 - 6$

66. $f(x) = x^4 - 7x^2 - 8$

Use a graphing calculator to do Exercises 67–70.

67. Business The demand equation for automobile oil filters is

$$p = -.000012q^3 - .00498q^2 + .1264q + 1508,$$

where p is in dollars and q is in thousands of items. The supply equation is

$$p = -.000001q^3 + .00097q^2 + 2q.$$

Find the equilibrium quantity and the equilibrium price.

68. Business The average cost (in dollars) per item of manufacturing x thousand cans of spray paint is given by

$$A(x) = -.000006x^4 + .0017x^3 + .03x^2 - 24x + 1110.$$

How many cans should be manufactured if the average cost is to be as low as possible? What is the average cost in that case?

69. Business The revenue (in millions of dollars) for the Exxon Mobil Corporation can be approximated by the function $R(x) = 1558x^3 - 36{,}587x^2 + 283{,}469x - 329{,}027$ where $x = 3$ corresponds to the year 2003. The cost function is approximated by $C(x) = 1261x^3 - 29{,}686x^2 + 233{,}069x - 249{,}868$ again with $x = 3$ corresponding to the year 2003. (Data from: www.morningstar.com.)

(a) Find the revenue for the year 2010.

(b) Find the costs for the year 2010.

(c) Find the profit function $P(x)$.

(d) Find the profit for the years 2010 and 2012.

70. Health The following table shows the average remaining life expectancy (in years) for a person in the United States at selected ages. (Data from: National Center for Health Statistics.)

Current Age	Birth	20	40	60	80	90	100
Life Expectancy	77.8	58.8	39.9	22.6	9.2	5.0	2.6

(a) Let birth $= 0$, and plot the data points.

(b) Use quartic regression to find a fourth-degree polynomial $f(x)$ that models the data.

(c) What is the remaining life expectancy of a person of age 25? age 35? age 50?

(d) What is the life expectancy of a person who is exactly your age?

List the vertical and horizontal asymptotes of each function, and sketch its graph.

71. $f(x) = \dfrac{1}{x - 3}$ **72.** $f(x) = \dfrac{-2}{x + 4}$

73. $f(x) = \dfrac{-3}{2x - 4}$ **74.** $f(x) = \dfrac{5}{3x + 7}$

75. $g(x) = \dfrac{5x - 2}{4x^2 - 4x - 3}$ **76.** $g(x) = \dfrac{x^2}{x^2 - 1}$

77. Business The average cost per carton of producing x cartons of cocoa is given by

$$A(x) = \frac{650}{2x + 40}.$$

Find the average cost per carton to make the given number of cartons.

(a) 10 cartons   (b) 50 cartons   (c) 70 cartons

(d) 100 cartons   (e) Graph $C(x)$.

78. Business The cost and revenue functions (in dollars) for a frozen-yogurt shop are given by

$$C(x) = \frac{400x + 400}{x + 4} \quad \text{and} \quad R(x) = 100x,$$

where x is measured in hundreds of units.

(a) Graph $C(x)$ and $R(x)$ on the same set of axes.

(b) What is the break-even point for this shop?

(c) If the profit function is given by $P(x)$, does $P(1)$ represent a profit or a loss?

(d) Does $P(4)$ represent a profit or a loss?

79. Business The supply and demand functions for the yogurt shop in Exercise 78 are

$$\text{supply: } p = \frac{q^2}{4} + 25 \quad \text{and} \quad \text{demand: } p = \frac{500}{q},$$

where p is the price in dollars for q hundred units of yogurt.

(a) Graph both functions on the same axes, and from the graph, estimate the equilibrium point.

(b) Give the q-intervals where supply exceeds demand.

(c) Give the q-intervals where demand exceeds supply.

80. Business A cost–benefit curve for pollution control is given by

$$y = \frac{9.2x}{106 - x},$$

where y is the cost, in thousands of dollars, of removing x percent of a specific industrial pollutant. Find y for each of the given values of x.

(a) $x = 50$ (b) $x = 98$

(c) What percent of the pollutant can be removed for $22,000?

Case Study 3 Architectural Arches

From ancient Roman bridges to medieval cathedrals, modern highway tunnels, and fast-food restaurants, arches are everywhere. For centuries builders and architects have used them for both structural and aesthetic reasons. There are arches of almost every material, from stone to steel. Some of the most common arch shapes are the parabolic arch, the semicircular arch, and the Norman arch (a semicircular arch set atop a rectangle, as shown here).

Parabolic   Semicircular   Norman

Note that every arch is symmetric around a vertical line through its center. The part of the arch on the left side of the line is mirror image of the part on the right side, with the line being the mirror. To describe these arches mathematically, suppose that each one is located on a coordinate plane with the origin at the intersection of the verticle symmetry line and a horizontal line at the base of the arch. For a parabolic arch, the situation looks like this, for some numbers k and c:

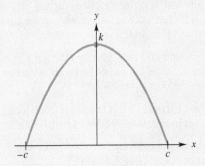

Since $(0, k)$ is the vertex, the arch is the graph of a function of the form

$$f(x) = a(x - 0)^2 + k,$$

or

$$f(x) = ax^2 + k.$$

Note that the point $(c, 0)$ is on the arch, which means that $f(c) = 0$. Therefore, we can make the following derivation:

$$f(x) = ax^2 + k$$
$$f(c) = ac^2 + k \qquad \text{Let } x = c.$$
$$0 = ac^2 + k \qquad f(c) = 0.$$
$$-k = ac^2 \qquad \text{Subtract } k \text{ from both sides.}$$
$$a = \frac{-k}{c^2} \qquad \text{Divide both sides by } c^2.$$

So the function whose graph is the shape of the parabolic arch is

$$f(x) = \frac{-k}{c^2}x^2 + k \qquad (-c \le x \le c),$$

where k is the height of the arch at its highest point and $2c$ (the distance from $-c$ to c) is the width of the arch at its base. For example, a 12-foot-high arch that is 14 feet wide at its base has $k = 12$ and $c = 7$, so it is the graph of

$$f(x) = \frac{-12}{49}x^2 + 12.$$

In order to describe semicircular and Norman arches, we must first find the equation of a circle of radius r with center at the origin. Consider a point (x, y) on the graph and the right triangle it determines:[*]

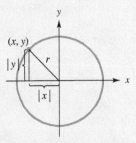

The horizontal side of the triangle has length $|x|$ (the distance from x to 0 on the x-axis), and the vertical side has length $|y|$ (the distance from y to 0 on the y-axis). The hypotenuse has length r (the radius of the circle). By the Pythagorean theorem,

$$|x|^2 + |y|^2 = r^2,$$

which is equivalent to

$$x^2 + y^2 = r^2,$$

because the absolute value of x is either x or $-x$ (see the definition on page 8), so $|x|^2 = (\pm x)^2 = x^2$, and similarly for y. Solving this equation for y shows that

$$y^2 = r^2 - x^2$$
$$y = \sqrt{r^2 - x^2} \quad \text{or} \quad y = -\sqrt{r^2 - x^2}.$$

In the first equation, y is always positive or 0 (because square roots are nonnegative), so its graph is the top half of the circle. Similarly, the second equation gives the bottom half of the circle.

Now consider a semicircle arch of radius r:

---

[*]The figure shows a point in the second quadrant, where x is negative and y is positive, but the same argument will work for points in other quadrants.

The arch is the top half of a circle with center at the origin. By the preceding paragraph, it is the graph of the function

$$g(x) = \sqrt{r^2 - x^2} \quad (-r \leq x \leq r).$$

For instance, a semicircular arch that is 8 feet high has $r = 8$ and is the graph of

$$g(x) = \sqrt{8^2 - x^2} = \sqrt{64 - x^2} \quad (-8 \leq x \leq 8).$$

A Norman arch is not the graph of a function (since its sides are vertical lines), but we can describe the semicircular top of the arch.

For example, consider a Norman arch whose top has radius 8 and whose sides are 10 feet high. If the top of the arch were at ground level, then its equation would be $g(x) = \sqrt{64 - x^2}$, as we just saw. But in the actual arch, this semicircular part is raised 10 feet, so it is the graph of

$$h(x) = g(x) + 10 = \sqrt{64 - x^2} + 10 \quad (-8 \leq x \leq 8),$$

as shown below.

$g(x) = \sqrt{64 - x^2}$ $h(x) = \sqrt{64 - x^2} + 10$ Norman Arch

Exercises

1. Write a function $f(x)$ that describes a parabolic arch which is 20 feet tall and 14 feet wide at the base.

2. Write a function $f(x)$ that describes a parabolic arch that is 25 feet tall and 30 feet wide at its base.

3. Write a function $g(x)$ that describes a semicircular arch that is 25 feet tall. How wide is the arch at its base?

4. Write a function $g(x)$ that describes a semicircular arch that is 40 feet tall. How wide is the arch at its base?

5. Write a function $h(x)$ that describes the top part of a Norman arch that is 20 feet tall and 24 feet wide at the base. How high are the vertical sides of this arch?

6. Write a function $h(x)$ that describes the top part of a Norman arch which is 32 feet tall and 44 feet wide at the base. How high are the vertical sides of this arch?

7. Would a truck that is 12 feet tall and 9 feet wide fit through all of the arches in Exercises 1, 3, and 5?

8. Would a truck that is 13 feet tall and 10 feet wide fit through all of the arches in Exercises 2, 4, and 6?

Extended Projects

1. Find an example of a parabolic, circular, or Norman arch (or all three) on your campus. Measure the dimensions and then write the equation for the arch in a manner similar to Exercises 1–8.

2. Find the dimensions of the fleet of Good Year Blimps that are currently in use. Determine the equation of a semicircular arch that would need to be built for the entrance to a facility that would house the blimps when not in use.

Exponential and Logarithmic Functions

4

CHAPTER

Population growth (of humans, fish, bacteria, etc.), compound interest, radioactive decay, and a host of other phenomena can be described by exponential functions. See Exercises 42–50 on page 191. Archeologists sometimes use carbon-14 dating to determine the approximate age of an artifact (such as a dinosaur skeleton or a mummy). This procedure involves using logarithms to solve an exponential equation. See Exercises 70–72 on page 217. The Richter scale for measuring the magnitude of an earthquake is a logarithmic function. See Exercises 73–74 on page 217.

Exponential and logarithmic functions play a key role in management, economics, the social and physical sciences, and engineering. We begin with exponential growth and exponential decay functions.

4.1 Exponential Functions

In polynomial functions such as $f(x) = x^2 + 5x - 4$, the variable is raised to various constant exponents. In **exponential functions,** such as

$$f(x) = 10^x, \quad g(x) = 750(1.05^x), \quad h(x) = 3^{.6x}, \quad \text{and} \quad k(x) = 2^{-x^2},$$

the variable is in the exponent and the **base** is a positive constant. We begin with the simplest type of exponential function, whose rule is of the form $f(x) = a^x$, with $a > 0$.

Example 1   Graph $f(x) = 2^x$, and estimate the height of the graph when $x = 50$.

Solution   Either use a graphing calculator or graph by hand: Make a table of values, plot the corresponding points, and join them by a smooth curve, as in Figure 4.1. The graph has y-intercept 1 and rises steeply to the right. Note that the graph gets very close to the x-axis on the left, but always lies *above* the axis (because *every* power of 2 is positive).

x	y
-3	1/8
-2	1/4
-1	1/2
0	1
1	2
2	4
3	8

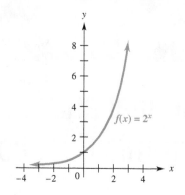

Figure 4.1

The graph illustrates **exponential growth,** which is far more explosive than polynomial growth. At $x = 50$, the graph would be 2^{50} units high. Since there are approximately 6 units to the inch in Figure 4.1, and since there are 12 inches to the foot and 5280 feet to the mile, the height of the graph at $x = 50$ would be approximately

$$\frac{2^{50}}{6 \times 12 \times 5280} \approx 2{,}961{,}647{,}482 \text{ miles!}$$

When $a > 1$, the graph of the exponential function $h(x) = a^x$ has the same basic shape as the graph of $f(x) = 2^x$, as illustrated in Figure 4.2 and summarized in the next box.

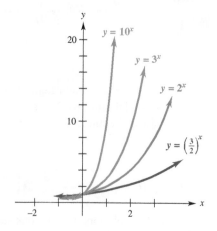

Figure 4.2

✓ **Checkpoint 1**

(a) Fill in this table:

x	$g(x) = 3^x$
-3	
-2	
-1	
0	
1	
2	
3	

(b) Sketch the graph of $g(x) = 3^x$.

Answers to Checkpoint exercises are found at the end of the section.

When $a > 1$, the function $f(x) = a^x$ has the set of all real numbers as its domain. Its graph has the shape shown on the following page and all five of the properties listed below.

1. The graph is above the x-axis.
2. The y-intercept is 1.
3. The graph climbs steeply to the right.
4. The negative x-axis is a horizontal asymptote.
5. The larger the base a, the more steeply the graph rises to the right.

Example 2 Consider the function $g(x) = 2^{-x}$.

(a) Rewrite the rule of g so that no minus signs appear in it.

Solution By the definition of negative exponents,

$$g(x) = 2^{-x} = \frac{1}{2^x} = \left(\frac{1}{2}\right)^x.$$

(b) Graph $g(x)$.

Solution Either use a graphing calculator or graph by hand in the usual way, as shown in Figure 4.3.

x	$y = 2^{-x}$
-3	8
-2	4
-1	2
0	1
1	$1/2$
2	$1/4$
3	$1/8$

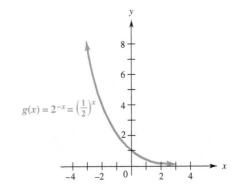

Figure 4.3

The graph falls sharply to the right, but never touches the x-axis, because every power of $\frac{1}{2}$ is positive. This is an example of **exponential decay**. ✓2

✓ **Checkpoint 2**

Graph $h(x) = (1/3)^x$.

When $0 < a < 1$, the graph of $k(x) = a^x$ has the same basic shape as the graph of $g(x) = (1/2)^x$, as illustrated in Figure 4.4 and summarized in the next box, on the following page.

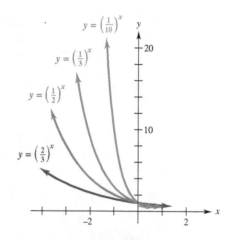

Figure 4.4

When $0 < a < 1$, the function $f(x) = a^x$ has the set of all real numbers as its domain. Its graph has the shape shown here and all five of the properties listed.

1. The graph is above the x-axis.
2. The y-intercept is 1.
3. The graph falls sharply to the right.
4. The positive x-axis is a horizontal asymptote.
5. The smaller the base a, the more steeply the graph falls to the right.

✓ **Checkpoint 3**

Use a graphing calculator to graph $f(x) = 4^x$ and $g(x) = \left(\frac{1}{4}\right)^x$ on the same screen.

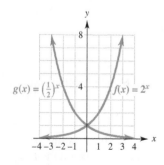

Figure 4.5

Example 3   In each case, graph $f(x)$ and $g(x)$ on the same set of axes and explain how the graphs are related.

(a) $f(x) = 2^x$ and $g(x) = (1/2)^x$

Solution   The graphs of f and g are shown in Figures 4.1 and 4.3, above. Placing them on the same set of axes, we obtain Figure 4.5. It shows that the graph of $g(x) = (1/2)^x$ is the mirror image of the graph of $f(x) = 2^x$, with the y-axis as the mirror. ✓3

(b) $f(x) = 3^{1-x}$ and $g(x) = 3^{-x}$

Solution   Choose values of x that make the exponent positive, zero, and negative, and plot the corresponding points. The graphs are shown in Figure 4.6, on the following page. The graph of $f(x) = 3^{1-x}$ has the same shape as the graph of $g(x) = 3^{-x}$, but is shifted 1 unit to the right, making the y-intercept $(0, 3)$ rather than $(0, 1)$.

(c) $f(x) = 2^{.6x}$ and $g(x) = 2^x$

Solution   Comparing the graphs of $f(x) = 2^{.6x}$ and $g(x) = 2^x$ in Figure 4.7, we see that the graphs are both increasing, but the graph of $f(x)$ rises at a slower rate. This happens because of the .6 in the exponent. If the coefficient of x were greater than 1, the graph would rise at a faster rate than the graph of $g(x) = 2^x$. ✓4

Figure 4.6

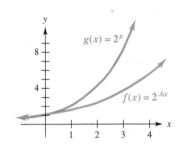

Figure 4.7

✓**Checkpoint 4**

Graph $f(x) = 2^{x+1}$.

When the exponent involves a nonlinear expression in x, the graph of an exponential function may have a much different shape than the preceding ones have.

Example 4   Graph $f(x) = 2^{-x^2}$.

Solution   Either use a graphing calculator or plot points and connect them with a smooth curve, as in Figure 4.8. The graph is symmetric about the y-axis; that is, if the figure were folded on the y-axis, the two halves would match. This graph has the x-axis as a horizontal asymptote. The domain is still all real numbers, but here the range is $0 < y \le 1$. Graphs such as this are important in probability, where the normal curve has an equation similar to $f(x)$ in this example. ✓5

✓**Checkpoint 5**

Graph $f(x) = \left(\frac{1}{2}\right)^{-x^2}$.

x	y
-2	$1/16$
-1.5	$.21$
-1	$1/2$
$-.5$	$.84$
0	1
$.5$	$.84$
1	$1/2$
1.5	$.21$
2	$1/16$

Figure 4.8

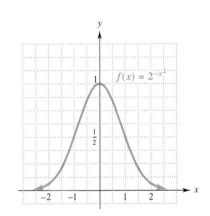

The Number e

In Case 5, we shall see that a certain irrational number, denoted e, plays an important role in the compounding of interest. This number e also arises naturally in a variety of other mathematical and scientific contexts. To 12 decimal places,

$$e \approx 2.718281828459.$$

Perhaps the single most useful exponential function is the function defined by $f(x) = e^x$.

e^(5)	
	148.4131591
e^(-1.4)	
	.2465969639
e^(1)	
	2.7182

Figure 4.9

 TECHNOLOGY TIP To evaluate powers of e with a calculator, use the e^x key, as in Figure 4.9. The figure also shows how to display the decimal expansion of e by calculating e^1. ✓ 6

In Figure 4.10, the functions defined by

$$g(x) = 2^x, \qquad f(x) = e^x, \qquad \text{and} \qquad h(x) = 3^x$$

are graphed for comparison.

✓ **Checkpoint 6**

Evaluate the following powers of e.

(a) $e^{.06}$

(b) $e^{-.06}$

(c) $e^{2.30}$

(d) $e^{-2.30}$

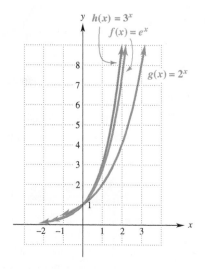

Figure 4.10

Example 5   **Business**   The amount of wine (in millions of gallons) consumed in the United States can be approximated by the function

$$f(x) = 139.6e^{.031x},$$

where $x = 0$ corresponds to the year 1950. (Data from: www.wineinstitute.org.)

(a) How much wine was consumed in the year 1970?

Solution   Since 1970 corresponds to $x = 20$, we evaluate $f(20)$:

$$f(20) = 139.6e^{.031(20)} \approx 260 \text{ million gallons.}$$

So the consumption was approximately 260 million gallons.

(b) How much wine was consumed in the year 2010?

Solution   Since 2010 corresponds to $x = 60$, we evaluate $f(60)$:

$$f(60) = 139.6e^{.031(60)} \approx 897 \text{ million gallons.}$$

So the consumption was approximately 897 million gallons.

 (c) Use a graphing calculator to determine when consumption will reach 1000 million gallons.

Solution   Since f measures consumption in millions of gallons, we must solve the equation $f(x) = 1000$, that is

$$139.6e^{.031x} = 1000.$$

Figure 4.11

 Checkpoint 7

Per-person wine consumption (in gallons) can be approximated by $g(x) = .875e^{.019x}$, where $x = 0$ corresponds to the year 1950.

(a) Estimate the per-person wine consumption in 1990.

(b) Determine when the per-person consumption reached 2.0 gallons.

Figure 4.12

One way to do this is to find the intersection point of the graphs of $y = 139.6e^{.031x}$ and $y = 1000$. (The calculator's intersection finder is in the same menu as its root [or zero] finder.) Figure 4.11 shows that this point is approximately $(63.5, 1000)$. Hence, consumption reached 1000 million gallons when $x \approx 63.5$, that is, in 2013.

Example 6   **Health**   When a patient is given a 300-mg dose of the drug cimetidine intravenously, the amount C of the drug in the bloodstream t hours later is given by $C(t) = 300e^{-.3466t}$.

(a) How much of the drug is in the bloodstream after 3 hours and after 10 hours?

Solution   Evaluate the function at $t = 3$ and $t = 10$:

$$C(3) = 300e^{-.3466*3} \approx 106.1 \text{ mg};$$
$$C(10) = 300e^{-.3466*10} \approx 9.4 \text{ mg}.$$

(b) Doctors want to give a patient a second 300-mg dose of cimetidine when its level in her bloodstream decreases to 75 mg. Use graphing technology to determine when this should be done.

Solution   The second dose should be given when $C(t) = 75$, so we must solve the equation

$$300e^{-.3466t} = 75.$$

Using the method of Example 5(c), we graph $y = 300e^{-.3466t}$ and $y = 75$ and find their intersection point. Figure 4.12 shows that this point is approximately $(4, 75)$. So the second dose should be given 4 hours after the first dose.

4.1 Exercises

Classify each function as linear, quadratic, or exponential.

1. $f(x) = 6^x$

2. $g(x) = -5x$

3. $h(x) = 4x^2 - x + 5$

4. $k(x) = 4^{x+3}$

5. $f(x) = 675(1.055^x)$

6. $g(x) = 12e^{x^2+1}$

Without graphing,

(a) *describe the shape of the graph of each function;*

(b) *find the second coordinates of the points with first coordinates 0 and 1. (See Examples 1–3.)*

7. $f(x) = .6^x$

8. $g(x) = 4^{-x}$

9. $h(x) = 2^{.5x}$

10. $k(x) = 5(3^x)$

11. $f(x) = e^{-x}$

12. $g(x) = 3(16^{x/4})$

Graph each function. (See Examples 1–3.)

13. $f(x) = 3^x$

14. $g(x) = 3^{.5x}$

15. $f(x) = 2^{x/2}$

16. $g(x) = e^{x/4}$

17. $f(x) = (1/5)^x$

18. $g(x) = 2^{3x}$

19. Graph these functions on the same axes.

(a) $f(x) = 2^x$ **(b)** $g(x) = 2^{x+3}$ **(c)** $h(x) = 2^{x-4}$

(d) If c is a positive constant, explain how the graphs of $y = 2^{x+c}$ and $y = 2^{x-c}$ are related to the graph of $f(x) = 2^x$.

20. Graph these functions on the same axes.

(a) $f(x) = 3^x$ **(b)** $g(x) = 3^x + 2$ **(c)** $h(x) = 3^x - 4$

(d) If c is a positive constant, explain how the graphs of $y = 3^x + c$ and $y = 3^x - c$ are related to the graph of $f(x) = 3^x$.

The accompanying figure shows the graphs of $y = a^x$ for $a = 1.8, 2.3, 3.2, 4, .75$, and $.31$. They are identified by letter, but not necessarily in the same order as the values just given. Use your knowledge of how the exponential function behaves for various powers of a to match each lettered graph with the correct value of a.

21. A

22. B

23. C

24. D

25. E

26. F

In Exercises 27 and 28, the graph of an exponential function with base a is given. Follow the directions in parts (a)–(f) in each exercise.

27.

$y \quad f(x) = a^x$

$(0, 1)$ $(1, a)$

0 x

(a) Is $a > 1$ or is $0 < a < 1$?

(b) Give the domain and range of f.

(c) Sketch the graph of $g(x) = -a^x$.

(d) Give the domain and range of g.

(e) Sketch the graph of $h(x) = a^{-x}$.

(f) Give the domain and range of h.

28.

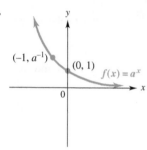

y

$(-1, a^{-1})$ $(0, 1)$

$f(x) = a^x$

0 x

(a) Is $a > 1$ or is $0 < a < 1$?

(b) Give the domain and range of f.

(c) Sketch the graph of $g(x) = a^x + 2$.

(d) Give the domain and range of g.

(e) Sketch the graph of $h(x) = a^{x+2}$.

(f) Give the domain and range of h.

29. If $f(x) = a^x$ and $f(3) = 27$, find the following values of $f(x)$.

(a) $f(1)$ (b) $f(-1)$ (c) $f(2)$ (d) $f(0)$

30. Give a rule of the form $f(x) = a^x$ to define the exponential function whose graph contains the given point.

(a) $(3, 8)$ (b) $(-3, 64)$

Graph each function. (See Example 4.)

31. $f(x) = 2^{-x^2+2}$ **32.** $g(x) = 2^{x^2-2}$

33. $f(x) = x \cdot 2^x$ **34.** $f(x) = x^2 \cdot 2^x$

Work the following exercises.

35. Finance   If $1 is deposited into an account paying 6% per year compounded annually, then after t years the account will contain

$$y = (1 + .06)^t = (1.06)^t$$

dollars.

(a) Use a calculator to complete the following table:

t	0	1	2	3	4	5	6	7	8	9	10
y	1					1.34					1.79

(b) Graph $y = (1.06)^t$.

36. Finance   If money loses value at the rate of 3% per year, the value of $1 in t years is given by

$$y = (1 - .03)^t = (.97)^t.$$

(a) Use a calculator to complete the following table:

t	0	1	2	3	4	5	6	7	8	9	10
y	1					.86					.74

(b) Graph $y = (.97)^t$.

Work these problems. (See Example 5.)

37. Finance   If money loses value, then as time passes, it takes more dollars to buy the same item. Use the results of Exercise 36(a) to answer the following questions.

(a) Suppose a house costs $105,000 today. Estimate the cost of the same house in 10 years. (*Hint:* Solve the equation $.74t = \$105,000$.)

(b) Estimate the cost of a $50 textbook in 8 years.

38. Natural Science   Biologists have found that the oxygen consumption of yearling salmon is given by $g(x) = 100e^{.7x}$, where x is the speed in feet per second. Find each of the following.

(a) the oxygen consumption when the fish are still;

(b) the oxygen consumption when the fish are swimming at a speed of 2 feet per second.

39. Business   The number of cell phone subscribers (in millions) can be approximated by

$$f(x) = 116.75e^{.101x},$$

where $x = 0$ corresponds to the year 2000. Estimate the number of cell phone subscribers in the following years. (Data from: CTIA-The Wireless Association.)

(a) 2004   (b) 2010   (c) 2011

40. Business   The monthly payment on a car loan at 12% interest per year on the unpaid balance is given by

$$f(n) = \frac{P}{\dfrac{1 - 1.01^{-n}}{.01}},$$

where P is the amount borrowed and n is the number of months over which the loan is paid back. Find the monthly payment for each of the following loans.

(a) $8000 for 48 months   **(b)** $8000 for 24 months

(c) $6500 for 36 months   **(d)** $6500 for 60 months

41. Natural Science The amount of plutonium remaining from 1 kilogram after x years is given by the function $W(x) = 2^{-x/24,360}$. How much will be left after

(a) 1000 years?   **(b)** 10,000 years?   **(c)** 15,000 years?

(d) Estimate how long it will take for the 1 kilogram to decay to half its original weight. Your answer may help to explain why nuclear waste disposal is a serious problem.

Business *The scrap value of a machine is the value of the machine at the end of its useful life. By one method of calculating scrap value, where it is assumed that a constant percentage of value is lost annually, the scrap value is given by*

$$S = C(1 - r)^n,$$

where C is the original cost, n is the useful life of the machine in years, and r is the constant annual percentage of value lost. Find the scrap value for each of the following machines.

42. Original cost, $68,000; life, 10 years; annual rate of value loss, 8%

43. Original cost, $244,000; life, 12 years; annual rate of value loss, 15%

44. Use the graphs of $f(x) = 2^x$ and $g(x) = 2^{-x}$ (not a calculator) to explain why $2^x + 2^{-x}$ is approximately equal to 2^x when x is very large.

Work the following problems. (See Examples 5 and 6.)

45. Social Science There were fewer than a billion people on Earth when Thomas Jefferson died in 1826, and there are now more than 6 billion. If the world population continues to grow as expected, the population (in billions) in year t will be given by the function $P(t) = 4.834(1.01^{(t-1980)})$. (Data from: U.S. Census Bureau.) Estimate the world population in the following years.

(a) 2005   **(b)** 2010   **(c)** 2030

(d) What will the world population be when you reach 65 years old?

46. Business The number of unique monthly visitors (in thousands) for Pinterest.com can be approximated by the function

$$g(x) = 325(1.29^x),$$

where $x = 1$ corresponds to the month of May, 2011. Estimate the number of unique monthly visitors for the following months. (Data from: cnet.com and techcrunch.com.)

(a) September 2011   **(b)** May 2012

(c) If the model remains accurate, find the month in which the number of unique visitors surpasses 40,000,000.

47. Economics Projections of the gross domestic product (GDP—in trillions of U.S. dollars), adjusted for purchasing power parity, are approximated as follows.

China: $f(x) = 10.21(1.103)^x$

United States: $g(x) = 14.28(1.046)^x,$

where $x = 1$ corresponds to the year 2011. (Data from: International Monetary Fund.) Find the projected GDP for the given years.

(a) 2012   **(b)** 2020   **(c)** 2050

(d) Use technology to determine when the Chinese GDP surpasses the U.S. GDP according to these projections. (*Hint:* Either graph both functions and find their intersection point or use the table feature of a graphing calculator.)

48. Business The amount of electricity (in trillion kilowatt hours) generated by natural gas in the United States can be approximated by the function

$$f(x) = .10(1.05)^x,$$

where $x = 0$ corresponds to the year 1960. (Data from: Energy Information Administration.) How many kilowatt hours were generated in the given years?

(a) 1990

(b) 2002

(c) In what year did the kilowatt hours hit 1 trillion?

49. Business The number of total subscribers (in millions) to Netflix, Inc. can be approximated by the function

$$g(x) = 9.78(1.07)^x,$$

where $x = 1$ corresponds to the first quarter of the year 2009, $x = 2$ corresponds to the second quarter of the year 2009, etc. Find the number of subscribers for the following quarters. (Data from: The *Wall Street Journal* and The *Associated Press.*)

(a) First quarter of 2010

(b) Fourth quarter of 2012

(c) Find the quarter and year when total subscribers surpassed 25 million.

50. Business The monthly rate for basic cable (in dollars) can be approximated by the function

$$h(x) = 8.71e^{.06x}, \quad (5 \le x \le 30)$$

where $x = 5$ corresponds to the year 1985. (Data from: ProQuest Statistical Abstract of the United States: 2013.)

(a) Find the rate in the year 2000 and the year 2009.

(b) When did spending reach $40 a month.

51. Business The amount of music (in billions of hours) listened to on the on-line streaming site Pandora can be approximated by the function

$$f(x) = .54e^{.191x},$$

where $x = 1$ corresponds to the first quarter of the year 2011, $x = 2$ corresponds to the second quarter of the year 2011, etc. Find the hours listened for the following quarters. (Data from: The *Wall Street Journal.*)

(a) Fourth quarter of 2011

(b) Third quarter of 2012

(c) When did the hours exceed 2.5 billion hours?

52. Business The stock price (in dollars) for Apple, Inc. can be approximated by the function

$$g(x) = 2.23e^{.404x} \quad (4 \le x \le 13),$$

where $x = 4$ corresponds to the year 2004. Use this model to approximate the price in the following years. (Data from: www.morningstar.com.)

(a) 2007   (b) 2013

(c) In what year, according to the model, did the price reach $300?

53. **Health** When a patient is given a 20-mg dose of aminophylline intravenously, the amount C of the drug in the bloodstream t hours later is given by $C(t) = 20e^{-.1155t}$. How much aminophylline remains in the bloodstream after the given numbers of hours?

(a) 4 hours

(b) 8 hours

(c) Approximately when does the amount of aminophylline decrease to 3.5 mg?

54. The accompanying figure shows the graph of an exponential growth function $f(x) = Pa^x$.

(a) Find P. [*Hint:* What is $f(0)$?]

(b) Find a. [*Hint:* What is $f(2)$?]

(c) Find $f(5)$.

✓ Checkpoint Answers

1. (a) The entries in the second column are 1/27, 1/9, 1/3, 1, 3, 9, 27, respectively.

(b)

2.

3.

4.

5.

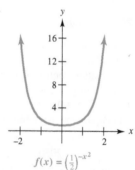

$$f(x) = \left(\tfrac{1}{2}\right)^{-x^2}$$

6. (a) 1.06184   (b) .94176

(c) 9.97418   (d) .10026

7. (a) About 1.87 gallons per person

(b) 1993

4.2 Applications of Exponential Functions

In many situations in biology, economics, and the social sciences, a quantity changes at a rate proportional to the quantity present. For example, a country's population might be increasing at a rate of 1.3% a year. In such cases, the amount present at time t is given by an **exponential growth function.**

It is understood that growth can involve either growing larger or growing smaller.

Exponential Growth Function

Under normal conditions, growth can be described by a function of the form

$$f(t) = y_0 e^{kt} \quad \text{or} \quad f(t) = y_0 b^t,$$

where $f(t)$ is the amount present at time t, y_0 is the amount present at time $t = 0$, and k and b are constants that depend on the rate of growth.

When $f(t) = y_0 e^{kt}$, and $k > 0$, we describe $f(t)$ as modeling exponential growth, and when $k < 0$, we describe $f(t)$ as modeling exponential decay. When $f(t) = y_0 b^t$, and $b > 1$, we describe $f(t)$ as modeling exponential growth, and when $0 < b < 1$, we describe $f(t)$ as modeling exponential decay.

Example 1 **Finance** Since the early 1970s, the amount of the total credit market (debt owed by the government, companies, or individuals) as a percentage of gross domestic product (GDP) can be approximated by the exponential function

$$f(t) = y_0 e^{.02t},$$

where t is time in years, $t = 0$ corresponds to the year 1970, and $f(t)$ is a percent. (Data from: Federal Reserve.)

(a) If the amount of total credit market was 155% of the GDP in 1970, find the percent in the year 2005.

Solution Since y_0 represents the percent when $t = 0$ (that is, in 1970) we have $y_0 = 155$. So the growth function is $f(t) = 155e^{.02t}$. To find the percent of the total credit market in the year 2005, evaluate $f(t)$ at $t = 35$ (which corresponds to the year 2005):

$$f(t) = 155e^{.02t}$$
$$f(35) = 155e^{.02(35)} \approx 312.$$

Hence, the percent of the total credit market in the year 2005 was approximately 312% of GDP.

(b) If the model remains accurate, what percent of GDP will the total credit market be in the year 2015?

Solution Since 2015 corresponds to $t = 45$, evaluate the function at $t = 45$:

$$f(45) = 155e^{.02(45)} \approx 381\%.$$

✓ **Checkpoint 1**

Suppose the number of bacteria in a culture at time t is

$$y = 500e^{.4t},$$

where t is measured in hours.

(a) How many bacteria are present initially?

(b) How many bacteria are present after 10 hours?

Example 2 **Business** Cigarette consumption in the United States has been decreasing for some time. Based on data from the Centers for Disease Control and Prevention, the number (in billions) of cigarettes consumed can be approximated by the function

$$g(x) = 436e^{-.036x},$$

with $x = 0$ corresponding to the year 2000.

(a) Find the number of cigarettes consumed in the years 2005 and 2010.

Solution The years 2005 and 2010 correspond to $x = 5$ and $x = 10$, respectively. We can evaluate $g(x)$ at these values for x:

$$g(5) = 436e^{-.036(5)} \approx 364 \text{ billion in the year 2005;}$$
$$g(10) = 436e^{-.036(10)} \approx 304 \text{ billion in the year 2010.}$$

Figure 4.13

(b) If this model remains accurate, when will cigarette consumption fall to 250 billion?

Solution   Graph $y = 436e^{-.036x}$ and $y = 250$ on the same screen and find the *x*-coordinate of their intersection point. Figure 4.13 shows that consumption is expected to be 250 billion in the year 2015 ($x = 15$).

When a quantity is known to grow exponentially, it is sometimes possible to find a function that models its growth from a small amount of data.

Example 3   **Finance**   When money is placed in a bank account that pays compound interest, the amount in the account grows exponentially, as we shall see in Chapter 5. Suppose such an account grows from $1000 to $1316 in 7 years.

(a) Find a growth function of the form $f(t) = y_0 b^t$ that gives the amount in the account at time *t* years.

Solution   The values of the account at time $t = 0$ and $t = 7$ are given; that is, $f(0) = 1000$ and $f(7) = 1316$. Solve the first of these equations for y_0:

$$f(0) = 1000$$
$$y_0 b^0 = 1000 \qquad \text{Rule of } f$$
$$y_0 = 1000. \qquad b^0 = 1$$

So the rule of *f* has the form $f(t) = 1000b^t$. Now solve the equation $f(7) = 1316$ for *b*:

$$f(7) = 1316$$
$$1000b^7 = 1316 \qquad \text{Rule of } f$$
$$b^7 = 1.316 \qquad \text{Divide both sides by 1000.}$$
$$b = (1.316)^{1/7} \approx 1.04. \qquad \text{Take the seventh root of each side.}$$

So the rule of the function is $f(t) = 1000(1.04)^t$.

(b) How much is in the account after 12 years?

Solution $f(12) = 1000(1.04)^{12} = \$1601.03.$

✓ **Checkpoint 2**

Suppose an investment grows exponentially from $500 to $587.12 in three years.

(a) Find a function of the form $f(t) = y_0 b^t$ that gives the value of the investment after *t* years.

(b) How much is the investment worth after 10 years?

Example 4   **Health**   Infant mortality rates in the United States are shown in the following table. (Data from: U.S. National Center for Health Statistics.)

Year	Rate	Year	Rate
1920	76.7	1980	12.6
1930	60.4	1990	9.2
1940	47.0	1995	7.6
1950	29.2	2000	6.9
1960	26.0	2005	6.9
1970	20.0	2008	6.6

(a) Let $t = 0$ correspond to 1920. Use the data for 1920 and 2008 to find a function of the form $f(t) = y_0 b^t$ that models these data.

Solution   Since the rate is 76.7 when $t = 0$, we have $y_0 = 76.7$. Hence, $f(t) = 76.7b^t$. Because 2008 corresponds to $t = 88$, we have $f(88) = 6.6$; that is,

$$76.7b^{88} = 6.6 \qquad \text{Rule of } f$$

$$b^{88} = \frac{6.6}{76.7} \qquad \text{Divide both sides by 76.7.}$$

$$b = \left(\frac{6.6}{76.7}\right)^{\frac{1}{88}} \approx .97251 \qquad \text{Take } 88^{th} \text{ roots on both sides.}$$

Therefore, the function is $f(t) = 76.7(.97251^t)$.

Figure 4.14

(b) Use exponential regression on a graphing calculator to find another model for the data.

Solution The procedure for entering the data and finding the function is the same as that for linear regression (just choose "exponential" instead of "linear"), as explained in Section 2.3. Depending on the calculator, one of the following functions will be produced:

$$g(t) = 79.2092*.9708^t \qquad \text{or} \qquad h(t) = 79.2092e^{-.0296t}.$$

Both functions give the same values (except for slight differences due to rounding of the coefficients). They fit the data reasonably well, as shown in Figure 4.14.

(c) Use the preceding models, and assume they continue to remain accurate, to estimate the infant mortality rate in the years 2012 and 2015.

Solution Evaluating each of the models in parts (a) and (b) at $t = 92$ and $t = 95$ shows that the models give slightly different results.

t	$f(t)$	$g(t)$
92	5.9	5.2
95	5.4	4.7

Other Exponential Models

When a quantity changes exponentially, but does not either grow very large or decrease practically to 0, as in Examples 1–3, different functions are needed.

Example 5   **Business**   Sales of a new product often grow rapidly at first and then begin to level off with time. Suppose the annual sales of an inexpensive can opener are given by

$$S(x) = 10,000(1 - e^{-.5x}),$$

where $x = 0$ corresponds to the time the can opener went on the market.

(a) What were the sales in each of the first three years?

Solution At the end of one year ($x = 1$), sales were

$$S(1) = 10,000(1 - e^{-.5(1)}) \approx 3935.$$

Sales in the next two years were

$$S(2) = 10,000(1 - e^{-.5(2)}) \approx 6321 \qquad \text{and} \qquad S(3) = 10,000(1 - e^{-.5(3)}) \approx 7769.$$

(b) What were the sales at the end of the 10th year?

Solution $S(10) = 10,000(1 - e^{-.5(10)}) \approx 9933.$

Figure 4.15

✓ Checkpoint 3

Suppose the value of the assets (in thousands of dollars) of a certain company after t years is given by

$$V(t) = 100 - 75e^{-.2t}.$$

(a) What is the initial value of the assets?

(b) What is the limiting value of the assets?

(c) Find the value after 10 years.

(d) Graph $V(t)$.

✓ Checkpoint 4

In Example 6,

(a) find the number of facts remembered after 10 days;

(b) use the graph to estimate when just one fact will be remembered.

⬈ TECHNOLOGY TIP

Many graphing calculators can find a logistic model for appropriate data.

(c) Graph the function S. What does it suggest?

Solution The graph can be obtained by plotting points and connecting them with a smooth curve or by using a graphing calculator, as in Figure 4.15. The graph indicates that sales will level off after the 12th year, to around 10,000 can openers per year. ✓3

A variety of activities can be modeled by **logistic functions,** whose rules are of the form

$$f(x) = \frac{c}{1 + ae^{kx}}.$$

The logistic function in the next example is sometimes called a **forgetting curve.**

Example 6 **Social Science** Psychologists have measured people's ability to remember facts that they have memorized. In one such experiment, it was found that the number of facts, $N(t)$, remembered after t days was given by

$$N(t) = \frac{10.003}{1 + .0003e^{.8t}}.$$

(a) How many facts were remembered at the beginning of the experiment?

Solution When $t = 0$,

$$N(0) = \frac{10.003}{1 + .0003e^{.8(0)}} = \frac{10.003}{1.0003} = 10.$$

So 10 facts were remembered at the beginning.

(b) How many facts were remembered after one week? after two weeks?

Solution One and two weeks respectively correspond to $t = 7$ and $t = 14$:

$$N(7) = \frac{10.003}{1 + .0003e^{.8(7)}} = \frac{10.003}{1.0811} \approx 9.25;$$

$$N(14) = \frac{10.003}{1 + .0003e^{.8(14)}} = \frac{10.003}{22.9391} \approx .44.$$

So 9 facts were remembered after one week, but effectively none were remembered after two weeks (because .44 is less than "half a fact"). The graph of the function in Figure 4.16 gives a picture of this forgetting process. ✓4

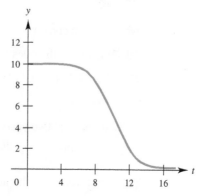

Figure 4.16

4.2 Exercises

1. **Finance** Suppose you owe $800 on your credit card and you decide to make no new purchases and to make the minimum monthly payment on the account. Assuming that the interest rate on your card is 1% per month on the unpaid balance and that the minimum payment is 2% of the total (balance plus interest), your balance after t months is given by

$$B(t) = 800(.9898^t).$$

Find your balance at each of the given times.

   (a) six months

   (b) one year (remember that t is in months)

   (c) five years

   (d) eight years

   (e) On the basis of your answers to parts (a)–(d), what advice would you give to your friends about minimum payments?

2. **Finance** Suppose you owe $1500 on your credit card and you decide to make no new purchases and to make the minimum monthly payment on the account. Assuming the interest rate on the card is 1.1% per month on the unpaid balance, and the minimum payment is 5% of the total (balance plus interest), your balance after t months is given by

$$B(t) = 1500(.9604)^t.$$

Find the balance at each of the given times.

   (a) five months

   (b) one year (remember that t is in months)

   (c) Is the balance paid off in two years?

3. **Business** The amount (in megawatts) of energy generated in the United States from wind power can be modeled by the function

$$W(t) = w_0(1.30)^t,$$

where $t = 0$ corresponds to the year 2000. (Data from: www.windpoweringamerica.gov.)

   (a) The amount generated in the year 2000 was 2540 megawatts. Find w_0.

   (b) Estimate the amount of energy generated by wind power in the years 2005 and 2012.

4. **Finance** The percent that public pension funds with assets over $1 billion hold in private-equity investments can be modeled by the function

$$f(t) = 2.214(1.142)^t,$$

where $t = 0$ corresponds to the year 2000. (Data from: The *Wall Street Journal*.)

Find the percent held in private-equity investments in the years:

   (a) 2008

   (b) 2011

   (c) If the model continues to be accurate, project the percent for the year 2015.

In each of the following problems, find an exponential function of the form $f(t) = y_0 b^t$ to model the data. (See Examples 3 and 4.)

5. **Business** The average asking price for rent in San Francisco was $1000 a month in the year 1990 and $2663 in the year 2012. (Data from: The *Wall Street Journal*.)

   (a) Find a model for these data in which $t = 0$ corresponds to the year 1990.

   (b) If this model remains accurate, what is the predicted average rent in the year 2015?

   (c) By experimenting with different values (or using a graphing calculator to solve an appropriate equation), estimate the year in which the average rent hit $2000 a month.

6. **Social Science** The U.S. Census Bureau predicts that the African-American population will increase from 35.3 million in 2000 to 61.8 million in 2060.

   (a) Find a model for these data, in which $t = 0$ corresponds to 2000.

   (b) What is the projected African-American population in 2020? in 2030?

   (c) By experimenting with different values of t (or by using a graphing calculator to solve an appropriate equation), estimate the year in which the African-American population will reach 55 million.

7. **Business** Sales of video and audio equipment, computers, and related services in the United States were about $81.1 billion in the year 1990 and $296 billion in the year 2010.

   (a) Let $t = 0$ correspond to the year 1990 and find a model for these data.

   (b) According to the model, what were sales in the year 2008?

   (c) If the model remains accurate, estimate sales for the year 2015.

8. **Health** Medicare expenditures were $110 billion in the year 1990 and increased to $554 billion in the year 2011.

   (a) Find a model for these data in which $t = 0$ corresponds to the year 1990 and expenditures are in billions of dollars.

   (b) Estimate Medicare expenditures in 2010.

   (c) If the model remains accurate, estimate Medicare expenditures for the year 2016.

In the following exercises, find the exponential model as follows: If you do not have suitable technology, use the first and last data points to find a function. (See Examples 3 and 4.) If you have a graphing calculator or other suitable technology, use exponential regression to find a function. (See Example 4.)

9. **Finance** The table shows the purchasing power of a dollar in recent years, with the year 2000 being the base year. For example, the entry .88 for 2005 means that a dollar in 2005 bought what $.88 did in the year 2000. (Data from: Bureau of Labor Statistics.)

Year	Purchasing Power of $1
2000	$1.00
2001	.97
2002	.96
2003	.94
2004	.91
2005	.88
2006	.85
2007	.83
2008	.79
2009	.80
2010	.79
2011	.77
2012	.75

(a) Find an exponential model for these data, where $t = 0$ corresponds to the year 2000.

(b) Assume the model remains accurate and predict the purchasing power of a dollar in 2015 and 2018.

(c) Use a graphing calculator (or trial and error) to determine the year in which the purchasing power of the 2000 dollar will drop to $.40.

10. **Physical Science** The table shows the atmospheric pressure (in millibars) at various altitudes (in meters).

Altitude	Pressure
0	1,013
1000	899
2000	795
3000	701
4000	617
5000	541
6000	472
7000	411
8000	357
9000	308
10,000	265

(a) Find an exponential model for these data, in which t is measured in thousands. (For instance, $t = 2$ is 2000 meters.)

(b) Use the function in part (a) to estimate the atmospheric pressure at 1500 meters and 11,000 meters. Compare your results with the actual values of 846 millibars and 227 millibars, respectively.

11. **Health** The table shows the age-adjusted death rates per 100,000 Americans for heart disease. (Data from: U.S. Center for Health Statistics.)

Year	Death Rate
2000	257.6
2002	240.8
2004	217.0
2006	210.2
2008	186.5
2010	178.5

(a) Find an exponential model for these data, where $t = 0$ corresponds to the year 2000.

(b) Assuming the model remains accurate, estimate the death rate in 2012 and 2016.

(c) Use a graphing calculator (or trial and error) to determine the year in which the death rate will fall to 100.

12. **Business** The table shows outstanding consumer credit (in billions of dollars) at the beginning of various years. (Data from: U.S. Federal Reserve.)

Year	Credit
1980	350.5
1985	524.0
1990	797.7
1995	1010.4
2000	1543.7
2005	2200.1
2010	2438.7

(a) Find an exponential model for these data, where $t = 0$ corresponds to the year 1980.

(b) If this model remains accurate, what will the outstanding consumer credit be in 2013 and 2016?

(c) In what year will consumer credit reach $6000 billion?

Work the following problems. (See Example 5.)

13. **Business** Assembly-line operations tend to have a high turnover of employees, forcing the companies involved to spend much time and effort in training new workers. It has been found that a worker who is new to the operation of a certain task on the assembly line will produce $P(t)$ items on day t, where

$$P(t) = 25 - 25e^{-.3t}.$$

(a) How many items will be produced on the first day?

(b) How many items will be produced on the eighth day?

(c) According to the function, what is the maximum number of items the worker can produce?

14. **Social Science** The number of words per minute that an average person can type is given by

$$W(t) = 60 - 30e^{-.5t},$$

where t is time in months after the beginning of a typing class. Find each of the following.

(a) $W(0)$ (b) $W(1)$

(c) $W(4)$ (d) $W(6)$

Natural Science   *Newton's law of cooling says that the rate at which a body cools is proportional to the difference in temperature between the body and an environment into which it is introduced. Using calculus, we can find that the temperature F(t) of the body at time t after being introduced into an environment having constant temperature T_0 is*

$$F(t) = T_0 + Cb^t,$$

where C and b are constants. Use this result in Exercises 15 and 16.

15. Boiling water at 100° Celsius is placed in a freezer at −18° Celsius. The temperature of the water is 50° Celsius after 24 minutes. Find the temperature of the water after 76 minutes.

16. Paisley refuses to drink coffee cooler than 95°F. She makes coffee with a temperature of 170°F in a room with a temperature of 70°F. The coffee cools to 120°F in 10 minutes. What is the longest amount of time she can let the coffee sit before she drinks it?

17. Social Science   A sociologist has shown that the fraction $y(t)$ of people in a group who have heard a rumor after t days is approximated by

$$y(t) = \frac{y_0 e^{kt}}{1 - y_0(1 - e^{kt})},$$

where y_0 is the fraction of people who heard the rumor at time $t = 0$ and k is a constant. A graph of $y(t)$ for a particular value of k is shown in the figure.

(a) If $k = .1$ and $y_0 = .05$, find $y(10)$.

(b) If $k = .2$ and $y_0 = .10$, find $y(5)$.

(c) Assume the situation in part (b). How many *weeks* will it take for 65% of the people to have heard the rumor?

18. Social Science   Data from the National Highway Traffic Safety Administration indicate that, in year t, the approximate percentage of people in the United States who wear seat belts when driving is given by

$$g(t) = \frac{97}{1 + .823e^{-.1401t}},$$

where $t = 0$ corresponds to the year 1994. What percentage used seat belts in

(a) 2000?

(b) 2003?

(c) 2004?

Assuming that this function is accurate after 2004, estimate seat belt use for the following years.

(d) 2011?

(e) 2013?

(f) 2015?

(g) Graph the function. Does the graph suggest that seat belt usage will ever reach 100%?

Use a graphing calculator or other technology to do the following problems. (See Example 6.)

19. Economics   The amount of U.S. expenditures on national defense (in billions of dollars) can by approximated by the function

$$f(x) = \frac{1084}{1 + 1.94e^{-.171x}},$$

where $x = 0$ corresponds to the year 2000. (Data from: U.S. Bureau of Economic Analysis.)

(a) Estimate the expenditures in the years 2005 and 2010.

(b) Assume the model remains accurate and graph the function from the year 2000 to the year 2020.

(c) Use the graph to determine the year in which expenditures reach $850 billion.

20. Natural Science   The population of fish in a certain lake at time t months is given by the function

$$p(t) = \frac{20,000}{1 + 24(2^{-.36t})}.$$

(a) Graph the population function from $t = 0$ to $t = 48$ (a four-year period).

(b) What was the population at the beginning of the period?

(c) Use the graph to estimate the one-year period in which the population grew most rapidly.

(d) When do you think the population will reach 25,000? What factors in nature might explain your answer?

21. Business   The amount (in billions of dollars) spent on legal services in the United States can be approximated by the function

$$g(x) = \frac{99.85}{1 + .527e^{-.258x}},$$

where $x = 0$ corresponds to the year 2000. (Data from: U.S. Bureau of Economic Analysis.)

(a) Estimate the amount spent on legal services in 2007 and 2011.

(b) Assume the model remains accurate and graph $g(x)$ from the year 2000 to the year 2025.

(c) Does the graph ever go over $110 billion dollars?

22. Social Science   The probability P percent of having an automobile accident is related to the alcohol level t of the driver's blood by the function $P(t) = e^{21.459t}$.

(a) Graph $P(t)$ in a viewing window with $0 \le t \le .2$ and $0 \le P(t) \le 100$.

(b) At what blood alcohol level is the probability of an accident at least 50%? What is the legal blood alcohol level in your state?

✓**Checkpoint Answers**

1. (a) 500
   (b) About 27,300

2. (a) $f(t) = 500(1.055)^t$
   (b) $854.07

3. (a) $25,000
   (b) $100,000
   (c) $89,850

(d)

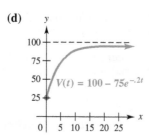

4. (a) 5
   (b) After about 12 days

4.3 Logarithmic Functions

Until the development of computers and calculators, logarithms were the only effective tool for large-scale numerical computations. They are no longer needed for this purpose, but logarithmic functions still play a crucial role in calculus and in many applications.

Common Logarithms

Logarithms are simply *a new language for old ideas*—essentially, a special case of exponents.

Definition of Common (Base 10) Logarithms

$$y = \log x \qquad \text{means} \qquad 10^y = x.$$

Log x, which is read "the logarithm of x," is the answer to the question,

To what exponent must 10 be raised to produce x?

✓**Checkpoint 1**

Find each common logarithm.

(a) log 100

(b) log 1000

(c) log .1

```
log(359)
           2.555094449
10^(2.5551)
              359.004589
log(.026)
             -1.585026652
```

Figure 4.17

✓**Checkpoint 2**

Find each common logarithm.

(a) log 27

(b) log 1089

(c) log .00426

Example 1   To find log 10,000, ask yourself, "To what exponent must 10 be raised to produce 10,000?" Since $10^4 = 10,000$, we see that log 10,000 = 4. Similarly,

$$\log 1 = 0 \qquad \text{because} \qquad 10^0 = 1;$$

$$\log .01 = -2 \qquad \text{because} \qquad 10^{-2} = \frac{1}{10^2} = \frac{1}{100} = .01;$$

$$\log \sqrt{10} = 1/2 \qquad \text{because} \qquad 10^{1/2} = \sqrt{10}. \qquad ✓_1$$

Example 2   Log (-25) is the exponent to which 10 must be raised to produce -25. But every power of 10 is positive! So there is no exponent that will produce -25. *Logarithms of negative numbers and 0 are not defined.*

Example 3   (a) We know that log 359 must be a number between 2 and 3 because $10^2 = 100$ and $10^3 = 1000$. By using the "log" key on a calculator, we find that log 359 (to four decimal places) is 2.5551. You can verify this statement by computing $10^{2.5551}$; the result (rounded) is 359. See the first two lines in Figure 4.17.

(b) When 10 is raised to a negative exponent, the result is a number less than 1. Consequently, the logarithms of numbers between 0 and 1 are negative. For instance, log .026 = -1.5850, as shown in the third line in Figure 4.17. ✓_2

📄 **NOTE** On most scientific calculators, enter the number followed by the log key. On graphing calculators, press the log key followed by the number, as in Figure 4.17.

Natural Logarithms

Although common logarithms still have some uses (one of which is discussed in Section 4.4), the most widely used logarithms today are defined in terms of the number e (whose decimal expansion begins 2.71828 . . .) rather than 10. They have a special name and notation.

> ### Definition of Natural (Base *e*) Logarithms
> $$y = \ln x \quad \text{means} \quad e^y = x.$$

Thus, the number **ln x** (which is sometimes read "el-en x") is the exponent to which e must be raised to produce the number x. For instance, $\ln 1 = 0$ because $e^0 = 1$. Although logarithms to the base e may not seem as "natural" as common logarithms, there are several reasons for using them, some of which are discussed in Section 4.4.

```
ln(85)
            4.442651256
e^4.4427
            85.0041433
ln(.38)
            -.9675840263
```

Figure 4.18

✓**Checkpoint 3**

Find the following.

(a) $\ln 6.1$

(b) $\ln 20$

(c) $\ln .8$

(d) $\ln .1$

Example 4 **(a)** To find ln 85, use the ⎡LN⎤ key of your calculator, as in Figure 4.18. The result is 4.4427. Thus, 4.4427 is the exponent (to four decimal places) to which e must be raised to produce 85. You can verify this result by computing $e^{4.4427}$; the answer (rounded) is 85. See Figure 4.18.

(b) A calculator shows that $\ln .38 = -.9676$ (rounded), which means that $e^{-.9676} \approx .38$. See Figure 4.18. ✓₃

Example 5 You don't need a calculator to find $\ln e^8$. Just ask yourself, "To what exponent must e be raised to produce e^8?" The answer, obviously, is 8. So $\ln e^8 = 8$.

Other Logarithms

The procedure used to define common and natural logarithms can be carried out with any positive number $a \neq 1$ as the base in place of 10 or e.

> ### Definition of Logarithms to the Base *a*
> $$y = \log_a x \quad \text{means} \quad a^y = x.$$

Read $y = \log_a x$ as "y is the logarithm of x to the base a." As was the case with common and natural logarithms, $\log_a x$ is an *exponent*; it is the answer to the question,

To what power must a be raised to produce x?

For example, suppose $a = 2$ and $x = 16$. Then $\log_2 16$ is the answer to the question,

To what power must 2 be raised to produce 16?

It is easy to see that $2^4 = 16$, so $\log_2 16 = 4$. In other words, the exponential statement $2^4 = 16$ is equivalent to the logarithmic statement $4 = \log_2 16$.

In the definition of a logarithm to base a, note carefully the relationship between the base and the exponent:

$$\text{Logarithmic form:} \quad y = \log_a x$$
$$\text{Exponential form:} \quad a^y = x$$

Common and natural logarithms are the special cases when $a = 10$ and when $a = e$, respectively. Both log u and $\log_{10} u$ mean the same thing. Similarly, ln u and $\log_e u$ mean the same thing.

Example 6 This example shows several statements written in both exponential and logarithmic form.

Exponential Form	Logarithmic Form
(a) $3^2 = 9$	$\log_3 9 = 2$
(b) $(1/5)^{-2} = 25$	$\log_{1/5} 25 = -2$
(c) $10^5 = 100{,}000$	$\log_{10} 100{,}000$ (or log 100,000) $= 5$
(d) $4^{-3} = 1/64$	$\log_4 (1/64) = -3$
(e) $2^{-4} = 1/16$	$\log_2 (1/16) = -4$
(f) $e^0 = 1$	$\log_e 1$ (or ln 1) $= 0$

✓ 4 ✓ 5

✓ **Checkpoint 4**

Write the logarithmic form of
(a) $5^3 = 125$;
(b) $3^{-4} = 1/81$;
(c) $8^{2/3} = 4$.

✓ **Checkpoint 5**

Write the exponential form of
(a) $\log_{16} 4 = 1/2$;
(b) $\log_3 (1/9) = -2$;
(c) $\log_{16} 8 = 3/4$.

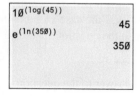

Figure 4.19

Properties of Logarithms

Some of the important properties of logarithms arise directly from their definition.

> Let x and a be any positive real numbers, with $a \neq 1$, and r be any real number. Then
>
> (a) $\log_a 1 = 0$; (b) $\log_a a = 1$;
> (c) $\log_a a^r = r$; (d) $a^{\log_a x} = x$.

Property (a) was discussed in Example 1 (with $a = 10$). Property (c) was illustrated in Example 5 (with $a = e$ and $r = 8$). Property (b) is property (c) with $r = 1$. To understand property (d), recall that $\log_a x$ is the exponent to which a must be raised to produce x. Consequently, when you raise a to this exponent, the result is x, as illustrated for common and natural logarithms in Figure 4.19.

The following properties are part of the reason that logarithms are so useful. They will be used in the next section to solve exponential and logarithmic equations.

The Product, Quotient, and Power Properties

Let x, y, and a be any positive real numbers, with $a \neq 1$. Let r be any real number. Then

$$\log_a xy = \log_a x + \log_a y \qquad \text{Product property}$$

$$\log_a \frac{x}{y} = \log_a x - \log_a y \qquad \text{Quotient property}$$

$$\log_a x^r = r \log_a x \qquad \text{Power property}$$

Each of these three properties is illustrated on a calculator in Figure 4.20.

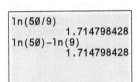

```
log(7*8)
            1.748188027
log(7)+log(8)
            1.748188027
```
```
ln(50/9)
            1.714798428
ln(50)-ln(9)
            1.714798428
```
```
log(12⁹)
            9.712631214
9*log(12)
            9.712631214
```

Figure 4.20

To prove the product property, let

$$m = \log_a x \qquad \text{and} \qquad n = \log_a y.$$

Then, by the definition of logarithm,

$$a^m = x \qquad \text{and} \qquad a^n = y.$$

Multiply to get

$$a^m \cdot a^n = x \cdot y,$$

or, by a property of exponents,

$$a^{m+n} = xy.$$

Use the definition of logarithm to rewrite this last statement as

$$\log_a xy = m + n.$$

Replace m with $\log_a x$ and n with $\log_a y$ to get

$$\log_a xy = \log_a x + \log_a y.$$

The quotient and power properties can be proved similarly.

Example 7   Using the properties of logarithms, we can write each of the following as a single logarithm:[*]

(a) $\log_a x + \log_a (x - 1) = \log_a x(x - 1);$ Product property

(b) $\log_a (x^2 + 4) - \log_a (x + 6) = \log_a \dfrac{x^2 + 4}{x + 6};$ Quotient property

(c) $\log_a 9 + 5 \log_a x = \log_a 9 + \log_a x^5 = \log_a 9x^5.$ Product and power properties

---

[*]Here and elsewhere, we assume that variable expressions represent positive numbers and that the base a is positive, with $a \neq 1$.

✓ Checkpoint 6

Write each expression as a single logarithm, using the properties of logarithms.

(a) $\log_a 5x + \log_a 3x^4$

(b) $\log_a 3p - \log_a 5q$

(c) $4 \log_a k - 3 \log_a m$

!️ **CAUTION** There is no logarithm property that allows you to simplify the logarithm of a sum, such as $\log_a (x^2 + 4)$. In particular, $\log_a (x^2 + 4)$ is *not* equal to $\log_a x^2 + \log_a 4$. The product property of logarithms shows that $\log_a x^2 + \log_a 4 = \log_a 4x^2$.

Example 8   Assume that $\log_6 7 \approx 1.09$ and $\log_6 5 \approx .90$. Use the properties of logarithms to find each of the following:

(a) $\log_6 35 = \log_6 (7 \cdot 5) = \log_6 7 + \log_6 5 \approx 1.09 + .90 = 1.99$;

(b) $\log_6 5/7 = \log_6 5 - \log_6 7 \approx .90 - 1.09 = -.19$;

(c) $\log_6 5^3 = 3 \log_6 5 \approx 3(.90) = 2.70$;

(d) $\log_6 6 = 1$;

(e) $\log_6 1 = 0$. ✓₇

✓ **Checkpoint 7**

Use the properties of logarithms to rewrite and evaluate each expression, given that $\log_3 7 \approx 1.77$ and $\log_3 5 \approx 1.46$.

(a) $\log_3 35$

(b) $\log_3 7/5$

(c) $\log_3 25$

(d) $\log_3 3$

(e) $\log_3 1$

In Example 8, several logarithms to the base 6 were given. However, they could have been found by using a calculator and the following formula.

Change-of-Base Theorem

For any positive numbers a and x (with $a \neq 1$),

$$\log_a x = \frac{\ln x}{\ln a}.$$

Example 9   To find $\log_7 3$, use the theorem with $a = 7$ and $x = 3$:

$$\log_7 3 = \frac{\ln 3}{\ln 7} \approx \frac{1.0986}{1.9459} \approx .5646.$$

You can check this result on your calculator by verifying that $7^{.5646} \approx 3$.

Example 10   **Natural Science** Environmental scientists who study the diversity of species in an ecological community use the *Shannon index* to measure diversity. If there are k different species, with n_1 individuals of species 1, n_2 individuals of species 2, and so on, then the Shannon index H is defined as

$$H = \frac{N \log_2 N - [n_1 \log_2 n_1 + n_2 \log_2 n_2 + \cdots + n_k \log_2 n_k]}{N},$$

where $N = n_1 + n_2 + n_3 + \cdots + n_k$. A study of the species that barn owls in a particular region typically eat yielded the following data:

Species	Number
Rats	143
Mice	1405
Birds	452

Find the index of diversity of this community.

Solution   In this case, $n_1 = 143, n_2 = 1405, n_3 = 452$, and

$$N = n_1 + n_2 + n_3 = 143 + 1405 + 452 = 2000.$$

So the index of diversity is

$$H = \frac{N \log_2 N - [n_1 \log_2 n_1 + n_2 \log_2 n_2 + \cdots + n_k \log_2 n_k]}{N}$$

$$= \frac{2000 \log_2 2000 - [143 \log_2 143 + 1405 \log_2 1405 + 452 \log_2 452]}{2000}.$$

To compute H, we use the change-of-base theorem:

$$H = \frac{2000 \dfrac{\ln 2000}{\ln 2} - \left[143 \dfrac{\ln 143}{\ln 2} + 1405 \dfrac{\ln 1405}{\ln 2} + 452 \dfrac{\ln 452}{\ln 2} \right]}{2000}$$

$$\approx 1.1149.$$

Logarithmic Functions

For a given *positive* value of x, the definition of logarithm leads to exactly one value of y, so that $y = \log_a x$ defines a function.

> If $a > 0$ and $a \neq 1$, the **logarithmic function** with base a is defined as
>
> $$f(x) = \log_a x.$$

The most important logarithmic function is the natural logarithmic function.

Example 11   Graph $f(x) = \ln x$ and $g(x) = e^x$ on the same axes.

Solution   For each function, use a calculator to compute some ordered pairs. Then plot the corresponding points and connect them with a curve to obtain the graphs in Figure 4.21.

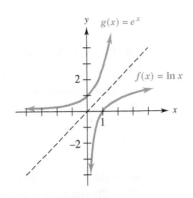

Figure 4.21

The dashed line in Figure 4.21 is the graph of $y = x$. Observe that the graph of $f(x) = \ln x$ is the mirror image of the graph of $g(x) = e^x$, with the line $y = x$ being the mirror. A pair of functions whose graphs are related in this way are said to be **inverses** of each other. A more complete discussion of inverse functions is given in many college algebra books. ✓ 8

When the base $a > 1$, the graph of $f(x) = \log_a x$ has the same basic shape as the graph of the natural logarithmic function in Figure 4.21, as summarized on the following page.

✓ **Checkpoint 8**

Verify that $f(x) = \log x$ and $g(x) = 10^x$ are inverses of each other by graphing $f(x)$ and $g(x)$ on the same axes.

Exponential Functions

$f(x) = a^x$

domain: set of all real numbers

range: set of all positive real numbers

horizontal asymptote
no vertical asymptote

Logarithmic Functions

$f(x) = \log_a x$

domain: set of all positive real numbers

range: set of all real numbers

vertical asymptote
no horizontal asymptote

As the information in the box suggests, the functions $f(x) = \log_a x$ and $g(x) = a^x$ are inverses of each other. (Their graphs are mirror images of each other, with the line $y = x$ being the mirror.)

Applications

Logarithmic functions are useful for, among other things, describing quantities that grow, but do so at a slower rate as time goes on.

Example 12 **Health** The life expectancy at birth of a person born in year x is approximated by the function

$$f(x) = 17.6 + 12.8 \ln x,$$

where $x = 10$ corresponds to 1910. (Data from: U.S. National Center for Health Statistics.)

(a) Find the life expectancy of persons born in 1910, 1960, and 2010.

Solution Since these years correspond to $x = 10, x = 60$, and $x = 110$, respectively, use a calculator to evaluate $f(x)$ at these numbers:

$$f(10) = 17.6 + 12.8 \ln(10) \approx 47.073;$$
$$f(60) = 17.6 + 12.8 \ln(60) \approx 70.008;$$
$$f(110) = 17.6 + 12.8 \ln(110) \approx 77.766.$$

So in the half-century from 1910 to 1960, life expectancy at birth increased from about 47 to 70 years, an increase of 23 years. But in the half-century from 1960 to 2010, it increased less than 8 years, from about 70 to 77.8 years.

 (b) If this function remains accurate, when will life expectancy at birth be 80.2 years?

Solution We must solve the equation $f(x) = 80.2$, that is,

$$17.6 + 12.8 \ln x = 80.2$$

Figure 4.22

In the next section, we shall see how to do this algebraically. For now, we solve the equation graphically by graphing $f(x)$ and $y = 80.2$ on the same screen and finding their intersection point. Figure 4.22 shows that the x-coordinate of this point is approximately 133. So life expectancy will be 80.2 years in 2033.

4.3 Exercises

Complete each statement in Exercises 1–4.

1. $y = \log_a x$ means $x =$ _____.

2. The statement $\log_5 125 = 3$ tells us that _____ is the power of _____ that equals _____.

3. What is wrong with the expression $y = \log_b$?

4. Logarithms of negative numbers are not defined because _____.

Translate each logarithmic statement into an equivalent exponential statement. (See Examples 1, 5, and 6.)

5. $\log 100{,}000 = 5$ **6.** $\log .001 = -3$

7. $\log_9 81 = 2$ **8.** $\log_2 (1/8) = -3$

Translate each exponential statement into an equivalent logarithmic statement. (See Examples 5 and 6.)

9. $10^{1.9823} = 96$ **10.** $e^{3.2189} = 25$

11. $3^{-2} = 1/9$ **12.** $16^{1/2} = 4$

Without using a calculator, evaluate each of the given expressions. (See Examples 1, 5, and 6.)

13. $\log 1000$ **14.** $\log .0001$

15. $\log_6 36$ **16.** $\log_3 81$

17. $\log_4 64$ **18.** $\log_5 125$

19. $\log_2 \dfrac{1}{4}$ **20.** $\log_3 \dfrac{1}{27}$

21. $\ln \sqrt{e}$ **22.** $\ln(1/e)$

23. $\ln e^{8.77}$ **24.** $\log 10^{74.3}$

Use a calculator to evaluate each logarithm to three decimal places. (See Examples 3 and 4.)

25. $\log 53$ **26.** $\log .005$

27. $\ln .0068$ **28.** $\ln 354$

29. Why does $\log_a 1$ always equal 0 for any valid base a?

Write each expression as the logarithm of a single number or expression. Assume that all variables represent positive numbers. (See Example 7.)

30. $\log 20 - \log 5$ **31.** $\log 6 + \log 8 - \log 2$

32. $3 \ln 2 + 2 \ln 3$ **33.** $2 \ln 5 - \frac{1}{2} \ln 25$

34. $5 \log x - 2 \log y$ **35.** $2 \log u + 3 \log w - 6 \log v$

36. $\ln(3x + 2) + \ln(x + 4)$ **37.** $2 \ln(x + 2) - \ln(x + 3)$

Write each expression as a sum and/or a difference of logarithms, with all variables to the first degree.

38. $\log 5x^2 y^3$ **39.** $\ln \sqrt{6m^4 n^2}$

40. $\ln \dfrac{3x}{5y}$ **41.** $\log \dfrac{\sqrt{xz}}{z^3}$

42. The calculator-generated table in the figure is for $y_1 = \log(4 - x)$. Why do the values in the y_1 column show ERROR for $x \geq 4$?

X	Y1	
0	.60206	
1	.47712	
2	.30103	
3	0	
	ERROR	
5	ERROR	
6	ERROR	
X=4		

Express each expression in terms of u and v, where $u = \ln x$ and $v = \ln y$. For example, $\ln x^3 = 3(\ln x) = 3u$.

43. $\ln(x^2 y^5)$ **44.** $\ln(\sqrt{x} \cdot y^2)$

45. $\ln(x^3 / y^2)$ **46.** $\ln(\sqrt{x}/y)$

Evaluate each expression. (See Example 9.)

47. $\log_6 384$ **48.** $\log_{30} 78$

49. $\log_{35} 5646$ **50.** $\log_6 60 - \log_{60} 6$

Find numerical values for b and c for which the given statement is FALSE.

51. $\log(b + c) = \log b + \log c$

52. $\dfrac{\ln b}{\ln c} = \ln\left(\dfrac{b}{c}\right)$

Graph each function. (See Example 11.)

53. $y = \ln(x + 2)$ **54.** $y = \ln x + 2$

55. $y = \log(x - 3)$ **56.** $y = \log x - 3$

57. Graph $f(x) = \log x$ and $g(x) = \log(x/4)$ for $-2 \leq x \leq 8$. How are these graphs related? How does the quotient rule support your answer?

In Exercises 58 and 59, the coordinates of a point on the graph of the indicated function are displayed at the bottom of the screen. Write the logarithmic and exponential equations associated with the display.

58.

59.

60. Match each equation with its graph. Each tick mark represents one unit.

(a) $y = \log x$ (b) $y = 10^x$

(c) $y = \ln x$ (d) $y = e^x$

(A)

(B)

(C)

(D)

61. Finance   The doubling function

$$D(r) = \frac{\ln 2}{\ln(1 + r)}$$

gives the number of years required to double your money when it is invested at interest rate r (expressed as a decimal), compounded annually. How long does it take to double your money at each of the following rates?

(a) 4%   (b) 8%   (c) 18%   (d) 36%

(e) Round each of your answers in parts (a)–(d) to the nearest year, and compare them with these numbers: 72/4, 72/8, 72/18, and 72/36. Use this evidence to state a "rule of thumb" for determining approximate doubling time without employing the function D. This rule, which has long been used by bankers, is called the *rule of 72*.

62. Health   Two people with the flu visited a college campus. The number of days, T, that it took for the flu virus to infect n people is given by

$$T = -1.43 \ln\left(\frac{10,000 - n}{4998n}\right).$$

How many days will it take for the virus to infect

(a) 500 people?   (b) 5000 people?

63. Business   The average annual expenditure (in dollars) for a consumer of gasoline and motor oil can be approximated by the function

$$g(x) = -771.9 + 1035 \ln x,$$

where $x = 5$ corresponds to the year 1995. (Data from: U.S. Bureau of Labor Statistics.)

(a) Estimate the average expenditure in 2008.

(b) Graph the function g for the period 1995 to 2011.

(c) Assuming the graph remains accurate, what does the shape of the graph suggest regarding the average expenditure on gasoline and motor oil?

64. Physical Science   The barometric pressure p (in inches of mercury) is related to the height h above sea level (in miles) by the equation

$$h = -5 \ln\left(\frac{p}{29.92}\right).$$

The pressure readings given in parts (a)–(c) were made by a weather balloon. At what heights were they made?

(a) 29.92 in.   (b) 20.05 in.   (c) 11.92 in.

(d) Use a graphing calculator to determine the pressure at a height of 3 miles.

65. Social Science   The number of residents (in millions) of the United States age 65 or older can be approximated by the function

$$h(x) = 1.58 + 10.15 \ln x,$$

where $x = 10$ corresponds to the year 1980. (Data from: U.S. Census Bureau.)

(a) Give the number of residents age 65 or older for the years 1990 and 2005.

(b) Graph the function h for $10 \le x \le 50$.

(c) What does the graph suggest regarding the number of older people as time goes on?

Natural Science   *These exercises deal with the Shannon index of diversity. (See Example 10.) Note that in two communities with the same number of species, a larger index indicates greater diversity.*

66. A study of barn owl prey in a particular area produced the following data:

Species	Number
Rats	662
Mice	907
Birds	531

Find the index of diversity of this community. Is this community more or less diverse than the one in Example 10?

67. An eastern forest is composed of the following trees:

Species	Number
Beech	2754
Birch	689
Hemlock	4428
Maple	629

What is the index of diversity of this community?

68. A community has high diversity when all of its species have approximately the same number of individuals. It has low diversity when a few of its species account for most of the total population. Illustrate this fact for the following two communities:

Community 1	Number
Species A	1000
Species B	1000
Species C	1000

Community 2	Number
Species A	2500
Species B	200
Species C	300

69. Business The total assets (in billions of dollars) held by credit unions can be approximated by the function

$$f(x) = -1237 + 580.6 \ln x,$$

where $x = 10$ corresponds to the year 1990. (Data from: U.S. Census Bureau.)

(a) What were the assets held by credit unions in 1998 and 2010?

✈ **(b)** If the model remains accurate, find the year the assets reach $1000 billion.

70. Finance The amount (in billions of dollars) held in private pension funds can be approximated by the function

$$h(x) = -11,052 + 5742 \ln x,$$

where $x = 10$ corresponds to the year 1990. (Data from: Board of Governors of the Federal Reserve System.)

(a) What was the amount in private pension funds in 2001 and 2009?

(b) If the model remains accurate, when will the amount reach $9000 billion?

71. Business The amount of milk (in gallons) consumed per person annually can be approximated by the function

$$g(x) = 28.29 - 1.948 \ln(x + 1),$$

where $x = 0$ corresponds to the year 1980. (Data from: U.S. Department of Agriculture.)

(a) How many gallons per person were consumed in the years 1985 and 2005?

(b) Assuming the model remains accurate, when will the per-person consumption be at 21 gallons?

72. Economics The median family income is the "middle income"—half the families have this income or more, and half have a lesser income. The median family income can be approximated by

$$f(x) = 22,751 + 8217 \ln(x + 1),$$

where $x = 0$ corresponds to the year 1990. (Data from: U.S. Census Bureau.)

(a) What is the median income in the years 2000 and 2010?

(b) If this model remains accurate, when will the median income reach $52,000?

✓ **Checkpoint Answers**

1. **(a)** 2 **(b)** 3 **(c)** −1

2. **(a)** 1.4314 **(b)** 3.0370 **(c)** −2.3706

3. **(a)** 1.8083 **(b)** 2.9957 **(c)** −.2231
(d) −2.3026

4. **(a)** $\log_5 125 = 3$ **(b)** $\log_3 (1/81) = -4$ **(c)** $\log_8 4 = 2/3$

5. **(a)** $16^{1/2} = 4$ **(b)** $3^{-2} = 1/9$ **(c)** $16^{3/4} = 8$

6. **(a)** $\log_a 15x^5$ **(b)** $\log_a (3p/5q)$ **(c)** $\log_a (k^4/m^3)$

7. **(a)** 3.23 **(b)** .31 **(c)** 2.92
(d) 1 **(e)** 0

8.

4.4 Logarithmic and Exponential Equations

Many applications involve solving logarithmic and exponential equations, so we begin with solution methods for such equations.

Logarithmic Equations

When an equation involves only logarithmic terms, use the logarithm properties to write each side as a single logarithm. Then use the following fact.

> Let u, v, and a be positive real numbers, with $a \neq 1$.
>
> If $\log_a u = \log_a v$, then $u = v$.

Example 1   Solve $\log x = \log(x + 3) - \log(x - 1)$.

Solution   First, use the quotient property of logarithms to write the right side as a single logarithm:

$$\log x = \log(x + 3) - \log(x - 1)$$

$$\log x = \log\left(\frac{x + 3}{x - 1}\right). \qquad \text{Quotient property of logarithms}$$

The fact in the preceding box now shows that

$$x = \frac{x + 3}{x - 1}$$

$$x(x - 1) = x + 3 \qquad \text{Cross multiply.}$$

$$x^2 - x = x + 3$$

$$x^2 - 2x - 3 = 0$$

$$(x - 3)(x + 1) = 0 \qquad \text{Factor.}$$

$$x = 3 \quad \text{or} \quad x = -1.$$

Since $\log x$ is not defined when $x = -1$, the only possible solution is $x = 3$. Use a calculator to verify that 3 actually is a solution. ✓1

✓ **Checkpoint 1**

Solve each equation.

(a) $\log_2(p + 9) - \log_2 p = \log_2(p + 1)$

(b) $\log_3(m + 1) - \log_3(m - 1) = \log_3 m$

When an equation involves constants and logarithmic terms, use algebra and the logarithm properties to write one side as a single logarithm and the other as a constant. Then use the following property of logarithms, which was discussed on pages 202–203.

> If a and u are positive real numbers, with $a \neq 1$, then
>
> $$a^{\log_a u} = u.$$

Example 2   Solve each equation.

(a) $\log_5(2x - 3) = 2$

Solution   Since the base of the logarithm is 5, raise 5 to the exponents given by the equation:

$$5^{\log_5(2x-3)} = 5^2$$

On the left side, use the fact in the preceding box (with $a = 5$ and $u = 2x - 3$) to conclude that

$$2x - 3 = 25$$

$$2x = 28$$

$$x = 14.$$

Verify that 14 is a solution of the original equation.

(b) $\log(x - 16) = 2 - \log(x - 1)$

Solution First rearrange the terms to obtain a single logarithm on the left side:

$$\log(x - 16) + \log(x - 1) = 2$$
$$\log[(x - 16)(x - 1)] = 2 \qquad \text{Product property of logarithms}$$
$$\log(x^2 - 17x + 16) = 2.$$

Since the base of the logarithm is 10, raise 10 to the given powers:

$$10^{\log(x^2 - 17x + 16)} = 10^2.$$

On the left side, apply the logarithm property in the preceding box (with $a = 10$ and $u = x^2 - 17x + 16$):

$$x^2 - 17x + 16 = 100$$
$$x^2 - 17x - 84 = 0$$
$$(x + 4)(x - 21) = 0$$
$$x = -4 \qquad \text{or} \qquad x = 21.$$

In the original equation, when $x = -4$, $\log(x - 16) = \log(-20)$, which is not defined. So -4 is not a solution. You should verify that 21 is a solution of the original equation.

(c) $\log_2 x - \log_2 (x - 1) = 1$

Solution Proceed as before, with 2 as the base of the logarithm:

$$\log_2 \frac{x}{x - 1} = 1 \qquad \text{Quotient property of logarithms}$$
$$2^{\log_2 x/(x-1)} = 2^1 \qquad \text{Exponentiate to the base 2.}$$
$$\frac{x}{x - 1} = 2 \qquad \text{Use the fact in the preceding box.}$$
$$x = 2(x - 1) \qquad \text{Multiply both sides by } x - 1.$$
$$x = 2x - 2$$
$$-x = -2$$
$$x = 2.$$

Verify that 2 is a solution of the original equation. ✓2

✓ **Checkpoint 2**

Solve each equation.

(a) $\log_5 x + 2 \log_5 x = 3$

(b) $\log_6 (a + 2) - \log_6 \dfrac{a - 7}{5} = 1$

Exponential Equations

An equation in which all the variables are exponents is called an exponential equation. When such an equation can be written as two powers of the same base, it can be solved by using the following fact.

> Let a be a positive real number, with $a \neq 1$.
>
> $$\text{If } a^u = a^v, \qquad \text{then} \qquad u = v.$$

Example 3   Solve $9^x = 27$.

Solution   First, write both sides as powers of the same base. Since $9 = 3^2$ and $27 = 3^3$, we have

$$9^x = 27$$
$$(3^2)^x = 3^3$$
$$3^{2x} = 3^3.$$

Apply the fact in the preceding box (with $a = 3$, $u = 2x$, and $v = 3$):

$$2x = 3$$

$$x = \frac{3}{2}.$$

✓ **Checkpoint 3**

Solve each equation.

(a) $8^{2x} = 4$

(b) $5^{3x} = 25^4$

(c) $36^{-2x} = 6$

Verify that $x = 3/2$ is a solution of the original equation. ✓₃

Exponential equations involving different bases can often be solved by using the power property of logarithms, which is repeated here for natural logarithms.

> If u and r are real numbers, with u positive, then
> $$\ln u^r = r \ln u.$$

Although natural logarithms are used in the following examples, logarithms to any base will produce the same solutions.

Example 4   Solve $3^x = 5$.

Solution   Take natural logarithms on both sides:

$$\ln 3^x = \ln 5.$$

Apply the power property of logarithms in the preceding box (with $r = x$) to the left side:

$$x \ln 3 = \ln 5$$

$$x = \frac{\ln 5}{\ln 3} \approx 1.465. \qquad \text{Divide both sides by the constant ln 3.}$$

To check, evaluate $3^{1.465}$; the answer should be approximately 5, which verifies that the solution of the given equation is 1.465 (to the nearest thousandth). ✓₄

✓ **Checkpoint 4**

Solve each equation. Round solutions to the nearest thousandth.

(a) $2^x = 7$

(b) $5^m = 50$

(c) $3^y = 17$

⊘ **CAUTION** Be careful: $\dfrac{\ln 5}{\ln 3}$ is *not* equal to $\ln\left(\dfrac{5}{3}\right)$ or $\ln 5 - \ln 3$.

Example 5   Solve $3^{2x-1} = 4^{x+2}$.

Solution   Taking natural logarithms on both sides gives

$$\ln 3^{2x-1} = \ln 4^{x+2}.$$

Now use the power property of logarithms and the fact that $\ln 3$ and $\ln 4$ are constants to rewrite the equation:

$$\begin{aligned}
(2x - 1)(\ln 3) &= (x + 2)(\ln 4) & \text{Power property} \\
2x(\ln 3) - 1(\ln 3) &= x(\ln 4) + 2(\ln 4) & \text{Distributive property} \\
2x(\ln 3) - x(\ln 4) &= 2(\ln 4) + 1(\ln 3). & \text{Collect terms with } x \text{ on one side.}
\end{aligned}$$

Factor out x on the left side to get

$$[2(\ln 3) - \ln 4]x = 2(\ln 4) + \ln 3.$$

Divide both sides by the coefficient of x:

$$x = \frac{2(\ln 4) + \ln 3}{2(\ln 3) - \ln 4}.$$

Using a calculator to evaluate this last expression, we find that

$$x = \frac{2\ln 4 + \ln 3}{2\ln 3 - \ln 4} \approx 4.774.$$ ✔5

Recall that $\ln e = 1$ (because 1 is the exponent to which e must be raised to produce e). This fact simplifies the solution of equations involving powers of e.

Solve $3e^{x^2} = 600$.

Solution   First divide each side by 3 to get

$$e^{x^2} = 200.$$

Now take natural logarithms on both sides; then use the power property of logarithms:

$$e^{x^2} = 200$$
$$\ln e^{x^2} = \ln 200$$
$$x^2 \ln e = \ln 200 \qquad \text{Power property}$$
$$x^2 = \ln 200 \qquad \ln e = 1.$$
$$x = \pm\sqrt{\ln 200}$$
$$x \approx \pm 2.302.$$

Verify that the solutions are ± 2.302, rounded to the nearest thousandth. (The symbol $\pm$ is used as a shortcut for writing the two solutions 2.302 and -2.302.) ✔6

Applications

Some of the most important applications of exponential and logarithmic functions arise in banking and finance. They will be thoroughly discussed in Chapter 5. The applications here are from other fields.

Example 7   **Business** The number of total subscribers (in millions) to Netflix, Inc. can be approximated by the function

$$g(x) = 9.78(1.07)^x,$$

where $x = 1$ corresponds to the first quarter of the year 2009, $x = 2$ corresponds to the second quarter of the year 2009, etc. Assume the model remains accurate and determine when the number of subscribers reached 28 million. (Data from: The *Wall Street Journal* and The *Associated Press.*)

Solution   You are being asked to find the value of x for which $g(x) = 28$—that is, to solve the following equation:

$$9.78(1.07)^x = 28$$
$$1.07^x = \frac{28}{9.78} \qquad \text{Divide both sides by 9.78.}$$
$$\ln(1.07^x) = \ln\left(\frac{28}{9.78}\right) \qquad \text{Take logarithms on both sides.}$$
$$x\ln(1.07) = \ln\left(\frac{28}{9.78}\right) \qquad \text{Power property of logarithms}$$
$$x = \frac{\ln(28/9.78)}{\ln(1.07)} \qquad \text{Divide both sides by } \ln(1.07).$$
$$x \approx 15.5.$$

The 15th quarter corresponds to the third quarter of the year 2012. Hence, according to this model, Netflix, Inc., reached 28 million subscribers in the third quarter of 2012. ✔7

✔ **Checkpoint 5**

Solve each equation. Round solutions to the nearest thousandth.

(a) $6^m = 3^{2m-1}$

(b) $5^{6a-3} = 2^{4a+1}$

✔ **Checkpoint 6**

Solve each equation. Round solutions to the nearest thousandth.

(a) $e^{.1x} = 11$

(b) $e^{3+x} = .893$

(c) $e^{2x^2-3} = 9$

📎 **TECHNOLOGY TIP**

Logarithmic and exponential equations can be solved on a graphing calculator. To solve $3^x = 5^{2x-1}$, for example, graph $y = 3^x$ and $y = 5^{2x-1}$ on the same screen. Then use the intersection finder to determine the x-coordinates of their intersection points. Alternatively, graph $y = 3^x - 5^{2x-1}$ and use the root finder to determine the x-intercepts of the graph.

✔ **Checkpoint 7**

Use the function in Example 7 to determine when Netflix reached 35 million subscribers.

The **half-life** of a radioactive substance is the time it takes for a given quantity of the substance to decay to one-half its original mass. The half-life depends only on the substance, not on the size of the sample. It can be shown that the amount of a radioactive substance at time t is given by the function

$$f(t) = y_0\left(\frac{1}{2}\right)^{t/h} = y_0(.5^{t/h}),$$

where y_0 is the initial amount (at time $t = 0$) and h is the half-life of the substance.

Radioactive carbon-14 is found in every living plant and animal. After the plant or animal dies, its carbon-14 decays exponentially, with a half-life of 5730 years. This fact is the basis for a technique called *carbon dating* for determining the age of fossils.

Example 8   **Natural Science**   A round wooden table hanging in Winchester Castle (England) was alleged to have belonged to King Arthur, who lived in the fifth century. A recent chemical analysis showed that the wood had lost 9% of its carbon-14.[*] How old is the table?

Solution   The decay function for carbon-14 is

$$f(t) = y_0(.5^{t/5730}),$$

where $t = 0$ corresponds to the time the wood was cut to make the table. (That is when the tree died.) Since the wood has lost 9% of its carbon-14, the amount in the table now is 91% of the initial amount y_0 (that is, $.91y_0$). We must find the value of t for which $f(t) = .91y_0$. So we must solve the equation

$y_0(.5^{t/5730}) = .91y_0$	Definition of $f(t)$
$.5^{t/5730} = .91$	Divide both sides by y_0.
$\ln .5^{t/5730} = \ln .91$	Take logarithms on both sides.
$\left(\dfrac{t}{5730}\right)\ln .5 = \ln .91$	Power property of logarithms
$t \ln .5 = 5730 \ln .91$	Multiply both sides by 5730.
$t = \dfrac{5730 \ln .91}{\ln .5} \approx 779.63.$	Divide both sides by $\ln .5$.

The table is about 780 years old and therefore could not have belonged to King Arthur. ✓ 8

✓ **Checkpoint 8**

How old is a skeleton that has lost 65% of its carbon-14?

Earthquakes are often in the news. The standard method of measuring their size, the **Richter scale,** is a logarithmic function (base 10).

Example 9   **Physical Science**   The intensity $R(i)$ of an earthquake, measured on the Richter scale, is given by

$$R(i) = \log\left(\frac{i}{i_0}\right),$$

where i is the intensity of the ground motion of the earthquake and i_0 is the intensity of the ground motion of the so-called *zero earthquake* (the smallest detectable earthquake, against which others are measured). The underwater earthquake that caused the disastrous 2004 tsunami in Southeast Asia measured 9.1 on the Richter scale.

---

[*]This is done by measuring the ratio of carbon-14 to nonradioactive carbon-12 in the table (a ratio that is approximately constant over long periods) and comparing it with the ratio in living wood.

(a) How did the ground motion of this tsunami compare with that of the zero earthquake?

Solution   In this case,

$$R(i) = 9.1$$

$$\log\left(\frac{i}{i_0}\right) = 9.1.$$

By the definition of logarithms, 9.1 is the exponent to which 10 must be raised to produce i/i_0, which means that

$$10^{9.1} = \frac{i}{i_0}, \qquad \text{or equivalently,} \qquad i = 10^{9.1}i_0.$$

So the earthquake that produced the tsunami had $10^{9.1}$ (about 1.26 *billion*) times more ground motion than the zero earthquake.

(b) What is the Richter-scale intensity of an earthquake with 10 times as much ground motion as the 2004 tsunami earthquake?

Solution   From (a), the ground motion of the tsunami quake was $10^{9.1}i_0$. So a quake with 10 times that motion would satisfy

$$i = 10(10^{9.1}i_0) = 10^1 \cdot 10^{9.1}i_0 = 10^{10.1}i_0.$$

Therefore, its Richter scale measure would be

$$R(i) = \log\left(\frac{i}{i_0}\right) = \log\left(\frac{10^{10.1}i_0}{i_0}\right) = \log 10^{10.1} = 10.1.$$

Thus, a tenfold increase in ground motion increases the Richter scale measure by only 1. ✔9

✔ **Checkpoint 9**

Find the Richter-scale intensity of an earthquake whose ground motion is 100 times greater than the ground motion of the 2004 tsunami earthquake discussed in Example 9.

Example 10   **Economics**   One action that government could take to reduce carbon emissions into the atmosphere is to place a tax on fossil fuels. This tax would be based on the amount of carbon dioxide that is emitted into the air when such a fuel is burned. The *cost–benefit* equation $\ln(1 - P) = -.0034 - .0053T$ describes the approximate relationship between a tax of T dollars per ton of carbon dioxide and the corresponding percent reduction P (in decimals) in emissions of carbon dioxide.[*]

(a) Write P as a function of T.

Solution   We begin by writing the cost–benefit equation in exponential form:

$$\ln(1 - P) = -.0034 - .0053T$$
$$1 - P = e^{-.0034 - .0053T}$$
$$P = P(T) = 1 - e^{-.0034 - .0053T}.$$

A calculator-generated graph of $P(T)$ is shown in Figure 4.23.

(b) Discuss the benefit of continuing to raise taxes on carbon dioxide emissions.

Solution   From the graph, we see that initially there is a rapid reduction in carbon dioxide emissions. However, after a while, there is little benefit in raising taxes further.

Figure 4.23

---

[*]"To Slow or Not to Slow: The Economics of The Greenhouse Effect," William D. Nordhaus, *The Economic Journal*, Vol. 101, No. 407 (July, 1991), pp. 920–937.

4.4 Exercises

Solve each logarithmic equation. (See Example 1.)

1. $\ln(x + 3) = \ln(2x - 5)$

2. $\ln(8k - 7) - \ln(3 + 4k) = \ln(9/11)$

3. $\ln(3x + 1) - \ln(5 + x) = \ln 2$

4. $\ln(5x + 2) = \ln 4 + \ln(x + 3)$

5. $2 \ln(x - 3) = \ln(x + 5) + \ln 4$

6. $\ln(k + 5) + \ln(k + 2) = \ln 18k$

Solve each logarithmic equation. (See Example 2.)

7. $\log_3 (6x - 2) = 2$

8. $\log_5 (3x - 4) = 1$

9. $\log x - \log(x + 4) = -1$

10. $\log m - \log(m + 4) = -2$

11. $\log_3 (y + 2) = \log_3 (y - 7) + \log_3 4$

12. $\log_8 (z - 6) = 2 - \log_8 (z + 15)$

13. $\ln(x + 9) - \ln x = 1$

14. $\ln(2x + 1) - 1 = \ln(x - 2)$

15. $\log x + \log(x - 9) = 1$

16. $\log(x - 1) + \log(x + 2) = 1$

Solve each equation for c.

17. $\log(3 + b) = \log(4c - 1)$

18. $\ln(b + 7) = \ln(6c + 8)$

19. $2 - b = \log(6c + 5)$

20. $8b + 6 = \ln(2c) + \ln c$

21. Suppose you overhear the following statement: "I must reject any negative answer when I solve an equation involving logarithms." Is this correct? Write an explanation of why it is or is not correct.

22. What values of x cannot be solutions of the following equation?
$$\log_a (4x - 7) + \log_a (x^2 + 4) = 0.$$

Solve these exponential equations without using logarithms. (See Example 3.)

23. $2^{x-1} = 8$

24. $16^{-x+2} = 8$

25. $25^{-3x} = 3125$

26. $81^{-2x} = 3^{x-1}$

27. $6^{-x} = 36^{x+6}$

28. $16^x = 64$

29. $\left(\dfrac{3}{4}\right)^x = \dfrac{16}{9}$

30. $2^{x^2 - 4x} = \dfrac{1}{16}$

Use logarithms to solve these exponential equations. (See Examples 4–6.)

31. $2^x = 5$

32. $5^x = 8$

33. $2^x = 3^{x-1}$

34. $4^{x+2} = 5^{x-1}$

35. $3^{1-2x} = 5^{x+5}$

36. $4^{3x-1} = 3^{x-2}$

37. $e^{3x} = 6$

38. $e^{-3x} = 5$

39. $2e^{5a+2} = 8$

40. $10e^{3z-7} = 5$

Solve each equation for c.

41. $10^{4c-3} = d$

42. $3 \cdot 10^{2c+1} = 4d$

43. $e^{2c-1} = b$

44. $3e^{5c-7} = b$

Solve these equations. (See Examples 1–6.)

45. $\log_7 (r + 3) + \log_7 (r - 3) = 1$

46. $\log_4 (z + 3) + \log_4 (z - 3) = 2$

47. $\log_3 (a - 3) = 1 + \log_3 (a + 1)$

48. $\log w + \log(3w - 13) = 1$

49. $\log_2 \sqrt{2y^2} - 1 = 3/2$ 50. $\log_2 (\log_2 x) = 1$

51. $\log_2 (\log_3 x) = 1$ 52. $\dfrac{\ln(2x + 1)}{\ln(3x - 1)} = 2$

53. $5^{-2x} = \dfrac{1}{25}$ 54. $5^{x^2 + x} = 1$

55. $2^{|x|} = 16$ 56. $5^{-|x|} = \dfrac{1}{25}$

57. $2^{x^2 - 1} = 10$ 58. $3^{2-x^2} = 8$

59. $2(e^x + 1) = 10$ 60. $5(e^{2x} - 2) = 15$

61. Explain why the equation $4^{x^2 + 1} = 2$ has no solutions.

62. Explain why the equation $\log(-x) = -4$ does have a solution, and find that solution.

Work these problems. (See Example 7.)

63. **Business** Gambling revenues (in billions of U.S. dollars) generated in Macau, China can be approximated by the function $g(x) = 1.104(1.346)^x$, where $x = 2$ corresponds to the year 2002. Assume the model remains accurate and find the years in which the gambling revenues reached the indicated amounts. (Data from: The *Wall Street Journal*.)

   (a) $20 billion   (b) $45 billion

64. **Social Science** The number of centenarians (in thousands) in the United States can be approximated by the function $h(x) = 2(1.056)^x$, where $x = 0$ corresponds to the year 1950. Find the year in which the number of centenarians reached the following levels. (Data from: U.S. Census Bureau.)

   (a) 30,000   (b) 50,000

65. **Health** As we saw in Example 12 of Section 4.3, the life expectancy at birth of a person born in year x is approximately
$$f(x) = 17.6 + 12.8 \ln x,$$
where $x = 10$ corresponds to the year 1910. Find the birth year of a person whose life expectancy at birth was

   (a) 75.5 years;   (b) 77.5 years;   (c) 81 years.

66. **Health** A drug's effectiveness decreases over time. If, each hour, a drug is only 90% as effective as during the previous hour, at some point the patient will not be receiving enough medication and must receive another dose. This situation can be modeled by the exponential function $y = y_0(.90)^{t-1}$. In this equation, y_0 is the amount of the initial dose and y is the amount of medication still available t hours after the drug was administered. Suppose 200 mg of the drug is administered. How long will it take for this initial dose to reach the dangerously low level of 50 mg?

67. **Economics** The percentage of the U.S. income earned by the top one percent of earners can be approximated by the function $f(x) = 7.9e^{.0254x}$, where $x = 0$ corresponds to the year 1970. (Data from: The *New York Times*.)

    (a) When did the percentage reach 15%?

    (b) If the model remains accurate, when will the percentage reach 30%?

68. **Health** The probability P percent of having an accident while driving a car is related to the alcohol level t of the driver's blood by the equation $P = e^{kt}$, where k is a constant. Accident statistics show that the probability of an accident is 25% when the blood alcohol level is $t = .15$.

    (a) Use the equation and the preceding information to find k (to three decimal places). *Note:* Use $P = 25$, and not .25.

    (b) Using the value of k from part (a), find the blood alcohol level at which the probability of having an accident is 50%.

Work these exercises. (See Example 8.)

69. **Natural Science** The amount of cobalt-60 (in grams) in a storage facility at time t is given by

    $$C(t) = 25e^{-.14t},$$

    where time is measured in years.

    (a) How much cobalt-60 was present initially?

    (b) What is the half-life of cobalt-60? (*Hint:* For what value of t is $C(t) = 12.5$?)

70. **Natural Science** A Native American mummy was found recently. It had 73.6% of the amount of radiocarbon present in living beings. Approximately how long ago did this person die?

71. **Natural Science** How old is a piece of ivory that has lost 36% of its radiocarbon?

72. **Natural Science** A sample from a refuse deposit near the Strait of Magellan had 60% of the carbon-14 of a contemporary living sample. How old was the sample?

Natural Science   *Work these problems. (See Example 9.)*

73. In May 2008, Sichuan province, China suffered an earthquake that measured 7.9 on the Richter scale.

    (a) Express the intensity of this earthquake in terms of i_0.

    (b) In July of the same year, a quake measuring 5.4 on the Richter scale struck Los Angeles. Express the intensity of this earthquake in terms of i_0.

(c) How many times more intense was the China earthquake than the one in Los Angeles?

74. Find the Richter-scale intensity of earthquakes whose ground motion is

    (a) $1000i_0$;   (b) $100,000i_0$;

    (c) $10,000,000i_0$.

    (d) Fill in the blank in this statement: Increasing the ground motion by a factor of 10^k increases the Richter intensity by _____ units.

75. The loudness of sound is measured in units called decibels. The decibel rating of a sound is given by

    $$D(i) = 10 \cdot \log\left(\frac{i}{i_0}\right),$$

    where i is the intensity of the sound and i_0 is the minimum intensity detectable by the human ear (the so-called *threshold sound*). Find the decibel rating of each of the sounds with the given intensities. Round answers to the nearest whole number.

    (a) Whisper, $115i_0$

    (b) Average sound level in the movie *Godzilla*, $10^{10}i_0$

    (c) Jackhammer, $31,600,000,000i_0$

    (d) Rock music, $895,000,000,000i_0$

    (e) Jetliner at takeoff, $109,000,000,000,000i_0$

76. (a) How much more intense is a sound that measures 100 decibels than the threshold sound?

    (b) How much more intense is a sound that measures 50 decibels than the threshold sound?

    (c) How much more intense is a sound measuring 100 decibels than one measuring 50 decibels?

77. **Natural Science** Refer to Example 10.

    (a) Determine the percent reduction in carbon dioxide when the tax is $60.

    (b) What tax will cause a 50% reduction in carbon dioxide emissions?

78. **Business** The revenue (in billions of dollars) for Walt Disney Company can be approximated by the function $R(x) = 16.20 + 9.992 \ln x$, where $x = 3$ corresponds to the year 2003. Find each of the following. (Data from: www.morningstar.com.)

    (a) $R(9)$ (b) $R(12)$

    (c) If the model remains accurate, in what year will revenue reach $50 billion?

79. **Business** Annual box office revenue (in billions of dollars) generated in North America can be approximated by the function $g(x) = 2.0 + 2.768 \ln x$, where $x = 2$ corresponds to the year 1992. (Data from: www.boxofficemojo.com.)

    (a) Graph the function g for the years 1992 through 2012.

    (b) According to the model, in what year did revenue reach $9 billion?

80. **Physical Science** The table on the following page gives some of the planets' average distances D from the sun and their period P of revolution around the sun in years. The distances

have been normalized so that Earth is one unit from the sun. Thus, Jupiter's distance of 5.2 means that Jupiter's distance from the sun is 5.2 times farther than Earth's.[*]

Planet	D	P
Earth	1	1
Jupiter	5.2	11.9
Saturn	9.54	29.5
Uranus	19.2	84.0

(a) Plot the points (D, P) for these planets. Would a straight line or an exponential curve fit these points best?

(b) Plot the points $(\ln D, \ln P)$ for these planets. Do these points appear to lie on a line?

(c) Determine a linear equation that approximates the data points, with $x = \ln D$ and $y = \ln P$. Use the first and last data points (rounded to 2 decimal places). Graph your line and the data on the same coordinate axes.

(d) Use the linear equation to predict the period of the planet Pluto if its distance is 39.5. Compare your answer with the true value of 248.5 years.

✓ Checkpoint Answers

1. (a) 3   (b) $1 + \sqrt{2} \approx 2.414$

2. (a) 5   (b) 52

3. (a) 1/3   (b) 8/3   (c) $-1/4$

4. (a) 2.807   (b) 2.431   (c) 2.579

5. (a) 2.710   (b) .802

6. (a) 23.979   (b) -3.113 (c) ± 1.612

7. Second quarter of 2013.

8. About 8679 years

9. 11.1

[*]C. Ronan, *The Natural History of the Universe.* New York: Macmillan Publishing Co., 1991.

CHAPTER 4 Summary and Review

Key Terms and Symbols

4.1 exponential function
exponential growth and
  decay
the number
  $e \approx 2.71828\ldots$

4.2 exponential growth function
logistic function

4.3 $\log x$ common (base-10)
  logarithm of x
$\ln x$ natural (base-e)
  logarithm of x
$\log_a x$ base-a logarithm
  of x

product, quotient, and
  power properties of
  logarithms
change-of-base theorem
Inverse logarithmic
  functions

4.4 logarithmic equations
exponential equations
half-life
Richter scale

Chapter 4 Key Concepts

Exponentialic Functions
An important application of exponents is the **exponential growth function,** defined as $f(t) = y_0 e^{kt}$ or $f(t) = y_0 b^t$, where y_0 is the amount of a quantity present at time $t = 0$, $e \approx 2.71828$, and k and b are constants.

Logarithmic Functions
The **logarithm** of x to the base a is defined as follows: For $a > 0$ and $a \neq 1$, $y = \log_a x$ means $a^y = x$. Thus, $\log_a x$ is an *exponent*, the power to which a must be raised to produce x.

Properties of Logarithms
Let x, y, and a be positive real numbers, with $a \neq 1$, and let r be any real number. Then

$$\log_a 1 = 0; \quad \log_a a = 1;$$
$$\log_a a^r = r; \quad a^{\log_a x} = x.$$

Product property $\log_a xy = \log_a x + \log_a y$

Quotient property $\log_a \dfrac{x}{y} = \log_a x - \log_a y$

Power property $\log_a x^r = r \log_a x$

Solving Exponential and Logarithmic Equations
Let $a > 0$, with $a \neq 1$.
If $\log_a u = \log_a v$, then $u = v$.
If $a^u = a^v$, then $u = v$.

Chapter 4 Review Exercises

Match each equation with the letter of the graph that most closely resembles the graph of the equation. Assume that $a > 1$.

1. $y = a^{x+2}$

2. $y = a^x + 2$

3. $y = -a^x + 2$

4. $y = a^{-x} + 2$

(a)

(b)

(c)

(d)

Consider the exponential function $y = f(x) = a^x$ graphed here. Answer each question on the basis of the graph.

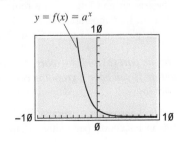

$y = f(x) = a^x$

5. What is true about the value of a in comparison to 1?

6. What is the domain of f?

7. What is the range of f?

8. What is the value of $f(0)$?

Graph each function.

9. $f(x) = 4^x$

10. $g(x) = 4^{-x}$

11. $f(x) = \ln x + 5$

12. $g(x) = \log x - 3$

Work these problems.

13. Economics The cumulative number of retail jobs (in thousands) added each month to the U.S. economy can be approximated by the function $f(x) = 39.61(1.118)^x$, where $x = 1$ corresponds to January, 2011. (Data from: U.S. Bureau of Labor Statistics.)

(a) Estimate the cumulative number of jobs added in September, 2012.

(b) In what month, according to the model, did the cumulative number of jobs hit 300,000?

14. Economics The cumulative number of construction jobs (in thousands) added each month to the U.S. economy can be approximated by the function $f(x) = 28.7(1.120)^x$, where $x = 1$ corresponds to January, 2011. (Data from: U.S. Bureau of Labor Statistics.)

(a) Estimate the cumulative number of jobs added in June, 2012.

(b) In what month, according to the model, did the cumulative number of jobs hit 250,000?

Translate each exponential statement into an equivalent logarithmic one.

15. $10^{2.53148} = 340$

16. $5^4 = 625$

17. $e^{3.8067} = 45$ **18.** $7^{1/2} = \sqrt{7}$

Translate each logarithmic statement into an equivalent exponential one.

19. $\log 10{,}000 = 4$ **20.** $\log 26.3 = 1.4200$

21. $\ln 81.1 = 4.3957$ **22.** $\log_2 4096 = 12$

Evaluate these expressions without using a calculator.

23. $\ln e^5$ **24.** $\log \sqrt[3]{10}$

25. $10^{\log 8.9}$ **26.** $\ln e^{3t^2}$

27. $\log_8 2$ **28.** $\log_8 32$

Write these expressions as a single logarithm. Assume all variables represent positive quantities.

29. $\log 4x + \log 5x^5$ **30.** $4 \log u - 5 \log u^6$

31. $3 \log b - 2 \log c$ **32.** $7 \ln x - 3(\ln x^3 + 5 \ln x)$

Solve each equation. Round to the nearest thousandth.

33. $\ln(m + 8) - \ln m = \ln 3$

34. $2 \ln(y + 1) = \ln(y^2 - 1) + \ln 5$

35. $\log(m + 3) = 2$ **36.** $\log x^3 = 2$

37. $\log_2 (3k + 1) = 4$ **38.** $\log_5 \left(\dfrac{5z}{z - 2} \right) = 2$

39. $\log x + \log(x - 3) = 1$ **40.** $\log_2 r + \log_2 (r - 2) = 3$

41. $2^{3x} = \dfrac{1}{64}$ **42.** $\left(\dfrac{9}{16} \right)^x = \dfrac{3}{4}$

43. $9^{2y+1} = 27^y$ **44.** $\dfrac{1}{2} = \left(\dfrac{b}{4} \right)^{1/4}$

45. $8^p = 19$ **46.** $3^z = 11$

47. $5 \cdot 2^{-m} = 35$ **48.** $2 \cdot 15^{-k} = 18$

49. $e^{-5-2x} = 5$ **50.** $e^{3x-1} = 12$

51. $6^{2-m} = 2^{3m+1}$ **52.** $5^{3r-1} = 6^{2r+5}$

53. $(1 + .003)^k = 1.089$ **54.** $(1 + .094)^z = 2.387$

Work these problems.

55. A population is increasing according to the growth law $y = 4e^{.03t}$, where y is in thousands and t is in months. Match each of the questions (a), (b), (c), and (d) with one of the solution (A), (B), (C), or (D).

  (a) How long will it take for the population to double?   **(A)** Solve $4e^{.03t} = 12$ for t.

  (b) When will the population reach 12 thousand?   **(B)** Evaluate $4e^{.03(72)}$.

  (c) How large will the population be in 6 months?   **(C)** Solve $4e^{.03t} = 2 \cdot 4$ for t.

  (d) How large will the population be in 6 years?   **(D)** Evaluate $4e^{.03(6)}$.

56. **Natural Science** A population is increasing according to the growth law $y = 2e^{.02t}$, where y is in millions and t is in

years. Match each of the questions (a), (b), (c), and (d) with one of the solutions (A), (B), (C), or (D).

  (a) How long will it take for the population to triple?   **(A)** Evaluate $2e^{.02(1/3)}$.

  (b) When will the population reach 3 million?   **(B)** Solve $2e^{.02t} = 3 \cdot 2$ for t.

  (c) How large will the population be in 3 years?   **(C)** Evaluate $2e^{.02(3)}$.

  (d) How large will the population be in 4 months?   **(D)** Solve $2e^{.02t} = 3$ for t.

57. **Natural Science** The amount of polonium (in grams) present after t days is given by

$$A(t) = 10e^{-.00495t}.$$

  (a) How much polonium was present initially?

  (b) What is the half-life of polonium?

  (c) How long will it take for the polonium to decay to 3 grams?

58. **Business** The annual average natural gas price (in dollars per million BTUs) can be approximated by the function $h(x) = 69.54e^{-.264x}$, where $x = 8$ corresponds to the year 2008. (Data from: Energy Information Administration.)

  (a) What was the average price per million BTUs in the year 2010?

  (b) According to the model, in what year did the average price per million BTUs hit $3.00?

59. **Natural Science** In April, 2013, Enarotali, Indonesia suffered an earthquake that measured 7.0 on the Richter scale.

  (a) Express the intensity of this earthquake in terms of i_0.

  (b) In March, 2013, Papua New Guinea suffered an earthquake that registered 6.5 on the Richter scale. Express the intensity of this earthquake in terms of i_0.

  (c) How many times more intense was the earthquake in Indonesia than the one in Papua New Guinea?

60. **Natural Science** One earthquake measures 4.6 on the Richter scale. A second earthquake has ground motion 1000 times greater than the first. What does the second one measure on the Richter scale?

📗 **Natural Science** *Another form of Newton's law of cooling (see Section 4.2, Exercises 15 and 16) is $F(t) = T_0 + Ce^{-kt}$, where C and k are constants.*

61. A piece of metal is heated to 300° Celsius and then placed in a cooling liquid at 50° Celsius. After 4 minutes, the metal has cooled to 175° Celsius. Find its temperature after 12 minutes.

62. A frozen pizza has a temperature of 3.4° Celsius when it is taken from the freezer and left out in a room at 18° Celsius. After half an hour, its temperature is 7.2° Celsius. How long will it take for the pizza to thaw to 10° Celsius?

In Exercises 63–66, do part (a) and skip part (b) if you do not have a graphing calculator. If you have a graphing calculator, then skip part (a) and do part (b).

63. **Business** The approximate average times (in minutes per month) spent on Facebook per unique visitor in the United

States on a mobile device are given in the following table for the last six months of 2012 and first two months of 2013. (Data from: www.comScore.com.)

Month	July 2012	Aug. 2012	Sept. 2012	Oct. 2012	Nov. 2012	Dec. 2012	Jan. 2013	Feb. 2013
Minutes	500	510	520	580	615	700	760	785

(a) Let $x = 0$ correspond to July, 2012. Use the data points from July, 2012 and February, 2013 to find a function of the form $f(x) = a(b^x)$ that models these data.

(b) Use exponential regression to find a function g that models these data, with $x = 0$ corresponding to July, 2012.

(c) Assume the model remains accurate and estimate the minutes per month in April, 2013.

(d) According to this model, when will the minutes per month reach 1000?

64. **Physical Science**   The atmospheric pressure (in millibars) at a given altitude (in thousands of meters) is listed in the table:

Altitude	0	2000	4000	6000	8000	10,000
Pressure	1013	795	617	472	357	265

(a) Use the data points for altitudes 0 and 10,000 to find a function of the form $f(x) = a(b^x)$ that models these data, where altitude x is measured in thousands of meters. (For example, $x = 4$ means 4000 meters.)

(b) Use exponential regression to find a function $g(x)$ that models these data, with x measured in thousands of meters.

(c) Estimate the pressure at 1500 m and 11,000 m, and compare the results with the actual values of 846 and 227 millibars, respectively.

(d) At what height is the pressure 500 millibars?

65. **Business**   The table shows the approximate digital share (in percent) of recorded music sales in the United States in recent years. (Data from: www.statista.com.)

Year	2006	2007	2008	2009	2010	2011	2012
Percent	18	25	39	43	47	50	59

(a) Let $x = 1$ correspond to the year 2006. Use the data points for 2006 and 2012 to find a function of the form $f(x) = a + b \ln x$ that models these data. [Hint: Use (1, 18) to find a; then use (7, 59) to find b.]

(b) Use logarithmic regression to find a function g that models these data, with $x = 1$ corresponding to the year 2006.

(c) Assume the model remains accurate and predict the percentage for 2014.

(d) According to the model, when will the share of digital music reach 70%?

66. **Health**   The number of kidney transplants (in thousands) in selected years is shown in the table. (Data from: National Network for Organ Sharing.)

Year	1991	1995	2000	2005	2011
Transplants	9.678	11.083	13.613	16.481	16.813

(a) Let $x = 1$ correspond to 1991. Use the data points for 1991 and 2011 to find a function of the form $f(x) = a + b \ln x$ that models these data. [See Exercise 65(a).]

(b) Use logarithmic regression to find a function $g(x)$ that models these data, with $x = 1$ corresponding to 1991.

(c) Estimate the number of kidney transplants in 2013.

(d) If the model remains accurate, when will the number of kidney transplants reach 17,500?

Case Study 4 Gapminder.org

The website www.gapminder.org is committed to displaying economic and health data for countries around the world in a visually compelling way. The goal is to make publicly available data easy for citizens of the world to understand so individuals and policy makers can comprehend trends and make data-driven conclusions. For example, the website uses the size of the bubble on a plot to indicate the population of the country, and the color indicates the region in which the country lies:

Yellow	America
Orange	Europe and Central Asia
Green	Middle East and Northern Africa
Dark Blue	Sub-Saharan Africa
Red	East Asia and the Pacific

Additionally, the website also uses animation to show how variables change over time.

Let's look at an example of two variables of interest as best we can on a printed page. We will use income per-person (in U.S. dollars and measured as gross domestic product per capita) as a measure of a country's wealth as the x-axis variable and life expectancy (in years) at birth as a measure of the health of a country on the y-axis. In Figure 4.24 on the following page we see a bubble for each country in the year 1800.

We see that all the countries are bunched together with quite low income per-person and average life expectancy ranging from 25–40 years. The two large bubbles you see are for the two most populous countries: China (red) and India (light blue). When you visit the website (please do so, it is very cool!) and press the "Play" button at the bottom left, you can see how income per-person and life expectancy change over time for each country. At its conclusion, you obtain Figure 4.25 on the following page, which shows the relationship between income per-person and average life expectancy in the year 2011.

Figure 4.24   Relationship Between Income per Person and Average Life Expectancy in 1800 from Gapminder Foundation. Reproduced by permission of Gapminder Foundation.

Figure 4.25   Relationship Between Income per Person and Average Life Expectancy in 2011 from Gapminder Foundation. Reproduced by permission of Gapminder Foundation.

We can see that a great deal has changed in 200 years! One great thing is that all countries now have average life expectancy that is over 45 years. This is simply incredible. Also, we see there is a great range of income per-person values for a variety of countries. The country to the far right (the little green dot) is the Middle Eastern country of Qatar. We see that many of the Sub-Sahara countries on the left (in dark blue) have the lowest per-person income and the lowest average life expectancy. The wealthier countries—for example, countries whose per-person income is greater than $20,000—all have life expectancy over 70 years.

We can actually use the per-person income x to predict the average life expectancy $f(x)$. Note that Gapminder.org has its default showing the income per-person on a logarithmic scale. When we see a linear pattern such as this where the x-axis is on a logarithmic scale and the y-axis is on the regular scale, a model of the form $f(x) = a + b \ln x$ often fits the data well. Since Gapminder.org makes all the data for their graphs available, we can fit a model to find values for a and b. Using regression, we obtain the following model:

$$f(x) = 15.32 + 6.178 \ln x. \tag{1}$$

Gapminder.org will also show the economic development for an individual country. Figure 4.26 shows per capita GDP on the *y*-axis for the country of Brazil over time. We can see that economic gains began close to the year 1900. The graph shows per-person income on the *y*-axis (again on a logarithmic scale) and the trend seems approx-imately linear since 1900. When this is the case, a model of the form $a(b^x)$ usually fits the data well. Letting $x = 0$ correspond to the year 1900, we obtain the following:

$$g(x) = 510.3(1.029)^x \qquad \textbf{(2)}$$

Figure 4.26   Relationship Between Time and per Capita GDP in 2011 from Gapminder Foundation. Reproduced by permission of Gapminder Foundation.

The trajectory of the United States (Figure 4.27) is a bit differ-ent, with rising incomes starting in the early 1800s and continuing to the present. Notice the dips that occur in the mid-1930s (the Great Depression) and the early 1940s (World War II). Fitting a model to the data for the United States (again with $x = 0$ corresponding to the year 1900) yields the model:

$$h(x) = 6229.2(1.018)^x \qquad \textbf{(3)}$$

Figure 4.27   Trajectory of United States from Gapminder Foundation. Reproduced by permission of Gapminder Foundation.

Exercises

For Exercises 1–6, use Equation (1) that provides a model using per-person income as the x-variable to predict life expectancy as the y-variable.

1. Create a graph of the function given in Equation (1) from $x = 0$ to 100,000.

2. Describe the shape of the graph.

3. The country farthest to the left in Figure 4.25 is the Democratic Republic of the Congo. In 2011, its income per-person was $387 and its life expectancy was 48. Suppose that the economic development improved so that the Democratic Republic of the Congo had a per-person income level of $4000. What does the model of Equation (1) predict for life expectancy?

4. In 2011, Russia had per-person income of $14,738 and life expectancy of 69 years. What does the model predict for life expectancy if the per-person income improved to $25,000?

5. According to the model, what per-person income level predicts a life expectancy of 60 years?

6. According to the model, what per-person income level predicts a life expectancy of 75 years?

For Exercises 7–10, use the model in Equation (2) that uses year (with $x = 0$ corresponding to the year 1900) to predict the per-person income for Brazil.

7. Graph the model of Equation (2) from $x = 0$ to 111.

8. Describe the shape of the model.

9. According to the model, what was the per-person income for Brazil in the year 1950? In the year 2000?

10. What year does the model indicate that per-person income reached $4000?

For Exercises 11–14, use the model in Equation (3) that uses year (with $x = 0$ corresponding to the year 1900) to predict the per-person income for the United States.

11. Graph the model of Equation (3) from $x = 0$ to 111.

12. Describe the shape of the model.

13. According to the model, what was the per-person income for the United States in the year 1960? In the year 2010?

14. What year does the model indicate that per-person income reached $20,000?

◢ Extended Project

Go to the website www.gapminder.org and explore different relationships. Examine the relationship between a variety of variables that look at relationships among health, climate, disasters, economy, education, family, global trends, HIV, and poverty. (*Hint:* When you have the graphic display showing, click on the button for "Open Graph Menu" to see a list of options in these areas all ready to be viewed.) When observing the different graphs, notice when the x-axis, the y-axis, or both are on a logarithmic scale.

1. Find a relationship that appears linear when the x-axis is on the logarithmic scale and the y-axis is not. Now click on the button to the right of the x-axis and observe the graph on a linear scale (rather than the logarithmic scale). Describe the shape.

2. Find a relationship that appears linear when the x-axis is not on the logarithmic scale, but the y-axis is on the logarithmic scale. Now click on the button above the y-axis and observe the graph on a linear scale (rather than the logarithmic scale). Describe the shape.

3. Find a relationship that appears linear when the x-axis is on the logarithmic scale, and the y-axis is on the logarithmic scale. Now click on the button to the right of the x-axis and click on the button above the y-axis and observe the graph on a linear scale (rather than the logarithmic scale) for both axes. Describe the shape.

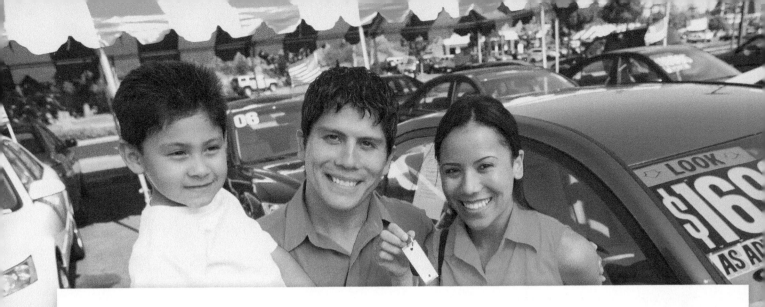

Mathematics of Finance

5

Most people must take out a loan for a big purchase, such as a car, a major appliance, or a house. People who carry a balance on their credit cards are, in effect, also borrowing money. Loan payments must be accurately determined, and it may take some work to find the "best deal." See Exercise 54 on page 262 and Exercise 57 on page 242. We must all plan for eventual retirement, which usually involves savings accounts and investments in stocks, bonds, and annuities to fund 401K accounts or individual retirement accounts (IRAs). See Exercises 40 and 41 on page 250.

It is important for both businesspersons and consumers to understand the mathematics of finance in order to make sound financial decisions. Interest formulas for borrowing and investing money are introduced in this chapter.

NOTE We try to present realistic, up-to-date applications in this text. Because interest rates change so frequently, however, it is very unlikely that the rates in effect when this chapter was written are the same as the rates today when you are reading it. Fortunately, the mathematics of finance is the same regardless of the level of interest rates. So we have used a variety of rates in the examples and exercises. Some will be realistic and some won't by the time you see them—but all of them have occurred in the past several decades.

5.1 Simple Interest and Discount

Interest is the fee paid to use someone else's money. Interest on loans of a year or less is frequently calculated as **simple interest,** which is paid only on the amount borrowed or invested and not on past interest. The amount borrowed or deposited is called the

principal. The **rate** of interest is given as a percent per year, expressed as a decimal. For example, 6% = .06 and $11\frac{1}{2}$% = .115. The **time** during which the money is accruing interest is calculated in years. Simple interest is the product of the principal, rate, and time.

> ## Simple Interest
>
> The simple interest I on P dollars at a rate of interest r per year for t years is
>
> $$I = Prt.$$

It is customary in financial problems to round interest to the nearest cent.

Example 1   To furnish her new apartment, Maggie Chan borrowed $4000 at 3% interest from her parents for 9 months. How much interest will she pay?

Solution   Use the formula $I = Prt$, with $P = 4000$, $r = 0.03$, and $t = 9/12 = 3/4$ years:

$$I = Prt$$

$$I = 4000 * .03 * \frac{3}{4} = 90.$$

Thus, Maggie pays a total of $90 in interest. ✓1

✓**Checkpoint 1**

Find the simple interest for each loan.

(a) $2000 at 8.5% for 10 months

(b) $3500 at 10.5% for $1\frac{1}{2}$ years

Answers to Checkpoint exercises are found at the end of the section.

Simple interest is normally used only for loans with a term of a year or less. A significant exception is the case of **corporate bonds** and similar financial instruments. A typical bond pays simple interest twice a year for a specified length of time, at the end of which the bond **matures.** At maturity, the company returns your initial investment to you.

Example 2   **Finance**   On January 8, 2013, Bank of America issued 10-year bonds at an annual simple interest rate of 3.3%, with interest paid twice a year. John Altiere buys a $10,000 bond. (Data from: www.finra.org.)

(a) How much interest will he earn every six months?

✓**Checkpoint 2**

For the given bonds, find the semiannual interest payment and the total interest paid over the life of the bond.

(a) $7500 Time Warner Cable, Inc. 30-year bond at 7.3% annual interest.

(b) $15,000 Clear Channel Communications 10-year bond at 9.0% annual interest.

Solution   Use the interest formula, $I = Prt$, with $P = 10,000$, $r = .033$, and $t = \frac{1}{2}$:

$$I = Prt = 10,000 * .033 * \frac{1}{2} = \$165.$$

(b) How much interest will he earn over the 10-year life of the bond?

Solution   Either use the interest formula with $t = 10$, that is,

$$I = Prt = 10,000 * .033 * 10 = \$3300,$$

or take the answer in part (a), which will be paid out every six months for 10 years for a total of twenty times. Thus, John would obtain $165 * 20 = $3300. ✓2

Future Value

If you deposit P dollars at simple interest rate r for t years, then the **future value** (or **maturity value**) A of this investment is the sum of the principal P and the interest I it has earned:

$$A = \text{Principal} + \text{Interest}$$
$$= P + I$$
$$= P + Prt \qquad\qquad I = Prt.$$
$$= P(1 + rt). \qquad\qquad \text{Factor out } P.$$

The following box summarizes this result.

Future Value (or Maturity Value) for Simple Interest

The future value (maturity value) A of P dollars for t years at interest rate r per year is

$$A = P + I, \qquad \text{or} \qquad A = P(1 + rt).$$

Example 3   Find each maturity value and the amount of interest paid.

(a) Rick borrows $20,000 from his parents at 5.25% to add a room on his house. He plans to repay the loan in 9 months with a bonus he expects to receive at that time.

Solution   The loan is for 9 months, or 9/12 of a year, so $t = .75, P = 20,000$, and $r = .0525$. Use the formula to obtain

$$A = P(1 + rt)$$
$$= 20{,}000[1 + .0525(.75)]$$
$$\approx 20{,}787.5, \qquad\qquad \text{Use a calculator.}$$

or $20,787.50. The maturity value A is the sum of the principal P and the interest I, that is, $A = P + I$. To find the amount of interest paid, rearrange this equation:

$$I = A - P$$
$$I = \$20{,}787.50 - \$20{,}000 = \$787.50.$$

(b) A loan of $11,280 for 85 days at 9% interest.

Solution   Use the formula $A = P(1 + rt)$, with $P = 11{,}280$ and $r = .09$. Unless stated otherwise, we assume a 365-day year, so the period in years is $t = 85/365$. The maturity value is

$$A = P(1 + rt)$$
$$A = 11{,}280\left(1 + .09 * \frac{85}{365}\right)$$
$$\approx 11{,}280(1.020958904) \approx \$11{,}516.42.$$

As in part (a), the interest is

$$I = A - P = \$11{,}516.42 - \$11{,}280 = \$236.42.$$

✓ **Checkpoint 3**

Find each future value.

(a) $1000 at 4.6% for 6 months

(b) $8970 at 11% for 9 months

(c) $95,106 at 9.8% for 76 days

Example 4   Suppose you borrow $15,000 and are required to pay $15,315 in 4 months to pay off the loan and interest. What is the simple interest rate?

Solution   One way to find the rate is to solve for r in the future-value formula when $P = 15{,}000, A = 15{,}315$, and $t = 4/12 = 1/3$:

$$P(1 + rt) = A$$

$$15{,}000\left(1 + r * \frac{1}{3}\right) = 15{,}315$$

$$15{,}000 + \frac{15{,}000r}{3} = 15{,}315 \qquad \text{Multiply out left side.}$$

$$\frac{15{,}000r}{3} = 315 \qquad \text{Subtract 15,000 from both sides.}$$

$$15{,}000r = 945 \qquad \text{Multiply both sides by 3.}$$

$$r = \frac{945}{15{,}000} = .063. \qquad \text{Divide both sides by 15,000.}$$

Therefore, the interest rate is 6.3%. ✓₄

✓**Checkpoint 4**

You lend a friend $500. She agrees to pay you $520 in 6 months. What is the interest rate?

Present Value

A sum of money that can be deposited today to yield some larger amount in the future is called the **present value** of that future amount. Present value refers to the principal to be invested or loaned, so we use the same variable P as we did for principal. In interest problems, P always represents the amount at the beginning of the period, and A always represents the amount at the end of the period. To find a formula for P, we begin with the future-value formula:

$$A = P(1 + rt).$$

Dividing each side by $1 + rt$ gives the following formula for the present value.

Present Value for Simple Interest

The **present value** P of a future amount of A dollars at a simple interest rate r for t years is

$$P = \frac{A}{1 + rt}.$$

Example 5   Find the present value of $32,000 in 4 months at 9% interest.

Solution

✓**Checkpoint 5**

Find the present value of the given future amounts. Assume 6% interest.

(a) $7500 in 1 year

(b) $89,000 in 5 months

(c) $164,200 in 125 days

$$P = \frac{A}{1 + rt} = \frac{32{,}000}{1 + (.09)\left(\dfrac{4}{12}\right)} = \frac{32{,}000}{1.03} = 31{,}067.96.$$

A deposit of $31,067.96 today at 9% interest would produce $32,000 in 4 months. These two sums, $31,067.96 today and $32,000.00 in 4 months, are equivalent (at 9%) because the first amount becomes the second amount in 4 months. ✓₅

Example 6   Because of a court settlement, Jeff Weidenaar owes $5000 to Chuck Synovec. The money must be paid in 10 months, with no interest. Suppose Weidenaar wants to pay the money today and that Synovec can invest it at an annual rate of 5%. What amount should Synovec be willing to accept to settle the debt?

Solution   The $5000 is the future value in 10 months. So Synovec should be willing to accept an amount that will grow to $5000 in 10 months at 5% interest. In other words, he should accept the present value of $5000 under these circumstances. Use the present-value formula with $A = 5000$, $r = .05$, and $t = 10/12 = 5/6$:

$$P = \frac{A}{1 + rt} = \frac{5000}{1 + .05 * \frac{5}{6}} = 4800.$$

Synovec should be willing to accept $4800 today in settlement of the debt.

Checkpoint 6

Jerrell Davis is owed $19,500 by Christine O'Brien. The money will be paid in 11 months, with no interest. If the current interest rate is 10%, how much should Davis be willing to accept today in settlement of the debt?

Example 7   Larry Parks owes $6500 to Virginia Donovan. The loan is payable in one year at 6% interest. Donovan needs cash to pay medical bills, so four months before the loan is due, she sells the note (loan) to the bank. If the bank wants a return of 9% on its investment, how much should it pay Donovan for the note?

Solution   First find the maturity value of the loan—the amount (with interest) that Parks must pay Donovan:

$$
\begin{aligned}
A &= P(1 + rt) && \text{Maturity-value formula}\\
&= 6500(1 + .06 * 1) && \text{Let } P = 6500, r = .06, \text{ and } t = 1.\\
&= 6500(1.06) = \$6890.
\end{aligned}
$$

In four months, the bank will receive $6890. Since the bank wants a 9% return, compute the present value of this amount at 9% for four months:

$$
\begin{aligned}
P &= \frac{A}{1 + rt} && \text{Present-value formula}\\
&= \frac{6890}{1 + .09\left(\frac{4}{12}\right)} = \$6689.32. && \text{Let } A = 6890, r = .09, \text{ and } t = 4/12.
\end{aligned}
$$

The bank pays Donovan $6689.32 and four months later collects $6890 from Parks.

Checkpoint 7

A firm accepts a $21,000 note due in 8 months, with interest of 10.5%. Two months before it is due, the firm sells the note to a broker. If the broker wants a 12.5% return on his investment, how much should he pay for the note?

Discount

The preceding examples dealt with loans in which money is borrowed and simple interest is charged. For most loans, both the principal (amount borrowed) and the interest are paid at the end of the loan period. With a corporate bond (which is a loan to a company by the investor who buys the bond), interest is paid during the life of the bond and the principal is paid back at maturity. In both cases,

the borrower receives the principal,

but pays back the principal *plus* the interest.

In a **simple discount loan,** however, the interest is deducted in advance from the amount of the loan and the *balance* is given to the borrower. The *full value* of the loan must be paid back at maturity. Thus,

the borrower receives the principal *less* the interest,

but pays back the principal.

The most common examples of simple discount loans are U.S. Treasury bills (T-bills), which are essentially short-term loans to the U.S. government by investors. T-bills are sold at a **discount** from their face value and the Treasury pays back the face value of the T-bill at maturity. The discount amount is the interest deducted in advance from the face value. The Treasury receives the face value less the discount, but pays back the full face value.

> **Example 8** **Finance** An investor bought a six-month $8000 treasury bill on February 28, 2013 that sold at a discount rate of .135%. What is the amount of the discount? What is the price of the T-bill? (Data from: www.treasurydirect.gov.)
>
> **Solution** The discount rate on a T-bill is always a simple *annual* interest rate. Consequently, the discount (interest) is found with the simple interest formula, using $P = 8000$ (face value), $r = .00135$ (discount rate), and $t = .5$ (because 6 months is half a year):
>
> $$\text{Discount} = Prt = 8000 * .00135 * .5 = \$5.40.$$
>
> So the price of the T-bill is
>
> $$\text{Face Value} - \text{Discount} = 8000 - 5.40 = \$7994.60. \quad \checkmark_8$$

✓ **Checkpoint 8**

The maturity times and discount rates for $10,000 T-bills sold on March 7, 2013, are given. Find the discount amount and the price of each T-bill.

(a) one year; .15%

(b) six months; .12%

(c) three months; .11%

In a simple discount loan, such as a T-bill, the discount rate is not the actual interest rate the borrower pays. In Example 8, the discount rate .135% was applied to the face value of $8000, rather than the $7994.60 that the Treasury (the borrower) received.

> **Example 9** **Finance** Find the actual interest rate paid by the Treasury in Example 8.
>
> **Solution** Use the formula for simple interest, $I = Prt$ with r as the unknown. Here, $P = 7994.60$ (the amount the Treasury received) and $I = 5.40$ (the discount amount). Since this is a six-month T-bill, $t = .5$, and we have
>
> $$I = Prt$$
> $$5.40 = 7994.60(r)(.5)$$
> $$5.40 = 3997.3r \qquad \text{Multiply out right side.}$$
> $$r = \frac{5.40}{3997.3} \approx .0013509. \qquad \text{Divide both sides by 3997.3.}$$
>
> So the actual interest rate is .13509%. $\quad \checkmark_9$

✓ **Checkpoint 9**

Find the actual interest rate paid by the Treasury for each T-bill in Checkpoint 8.

5.1 Exercises

Unless stated otherwise, "interest" means simple interest, and "interest rate" and "discount rate" refer to annual rates. Assume 365 days in a year.

1. What factors determine the amount of interest earned on a fixed principal?

Find the interest on each of these loans. (See Example 1.)

2. $35,000 at 6% for 9 months

3. $2850 at 7% for 8 months

4. $1875 at 5.3% for 7 months

5. $3650 at 6.5% for 11 months

6. $5160 at 7.1% for 58 days

7. $2830 at 8.9% for 125 days

8. $8940 at 9%; loan made on May 7 and due September 19

9. $5328 at 8%; loan made on August 16 and due December 30

10. $7900 at 7%; loan made on July 7 and due October 25

Finance *For each of the given corporate bonds, whose interest rates are provided, find the semiannual interest payment and the total interest earned over the life of the bond. (See Example 2, Data from: www.finra.org.)*

11. $5000 IBM, 3-year bond; 1.25%

12. $9000 Barrick Gold Corp., 10-year bond; 3.85%

13. $12,500 Morgan Stanley, 10-year bond; 3.75%

14. $4500 Goldman Sachs, 3-year bond; 6.75%

15. $6500 Amazon.com Corp, 10-year bond; 2.5%

16. $10,000 Wells Fargo, 10-year bond; 3.45%

Find the future value of each of these loans. (See Example 3.)

17. $12,000 loan at 3.5% for 3 months

18. $3475 loan at 7.5% for 6 months

19. $6500 loan at 5.25% for 8 months

20. $24,500 loan at 9.6% for 10 months

21. What is meant by the *present value* of money?

22. In your own words, describe the *maturity value* of a loan.

Find the present value of each future amount. (See Examples 5 and 6.)

23. $15,000 for 9 months; money earns 6%

24. $48,000 for 8 months; money earns 5%

25. $15,402 for 120 days; money earns 6.3%

26. $29,764 for 310 days; money earns 7.2%

Finance   *The given treasury bills were sold on April 4, 2013. Find (a) the price of the T-bill, and (b) the actual interest rate paid by the Treasury. (See Examples 8 and 9. Data from: www.treasurydirect.gov.)*

27. Three-month $20,000 T-bill with discount rate of .075%

28. One-month $12,750 T-bill with discount rate of .070%

29. Six-month $15,500 T-bill with discount rate of .105%

30. One-year $7000 T-bill with discount rate of .140%

Finance   *Historically, treasury bills offered higher rates. On March 9, 2007 the discount rates were substantially higher than in April, 2013. For the following treasury bills bought in 2007, find (a) the price of the T-bill, and (b) the actual interest rate paid by the Treasury. (See Examples 8 and 9. Data from: www.treasury.gov.)*

31. Three-month $20,000 T-bill with discount rate of 4.96%

32. One-month $12,750 T-bill with discount rate of 5.13%

33. Six-month $15,500 T-bill with discount rate of 4.93%

34. Six-month $9000 T-bill with discount rate of 4.93%

Finance   *Work the following applied problems.*

35. In March 1868, Winston Churchill's grandfather, L.W. Jerome, issued $1000 bonds (to pay for a road to a race track he owned in what is now the Bronx). The bonds carried a 7% annual interest rate payable semiannually. Mr. Jerome paid the interest until March 1874, at which time New York City assumed responsibility for the bonds (and the road they financed). (Data from: *New York Times,* February 13, 2009.)

   (a) The first of these bonds matured in March 2009. At that time, how much interest had New York City paid on this bond?

   (b) Another of these bonds will not mature until March 2147! At that time, how much interest will New York City have paid on it?

36. An accountant for a corporation forgot to pay the firm's income tax of $725,896.15 on time. The government charged a penalty of 9.8% interest for the 34 days the money was late. Find the total amount (tax and penalty) that was paid.

37. Mike Branson invested his summer earnings of $3000 in a savings account for college. The account pays 2.5% interest. How much will this amount to in 9 months?

38. To pay for textbooks, a student borrows $450 from a credit union at 6.5% simple interest. He will repay the loan in 38 days, when he expects to be paid for tutoring. How much interest will he pay?

39. An account invested in a money market fund grew from $67,081.20 to $67,359.39 in a month. What was the interest rate, to the nearest tenth?

40. A $100,000 certificate of deposit held for 60 days is worth $101,133.33. To the nearest tenth of a percent, what interest rate was earned?

41. Dave took out a $7500 loan at 7% and eventually repaid $7675 (principal and interest). What was the time period of the loan?

42. What is the time period of a $10,000 loan at 6.75%, in which the total amount of interest paid was $618.75?

43. Tuition of $1769 will be due when the spring term begins in 4 months. What amount should a student deposit today, at 3.25%, to have enough to pay the tuition?

44. A firm of accountants has ordered 7 new computers at a cost of $5104 each. The machines will not be delivered for 7 months. What amount could the firm deposit in an account paying 6.42% to have enough to pay for the machines?

45. John Sun Yee needs $6000 to pay for remodeling work on his house. A contractor agrees to do the work in 10 months. How much should Yee deposit at 3.6% to accumulate the $6000 at that time?

46. Lorie Reilly decides to go back to college. For transportation, she borrows money from her parents to buy a small car for $7200. She plans to repay the loan in 7 months. What amount can she deposit today at 5.25% to have enough to pay off the loan?

47. A six-month $4000 Treasury bill sold for $3930. What was the discount rate?

48. A three-month $7600 Treasury bill carries a discount of $80.75. What is the discount rate for this T-bill?

Finance   *Work the next set of problems, in which you are to find the annual simple interest rate. Consider any fees, dividends, or profits as part of the total interest.*

49. A stock that sold for $22 at the beginning of the year was selling for $24 at the end of the year. If the stock paid a dividend of $.50 per share, what is the simple interest rate on an investment in this stock? (*Hint:* Consider the interest to be the increase in value plus the dividend.)

50. Jerry Ryan borrowed $8000 for nine months at an interest rate of 7%. The bank also charges a $100 processing fee. What is the actual interest rate for this loan?

51. You are due a tax refund of $760. Your tax preparer offers you a no-interest loan to be repaid by your refund check, which will arrive in four weeks. She charges a $60 fee for this service. What actual interest rate will you pay for this loan? (*Hint:* The time period of this loan is not 4/52, because a 365-day year is 52 weeks and 1 day. So use days in your computations.)

52. Your cousin is due a tax refund of $400 in six weeks. His tax preparer has an arrangement with a bank to get him the $400 now. The bank charges an administrative fee of $29 plus interest at 6.5%. What is the actual interest rate for this loan? (See the hint for Exercise 51.)

Finance *Work these problems. (See Example 7.)*

53. A building contractor gives a $13,500 promissory note to a plumber who has loaned him $13,500. The note is due in nine months with interest at 9%. Three months after the note is signed, the plumber sells it to a bank. If the bank gets a 10% return on its investment, how much will the plumber receive? Will it be enough to pay a bill for $13,650?

54. Shalia Johnson owes $7200 to the Eastside Music Shop. She has agreed to pay the amount in seven months at an interest rate of 10%. Two months before the loan is due, the store needs $7550 to pay a wholesaler's bill. The bank will buy the note, provided that its return on the investment is 11%. How much will the store receive? Is it enough to pay the bill?

55. Let y_1 be the future value after t years of $100 invested at 8% annual simple interest. Let y_2 be the future value after t years of $200 invested at 3% annual simple interest.

(a) Think of y_1 and y_2 as functions of t and write the rules of these functions.

(b) Without graphing, describe the graphs of y_1 and y_2.

(c) Verify your answer to part (b) by graphing y_1 and y_2 in the first quadrant.

(d) What do the slopes and y-intercepts of the graphs represent (in terms of the investment situation that they describe)?

56. If $y = 16.25t + 250$ and y is the future value after t years of P dollars at interest rate r, what are P and r? (*Hint:* See Exercise 55.)

✓**Checkpoint Answers**

1. **(a)** $141.67   **(b)** $551.25

2. **(a)** $273.75; $16,425   **(b)** $675; $13,500

3. **(a)** $1023   **(b)** $9710.03   **(c)** $97,046.68

4. 8%

5. **(a)** $7075.47   **(b)** $86,829.27   **(c)** $160,893.96

6. $17,862.60

7. $22,011.43

8. **(a)** $15; $9985   **(b)** $6; $9994
    (c) $2.75; $9997.25

9. **(a)** About .15023%   **(b)** About .12007%
    (c) About .11003%

5.2 Compound Interest

With annual simple interest, you earn interest each year on your original investment. With annual **compound interest,** however, you earn interest both on your original investment *and* on any previously earned interest. To see how this process works, suppose you deposit $1000 at 5% annual interest. The following chart shows how your account would grow with both simple and compound interest:

End of Year	SIMPLE INTEREST		COMPOUND INTEREST	
	Interest Earned	Balance	Interest Earned	Balance
	Original Investment: $1000		*Original Investment:* $1000	
1	1000(.05) = $50	$1050	1000(.05) = $50	$1050
2	1000(.05) = $50	$1100	1050(.05) = $52.50	$1102.50
3	1000(.05) = $50	$1150	1102.50(.05) = $55.13*	$1157.63

As the chart shows, simple interest is computed each year on the original investment, but compound interest is computed on the entire balance at the end of the preceding year. So simple interest always produces $50 per year in interest, whereas compound interest

*Rounded to the nearest cent.

✓ **Checkpoint 1**

Extend the chart in the text by finding the interest earned and the balance at the end of years 4 and 5 for **(a)** simple interest and **(b)** compound interest.

produces $50 interest in the first year and increasingly larger amounts in later years (because you earn interest on your interest). ✓₁

Example 1   If $7000 is deposited in an account that pays 4% interest compounded annually, how much money is in the account after nine years?

Solution   After one year, the account balance is

$$7000 + 4\% \text{ of } 7000 = 7000 + (.04)7000$$
$$= 7000(1 + .04) \qquad \text{Distributive property}$$
$$= 7000(1.04) = \$7280.$$

The initial balance has grown by a factor of 1.04. At the end of the second year, the balance is

$$7280 + 4\% \text{ of } 7280 = 7280 + (.04)7280$$
$$= 7280(1 + .04) \qquad \text{Distributive property}$$
$$= 7280(1.04) = 7571.20.$$

Once again, the balance at the beginning of the year has grown by a factor of 1.04. This is true in general: If the balance at the beginning of a year is P dollars, then the balance at the end of the year is

$$P + 4\% \text{ of } P = P + .04P$$
$$= P(1 + .04)$$
$$= P(1.04).$$

So the account balance grows like this:

Year 1	**Year 2**	**Year 3**
$7000 \rightarrow 7000(1.04) \rightarrow$	$\underbrace{[7000(1.04)](1.04)}_{7000(1.04)^2} \rightarrow$	$\underbrace{[7000(1.04)(1.040)](1.04)}_{7000(1.04)^3} \rightarrow \cdots .$

At the end of nine years, the balance is

$$7000(1.04)^9 = \$9963.18 \qquad \text{(rounded to the nearest penny)}.$$

The argument used in Example 1 applies in the general case and leads to this conclusion.

Compound Interest

If P dollars are invested at interest rate i per period, then the **compound amount** (future value) A after n compounding periods is

$$A = P(1 + i)^n.$$

In Example 1, for instance, we had $P = 7000$, $n = 9$, and $i = .04$ (so that $1 + i = 1 + .04 = 1.04$).

📄 **NOTE** Compare this future value formula for compound interest with the one for simple interest from the previous section, using t as the number of years:

Compound interest $A = P(1 + r)^t$;

Simple interest $A = P(1 + rt)$.

The important distinction between the two formulas is that, in the compound interest formula, the number of years, t, is an *exponent*, so that money grows much more rapidly when interest is compounded.

Example 2 Suppose $1000 is deposited for six years in an account paying 8.31% per year compounded annually.

(a) Find the compound amount.

Solution In the formula above, $P = 1000$, $i = .0831$, and $n = 6$. The compound amount is

$$A = P(1 + i)^n$$
$$A = 1000(1.0831)^6$$
$$A = \$1614.40.$$

(b) Find the amount of interest earned.

Solution Subtract the initial deposit from the compound amount:

$$\text{Amount of interest} = \$1614.40 - \$1000 = \$614.40.$$

✓**Checkpoint 2**

Suppose $17,000 is deposited at 4% compounded annually for 11 years.

(a) Find the compound amount.

(b) Find the amount of interest earned.

TECHNOLOGY TIP
Spreadsheets are ideal for performing financial calculations. Figure 5.1 shows a Microsoft Excel spreadsheet with the formulas for compound and simple interest used to create columns *B* and *C*, respectively, when $1000 is invested at an annual rate of 10%. Notice how rapidly the compound amount increases compared with the maturity value with simple interest. For more details on the use of spreadsheets in the mathematics of finance, see the *Spreadsheet Manual* that is available with this text.

	A	B	C
1	period	compound	simple
2	1	1100	1100
3	2	1210	1200
4	3	1331	1300
5	4	1464.1	1400
6	5	1610.51	1500
7	6	1771.561	1600
8	7	1948.7171	1700
9	8	2143.58881	1800
10	9	2357.947691	1900
11	10	2593.74246	2000
12	11	2853.116706	2100
13	12	3138.428377	2200
14	13	3452.271214	2300
15	14	3797.498336	2400
16	15	4177.248169	2500
17	16	4594.972986	2600
18	17	5054.470285	2700
19	18	5559.917313	2800
20	19	6115.909045	2900
21	20	6727.499949	3000

Figure 5.1

Example 3 If a $16,000 investment grows to $50,000 in 18 years, what is the interest rate (assuming annual compounding)?

Solution Use the compound interest formula, with $P = 16{,}000$, $A = 50{,}000$, and $n = 18$, and solve for i:

$$P(1 + i)^n = A$$
$$16{,}000(1 + i)^{18} = 50{,}000$$
$$(1 + i)^{18} = \frac{50{,}000}{16{,}000} = 3.125 \qquad \text{Divide both sides by 16,000.}$$
$$\sqrt[18]{(1 + i)^{18}} = \sqrt[18]{3.125} \qquad \text{Take 18th roots on both sides.}$$
$$1 + i = \sqrt[18]{3.125}$$
$$i = \sqrt[18]{3.125} - 1 \approx .06535. \qquad \text{Subtract 1 from both sides.}$$

So the interest rate is about 6.535%.

Interest can be compounded more than once a year. Common **compounding periods** include

semiannually (2 periods per year),

quarterly (4 periods per year),

monthly (12 periods per year), and

daily (usually 365 periods per year).

When the annual interest i is compounded m times per year, the interest rate per period is understood to be i/m.

Example 4   **Finance**   In April 2013, www.bankrate.com advertised a one-year certificate of deposit (CD) for GE Capital Retail Bank at an interest rate of 1.05%. Find the value of the CD if $10,000 is invested for one year and interest is compounded according to the given periods.

(a) Annually

Solution   Apply the formula $A = P(1 + i)^n$ with $P = 10,000$, $i = .0105$, and $n = 1$:

$$A = P(1 + i)^n = 10,000(1 + .0105)^1 = 10,000(1.0105) = \$10,105.$$

(b) Semiannually

Solution   Use the same formula and value of P. Here interest is compounded twice a year, so the number of periods is $n = 2$ and the interest rate per period is $i = \dfrac{.0105}{2}$:

$$A = P(1 + i)^n = 10,000\left(1 + \frac{.0105}{2}\right)^2 = \$10,105.28.$$

(c) Quarterly

Solution   Proceed as in part (b), but now interest is compounded 4 times a year, and so $n = 4$ and the interest rate per period is $i = \dfrac{.0105}{4}$:

$$A = P(1 + i)^n = 10,000\left(1 + \frac{.0105}{4}\right)^4 = \$10,105.41.$$

(d) Monthly

Solution   Interest is compounded 12 times a year, so $n = 12$ and $i = \dfrac{.0105}{12}$:

$$A = P(1 + i)^n = 10,000\left(1 + \frac{.0105}{12}\right)^{12} = \$10,105.51.$$

(e) Daily

Solution   Interest is compounded 365 times a year, so $n = 365$ and $i = \dfrac{.0105}{365}$:

$$A = P(1 + i)^n = 10,000\left(1 + \frac{.0105}{365}\right)^{365} = \$10,105.55.$$

Example 5   **Finance**   The given CDs were advertised online by various banks in April 2013. Find the future value of each one. (Data from: cdrates.bankaholic.com.)

(a) Nationwide Bank: $100,000 for 5 years at 1.73% compounded daily.

Solution   Use the compound interest formula with $P = 100,000$. Interest is compounded 365 times a year, so the interest rate per period is $i = \dfrac{.0173}{365}$. Since there are five years, the number of periods in 5 years is $n = 365(5) = 1825$. The future value is

$$A = P(1 + i)^n = 100,000\left(1 + \frac{.0173}{365}\right)^{1825} = \$109,034.91.$$

(b) California First National Bank: $5000 for 2 years at 1.06% compounded monthly.

Solution   Use the compound interest formula with $P = 5000$. Interest is compounded 12 times a year, so the interest rate per period is $i = \dfrac{.0106}{12}$. Since there are two years, the number of periods in 2 years is $n = 12(2) = 24$. The future value is

$$A = P(1 + i)^n = 5000\left(1 + \frac{.0106}{12}\right)^{24} = \$5107.08. \quad $$

 Checkpoint 3

Find the future value for these CDs.

(a) National Republic Bank of Chicago: $1000 at 1.3% compounded monthly for 3 years.

(b) Discover Bank: $2500 at .8% compounded daily for 9 months (assume 30 days in each month).

 Example 4 shows that the more often interest is compounded, the larger is the amount of interest earned. Since interest is rounded to the nearest penny, however, there is a limit on how much can be earned. In Example 4, part (e), for instance, that limit of $10,105.55 has been reached. Nevertheless, the idea of compounding more and more frequently leads to a method of computing interest called **continuous compounding** that is used in certain financial situations The formula for continuous compounding is developed in Case 5, but the formula is given in the following box where $e = 2.7182818\ldots$, which was introduced in Chapter 4.

Continuous Compound Interest

The compound amount A for a deposit of P dollars at an interest rate r per year compounded continuously for t years is given by

$$A = Pe^{rt}.$$

Example 6   Suppose that $5000 is invested at an annual interest rate of 3.1% compounded continuously for 4 years. Find the compound amount.

Solution   In the formula for continuous compounding, let $P = 5000, r = .031$, and $t = 4$. Then a calculator with an e^x key shows that

$$A = Pe^{rt} = 5000e^{.031(4)} = \$5660.08. \quad \boxed{4}$$

 Checkpoint 4

Find the compound amount for $7500 invested at an annual interest rate of 2.07% compounded continuously for 3 years.

```
N=365
I%=1.05
PV=-10000
PMT=0
•FV=10105.55166
P/Y=365
C/Y=365
PMT:END BEGIN
```

Figure 5.2

TECHNOLOGY TIP   TI-84+ and most Casios have a "TVM solver" for financial computations (in the TI APPS/financial menu or the Casio main menu); a similar one can be downloaded for TI-89. Figure 5.2 shows the solution of Example 4(e) on such a solver (FV means future value). The use of these solvers is explained in the next section. Most of the problems in this section can be solved just as quickly with an ordinary calculator.

Ordinary corporate or municipal bonds usually make semiannual simple interest payments. With a **zero-coupon bond,** however, there are no interest payments during the life of the bond. The investor receives a single payment when the bond matures, consisting of his original investment and the interest (compounded semiannually) that it has earned. Zero-coupon bonds are sold at a substantial discount from their face value, and the buyer receives the face value of the bond when it matures. The difference between the face value and the price of the bond is the interest earned.

Example 7   Doug Payne bought a 15-year zero-coupon bond paying 4.5% interest (compounded semiannually) for $12,824.50. What is the face value of the bond?

Solution   Use the compound interest formula with $P = 12{,}824.50$. Interest is paid twice a year, so the rate per period is $i = .045/2$, and the number of periods in 15 years is $n = 30$. The compound amount will be the face value:

$$A = P(1 + i)^n = 12{,}824.50(1 + .045/2)^{30} = 24{,}999.99618.$$

Rounding to the nearest cent, we see that the face value of the bond in $25,000.

Checkpoint 5

Find the face value of the zero coupon.

(a) 30-year bond at 6% sold for $2546

(b) 15-year bond at 5% sold for $16,686

Example 8   Suppose that the inflation rate is 3.5% (which means that the overall level of prices is rising 3.5% a year). How many years will it take for the overall level of prices to double?

Solution   We want to find the number of years it will take for $1 worth of goods or services to cost $2. Think of $1 as the present value and $2 as the future value, with an interest rate of 3.5%, compounded annually. Then the compound amount formula becomes

$$P(1 + i)^n = A$$
$$1(1 + .035)^n = 2,$$

which simplifies as

$$1.035^n = 2.$$

We must solve this equation for n. There are several ways to do this.

Graphical   Use a graphing calculator (with x in place of n) to find the intersection point of the graphs of $y_1 = 1.035^x$ and $y_2 = 2$. Figure 5.3 shows that the intersection point has (approximate) x-coordinate 20.14879. So it will take about 20.15 years for prices to double.

Figure 5.3

Algebraic   The same answer can be obtained by using natural logarithms, as in Section 4.4:

$$1.035^n = 2$$
$$\ln 1.035^n = \ln 2 \qquad \text{Take the logarithm of each side.}$$
$$n \ln 1.035 = \ln 2 \qquad \text{Power property of logarithms.}$$
$$n = \frac{\ln 2}{\ln 1.035} \qquad \text{Divide both sides by } \ln 1.035.$$
$$n \approx 20.14879. \qquad \text{Use a calculator.}$$

Checkpoint 6

Using a calculator, find the number of years it will take for $500 to increase to $750 in an account paying 6% interest compounded semiannually.

Effective Rate (APY)

If you invest $100 at 9%, compounded monthly, then your balance at the end of one year is

$$A = P(1 + i)^n = 100\left(1 + \frac{.09}{12}\right)^{12} = \$109.38.$$

You have earned $9.38 in interest, which is 9.38% of your original $100. In other words, $100 invested at 9.38% compounded *annually* will produce the same amount of interest (namely, $100 * .0938 = 9.38) as does 9% compounded monthly. In this situation, 9% is called the **nominal** or **stated rate,** while 9.38% is called the **effective rate** or **annual percentage yield (APY).**

In the discussion that follows, the nominal rate is denoted r and the APY (effective rate) is denoted r_E.

Effective Rate (r_E) or Annual Percentage Yield (APY)

The *APY* r_E is the annual compounding rate needed to produce the same amount of interest in one year, as the nominal rate does with more frequent compounding.

Example 9   **Finance**   In April 2013, Nationwide Bank offered its customers a 5-year $100,000 CD at 1.73% interest, compounded daily. Find the APY. (Data from: cdrates.bankaholic.com.)

Solution   The box given previously means that we must have the following:

$$\frac{\$100,000 \text{ at rate } r_E}{\text{compounded annually}} = \frac{\$100,000 \text{ at } 1.73\%,}{\text{compounded daily}}$$

$$100,000(1 + r_E)^1 = 100,000\left(1 + \frac{.0173}{365}\right)^{365} \qquad \text{Compound interest formula.}$$

$$(1 + r_E) = \left(1 + \frac{.0173}{365}\right)^{365} \qquad \text{Divide both sides by 100,000.}$$

$$r_E = \left(1 + \frac{.0173}{365}\right)^{365} - 1 \qquad \text{Subtract 1 from both sides.}$$

$$r_E \approx .0175.$$

So the APY is about 1.75%.

The argument in Example 9 can be carried out with 100,000 replaced by P, .0173 by r, and 365 by m. The result is the effective-rate formula.

Effective Rate (APY)

The effective rate (APY) corresponding to a stated rate of interest r compounded m times per year is

$$r_E = \left(1 + \frac{r}{m}\right)^m - 1.$$

Example 10   **Finance**   When interest rates are low (as they were when this text went to press), the interest rate and the APY are insignificantly different. To see when the difference is more pronounced, we will find the APY for each of the given money market checking accounts (with balances between $50,000 and $100,000), which were advertised in October 2008 when offered rates were higher.

(a)   Imperial Capital Bank: 3.35% compounded monthly.

Solution   Use the effective-rate formula with $r = .0335$ and $m = 12$:

$$r_E = \left(1 + \frac{r}{m}\right)^m - 1 = \left(1 + \frac{.0335}{12}\right)^{12} - 1 = .034019.$$

So the APY is about 3.40%, a slight increase over the nominal rate of 3.35%.

(b) U.S. Bank: 2.33% compounded daily.

Solution   Use the formula with $r = .0233$ and $m = 365$:

$$r_E = \left(1 + \frac{r}{m}\right)^m - 1 = \left(1 + \frac{.0233}{365}\right)^{365} - 1 = .023572.$$

The APY is about 2.36%.

Checkpoint 7

Find the APY corresponding to a nominal rate of

(a) 12% compounded monthly;

(b) 8% compounded quarterly.

Example 11   Bank A is now lending money at 10% interest compounded annually. The rate at Bank B is 9.6% compounded monthly, and the rate at Bank C is 9.7% compounded quarterly. If you need to borrow money, at which bank will you pay the least interest?

Solution   Compare the APYs:

$$\text{Bank } A: \quad \left(1 + \frac{.10}{1}\right)^1 - 1 = .10 = 10\%;$$

$$\text{Bank } B: \quad \left(1 + \frac{.096}{12}\right)^{12} - 1 \approx .10034 = 10.034\%;$$

$$\text{Bank } C: \quad \left(1 + \frac{.097}{4}\right)^4 - 1 \approx .10059 = 10.059\%.$$

The lowest APY is at Bank A, which has the highest nominal rate.

TECHNOLOGY TIP
Effective rates (APYs) can be computed on TI-84+ by using "Eff" in the APPS financial menu, as shown in Figure 5.4 for Example 11.

```
▶Eff(10.1)
                    10
▶Eff(9.6,12)
          10.03386937
▶Eff(9.7,4)
          10.05857629
```

Figure 5.4

NOTE   Although you can find both the stated interest rate and the APY for most certificates of deposit and other interest-bearing accounts, most bank advertisements mention only the APY.

Checkpoint 8

Find the APY corresponding to a nominal rate of

(a) 4% compounded quarterly;

(b) 7.9% compounded daily.

Present Value for Compound Interest

The formula for compound interest, $A = P(1 + i)^n$, has four variables: A, P, i, and n. Given the values of any three of these variables, the value of the fourth can be found. In particular, if A (the future amount), i, and n are known, then P can be found. Here, P is the amount that should be deposited today to produce A dollars in n periods.

Example 12   Keisha Jones must pay a lump sum of $6000 in 5 years. What amount deposited today at 6.2% compounded annually will amount to $6000 in 5 years?

Solution   Here, $A = 6000$, $i = .062$, $n = 5$, and P is unknown. Substituting these values into the formula for the compound amount gives

$$6000 = P(1.062)^5$$

$$P = \frac{6000}{(1.062)^5} = 4441.49,$$

or $4441.49. If Jones leaves $4441.49 for 5 years in an account paying 6.2% compounded annually, she will have $6000 when she needs it. To check your work, use the compound interest formula with $P = \$4441.49$, $i = .062$, and $n = 5$. You should get $A = \$6000.00$.

Checkpoint 9

Find P in Example 12 if the interest rate is

(a) 6%;

(b) 10%.

As Example 12 shows, $6000 in 5 years is (approximately) the same as $4441.49 today (if money can be deposited at 6.2% annual interest). An amount that can be deposited today to yield a given amount in the future is called the *present value* of the future amount. By solving $A = P(1 + i)^n$ for P, we get the following general formula for present value.

Present Value for Compound Interest

The **present value** of A dollars compounded at an interest rate i per period for n periods is

$$P = \frac{A}{(1 + i)^n}, \quad \text{or} \quad P = A(1 + i)^{-n}.$$

Example 13 A zero-coupon bond with face value $15,000 and a 6% interest rate (compounded semiannually) will mature in 9 years. What is a fair price to pay for the bond today?

Solution Think of the bond as a 9-year investment paying 6%, compounded semiannually, whose future value is $15,000. Its present value (what it is worth today) would be a fair price. So use the present value formula with $A = 15,000$. Since interest is compounded twice a year, the interest rate per period is $i = .06/2 = .03$ and the number of periods in nine years is $n = 9(2) = 18$. Hence,

$$P = \frac{A}{(1 + i)^n} = \frac{15,000}{(1 + .03)^{18}} \approx 8810.919114.$$

✓**Checkpoint 10**

Find the fair price (present value) in Example 13 if the interest rate is 7.5%.

So a fair price would be the present value of $8810.92. ✓₁₀

Example 14 **Economics** The average annual inflation rate for the years 2010–2012 was 2.29%. How much did an item that sells for $1000 in early 2013 cost three years before? (Data from: inflationdata.com.)

Solution Think of the price three years prior as the present value P and $1000 as the future value A. Then $i = .0229, n = 3$, and the present value is

$$P = \frac{A}{(1 + i)^n} = \frac{1000}{(1 + .0229)^3} = \$934.33.$$

✓**Checkpoint 11**

What did a $1000 item sell for 5 years prior if the annual inflation rate has been 3.2%?

So the item cost $934.33 three years prior. ✓₁₁

Summary

At this point, it seems helpful to summarize the notation and the most important formulas for simple and compound interest. We use the following variables:

- P = principal or present value;
- A = future or maturity value;
- r = annual (stated or nominal) interest rate;
- t = number of years;
- m = number of compounding periods per year;
- i = interest rate per period;
- n = total number of compounding periods;
- r_E = effective rate (APY).

Simple Interest	Compound Interest	Continuous Compounding
$A = P(1 + rt)$	$A = P(1 + i)^n$	$A = Pe^{rt}$
$P = \dfrac{A}{1 + rt}$	$P = \dfrac{A}{(1 + i)^n} = A(1 + i)^{-n}$	$P = \dfrac{A}{e^{rt}}$
	$r_E = \left(1 + \dfrac{r}{m}\right)^m - 1$	

5.2 Exercises

Interest on the zero-coupon bonds here is compounded semiannually.

✎ **1.** In the preceding summary what is the difference between *r* and *i*? between *t* and *n*?

✎ **2.** Explain the difference between simple interest and compound interest.

3. What factors determine the amount of interest earned on a fixed principal?

✎ **4.** In your own words, describe the *maturity value* of a loan.

✎ **5.** What is meant by the *present value* of money?

6. If interest is compounded more than once per year, which rate is higher, the stated rate or the effective rate?

Find the compound amount and the interest earned for each of the following deposits. (See Examples 1, 2, 4, and 5.)

7. $1000 at 4% compounded annually for 6 years

8. $1000 at 6% compounded annually for 10 years

9. $470 at 8% compounded semiannually for 12 years

10. $15,000 at 4.6% compounded semiannually for 11 years

11. $6500 at 4.5% compounded quarterly for 8 years

12. $9100 at 6.1% compounded quarterly for 4 years

Finance *The following CDs were available on www.bankrate. com on April 13, 2013. Find the compound amount and the interest earned for each of the following. (See Example 5.)*

13. Virtual Bank: $10,000 at .9% compounded daily for 1 year

14. AloStar Bank of Commerce: $1000 at .85% compounded daily for 1 year

15. USAA: $5000 at .81% compounded monthly for 2 years

16. Centennial Bank: $20,000 at .45% compounded monthly for 2 years

17. E-LOAN: $100,000 at 1.52% compounded daily for 5 years

18. Third Federal Savings and Loans: $150,000 at 1.15% compounded quarterly for 5 years

Find the interest rate (with annual compounding) that makes the statement true. (See Example 3.)

19. $3000 grows to $3606 in 5 years

20. $2550 grows to $3905 in 11 years

21. $8500 grows to $12,161 in 7 years

22. $9000 grows to $17,118 in 16 years

Find the compound amount and the interest earned when the following investments have continuous compounding. (See Example 6.)

23. $20,000 at 3.5% for 5 years

24. $15,000 at 2.9% for 10 years

25. $30,000 at 1.8% for 3 years

26. $100,000 at 5.1% for 20 years

Find the face value (to the nearest dollar) of the zero-coupon bond. (See Example 7.)

27. 15-year bond at 5.2%; price $4630

28. 10-year bond at 4.1%; price $13,328

29. 20-year bond at 3.5%; price $9992

✎ **30.** How do the nominal, or stated, interest rate and the effective interest rate (APY) differ?

Find the APY corresponding to the given nominal rates. (See Examples 9–11).

31. 4% compounded semiannually

32. 6% compounded quarterly

33. 5% compounded quarterly

34. 4.7% compounded semiannually

Find the present value of the given future amounts. (See Example 12.)

35. $12,000 at 5% compounded annually for 6 years

36. $8500 at 6% compounded annually for 9 years

37. $17,230 at 4% compounded quarterly for 10 years

38. $5240 at 6% compounded quarterly for 8 years

What price should you be willing to pay for each of these zero-coupon bonds? (See Example 13.)

39. 5-year $5000 bond; interest at 3.5%

40. 10-year $10,000 bond; interest at 4%

41. 15-year $20,000 bond; interest at 4.7%

42. 20-year $15,000 bond; interest at 5.3%

Finance *For Exercises 43 and 44, assume an annual inflation rate of 2.07% (the annual inflation rate of 2012 according to www.InflationData.com). Find the previous price of the following items. (See Example 14.)*

43. How much did an item that costs $5000 now cost 4 years prior?

44. How much did an item that costs $7500 now cost 5 years prior?

45. If the annual inflation rate is 3.6%, how much did an item that costs $500 now cost 2 years prior?

46. If the annual inflation rate is 1.18%, how much did an item that costs $1250 now cost 6 years prior?

47. If money can be invested at 8% compounded quarterly, which is larger, $1000 now or $1210 in 5 years? Use present value to decide.

48. If money can be invested at 6% compounded annually, which is larger, $10,000 now or $15,000 in 6 years? Use present value to decide.

Finance *Work the following applied problems.*

49. A small business borrows $50,000 for expansion at 9% compounded monthly. The loan is due in 4 years. How much interest will the business pay?

50. A developer needs $80,000 to buy land. He is able to borrow the money at 10% per year compounded quarterly. How much will the interest amount to if he pays off the loan in 5 years?

51. Lora Reilly has inherited $10,000 from her uncle's estate. She will invest the money for 2 years. She is considering two investments: a money market fund that pays a guaranteed 5.8% interest compounded daily and a 2-year Treasury note at 6% annual interest. Which investment pays the most interest over the 2-year period?

52. Which of these 20-year zero-coupon bonds will be worth more at maturity: one that sells for $4510, with a 6.1% interest rate, or one that sells for $5809, with a 4.8% interest rate?

53. As the prize in a contest, you are offered $1000 now or $1210 in 5 years. If money can be invested at 6% compounded annually, which is larger?

54. Two partners agree to invest equal amounts in their business. One will contribute $10,000 immediately. The other plans to contribute an equivalent amount in 3 years, when she expects to acquire a large sum of money. How much should she contribute at that time to match her partner's investment now, assuming an interest rate of 6% compounded semiannually?

55. In the Capital Appreciation Fund, a mutual fund from T. Rowe Price, a $10,000 investment grew to $11,115 over the 3-year period 2010–2013. Find the annual interest rate, compounded yearly, that this investment earned.

56. In the Vanguard Information Technology Index Fund, a $10,000 investment grew to $16,904.75 over the 10-year period 2003–2013. Find the annual interest rate, compounded yearly, that this investment earned.

57. The Flagstar Bank in Michigan offered a 5-year certificate of deposit (CD) at 4.38% interest compounded quarterly in June 2005. On the same day on the Internet, Principal Bank offered a 5-year CD at 4.37% interest compounded monthly. Find the APY for each CD. Which bank paid a higher APY?

58. The Westfield Bank in Ohio offered the CD rates shown in the accompanying table in October 2008. The APY rates shown assume monthly compounding. Find the corresponding nominal rates to the nearest hundredth. (*Hint:* Solve the effective-rate equation for r.)

Term	6 mo	1 yr	2 yr	3 yr	5 yr
APY (%)	2.25	2.50	3.00	3.25	3.75

59. A company has agreed to pay $2.9 million in 5 years to settle a lawsuit. How much must it invest now in an account paying 5% interest compounded monthly to have that amount when it is due?

60. Bill Poole wants to have $20,000 available in 5 years for a down payment on a house. He has inherited $16,000. How much of the inheritance should he invest now to accumulate the $20,000 if he can get an interest rate of 5.5% compounded quarterly?

61. If inflation has been running at 3.75% per year and a new car costs $23,500 today, what would it have cost three years ago?

62. If inflation is 2.4% per year and a washing machine costs $345 today, what did a similar model cost five years ago?

Economics *Use the approach in Example 8 to find the time it would take for the general level of prices in the economy to double at the average annual inflation rates in Exercises 63–66.*

63. 3%   **64.** 4%   **65.** 5%   **66.** 5.5%

67. The consumption of electricity has increased historically at 6% per year. If it continues to increase at this rate indefinitely, find the number of years before the electric utility companies will need to double their generating capacity.

68. Suppose a conservation campaign coupled with higher rates causes the demand for electricity to increase at only 2% per year, as it has recently. Find the number of years before the utility companies will need to double their generating capacity.

69. You decide to invest a $16,000 bonus in a money market fund that guarantees a 5.5% annual interest rate compounded monthly for 7 years. A one-time fee of $30 is charged to set up the account. In addition, there is an annual administrative charge of 1.25% of the balance in the account at the end of each year.

(a) How much is in the account at the end of the first year?

(b) How much is in the account at the end of the seventh year?

70. Joe Marusa decides to invest $12,000 in a money market fund that guarantees a 4.6% annual interest rate compounded daily for 6 years. A one-time fee of $25 is charged to set up the account. In addition, there is an annual administration charge of .9% of the balance in the account at the end of each year.

(a) How much is in the account at the end of the first year?

(b) How much is in the account at the end of the sixth year?

The following exercises are from professional examinations.

71. On January 1, 2002, Jack deposited $1000 into Bank X to earn interest at the rate of j per annum compounded semiannually. On January 1, 2007, he transferred his account to Bank Y to earn interest at the rate of k per annum compounded quarterly. On January 1, 2010, the balance at Bank Y was $1990.76. If Jack could have earned interest at the rate of k per annum compounded quarterly from January 1, 2002, through January 1, 2010, his balance would have been $2203.76. Which of the following represents the ratio k/j? (Deposit of Jack in Bank X from Course 140 Examination, Mathematics of Compound Interest. Copyright © Society of Actuaries. Reproduced by permission of Society of Actuaries.)

(a) 1.25   (b) 1.30   (c) 1.35   (d) 1.40   (e) 1.45

72. On January 1, 2009, Tone Company exchanged equipment for a $200,000 non-interest-bearing note due on January 1, 2012. The prevailing rate of interest for a note of this type on January 1, 2009, was 10%. The present value of $1 at 10% for three periods is 0.75. What amount of interest revenue should be included in Tone's 2010 income statement? (Adapted from the Uniform CPA Examination, American Institute of Certified Public Accountants.)

(a) $7500   (b) $15,000

(c) $16,500   (d) $20,000

✓**Checkpoint Answers**

1. (a)

Year	Interest	Balance
4	$50	$1200
5	$50	$1250

(b)

Year	Interest	Balance
4	$57.88	$1215.51
5	$60.78	$1276.29

2. (a) $26,170.72   (b) $9170.72

3. (a) $1039.75   (b) $2514.84

4. $7980.52

5. (a) $15,000   (b) $35,000

6. About 7 years ($n = 6.86$)

7. (a) 12.68%   (b) 8.24%

8. (a) 4.06%   (b) 8.220%

9. (a) $4483.55   (b) $3725.53

10. $7732.24   11. $854.28

5.3 Annuities, Future Value, and Sinking Funds

So far in this chapter, only lump-sum deposits and payments have been discussed. Many financial situations, however, involve a sequence of payments at regular intervals, such as weekly deposits in a savings account or monthly payments on a mortgage or car loan. Such periodic payments are the subject of this section and the next.

The analysis of periodic payments will require an algebraic technique that we now develop. Suppose x is a real number. For reasons that will become clear later, we want to find the product

$$(x - 1)(1 + x + x^2 + x^3 + \cdots + x^{11}).$$

Using the distributive property to multiply this expression out, we see that all but two of the terms cancel:

$$x(1 + x + x^2 + x^3 + \cdots + x^{11}) - 1(1 + x + x^2 + x^3 + \cdots + x^{11})$$
$$= (x + x^2 + x^3 + \cdots + x^{11} + x^{12}) - 1 - x - x^2 - x^3 - \cdots - x^{11}$$
$$= x^{12} - 1.$$

Hence, $(x - 1)(1 + x + x^2 + x^3 + \cdots + x^{11}) = x^{12} - 1$. Dividing both sides by $x - 1$, we have

$$1 + x + x^2 + x^3 + \cdots + x^{11} = \frac{x^{12} - 1}{x - 1}.$$

The same argument, with any positive integer n in place of 12 and $n - 1$ in place of 11, produces the following result:

> If x is a real number and n is a positive integer, then
> $$1 + x + x^2 + x^3 + \cdots + x^{n-1} = \frac{x^n - 1}{x - 1}.$$

```
1+5+5²+5³+5⁴+5⁵+5⁶
                   19531
5⁷-1
─────
5-1
                   19531
```

Figure 5.5

For example, when $x = 5$ and $n = 7$, we see that

$$1 + 5 + 5^2 + 5^3 + 5^4 + 5^5 + 5^6 = \frac{5^7 - 1}{5 - 1} = \frac{78,124}{4} = 19,531.$$

A calculator can easily add up the terms on the left side, but it is faster to use the formula (Figure 5.5).

Ordinary Annuities

A sequence of equal payments made at equal periods of time is called an **annuity.** The time between payments is the **payment period,** and the time from the beginning of the first payment period to the end of the last period is called the **term of the annuity.** Annuities can be used to accumulate funds—for example, when you make regular deposits in a savings account. Or they can be used to pay out funds—as when you receive regular payments from a pension plan after you retire.

Annuities that pay out funds are considered in the next section. This section deals with annuities in which funds are accumulated by regular payments into an account or investment that earns compound interest. The **future value** of such an annuity is the final sum on deposit—that is, the total amount of all deposits and all interest earned by them.

We begin with **ordinary annuities**—ones where the payments are made at the *end* of each period and the frequency of payments is the same as the frequency of compounding the interest.

Example 1 $1500 is deposited at the end of each year for the next 6 years in an account paying 8% interest compounded annually. Find the future value of this annuity.

Solution   Figure 5.6 shows the situation schematically.

Figure 5.6

To find the future value of this annuity, look separately at each of the $1500 payments. The first $1500 is deposited at the end of period 1 and earns interest for the remaining 5 periods. From the formula in the box on page 233, the compound amount produced by this payment is

$$1500(1 + .08)^5 = 1500(1.08)^5.$$

The second $1500 payment is deposited at the end of period 2 and earns interest for the remaining 4 periods. So the compound amount produced by the second payment is

$$1500(1 + .08)^4 = 1500(1.08)^4.$$

Continue to compute the compound amount for each subsequent payment, as shown in Figure 5.7. Note that the last payment earns no interest.

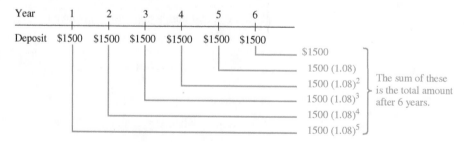

Figure 5.7

The last column of Figure 5.7 shows that the total amount after 6 years is the sum

$$1500 + 1500 \cdot 1.08 + 1500 \cdot 1.08^2 + 1500 \cdot 1.08^3 + 1500 \cdot 1.08^4 + 1500 \cdot 1.08^5$$
$$= 1500(1 + 1.08 + 1.08^2 + 1.08^3 + 1.08^4 + 1.08^5). \tag{1}$$

Now apply the algebraic fact in the box on page 243 to the expression in parentheses (with $x = 1.08$ and $n = 6$). It shows that the sum (the future value of the annuity) is

$$1500 \cdot \frac{1.08^6 - 1}{1.08 - 1} = \$11{,}003.89. \quad \boxed{✓_1}$$

✓

Checkpoint 1

Complete these steps for an annuity of $2000 at the end of each year for 3 years. Assume interest of 6% compounded annually.

(a) The first deposit of $2000 produces a total of _____.

(b) The second deposit becomes _____.

(c) No interest is earned on the third deposit, so the total in the account is _____.

Example 1 is the model for finding a formula for the future value of any annuity. Suppose that a payment of R dollars is deposited at the end of each period for n periods, at an interest rate of i per period. Then the future value of this annuity can be found by using the procedure in Example 1, with these replacements:

1500	.08	1.08	6	5
↓	↓	↓	↓	↓
R	i	$1 + i$	n	$n - 1$

The future value S in Example 1—call it S—is the sum **(1)**, which now becomes

$$S = R[1 + (1 + i) + (1 + i)^2 + \cdots + (1 + i)^{n-2} + (1 + i)^{n-1}].$$

Apply the algebraic fact in the box on page 243 to the expression in brackets (with $x = 1 + i$). Then we have

$$S = R\left[\frac{(1 + i)^n - 1}{(1 + i) - 1}\right] = R\left[\frac{(1 + i)^n - 1}{i}\right].$$

The quantity in brackets in the right-hand part of the preceding equation is sometimes written $s_{\overline{n}|i}$ (read "s-angle-n at i"). So we can summarize as follows.[*]

Future Value of an Ordinary Annuity

The future value S of an ordinary annuity used to accumulate funds is given by

$$S = R\left[\frac{(1 + i)^n - 1}{i}\right], \quad \text{or} \quad S = R \cdot s_{\overline{n}|i,}$$

where

    R is the payment at the end of each period,

    i is the interest rate per period, and

    n is the number of periods.

TECHNOLOGY TIP Most computations with annuities can be done quickly with a spreadsheet program or a graphing calculator. On a calculator, use the TVM solver if there is one (see the Technology Tip on page 236); otherwise, use the programs in the Program Appendix.

Figure 5.8 shows how to do Example 1 on a TI-84+ TVM solver. First, enter the known quantities: N = number of payments, I % = annual interest rate, PV = present value, PMT = payment per period (entered as a negative amount), P/Y = number of payments per year, and C/Y = number of compoundings per year. At the bottom of the screen, set PMT: to "END" for ordinary annuities. Then put the cursor next to the unknown amount FV (future value), and press SOLVE.

Note: P/Y and C/Y should always be the same for problems in this text. If you use the solver for ordinary compound interest problems, set PMT = 0 and enter either PV or FV (whichever is known) as a negative amount.

```
N=6
I%=8
PV=0
PMT=-1500
•FV=11003.89356
P/Y=1
C/Y=1
PMT:END BEGIN
```

Figure 5.8

Example 2 A rookie player in the National Football League just signed his first 7-year contract. To prepare for his future, he deposits $150,000 at the end of each year for 7 years in an account paying 4.1% compounded annually. How much will he have on deposit after 7 years?

[*]We use S for the future value here instead of A, as in the compound interest formula, to help avoid confusing the two formulas.

Solution His payments form an ordinary annuity with $R = 150{,}000, n = 7$, and $i = .041$. The future value of this annuity (by the previous formula) is

$$S = 150{,}000\left[\frac{(1.041)^7 - 1}{.041}\right] = \$1{,}188{,}346.11.\ \checkmark_2$$

✓ **Checkpoint 2**

Johnson Building Materials deposits $2500 at the end of each year into an account paying 8% per year compounded annually. Find the total amount on deposit after

(a) 6 years;

(b) 10 years.

Example 3   Allyson, a college professor, contributed $950 a month to the CREF stock fund (an investment vehicle available to many college and university employees). For the past 10 years this fund has returned 4.25%, compounded monthly.

(a) How much did Allyson earn over the course of the last 10 years?

Solution Allyson's payments form an ordinary annuity, with monthly payment $R = 950$. The interest per month is $i = \dfrac{.0425}{12}$, and the number of months in 10 years is $n = 10 * 12 = 120$. The future value of this annuity is

$$S = R\left[\frac{(1 + i)^n - 1}{i}\right] = 950\left[\frac{(1 + .0425/12)^{120} - 1}{.0425/12}\right] = \$141{,}746.90.$$

(b) As of April 14, 2013, the year to date return was 9.38%, compounded monthly. If this rate were to continue, and Allyson continues to contribute $950 a month, how much would the account be worth at the end of the next 15 years?

Solution Deal separately with the two parts of her account (the $950 contributions in the future and the $141,746.90 already in the account). The contributions form an ordinary annuity as in part (a). Now we have $R = 950, i = .0938/12$, and $n = 12 * 15 = 180$. So the future value is

$$S = R\left[\frac{(1 + i)^n - 1}{i}\right] = 950\left[\frac{(1 + .0938/12)^{180} - 1}{.0938/12}\right] = \$372{,}068.65.$$

Meanwhile, the $141,746.90 from the first 10 years is also earning interest at 9.38%, compounded monthly. By the compound amount formula (Section 5.2), the future value of this money is

$$141{,}746.90(1 + .0938/12)^{180} = \$575{,}691.85.$$

So the total amount in Allyson's account after 25 years is the sum

$$\$372{,}068.65 + \$575{,}691.85 = \$947{,}760.50.\ \checkmark_3$$

✓ **Checkpoint 3**

Find the total value of the account in part (b) of Example 3 if the fund's return for the last 15 years is 8.72%, compounded monthly.

Sinking Funds

A **sinking fund** is a fund set up to receive periodic payments. Corporations and municipalities use sinking funds to repay bond issues, to retire preferred stock, to provide for replacement of fixed assets, and for other purposes. If the payments are equal and are made at the end of regular periods, they form an ordinary annuity.

Example 4   A business sets up a sinking fund so that it will be able to pay off bonds it has issued when they mature. If it deposits $12,000 at the end of each quarter in an account that earns 5.2% interest, compounded quarterly, how much will be in the sinking fund after 10 years?

Solution The sinking fund is an annuity, with $R = 12{,}000, i = .052/4$, and $n = 4(10) = 40$. The future value is

$$S = R\left[\frac{(1 + i)^n - 1}{i}\right] = 12{,}000\left[\frac{(1 + .052/4)^{40} - 1}{.052/4}\right] = \$624{,}369.81.$$

So there will be about $624,370 in the sinking fund.

Example 5 A firm borrows $6 million to build a small factory. The bank requires it to set up a $200,000 sinking fund to replace the roof after 15 years. If the firm's deposits earn 6% interest, compounded annually, find the payment it should make at the end of each year into the sinking fund.

Solution This situation is an annuity with future value $S = 200,000$, interest rate $i = .06$, and $n = 15$. Solve the future-value formula for R:

$$S = R\left[\frac{(1 + i)^n - 1}{i}\right]$$

$$200,000 = R\left[\frac{(1 + .06)^{15} - 1}{.06}\right] \qquad \text{Let } S = 200,000, i = .06, \text{ and } n = 15.$$

$$200,000 = R[23.27597] \qquad \text{Compute the quantity in brackets.}$$

$$R = \frac{200,000}{23.27597} = \$8592.55. \qquad \text{Divide both sides by 23.27597.}$$

So the annual payment is about $8593.

✓ Checkpoint 4

Francisco Arce needs $8000 in 6 years so that he can go on an archaeological dig. He wants to deposit equal payments at the end of each quarter so that he will have enough to go on the dig. Find the amount of each payment if the bank pays

(a) 12% interest compounded quarterly;

(b) 8% interest compounded quarterly.

Example 6 As an incentive for a valued employee to remain on the job, a company plans to offer her a $100,000 bonus, payable when she retires in 20 years. If the company deposits $200 a month in a sinking fund, what interest rate must it earn, with monthly compounding, in order to guarantee that the fund will be worth $100,000 in 20 years?

Solution The sinking fund is an annuity with $R = 200$, $n = 12(20) = 240$, and future value $S = 100,000$. We must find the interest rate. If x is the annual interest rate in decimal form, then the interest rate per month is $i = x/12$. Inserting these values into the future-value formula, we have

$$R\left[\frac{(1 + i)^n - 1}{i}\right] = S$$

$$200\left[\frac{(1 + x/12)^{240} - 1}{x/12}\right] = 100,000.$$

This equation is hard to solve algebraically. You can get a rough approximation by using a calculator and trying different values for x. With a graphing calculator, you can get an accurate solution by graphing

$$y_1 = 200\left[\frac{(1 + x/12)^{240} - 1}{x/12}\right] \quad \text{and} \quad y_2 = 100,000$$

and finding the x-coordinate of the point where the graphs intersect. Figure 5.9 shows that the company needs an interest rate of about 6.661%. The same answer can be obtained on a TVM solver (Figure 5.10).

500,000

Ø	0.2

Intersection
X=.06660938   Y=100000

Figure 5.9

N=240
• I%=6.660938285
PV=0
PMT=-200
FV=100000
P/Y=12
C/Y=12
PMT:**END** BEGIN

Figure 5.10

✓ Checkpoint 5

Pete's Pizza deposits $5800 at the end of each quarter for 4 years.

(a) Find the final amount on deposit if the money earns 6.4% compounded quarterly.

(b) Pete wants to accumulate $110,000 in the 4-year period. What interest rate (to the nearest tenth) will be required?

Annuities Due

The formula developed previously is for *ordinary annuities*—annuities with payments at the *end* of each period. The results can be modified slightly to apply to **annuities due**—annuities where payments are made at the *beginning* of each period.

An example will illustrate how this is done. Consider an annuity due in which payments of $100 are made for 3 years, and an ordinary annuity in which payments of $100 are made for 4 years, both with 5% interest, compounded annually. Figure 5.11 computes the growth of each payment separately (as was done in Example 1).

Annuity Due (payments at beginning of year for 3 years)

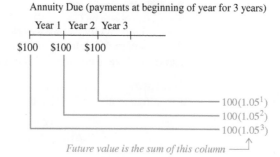

Ordinary Annuity (payments at end of year for 4 years)

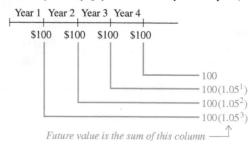

Figure 5.11

Figure 5.11 shows that the future values are the same, *except* for one $100 payment on the ordinary annuity (shown in red). So we can use the formula on page 245 to find the future value of the 4-year ordinary annuity and then subtract one $100 payment to get the future value of the 3-year annuity due:

Future value of = **Future value of** − **One payment**
3-year annuity due   **4-year ordinary annuity**

$$S = 100\left[\frac{1.05^4 - 1}{.05}\right] - 100 = \$331.01.$$

Essentially the same argument works in the general case.

Future Value of an Annuity Due

The future value S of an annuity due used to accumulate funds is given by

$$S = R\left[\frac{(1 + i)^{n+1} - 1}{i}\right] - R$$

$$S = \text{an ordinary annuity} - \text{One payment,}$$
$$\text{of } n + 1 \text{ payments}$$

Future value of

where

   R is the payment at the beginning of each period,

   i is the interest rate per period, and

   n is the number of periods.

Example 7   Payments of $500 are made at the beginning of each quarter for 7 years in an account paying 8% interest, compounded quarterly. Find the future value of this annuity due.

✓ **Checkpoint 6**

(a) Ms. Black deposits $800 at the beginning of each 6-month period for 5 years. Find the final amount if the account pays 6% compounded semiannually.

(b) Find the final amount if this account were an ordinary annuity.

Solution In 7 years, there are $n = 28$ quarterly periods. For an annuity due, add one period to get $n + 1 = 29$, and use the formula with $i = .08/4 = .02$:

$$S = R\left[\frac{(1 + i)^{n+1} - 1}{i}\right] - R = 500\left[\frac{(1 + .02)^{29} - 1}{.02}\right] - 500 = \$18,896.12.$$

After 7 years, the account balance will be $18,896.12. ✓₆

Example 8 Jay Rechtien plans to have a fixed amount from his paycheck directly deposited into an account that pays 5.5% interest, compounded monthly. If he gets paid on the first day of the month and wants to accumulate $13,000 in the next three-and-a-half years, how much should he deposit each month?

Solution Jay's deposits form an annuity due whose future value is $S = 13,000$. The interest rate is $i = .055/12$. There are 42 months in three-and-a-half years. Since this is an annuity due, add one period, so that $n + 1 = 43$. Then solve the future-value formula for the payment R:

$$R\left[\frac{(1 + i)^{n+1} - 1}{i}\right] - R = S$$

$$R\left[\frac{(1 + .055/12)^{43} - 1}{.055/12}\right] - R = 13,000 \qquad \text{Let } i = .055/12, n = 43, \text{ and } S = 13,000.$$

$$R\left(\left[\frac{(1 + .055/12)^{43} - 1}{.055/12}\right] - 1\right) = 13,000 \qquad \text{Factor out } R \text{ on left side.}$$

$$R(46.4103) = 13,000 \qquad \text{Compute left side.}$$

$$R = \frac{13,000}{46.4103} = 280.110. \qquad \text{Divide both sides by 46.4103.}$$

Jay should have $280.11 deposited from each paycheck.

📐 **TECHNOLOGY TIP**
When a TVM solver is used for annuities due, the PMT: setting at the bottom of the screen should be "BEGIN". See Figure 5.12, which shows the solution of Example 8.

```
N=42
I%=5.5
PV=0
•PMT=-280.110136
FV=13000
P/Y=12
C/Y=12
PMT:END BEGIN
```

Figure 5.12

5.3 Exercises

Note: Unless stated otherwise, all payments are made at the end of the period.

Find each of these sums (to 4 decimal places).

1. $1 + 1.05 + 1.05^2 + 1.05^3 + \cdots + 1.05^{14}$

2. $1 + 1.046 + 1.046^2 + 1.046^3 + \cdots + 1.046^{21}$

Find the future value of the ordinary annuities with the given payments and interest rates. (See Examples 1, 2, 3(a), and 4.)

3. $R = \$12,000, 6.2\%$ interest compounded annually for 8 years

4. $R = \$20,000, 4.5\%$ interest compounded annually for 12 years

5. $R = \$865, 6\%$ interest compounded semiannually for 10 years

6. $R = \$7300, 9\%$ interest compounded semiannually for 6 years

7. $R = \$1200, 8\%$ interest compounded quarterly for 10 years

8. $R = \$20,000, 6\%$ interest compounded quarterly for 12 years

Find the final amount (rounded to the nearest dollar) in each of these retirement accounts, in which the rate of return on the account and the regular contribution change over time. (See Example 3.)

9. $400 per month invested at 4%, compounded monthly, for 10 years; then $600 per month invested at 6%, compounded monthly, for 10 years.

10. $500 per month invested at 5%, compounded monthly, for 20 years; then $1000 per month invested at 8%, compounded monthly, for 20 years.

11. $1000 per quarter invested at 4.2%, compounded quarterly, for 10 years; then $1500 per quarter invested at 7.4%, compounded quarterly, for 15 years.

12. $1500 per quarter invested at 7.4%, compounded quarterly, for 15 years; then $1000 per quarter invested at 4.2%, compounded quarterly, for 10 years. (Compare with Exercise 11.)

Find the amount of each payment to be made into a sinking fund to accumulate the given amounts. Payments are made at the end of each period. (See Example 5.)

13. $11,000; money earns 5% compounded semiannually for 6 years

14. $65,000; money earns 6% compounded semiannually for $4\frac{1}{2}$ years

15. $50,000; money earns 8% compounded quarterly for $2\frac{1}{2}$ years

16. $25,000; money earns 9% compounded quarterly for $3\frac{1}{2}$ years

17. $6000; money earns 6% compounded monthly for 3 years

18. $9000; money earns 7% compounded monthly for $2\frac{1}{2}$ years

↗ *Find the interest rate needed for the sinking fund to reach the required amount. Assume that the compounding period is the same as the payment period. (See Example 6.)*

19. $50,000 to be accumulated in 10 years; annual payments of $3940.

20. $100,000 to be accumulated in 15 years; quarterly payments of $1200.

21. $38,000 to be accumulated in 5 years; quarterly payments of $1675.

22. $77,000 to be accumulated in 20 years; monthly payments of $195.

◣**23.** What is meant by a sinking fund? List some reasons for establishing a sinking fund.

◣**24.** Explain the difference between an ordinary annuity and an annuity due.

Find the future value of each annuity due. (See Example 7.)

25. Payments of $500 for 10 years at 5% compounded annually

26. Payments of $1050 for 8 years at 3.5% compounded annually

27. Payments of $16,000 for 11 years at 4.7% compounded annually

28. Payments of $25,000 for 12 years at 6% compounded annually

29. Payments of $1000 for 9 years at 8% compounded semiannually

30. Payments of $750 for 15 years at 6% compounded semiannually

31. Payments of $100 for 7 years at 9% compounded quarterly

32. Payments of $1500 for 11 years at 7% compounded quarterly

Find the payment that should be used for the annuity due whose future value is given. Assume that the compounding period is the same as the payment period. (See Example 8.)

33. $8000; quarterly payments for 3 years; interest rate 4.4%

34. $12,000; annual payments for 6 years; interest rate 5.1%

35. $55,000; monthly payments for 12 years; interest rate 5.7%

36. $125,000; monthly payments for 9 years; interest rate 6%

Finance *Work the following applied problems.*

37. A typical pack-a-day smoker in Ohio spends about $170 per month on cigarettes. Suppose the smoker invests that amount at the end of each month in an investment fund that pays a return

of 5.3% compounded monthly. What would the account be worth after 40 years? (Data from: www.theawl.com.)

38. A typical pack-a-day smoker in Illinois spends about $307.50 per month on cigarettes. Suppose the smoker invests that amount at the end of each month in an investment fund that pays a return of 4.9% compounded monthly. What would the account be worth after 40 years? (Data from: www.theawl.com.)

39. The Vanguard Explorer Value fund had as of April 2013 a 10-year average return of 10.99%. (Data from: www.vanguard.com.)

    (a) If Becky Anderson deposited $800 a month in the fund for 10 years, find the final value of the amount of her investments. Assume monthly compounding.

    (b) If Becky had invested instead with the Vanguard Growth and Income fund, which had an average annual return of 7.77%, what would the final value of the amount of her investments be? Assume monthly compounding.

    (c) How much more did the Explorer Value fund generate than the Growth and Income fund?

40. The Janus Enterprise fund had as of April 2013 a 10-year average return of 12.54%. (Data from: www.janus.com.)

    (a) If Elaine Chuha deposited $625 a month in the fund for 8 years, find the final value of the amount of her investments. Assume monthly compounding.

    (b) If Elaine had invested instead with the Janus Twenty fund, which had an average annual return of 10.63%, what would the final value of the amount of her investments be? Assume monthly compounding.

    (c) How much more did the Janus Enterprise fund generate than the Janus Twenty fund?

◳**41.** Brian Feister, a 25-year-old professional, invests $200 a month in the T. Rowe Price Capital Opportunity fund, which has a 10-year average return of 8.75%. (Data from: www.troweprice.com.)

    (a) Brian wants to estimate what he will have for retirement when he is 60 years old if the rate stays constant. Assume monthly compounding.

    (b) If Brian makes no further deposits and makes no withdrawals after age 60, how much will he have for retirement at age 65?

◳**42.** Ian Morrison, a 30-year-old professional, invests $250 a month in the T. Rowe Price Equity Income fund, which has a 10-year average return of 9.04%. (Data from: www.troweprice.com.)

    (a) Ian wants to estimate what he will have for retirement when he is 65 years old if the rate stays constant. Assume monthly compounding.

    (b) If Ian makes no further deposits and makes no withdrawals after age 65, how much will he have for retirement at age 75? Assume monthly compounding.

43. A mother opened an investment account for her son on the day he was born, investing $1000. Each year on his birthday, she deposits another $1000, making the last deposit on his 18th birthday. If the account paid a return rate of 5.6% compounded annually, how much is in the account at the end of the day on the son's 18th birthday?

44. A grandmother opens an investment account for her only grand-daughter on the day she was born, investing $500. Each year on her birthday, she deposits another $500, making the last deposit on her 25th birthday. If the account paid a return rate of 6.2% compounded annually, how much is in the account at the end of the day on the granddaughter's 25th birthday?

45. Chuck Hickman deposits $10,000 at the beginning of each year for 12 years in an account paying 5% compounded annually. He then puts the total amount on deposit in another account paying 6% compounded semi-annually for another 9 years. Find the final amount on deposit after the entire 21-year period.

46. Suppose that the best rate that the company in Example 6 can find is 6.3%, compounded monthly (rather than the 6.661% it wants). Then the company must deposit more in the sinking fund each month. What monthly deposit will guarantee that the fund will be worth $100,000 in 20 years?

47. David Horwitz needs $10,000 in 8 years.

   (a) What amount should he deposit at the end of each quarter at 5% compounded quarterly so that he will have his $10,000?

   (b) Find Horwitz's quarterly deposit if the money is deposited at 5.8% compounded quarterly.

48. Harv's Meats knows that it must buy a new machine in 4 years. The machine costs $12,000. In order to accumulate enough money to pay for the machine, Harv decides to deposit a sum of money at the end of each 6 months in an account paying 6% compounded semiannually. How much should each payment be?

49. Barbara Margolius wants to buy a $24,000 car in 6 years. How much money must she deposit at the end of each quarter in an account paying 5% compounded quarterly so that she will have enough to pay for her car?

50. The Chinns agree to sell an antique vase to a local museum for $19,000. They want to defer the receipt of this money until they retire in 5 years (and are in a lower tax bracket). If the museum can earn 5.8%, compounded annually, find the amount of each annual payment it should make into a sinking fund so that it will have the necessary $19,000 in 5 years.

51. Diane Gray sells some land in Nevada. She will be paid a lump sum of $60,000 in 7 years. Until then, the buyer pays 8% simple interest quarterly.

   (a) Find the amount of each quarterly interest payment.

   (b) The buyer sets up a sinking fund so that enough money will be present to pay off the $60,000. The buyer wants to make semiannual payments into the sinking fund; the account pays 6% compounded semiannually. Find the amount of each payment into the fund.

52. Joe Seniw bought a rare stamp for his collection. He agreed to pay a lump sum of $4000 after 5 years. Until then, he pays 6% simple interest semiannually.

   (a) Find the amount of each semiannual interest payment.

   (b) Seniw sets up a sinking fund so that enough money will be present to pay off the $4000. He wants to make annual payments into the fund. The account pays 8% compounded annually. Find the amount of each payment.

53. To save for retirement, Karla Harby put $300 each month into an ordinary annuity for 20 years. Interest was compounded monthly. At the end of the 20 years, the annuity was worth $147,126. What annual interest rate did she receive?

54. Jennifer Wall made payments of $250 per month at the end of each month to purchase a piece of property. After 30 years, she owned the property, which she sold for $330,000. What annual interest rate would she need to earn on an ordinary annuity for a comparable rate of return?

55. When Joe and Sarah graduate from college, each expects to work a total of 45 years. Joe begins saving for retirement immediately. He plans to deposit $600 at the end of each quarter into an account paying 8.1% interest, compounded quarterly, for 10 years. He will then leave his balance in the account, earning the same interest rate, but make no further deposits for 35 years. Sarah plans to save nothing during the first 10 years and then begin depositing $600 at the end of each quarter in an account paying 8.1% interest, compounded quarterly, for 35 years.

   (a) Without doing any calculations, predict which one will have the most in his or her retirement account after 45 years. Then test your prediction by answering the following questions (calculation required to the nearest dollar).

   (b) How much will Joe contribute to his retirement account?

   (c) How much will be in Joe's account after 45 years?

   (d) How much will Sarah contribute to her retirement account?

   (e) How much will be in Sarah's account after 45 years?

56. In a 1992 Virginia lottery, the jackpot was $27 million. An Australian investment firm tried to buy all possible combinations of numbers, which would have cost $7 million. In fact, the firm ran out of time and was unable to buy all combinations, but ended up with the only winning ticket anyway. The firm received the jackpot in 20 equal annual payments of $1.35 million. Assume these payments meet the conditions of an ordinary annuity. (Data from: *Washington Post*, March 10, 1992, p. A1.)

   (a) Suppose the firm can invest money at 8% interest compounded annually. How many years would it take until the investors would be further ahead than if they had simply invested the $7 million at the same rate? (*Hint:* Experiment with different values of n, the number of years, or use a graphing calculator to plot the value of both investments as a function of the number of years.)

   (b) How many years would it take in part (a) at an interest rate of 12%?

✓ Checkpoint Answers

1. (a) $2247.20   **(b)** $2120.00   **(c)** $6367.20

2. (a) $18,339.82   **(b)** $36,216.41

3. $872,354.36

4. (a) $232.38   **(b)** $262.97

5. (a) $104,812.44   **(b)** 8.9%

6. (a) $9446.24   **(b)** $9171.10

5.4 Annuities, Present Value, and Amortization

In the annuities studied previously, regular deposits were made into an interest-bearing account and the value of the annuity increased from 0 at the beginning to some larger amount at the end (the future value). Now we expand the discussion to include annuities that begin with an amount of money and make regular payments each period until the value of the annuity decreases to 0. Examples of such annuities are lottery jackpots, structured settlements imposed by a court in which the party at fault (or his or her insurance company) makes regular payments to the injured party, and trust funds that pay the recipients a fixed amount at regular intervals.

In order to develop the essential formula for dealing with "payout annuities," we need another useful algebraic fact. If x is a nonzero number and n is a positive integer, verify the following equality by multiplying out the right-hand side:*

$$x^{-1} + x^{-2} + x^{-3} + \cdots + x^{-(n-1)} + x^{-n} = x^{-n}(x^{n-1} + x^{n-2} + x^{n-3} + \cdots + x^1 + 1).$$

Now use the sum formula in the box on page 243 to rewrite the expression in parentheses on the right-hand side:

$$x^{-1} + x^{-2} + x^{-3} + \cdots + x^{-(n-1)} + x^{-n} = x^{-n}\left(\frac{x^n - 1}{x - 1}\right)$$

$$= \frac{x^{-n}(x^n - 1)}{x - 1} = \frac{x^0 - x^{-n}}{x - 1} = \frac{1 - x^{-n}}{x - 1}.$$

We have proved the following result:

> If x is a nonzero real number and n is a positive integer, then
> $$x^{-1} + x^{-2} + x^{-3} + \cdots + x^{-n} = \frac{1 - x^{-n}}{x - 1}.$$

Present Value

In Section 5.2, we saw that the present value of A dollars at interest rate i per period for n periods is the amount that must be deposited today (at the same interest rate) in order to produce A dollars in n periods. Similarly, the **present value of an annuity** is the amount that must be deposited today (at the same compound interest rate as the annuity) to provide all the payments for the term of the annuity. It does not matter whether the payments are invested to accumulate funds or are paid out to disperse funds; the amount needed to provide the payments is the same in either case. We begin with ordinary annuities.

Example 1 Your rich aunt has funded an annuity that will pay you $1500 at the end of each year for six years. If the interest rate is 8%, compounded annually, find the present value of this annuity.

Solution Look separately at each payment you will receive. Then find the present value of each payment—the amount needed now in order to make the payment in the future. The sum of these present values will be the present value of the annuity, since it will provide all of the payments.

---

*Remember that powers of x are multiplied by *adding* exponents and that $x^n x^{-n} = x^{n-n} = x^0 = 1$.

To find the first $1500 payment (due in one year), the present value of $1500 at 8% annual interest is needed now. According to the present-value formula for compound interest on page 240 (with $A = 1500$, $i = .08$, and $n = 1$), this present value is

$$\frac{1500}{1 + .08} = \frac{1500}{1.08} = 1500(1.08^{-1}) \approx \$1388.89.$$

This amount will grow to $1500 in one year.

For the second $1500 payment (due in two years), we need the present value of $1500 at 8% interest, compounded annually for two years. The present-value formula for compound interest (with $A = 1500$, $i = .08$, and $n = 2$) shows that this present value is

$$\frac{1500}{(1 + .08)^2} = \frac{1500}{1.08^2} = 1500(1.08^{-2}) \approx \$1286.01.$$

Less money is needed for the second payment because it will grow over two years instead of one.

A similar calculation shows that the third payment (due in three years) has present value $1500(1.08^{-3})$. Continue in this manner to find the present value of each of the remaining payments, as summarized in Figure 5.13.

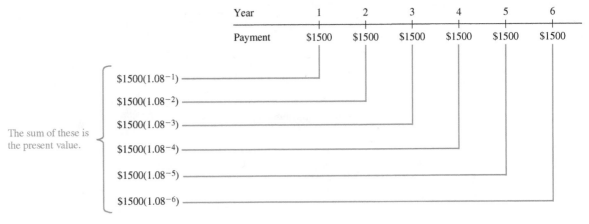

Figure 5.13

The left-hand column of Figure 5.13 shows that the present value is

$$1500 \cdot 1.08^{-1} + 1500 \cdot 1.08^{-2} + 1500 \cdot 1.08^{-3} + 1500 \cdot 1.08^{-4}$$
$$+ 1500 \cdot 1.08^{-5} + 1500 \cdot 1.08^{-6}$$
$$= 1500(1.08^{-1} + 1.08^{-2} + 1.08^{-3} + 1.08^{-4} + 1.08^{-5} + 1.08^{-6}). \qquad \textbf{(1)}$$

Now apply the algebraic fact in the box on page 252 to the expression in parentheses (with $x = 1.08$ and $n = 6$). It shows that the sum (the present value of the annuity) is

$$1500\left[\frac{1 - 1.08^{-6}}{1.08 - 1}\right] = 1500\left[\frac{1 - 1.08^{-6}}{.08}\right] = \$6934.32.$$

This amount will provide for all six payments and leave a zero balance at the end of six years (give or take a few cents due to rounding to the nearest penny at each step).

✓ **Checkpoint 1**

Show that $6934.32 will provide all the payments in Example 1 as follows:

(a) Find the balance at the end of the first year after the interest has been added and the $1500 payment subtracted.

(b) Repeat part (a) to find the balances at the ends of years 2 through 6.

Example 1 is the model for finding a formula for the future value of any ordinary annuity. Suppose that a payment of R dollars is made at the end of each period for n

periods, at interest rate i per period. Then the present value of this annuity can be found by using the procedure in Example 1, with these replacements:

$$
\begin{array}{cccc}
1500 & .08 & 1.08 & 6 \\
\downarrow & \downarrow & \downarrow & \downarrow \\
R & i & 1+i & n
\end{array}
$$

The future value in Example 1 is the sum in equation (**1**), which now becomes

$$P = R[(1 + i)^{-1} + (1 + i)^{-2} + (1 + i)^{-3} + \cdots + (1 + i)^{-n}].$$

Apply the algebraic fact in the box on page 252 to the expression in brackets (with $x = 1 + i$). Then we have

$$P = R\left[\frac{1 - (1 + i)^{-n}}{(1 + i) - 1}\right] = R\left[\frac{1 - (1 + i)^{-n}}{i}\right].$$

The quantity in brackets in the right-hand part of the preceding equation is sometimes written $a_{\overline{n}|i}$ (read "a-angle-n at i"). So we can summarize as follows.

Present Value of an Ordinary Annuity

The present value P of an ordinary annuity is given by

$$P = R\left[\frac{1 - (1 + i)^{-n}}{i}\right], \quad \text{or} \quad P = R \cdot a_{\overline{n}|i},$$

where

    R is the payment at the end of each period,

    i is the interest rate per period, and

    n is the number of periods.

⊘ CAUTION Do not confuse the formula for the present value of an annuity with the one for the future value of an annuity. Notice the difference: The numerator of the fraction in the present-value formula is $1 - (1 + i)^{-n}$, but in the future-value formula, it is $(1 + i)^n - 1$.

Example 2   Jim Riles was in an auto accident. He sued the person at fault and was awarded a structured settlement in which an insurance company will pay him $600 at the end of each month for the next seven years. How much money should the insurance company invest now at 4.7%, compounded monthly, to guarantee that all the payments can be made?

Solution The payments form an ordinary annuity. The amount needed to fund all the payments is the present value of the annuity. Apply the present-value formula with $R = 600$, $n = 7 \cdot 12 = 84$, and $i = .047/12$ (the interest rate per month). The insurance company should invest

$$P = R\left[\frac{1 - (1 + i)^{-n}}{i}\right] = 600\left[\frac{1 - (1 + .047/12)^{-84}}{.047/12}\right] = \$42,877.44. \ \checkmark_2$$

✓Checkpoint 2

An insurance company offers to pay Jane Parks an ordinary annuity of $1200 per quarter for five years *or* the present value of the annuity now. If the interest rate is 6%, find the present value.

Example 3   To supplement his pension in the early years of his retirement, Ralph Taylor plans to use $124,500 of his savings as an ordinary annuity that will make monthly payments to him for 20 years. If the interest rate is 5.2%, how much will each payment be?

Solution The present value of the annuity is $P = \$124{,}500$, the monthly interest rate is $i = .052/12$, and $n = 12 \cdot 20 = 240$ (the number of months in 20 years). Solve the present-value formula for the monthly payment R:

$$P = R\left[\frac{1 - (1 + i)^{-n}}{i}\right]$$

$$124{,}500 = R\left[\frac{1 - (1 + .052/12)^{-240}}{.052/12}\right]$$

$$R = \frac{124{,}500}{\left[\dfrac{1 - (1 + .052/12)^{-240}}{.052/12}\right]} = \$835.46.$$

✓ **Checkpoint 3**

Carl Dehne has $80,000 in an account paying 4.8% interest, compounded monthly. He plans to use up all the money by making equal monthly withdrawals for 15 years. If the interest rate is 4.8%, find the amount of each withdrawal.

Taylor will receive $835.46 a month (about $10,026 per year) for 20 years.

Example 4 Surinder Sinah and Maria Gonzalez are graduates of Kenyon College. They both agree to contribute to an endowment fund at the college. Sinah says he will give $500 at the end of each year for 9 years. Gonzalez prefers to give a single donation today. How much should she give to equal the value of Sinah's gift, assuming that the endowment fund earns 7.5% interest, compounded annually?

Solution Sinah's gift is an ordinary annuity with annual payments of $500 for 9 years. Its *future* value at 7.5% annual compound interest is

$$S = R\left[\frac{(1 + i)^n - 1}{i}\right] = 500\left[\frac{(1 + .075)^9 - 1}{.075}\right] = 500\left[\frac{1.075^9 - 1}{.075}\right] = \$6114.92.$$

We claim that for Gonzalez to equal this contribution, she should today contribute an amount equal to the *present* value of this annuity, namely,

$$P = R\left[\frac{1 - (1 + i)^{-n}}{i}\right] = 500\left[\frac{1 - (1 + .075)^{-9}}{.075}\right] = 500\left[\frac{1 - 1.075^{-9}}{.075}\right] = \$3189.44.$$

To confirm this claim, suppose the present value $P = \$3189.44$ is deposited today at 7.5% interest, compounded annually for 9 years. According to the compound interest formula on page 233, P will grow to

$$3189.44(1 + .075)^9 = \$6114.92,$$

the future value of Sinah's annuity. So at the end of 9 years, Gonzalez and Sinah will have made identical gifts.

Example 4 illustrates the following alternative description of the present value of an "accumulation annuity."

> The present value of an annuity for accumulating funds is the single deposit that would have to be made today to produce the future value of the annuity (assuming the same interest rate and period of time.) ✓ 4

✓ **Checkpoint 4**

What lump sum deposited today would be equivalent to equal payments of

(a) $650 at the end of each year for 9 years at 4% compounded annually?

(b) $1000 at the end of each quarter for 4 years at 4% compounded quarterly?

Corporate bonds, which were introduced in Section 5.1, are routinely bought and sold in financial markets. In most cases, interest rates when a bond is sold differ from the interest rate paid by the bond (known as the **coupon rate**). In such cases, the price of a bond will not be its face value, but will instead be based on current interest rates. The next example shows how this is done.

Example 5 A 15-year $10,000 bond with a 5% coupon rate was issued five years ago and is now being sold. If the current interest rate for similar bonds is 7%, what price should a purchaser be willing to pay for this bond?

Solution   According to the simple interest formula (page 226), the interest paid by the bond each half-year is

$$I = Prt = 10{,}000 \cdot .05 \cdot \frac{1}{2} = \$250.$$

Think of the bond as a two-part investment: The first is an annuity that pays $250 every six months for the next 10 years; the second is the $10,000 face value of the bond, which will be paid when the bond matures, 10 years from now. The purchaser should be willing to pay the present value of each part of the investment, assuming 7% interest, compounded semiannually.[*] The interest rate per period is $i = .07/2$, and the number of six-month periods in 10 years is $n = 20$. So we have:

Present value of annuity

$$P = R\left[\frac{1 - (1 + i)^{-n}}{i}\right]$$

$$= 250\left[\frac{1 - (1 + .07/2)^{-20}}{.07/2}\right]$$

$$= \$3553.10$$

Present value of $10,000 in 10 years

$$P = A(1 + i)^{-n}$$

$$= 10{,}000(1 + .07/2)^{-20}$$

$$= \$5025.66.$$

So the purchaser should be willing to pay the sum of these two present values:

$$\$3553.10 + \$5025.66 = \$8578.76. \quad \boxed{5}$$

 Checkpoint 5

Suppose the current interest rate for bonds is 4% instead of 7% when the bond in Example 5 is sold. What price should a purchaser be willing to pay for it?

📄 **NOTE** Example 5 and Checkpoint 5 illustrate the inverse relation between interest rates and bond prices: If interest rates rise, bond prices fall, and if interest rates fall, bond prices rise.

Loans and Amortization

If you take out a car loan or a home mortgage, you repay it by making regular payments to the bank. From the bank's point of view, your payments are an annuity that is paying it a fixed amount each month. The present value of this annuity is the amount you borrowed.

> **Example 6**   **Finance**   Chase Bank in April 2013 advertised a new car auto loan rate of 2.23% for a 48-month loan. Shelley Fasulko will buy a new car for $25,000 with a down payment of $4500. Find the amount of each payment. (Data from: www.chase.com.)
>
> **Solution**   After a $4500 down payment, the loan amount is $20,500. Use the present-value formula for an annuity, with $P = 20{,}500$, $n = 48$, and $i = .0223/12$ (the monthly interest rate). Then solve for payment R.
>
> $$P = R\left[\frac{1 - (1 + i)^{-n}}{i}\right]$$
>
> $$20{,}500 = R\left[\frac{1 - (1 + .0223/12)^{-48}}{.0223/12}\right]$$
>
> $$R = \frac{20{,}500}{\left[\dfrac{1 - (1 + .0223/12)^{-48}}{.0223/12}\right]} \qquad \text{Solve for } R.$$
>
> $$R = \$446.81 \quad \boxed{6}$$

✓ **Checkpoint 6**

Suzanne Bellini uses a Chase auto loan to purchase a used car priced at $28,750 at an interest rate of 3.64% for a 60-month loan. What is the monthly payment?

A loan is **amortized** if both the principal and interest are paid by a sequence of equal periodic payments. The periodic payment needed to amortize a loan may be found, as in Example 6, by solving the present-value formula for R.

[*]The analysis here does not include any commissions or fees charged by the financial institution that handles the bond sale.

Amortization Payments

A loan of P dollars at interest rate i per period may be amortized in n equal periodic payments of R dollars made at the end of each period, where

$$R = \frac{P}{\left[\dfrac{1 - (1 + i)^{-n}}{i}\right]} = \frac{Pi}{1 - (1 + i)^{-n}}.$$

Example 7 **Finance** In April 2013, the average rate for a 30-year fixed mortgage was 3.43%. Assume a down payment of 20% on a home purchase of $272,900. (Data from: Freddie Mac.)

(a) Find the monthly payment needed to amortize this loan.

Solution The down payment is $.20(272,900) = \$54,580$. Thus, the loan amount P is $\$272,900 - 54,580 = \$218,320$. We can now apply the formula in the preceding box, with $n = 12(30) = 360$ (the number of monthly payments in 30 years), and monthly interest rate $i = .0343/12$.[*]

$$R = \frac{Pi}{1 - (1 + i)^{-n}} = \frac{(218,320)(.0343/12)}{1 - (1 + .0343/12)^{-360}} = \$971.84$$

Monthly payments of $971.84 are required to amortize the loan.

(b) After 10 years, approximately how much is owed on the mortgage?

Solution You may be tempted to say that after 10 years of payments on a 30-year mortgage, the balance will be reduced by a third. However, a significant portion of each payment goes to pay interest. So, much less than a third of the mortgage is paid off in the first 10 years, as we now see.

After 10 years (120 payments), the 240 remaining payments can be thought of as an annuity. The present value for this annuity is the (approximate) remaining balance on the mortgage. Hence, we use the present-value formula with $R = 971.84$, $i = .0343/12$, and $n = 240$:

$$P = 971.84\left[\frac{1 - (1 + .0343/12)^{-240}}{(.0343/12)}\right] = \$168,614.16.$$

So the remaining balance is about $168,614.16. The actual balance probably differs slightly from this figure because payments and interest amounts are rounded to the nearest penny. ✓ 7

✓ Checkpoint 7

Find the remaining balance after 20 years.

```
N=360
I%=3.43
PV=218320
•PMT=-971.8435089
FV=0
P/Y=12
C/Y=12
PMT:END BEGIN
```

Figure 5.14

▸ TECHNOLOGY TIP A TVM solver on a graphing calculator can find the present value of an annuity or the payment on a loan: Fill in the known information, put the cursor next to the unknown item (PV or PMT), and press SOLVE. Figure 5.14 shows the solution to Example 7(a) on a TVM solver. Alternatively, you can use the program in the Program Appendix.

Example 7(b) illustrates an important fact: Even though equal *payments* are made to amortize a loan, the loan *balance* does not decrease in equal steps. The method used to estimate the remaining balance in Example 7(b) works in the general case. If n payments

---

[*]Mortgage rates are quoted in terms of annual interest, but it is always understood that the monthly rate is $\frac{1}{12}$ of the annual interest rate and that interest is compounded monthly.

are needed to amortize a loan and x payments have been made, then the remaining payments form an annuity of $n - x$ payments. So we apply the present-value formula with $n - x$ in place of n to obtain this result.

Remaining Balance

If a loan can be amortized by n payments of R dollars each at an interest rate i per period, then the *approximate* remaining balance B after x payments is

$$B = R\left[\frac{1 - (1 + i)^{-(n-x)}}{i}\right].$$

Amortization Schedules

The remaining-balance formula is a quick and convenient way to get a reasonable estimate of the remaining balance on a loan, but it is not accurate enough for a bank or business, which must keep its books exactly. To determine the exact remaining balance after each loan payment, financial institutions normally use an **amortization schedule,** which lists how much of each payment is interest, how much goes to reduce the balance, and how much is still owed after each payment.

Example 8   Beth Hill borrows $1000 for one year at 12% annual interest, compounded monthly.

(a) Find her monthly payment.

Solution   Apply the amortization payment formula with $P = 1000, n = 12$, and monthly interest rate $i = .12/12 = .01$. Her payment is

$$R = \frac{Pi}{1 - (1 + i)^{-n}} = \frac{1000(.01)}{1 - (1 + .01)^{-12}} = \$88.85.$$

(b) After making five payments, Hill decides to pay off the remaining balance. Approximately how much must she pay?

Solution   Apply the remaining-balance formula just given, with $R = 88.85, i = .01$, and $n - x = 12 - 5 = 7$. Her approximate remaining balance is

$$B = R\left[\frac{1 - (1 + i)^{-(n-x)}}{i}\right] = 88.85\left[\frac{1 - (1 + .01)^{-7}}{.01}\right] = \$597.80.$$

(c) Construct an amortization schedule for Hill's loan.

Solution   An amortization schedule for the loan is shown in the table on the next page. It was obtained as follows: The annual interest rate is 12% compounded monthly, so the interest rate per month is $12\%/12 = 1\% = .01$. When the first payment is made, one month's interest, namely, $.01(1000) = \$10$, is owed. Subtracting this from the $88.85 payment leaves $78.85 to be applied to repayment. Hence, the principal at the end of the first payment period is $1000 - 78.85 = \$921.15$, as shown in the "payment 1" line of the table.

When payment 2 is made, one month's interest on the new balance of $921.15 is owed, namely, $.01(921.15) = \$9.21$. Continue as in the preceding paragraph to compute the entries in this line of the table. The remaining lines of the table are found in a similar fashion.

Payment Number	Amount of Payment	Interest for Period	Portion to Principal	Principal at End of Period
0	—	—	—	$1000.00
1	$88.85	$10.00	$78.85	921.15
2	88.85	9.21	79.64	841.51
3	88.85	8.42	80.43	761.08
4	88.85	7.61	81.24	679.84
5	88.85	6.80	82.05	597.79
6	88.85	5.98	82.87	514.92
7	88.85	5.15	83.70	431.22
8	88.85	4.31	84.54	346.68
9	88.85	3.47	85.38	261.30
10	88.85	2.61	86.24	175.06
11	88.85	1.75	87.10	87.96
12	88.84	.88	87.96	0

Note that Hill's remaining balance after five payments differs slightly from the estimate made in part (b).

The final payment in the amortization schedule in Example 8(c) differs from the other payments. It often happens that the last payment needed to amortize a loan must be adjusted to account for rounding earlier and to ensure that the final balance will be exactly 0.

 TECHNOLOGY TIP Most Casio graphing calculators can produce amortization schedules. For other calculators, use the amortization table program in the Program Appendix. Spreadsheets are another useful tool for creating amortization tables. Microsoft Excel (Microsoft Corporation Excel © 2013) has a built-in feature for calculating monthly payments. Figure 5.15 shows an Excel amortization table for Example 8. For more details, see the *Spreadsheet Manual,* also available with this text.

	A	B	C	D	E	F
1	Prnt#	Payment	Interest	Principal	End Principal	
2	0				1000	
3	1	88.85	10.00	78.85	921.15	
4	2	88.85	9.21	79.64	841.51	
5	3	88.85	8.42	80.43	761.08	
6	4	88.85	7.61	81.24	679.84	
7	5	88.85	6.80	82.05	597.79	
8	6	88.85	5.98	82.87	514.92	
9	7	88.85	5.15	83.70	431.22	
10	8	88.85	4.31	84.54	346.68	
11	9	88.85	3.47	85.38	261.30	
12	10	88.85	2.61	86.24	175.06	
13	11	88.85	1.75	87.10	87.96	
14	12	88.85	0.88	87.97	-0.01	

Figure 5.15

Annuities Due

We want to find the present value of an annuity due in which 6 payments of R dollars are made at the *beginning* of each period, with interest rate i per period, as shown schematically in Figure 5.16.

```
  1     2     3     4     5     6
  |——————|——————|——————|——————|——————|——————
  R     R     R     R     R     R
```

Figure 5.16

The present value is the amount needed to fund all 6 payments. Since the first payment earns no interest, R dollars are needed to fund it. Now look at the last 5 payments by themselves in Figure 5.17.

Figure 5.17

If you think of these 5 payments as being made at the end of each period, you see that they form an ordinary annuity. The money needed to fund them is the present value of this ordinary annuity. So the present value of the annuity due is given by

$$R + \begin{array}{c} \text{Present value of the ordinary} \\ \text{annuity of 5 payments} \end{array}$$

$$R + R\left[\frac{1 - (1 + i)^{-5}}{i}\right].$$

Replacing 6 by n and 5 by $n - 1$, and using the argument just given, produces the general result that follows.

> ## Present Value of an Annuity Due
>
> The present value P of an annuity due is given by
>
> $$P = R + R\left[\frac{1 - (1 + i)^{-(n-1)}}{i}\right],$$
>
> $$P = \underset{\text{payment}}{\text{One}} + \begin{array}{c} \text{Present value of} \\ \text{an ordinary annuity} \\ \text{of } n - 1 \text{ payments} \end{array}$$
>
> where
>
> R is the payment at the beginning of each period,
>
> i is the interest rate per period, and
>
> n is the number of periods.

Example 9 **Finance** The *Illinois Lottery Winner's Handbook* discusses the options of how to receive the winnings for a $12 million Lotto jackpot. One option is to take 26 annual payments of approximately $461,538.46, which is $12 million divided into 26 equal payments. The other option is to take a lump-sum payment (which is often called the "cash value"). If the Illinois lottery commission can earn 4.88% annual interest, how much is the cash value?

Solution The yearly payments form a 26-payment annuity due. An equivalent amount now is the present value of this annuity. Apply the present-value formula with $R = 461,538.46$, $i = .0488$, and $n = 26$:

$$P = R + R\left[\frac{1 - (1 + i)^{-(n-1)}}{i}\right] = 461,538.46 + 461,538.46\left[\frac{1 - (1 + .0488)^{-25}}{.0488}\right]$$

$$= \$7,045,397.39.$$

The cash value is $7,045,397.39. ✓8

TECHNOLOGY TIP Figure 5.18 shows the solution of Example 9 on a TVM solver. Since this is an annuity due, the PMT: setting at the bottom of the screen is "BEGIN".

✓ **Checkpoint 8**

What is the cash value for a Lotto jackpot of $25 million if the Illinois Lottery can earn 6.2% annual interest?

```
N=26
I%=4.88
•PV=7045397.393
PMT=-461538.46
FV=0
P/Y=1
C/Y=1
PMT:END BEGIN
```

Figure 5.18

5.4 Exercises

Unless noted otherwise, all payments and withdrawals are made at the end of the period.

1. Explain the difference between the present value of an annuity and the future value of an annuity.

Find the present value of each ordinary annuity. (See Examples 1, 2, and 4.)

2. Payments of $890 each year for 16 years at 6% compounded annually

3. Payments of $1400 each year for 8 years at 6% compounded annually

4. Payments of $10,000 semiannually for 15 years at 7.5% compounded semiannually

5. Payments of $50,000 quarterly for 10 years at 5% compounded quarterly

6. Payments of $15,806 quarterly for 3 years at 6.8% compounded quarterly

Find the amount necessary to fund the given withdrawals. (See Examples 1 and 2.)

7. Quarterly withdrawals of $650 for 5 years; interest rate is 4.9%, compounded quarterly.

8. Yearly withdrawals of $1200 for 14 years; interest rate is 5.6%, compounded annually.

9. Monthly withdrawals of $425 for 10 years; interest rate is 6.1%, compounded monthly.

10. Semiannual withdrawals of $3500 for 7 years; interest rate is 5.2%, compounded semiannually.

Find the payment made by the ordinary annuity with the given present value. (See Example 3.)

11. $90,000; monthly payments for 22 years; interest rate is 4.9%, compounded monthly.

12. $45,000; monthly payments for 11 years; interest rate is 5.3%, compounded monthly.

13. $275,000; quarterly payments for 18 years; interest rate is 6%, compounded quarterly.

14. $330,000; quarterly payments for 30 years; interest rate is 6.1% compounded quarterly.

Find the lump sum deposited today that will yield the same total amount as payments of $10,000 at the end of each year for 15 years at each of the given interest rates. (See Example 4 and the box following it.)

15. 3% compounded annually

16. 4% compounded annually

17. 6% compounded annually

18. What sum deposited today at 5% compounded annually for 8 years will provide the same amount as $1000 deposited at the end of each year for 8 years at 6% compounded annually?

19. What lump sum deposited today at 8% compounded quarterly for 10 years will yield the same final amount as deposits of $4000 at the end of each 6-month period for 10 years at 6% compounded semiannually?

Find the price a purchaser should be willing to pay for the given bond. Assume that the coupon interest is paid twice a year. (See Example 5.)

20. $20,000 bond with coupon rate 4.5% that matures in 8 years; current interest rate is 5.9%.

21. $15,000 bond with coupon rate 6% that matures in 4 years; current interest rate is 5%.

22. $25,000 bond with coupon rate 7% that matures in 10 years; current interest rate is 6%.

23. $10,000 bond with coupon rate 5.4% that matures in 12 years; current interest rate is 6.5%.

24. What does it mean to amortize a loan?

Find the payment necessary to amortize each of the given loans. (See Examples 6, 7(a), and 8(a).)

25. $2500; 8% compounded quarterly; 6 quarterly payments

26. $41,000; 9% compounded semiannually; 10 semiannual payments

27. $90,000; 7% compounded annually; 12 annual payments

28. $140,000; 12% compounded quarterly; 15 quarterly payments

29. $7400; 8.2% compounded semiannually; 18 semiannual payments

30. $5500; 9.5% compounded monthly; 24 monthly payments

Finance *In April 2013, the mortgage interest rates listed in Exercises 31–34 for the given companies were listed at www.hsh.com. Find the monthly payment necessary to amortize the given loans. (See Example 7(a).)*

31. $225,000 at 3.25% for 30 years from Amerisave

32. $330,000 at 3.125% for 20 years from Quicken Loans

33. $140,000 at 2.375% for 15 years from Discover Home Loans

34. $180,000 at 2.25% for 10 years from Roundpoint Mortgage Company

Finance *Find the monthly payment and estimate the remaining balance (to the nearest dollar). Assume interest is on the unpaid balance. The interest rates are from national averages from www.bankrate.com in April 2013. (See Examples 7 and 8.)*

35. Four-year new car loan for $26,799 at 3.13%; remaining balance after 2 years

36. Three-year used car loan for $15,875 at 2.96%; remaining balance after 1 year

37. Thirty-year mortgage for $210,000 at 3.54%; remaining balance after 12 years

38. Fifteen-year mortgage for $195,000 at 2.78%; remaining balance after 4.5 years

Use the amortization table in Example 8(c) to answer the questions in Exercises 39–42.

39. How much of the 5th payment is interest?

40. How much of the 10th payment is used to reduce the debt?

41. How much interest is paid in the first 5 months of the loan?

42. How much interest is paid in the last 5 months of the loan?

Find the cash value of the lottery jackpot (to the nearest dollar). Yearly jackpot payments begin immediately (26 for Mega Millions and 30 for Powerball). Assume the lottery can invest at the given interest rate. (See Example 9.)

43. Powerball: $57.6 million; 5.1% interest

44. Powerball: $207 million; 5.78% interest

45. Mega Millions: $41.6 million; 4.735% interest

46. Mega Millions: $23.4 million; 4.23% interest

Finance   *Work the following applied problems.*

47. An auto stereo dealer sells a stereo system for $600 down and monthly payments of $30 for the next 3 years. If the interest rate is 1.25% *per month* on the unpaid balance, find

(a) the cost of the stereo system;

(b) the total amount of interest paid.

48. John Kushida buys a used car costing $6000. He agrees to make payments at the end of each monthly period for 4 years. He pays 12% interest, compounded monthly.

(a) What is the amount of each payment?

(b) Find the total amount of interest Kushida will pay.

49. A speculator agrees to pay $15,000 for a parcel of land; this amount, with interest, will be paid over 4 years with semiannual payments at an interest rate of 10% compounded semiannually. Find the amount of each payment.

50. Alan Stasa buys a new car costing $26,750. What is the monthly payment if the interest rate is 4.2%, compounded monthly, and the loan is for 60 months? Find the total amount of interest Alan will pay.

Finance   *A student education loan has two repayment options. The standard plan repays the loan in 10 years with equal monthly payments. The extended plan allows from 12 to 30 years to repay the loan. A student borrows $35,000 at 7.43% compounded monthly.*

51. Find the monthly payment and total interest paid under the standard plan.

52. Find the monthly payment and total interest paid under the extended plan with 20 years to pay off the loan.

Finance   *Use the formula for the approximate remaining balance to work each problem. (See Examples 7(b) and 8(b).)*

53. When Teresa Flores opened her law office, she bought $14,000 worth of law books and $7200 worth of office furniture. She paid $1200 down and agreed to amortize the balance with semiannual payments for 5 years at 12% compounded semiannually.

(a) Find the amount of each payment.

(b) When her loan had been reduced below $5000, Flores received a large tax refund and decided to pay off the loan. How many payments were left at this time?

54. Kareem Adams buys a house for $285,000. He pays $60,000 down and takes out a mortgage at 6.9% on the balance. Find his monthly payment and the total amount of interest he will pay if the length of the mortgage is

(a) 15 years;

(b) 20 years;

(c) 25 years.

(d) When will half the 20-year loan be paid off?

55. Susan Carver will purchase a home for $257,000. She will use a down payment of 20% and finance the remaining portion at 3.9%, compounded monthly for 30 years.

(a) What will be the monthly payment?

(b) How much will remain on the loan after making payments for 5 years?

(c) How much interest will be paid on the total amount of the loan over the course of 30 years?

56. Mohsen Manouchehri will purchase a $230,000 home with a 20-year mortgage. If he makes a down payment of 20% and the interest rate is 3.3%, compounded monthly,

(a) what will the monthly payment be?

(b) how much will he owe after making payments for 8 years?

(c) how much in total interest will he pay over the course of the 20-year loan?

Work each problem.

57. Elizabeth Bernardi and her employer contribute $400 at the end of each month to her retirement account, which earns 7% interest, compounded monthly. When she retires after 45 years, she plans to make monthly withdrawals for 30 years. If her account earns 5% interest, compounded monthly, then when she retires, what is her maximum possible monthly withdrawal (without running out of money)?

58. Jim Milliken won a $15,000 prize. On March 1, he deposited it in an account earning 5.2% interest, compounded monthly. On March 1 one year later, he begins to withdraw the same amount at the beginning of each month for a year. Assuming that he uses up all the money in the account, find the amount of each monthly withdrawal.

59. Catherine Dohanyos plans to retire in 20 years. She will make 20 years of monthly contributions to her retirement account. One month after her last contribution, she will begin the first of 10 years of withdrawals. She wants to withdraw $2500 per month. How large must her monthly contributions be in order to accomplish her goal if the account earns interest of 7.1% compounded monthly for the duration of her contributions and the 120 months of withdrawals?

60. David Turner plans to retire in 25 years. He will make 25 years of monthly contributions to his retirement account. One month after his last contribution, he will begin the first of 10 years of withdrawals. He wants to withdraw $3000 per month. How large must his monthly contributions be in order to accomplish his goal if the account earns interest of 6.8% compounded monthly for the duration of his contributions and the 120 months of withdrawals?

61. William Blake plans to retire in 20 years. William will make 10 years (120 months) of equal monthly payments into his account. Ten years after his last contribution, he will begin the first of 120 monthly withdrawals of $3400 per month. Assume that the retirement account earns interest of 8.2% compounded monthly for the duration of his contributions, the 10 years in between his contributions and the beginning of his withdrawals, and the 10 years of withdrawals. How large must William's monthly contributions be in order to accomplish his goal?

62. Gil Stevens plans to retire in 25 years. He will make 15 years (180 months) of equal monthly payments into his account. Ten years after his last contribution, he will begin the first of 120 monthly withdrawals of $2900 per month. Assume that the retirement account earns interest of 5.4% compounded monthly for the duration of his contributions, the 10 years in between his contributions and the beginning of his withdrawals, and the 10 years of withdrawals. How large must Gil's monthly contributions be in order to accomplish his goal?

Finance *In Exercises 63–66, prepare an amortization schedule showing the first four payments for each loan. (See Example 8(c).)*

63. An insurance firm pays $4000 for a new printer for its computer. It amortizes the loan for the printer in 4 annual payments at 8% compounded annually.

64. Large semitrailer trucks cost $72,000 each. Ace Trucking buys such a truck and agrees to pay for it by a loan that will be amortized with 9 semiannual payments at 6% compounded semiannually.

65. One retailer charges $1048 for a certain computer. A firm of tax accountants buys 8 of these computers. It makes a down payment of $1200 and agrees to amortize the balance with monthly payments at 12% compounded monthly for 4 years.

66. Joan Varozza plans to borrow $20,000 to stock her small boutique. She will repay the loan with semiannual payments for 5 years at 7% compounded semiannually.

✓ Checkpoint Answers

1. (a) $5989.07

   (b) $4968.20; $3865.66; $2674.91; $1388.90; $0.01

2. $20,602.37

3. $624.33

4. (a) $4832.97   **(b)** $14,717.87

5. $10,817.57

6. $524.82

7. $98,605.61

8. $13,023,058.46

CHAPTER 5 Summary and Review

Key Terms and Symbols

5.1 simple interest
   principal
   rate
   time
   future value (maturity value)
   present value
   discount and T-bills

5.2 compound interest
   compound amount
   compounding period
   nominal rate (stated rate)
   effective rate (APY)
   present value

5.3 annuity
   payment period

   term of an annuity
   ordinary annuity
   future value of an ordinary annuity
   sinking fund
   annuity due
   future value of an annuity due

5.4 present value of an ordinary annuity
   amortization payments
   remaining balance
   amortization schedule
   present value of an annuity due

Chapter 5 Key Concepts

A Strategy for Solving Finance Problems

We have presented a lot of new formulas in this chapter. By answering the following questions, you can decide which formula to use for a particular problem.

1. Is simple or compound interest involved?

    Simple interest is normally used for investments or loans of a year or less; compound interest is normally used in all other cases.

2. If simple interest is being used, what is being sought—interest amount, future value, present value, or discount?

3. If compound interest is being used, does it involve a lump sum (single payment) or an annuity (sequence of payments)?

    (a) For a lump sum,

      (i) is ordinary compound interest involved?

      (ii) what is being sought—present value, future value, number of periods, or effective rate (APY)?

    (b) For an annuity,

      (i) is it an ordinary annuity (payment at the end of each period) or an annuity due (payment at the beginning of each period)?

      (ii) what is being sought—present value, future value, or payment amount?

    Once you have answered these questions, choose the appropriate formula and work the problem. As a final step, consider whether the answer you get makes sense. For instance, the amount of interest or the payments in an annuity should be fairly small compared with the total future value.

Key Formulas

List of Variables

r is the annual interest rate.

m is the number of periods per year.

i is the interest rate per period. $i = \dfrac{r}{m}$

t is the number of years.

n is the number of periods. $n = tm$

P is the principal or present value.

A is the future value of a lump sum.

S is the future value of an annuity.

R is the periodic payment in an annuity.

B is the remaining balance on a loan.

Interest	Simple Interest	Compound Interest
Interest	$I = Prt$	$I = A - P$
Future value	$A = P(1 + rt)$	$A = P(1 + i)^n$
Present value	$P = \dfrac{A}{1 + rt}$	$P = \dfrac{A}{(1 + i)^n} = A(1 + i)^{-n}$

Effective rate (or APY) $r_E = \left(1 + \dfrac{r}{m}\right)^m - 1$

Discount

If D is the **discount** on a T-bill with face value P at simple interest rate r for t years, then $D = Prt$.

Continuous Interest

If P dollars are deposited for t years at interest rate r per year, compounded continuously, the **compound amount (future value)** is $A = Pe^{rt}$.

The **present value** P of A dollars at interest rate r per year compounded continuously for t years is

$$P = \dfrac{A}{e^{rt}}.$$

Annuities

Ordinary annuity	Future value	$S = R\left[\dfrac{(1 + i)^n - 1}{i}\right] = R \cdot s_{\overline{n}|i}$	
	Present value	$P = R\left[\dfrac{1 - (1 + i)^{-n}}{i}\right] = R \cdot a_{\overline{n}|i}$	
Annuity due	Future value	$S = R\left[\dfrac{(1 + i)^{n+1} - 1}{i}\right] - R$	
	Present value	$P = R + R\left[\dfrac{1 - (1 + i)^{-(n-1)}}{i}\right]$	

Chapter 5 Review Exercises

Find the simple interest for the following loans.

1. $4902 at 6.5% for 11 months

2. $42,368 at 9.22% for 5 months

3. $3478 at 7.4% for 88 days

4. $2390 at 8.7% from May 3 to July 28

Find the semiannual (simple) interest payment and the total interest earned over the life of the bond.

5. $12,000 Merck Company 6-year bond at 4.75% annual interest

6. $20,000 General Electric 9-year bond at 5.25% annual interest

Find the maturity value for each simple interest loan.

7. $7750 at 6.8% for 4 months

8. $15,600 at 8.2% for 9 months

9. What is meant by the present value of an amount A?

Find the present value of the given future amounts; use simple interest.

10. $459.57 in 7 months; money earns 5.5%

11. $80,612 in 128 days; money earns 6.77%

12. A 9-month $7000 Treasury bill sells at a discount rate of 3.5%. Find the amount of the discount and the price of the T-bill.

13. A 6-month $10,000 T-bill sold at a 4% discount. Find the actual rate of interest paid by the Treasury.

14. For a given amount of money at a given interest rate for a given period greater than 1 year, does simple interest or compound interest produce more interest? Explain.

Find the compound amount and the amount of interest earned in each of the given scenarios.

15. $2800 at 6% compounded annually for 12 years

16. $57,809.34 at 4% compounded quarterly for 6 years

17. $12,903.45 at 6.37% compounded quarterly for 29 quarters

18. $4677.23 at 4.57% compounded monthly for 32 months

Find the amount of compound interest earned by each deposit.

19. $22,000 at 5.5%, compounded quarterly for 6 years

20. $2975 at 4.7%, compounded monthly for 4 years

Find the face value (to the nearest dollar) of the zero-coupon bond.

21. 5-year bond at 3.9%; price $12,366

22. 15-year bond at 5.2%; price $11,575

Find the APY corresponding to the given nominal rate.

23. 5% compounded semiannually

24. 6.5% compounded daily

Find the present value of the given amounts at the given interest rate.

25. $42,000 in 7 years; 12% compounded monthly

26. $17,650 in 4 years; 8% compounded quarterly

27. $1347.89 in 3.5 years; 6.2% compounded semiannually

28. $2388.90 in 44 months; 5.75% compounded monthly

Find the price that a purchaser should be willing to pay for these zero-coupon bonds.

29. 10-year $15,000 bond; interest at 4.4%

30. 25-year $30,000 bond; interest at 6.2%

31. What is meant by the future value of an annuity?

Find the future value of each annuity.

32. $1288 deposited at the end of each year for 14 years; money earns 7% compounded annually

33. $4000 deposited at the end of each quarter for 8 years; money earns 6% compounded quarterly

34. $233 deposited at the end of each month for 4 years; money earns 6% compounded monthly

35. $672 deposited at the beginning of each quarter for 7 years; money earns 5% compounded quarterly

36. $11,900 deposited at the beginning of each month for 13 months; money earns 7% compounded monthly

37. What is the purpose of a sinking fund?

Find the amount of each payment that must be made into a sinking fund to accumulate the given amounts. Assume payments are made at the end of each period.

38. $6500; money earns 5% compounded annually; 6 annual payments

39. $57,000; money earns 6% compounded semiannually for $8\frac{1}{2}$ years

40. $233,188; money earns 5.7% compounded quarterly for $7\frac{3}{4}$ years

41. $56,788; money earns 6.12% compounded monthly for $4\frac{1}{2}$ years

Find the present value of each ordinary annuity.

42. Payments of $850 annually for 4 years at 5% compounded annually

43. Payments of $1500 quarterly for 7 years at 8% compounded quarterly

44. Payments of $4210 semiannually for 8 years at 5.6% compounded semiannually

45. Payments of $877.34 monthly for 17 months at 6.4% compounded monthly

Find the amount necessary to fund the given withdrawals (which are made at the end of each period).

46. Quarterly withdrawals of $800 for 4 years with interest rate 4.6%, compounded quarterly

47. Monthly withdrawals of $1500 for 10 years with interest rate 5.8%, compounded monthly

48. Yearly withdrawals of $3000 for 15 years with interest rate 6.2%, compounded annually

Find the payment for the ordinary annuity with the given present value.

49. $150,000; monthly payments for 15 years, with interest rate 5.1%, compounded monthly

50. $25,000; quarterly payments for 8 years, with interest rate 4.9%, compounded quarterly

51. Find the lump-sum deposit today that will produce the same total amount as payments of $4200 at the end of each year for 12 years. The interest rate in both cases is 4.5%, compounded annually.

52. If the current interest rate is 6.5%, find the price (to the nearest dollar) that a purchaser should be willing to pay for a $24,000 bond with coupon rate 5% that matures in 6 years.

Find the amount of the payment necessary to amortize each of the given loans.

53. $32,000 at 8.4% compounded quarterly; 10 quarterly payments

54. $5607 at 7.6% compounded monthly; 32 monthly payments

Find the monthly house payments for the given mortgages.

55. $95,000 at 3.67% for 30 years

56. $167,000 at 2.91% for 15 years

57. Find the approximate remaining balance after 5 years of payments on the loan in Exercise 55.

58. Find the approximate remaining balance after 7.5 years of payments on the loan in Exercise 56.

Finance *According to www.studentaid.ed.gov, in 2013 the interest rate for a direct unsubsidized student loan was 6.8%. A*

portion of an amortization table is given here for a $15,000 direct unsubsidized student loan compounded monthly to be paid back in 10 years. Use the table to answer Exercises 59–62.

Payment Number	Amount of Payment	Interest for Period	Portion to Principal	Principal at End of Period
0				15,000.00
1	172.62	85.00	87.62	14,912.38
2	172.62	84.50	88.12	14,824.26
3	172.62	84.00	88.62	14,735.64
4	172.62	83.50	89.12	14,646.52
5	172.62	83.00	89.62	14,556.90
6	172.62	82.49	90.13	14,466.77
7	172.62	81.98	90.64	14,376.13
8	172.62	81.46	91.16	14,284.97

59. How much of the seventh payment is interest?

60. How much of the fourth payment is used to reduce the debt?

61. How much interest is paid in the first 6 months of the loan?

62. How much has the debt been reduced at the end of the first 8 months?

Finance *Work the following applied problems.*

63. In February 2013, a Virginia family won a Powerball lottery prize of $217,000,000.

   (a) If they had chosen to receive the money in 30 yearly payments, beginning immediately, what would have been the amount of each payment?

   (b) The family chose the one-time lump-sum cash option. If the interest rate is 3.58%, approximately how much did they receive?

64. A firm of attorneys deposits $15,000 of profit-sharing money in an account at 6% compounded semiannually for $7\frac{1}{2}$ years. Find the amount of interest earned.

65. Tom, a graduate student, is considering investing $500 now, when he is 23, or waiting until he is 40 to invest $500. How much more money will he have at age 65 if he invests now, given that he can earn 5% interest compounded quarterly?

66. According to a financial Web site, on June 15, 2005, Frontenac Bank of Earth City, Missouri, paid 3.94% interest, compounded quarterly, on a 2-year CD, while E*TRADE Bank of Arlington, Virginia, paid 3.93% compounded daily. What was the effective rate for the two CDs, and which bank paid a higher effective rate? (Data from: www.bankrate.com.)

67. Chalon Bridges deposits semiannual payments of $3200, received in payment of a debt, in an ordinary annuity at 6.8% compounded semiannually. Find the final amount in the account and the interest earned at the end of 3.5 years.

68. Each year, a firm must set aside enough funds to provide employee retirement benefits of $52,000 in 20 years. If the firm can invest money at 7.5% compounded monthly, what amount must be invested at the end of each month for this purpose?

69. A benefactor wants to be able to leave a bequest to the college she attended. If she wants to make a donation of $2,000,000 in 10 years, how much each month does she need to place in an investment account that pays an interest rate of 5.5%, compounded monthly?

70. Suppose you have built up a pension with $12,000 annual payments by working 10 years for a company when you leave to accept a better job. The company gives you the option of collecting half the full pension when you reach age 55 or the full pension at age 65. Assume an interest rate of 8% compounded annually. By age 75, how much will each plan produce? Which plan would produce the larger amount?

71. In 3 years, Ms. Nguyen must pay a pledge of $7500 to her favorite charity. What lump sum can she deposit today at 10% compounded semiannually so that she will have enough to pay the pledge?

72. To finance the $15,000 cost of their kitchen remodeling, the Chews will make equal payments at the end of each month for 36 months. They will pay interest at the rate of 7.2% compounded monthly. Find the amount of each payment.

73. To expand her business, the owner of a small restaurant borrows $40,000. She will repay the money in equal payments at the end of each semiannual period for 8 years at 9% interest compounded semiannually. What payments must she make?

74. The Fix family bought a house for $210,000. They paid $42,000 down and took out a 30-year mortgage for the balance at 3.75%.

(a) Find the monthly payment.

(b) How much of the first payment is interest?

After 15 years, the family sold their house for $255,000.

(c) Estimate the current mortgage balance at the time of the sale.

(d) Find the amount of money they received from the sale after paying off the mortgage.

75. Over a 20-year period, the class A shares of the Davis New York Venture mutual fund increased in value at the rate of 11.2%, compounded monthly. If you had invested $250 at the end of each month in this fund, what would have the value of your account been at the end of those 20 years?

76. Dan Hook deposits $400 a month to a retirement account that has an interest rate of 3.1%, compounded monthly. After making 60 deposits, Dan changes his job and stops making payments for 3 years. After 3 years, he starts making deposits again, but now he deposits $525 per month. What will the value of the retirement account be after Dan makes his $525 monthly deposits for 5 years?

77. The proceeds of a $10,000 death benefit are left on deposit with an insurance company for 7 years at an annual effective interest rate of 5%.* The balance at the end of 7 years is paid to the beneficiary in 120 equal monthly payments of X, with the first payment made immediately. During the payout period, interest is credited at an annual effective interest rate of 3%. Which of the following is the correct value of X?

(a) 117   (b) 118   (c) 129   (d) 135   (e) 158

78. Eileen Gianiodis wants to retire on $75,000 per year for her life expectancy of 20 years after she retires. She estimates that she will be able to earn an interest rate of 10.1%, compounded annually, throughout her lifetime. To reach her retirement goal, Eileen will make annual contributions to her account for the next 30 years. One year after making her last deposit, she will receive her first retirement check. How large must her yearly contributions be?

---

*The Proceeds of Death Benefit Left on Deposit with an Insurance Company from Course 140 Examination, Mathematics of Compound Interest. Copyright © Society of Actuaries. Reproduced by permission of Society of Actuaries.

Case Study 5 Continuous Compounding

Informally, you can think of *continuous compounding* as a process in which interest is compounded *very* frequently (for instance, every nanosecond). You will occasionally see an ad for a certificate of deposit in which interest is compounded continuously. That's pretty much a gimmick in most cases, because it produces only a few more cents than daily compounding. However, continuous compounding does play a serious role in certain financial situations, notably in the pricing of derivatives.* So let's see what is involved in continuous compounding.

As a general rule, the more often interest is compounded, the better off you are as an investor. (See Example 4 of Section

5.2.) But there is, alas, a limit on the amount of interest, no matter how often it is compounded. To see why this is so, suppose you have $1 to invest. The Exponential Bank offers to pay 100% annual interest, compounded n times per year and rounded to the nearest penny. Furthermore, you may pick any value for n that you want. Can you choose n so large that your $1 will grow to $5 in a year? We will test several values of n in the formula for the compound amount, with $P = 1$. In this case, the annual interest rate (in decimal form) is also 1. If there are n periods in the year, the interest rate per period is $i = 1/n$. So the amount that your dollar grows to is:

$$A = P(1 + i)^n = 1\left(1 + \frac{1}{n}\right)^n.$$

---

*Derivatives are complicated financial instruments. But investors have learned the hard way that they can sometimes cause serious problems—as was the case in the recession that began in 2008, which was blamed in part on the misuse of derivatives.

A computer gives the following results for various values of n:

Interest Is Compounded ...	n	$\left(1 + \dfrac{1}{n}\right)^n$
Annually	1	$\left(1 + \dfrac{1}{1}\right)^1 = 2$
Semiannually	2	$\left(1 + \dfrac{1}{2}\right)^2 = 2.25$
Quarterly	4	$\left(1 + \dfrac{1}{4}\right)^4 \approx 2.4414$
Monthly	12	$\left(1 + \dfrac{1}{12}\right)^{12} \approx 2.6130$
Daily	365	$\left(1 + \dfrac{1}{365}\right)^{365} \approx 2.71457$
Hourly	8760	$\left(1 + \dfrac{1}{8760}\right)^{8760} \approx 2.718127$
Every minute	525,600	$\left(1 + \dfrac{1}{525,600}\right)^{525,600} \approx 2.7182792$
Every second	31,536,000	$\left(1 + \dfrac{1}{31,536,000}\right)^{31,536,000} \approx 2.7182818$

Because interest is rounded to the nearest penny, the compound amount never exceeds $2.72, no matter how big n is. (A computer was used to develop the table, and the figures in it are accurate. If you try these computations with your calculator, however, your answers may not agree exactly with those in the table because of round-off error in the calculator.)

The preceding table suggests that as n takes larger and larger values, the corresponding values of $\left(1 + \dfrac{1}{n}\right)^n$ get closer and closer to a specific real number whose decimal expansion begins $2.71828 \cdots$. This is indeed the case, as is shown in calculus, and the number $2.71828 \cdots$ is denoted e. This fact is sometimes expressed by writing

$$\lim_{n \to \infty}\left(1 + \frac{1}{n}\right)^n = e,$$

which is read "the limit of $\left(1 + \dfrac{1}{n}\right)^n$ as n approaches infinity is e."

The preceding example is typical of what happens when interest is compounded n times per year, with larger and larger values of n. It can be shown that no matter what interest rate or principal is used, there is always an upper limit (involving the number e) on the compound amount, which is called the compound amount from **continuous compounding**.

Continuous Compounding

The compound amount A for a deposit of P dollars at an interest rate r per year compounded continuously for t years is given by

$$A = Pe^{rt}.$$

Most calculators have an e^x key for computing powers of e. See the Technology Tip on page 188 for details on using a calculator to evaluate e^x.

Example 1 Suppose $5000 is invested at an annual rate of 4% compounded continuously for 5 years. Find the compound amount.

Solution In the formula for continuous compounding, let $P = 5000, r = .04$, and $t = 5$. Then a calculator with an e^x key shows that

$$A = 5000e^{(.04)5} = 5000e^{.2} \approx \$6107.01.$$

You can readily verify that daily compounding would have produced a compound amount about 6¢ less.

Exercises

1. Find the compound amount when $20,000 is invested at 6% compounded continuously for
   (a) 2 years;   (b) 10 years;   (c) 20 years.

2. (a) Find the compound amount when $2500 is invested at 5.5%, compounded monthly for two years.
   (b) Do part (a) when the interest rate is 5.5% compounded continuously.

3. Determine the compounded amount from a deposit of $25,000 when it is invested at 5% for 10 years and compounded in the following time periods:
   (a) annually   (b) quarterly   (c) monthly
   (d) daily   (e) continuously

4. Determine the compounded amount from a deposit of $250,000 when it is invested at 5% for 10 years and compounded in the following time periods:

   (a) annually   (b) quarterly   (c) monthly
   (d) daily   (e) continuously

5. It can be shown that if interest is compounded continuously at nominal rate r, then the effective rate r_E is $e^r - 1$. Find the effective rate of continuously compounded interest if the nominal rate is

   (a) 4.5%;   (b) 5.7%;   (c) 7.4%.

6. Suppose you win a court case and the defendant has up to 8 years to pay you $5000 in damages. Assume that the defendant will wait until the last possible minute to pay you.

   (a) If you can get an interest rate of 3.75% compounded continuously, what is the present value of the $5000? [*Hint:* Solve the continuous-compounding formula for P.]

   (b) If the defendant offers you $4000 immediately to settle his debt, should you take the deal?

Extended Projects

1. Investigate the interest rates for the subsidized and unsubsidized student loans. If you have taken out student loans or plan to take out student loans before graduating, calculate your own monthly payment and how much interest you will pay over the course of the repayment period. If you have not taken out, and you do not plan to take out a student loan, contact the financial aid office of your college and university to determine the median amount borrowed with student loans at your institution. Determine the monthly payment and how much interest is paid during repayment for the typical borrowing student.

2. Determine the best interest rate for a new car purchase for a 48-month loan at a bank near you. If you finance $25,999 with such a loan, determine the payment and the total interest paid over the course of the loan. Also, determine the best interest rate for a new car purchase for a 48-month loan at a credit union near you. Determine the monthly payment and total interest paid if the same auto loan is financed through the credit union. Is it true that the credit union would save you money?

Systems of Linear Equations and Matrices

A variety of resource allocation problems involving many variables can be handled by solving an appropriate system of linear equations. Technology (such as graphing calculators, WolframAlpha.com, computer algebra systems, and smart phone apps) is very helpful for handling large systems. Smaller ones can easily be solved by hand. See Exercises 22 and 23 on page 296.

This chapter deals with **linear** (or **first-degree**) **equations** such as

$$2x + 3y = 14 \qquad \text{linear equation in two variables,}$$

$$4x - 2y + 5z = 8 \qquad \text{linear equation in three variables,}$$

and so on. A **solution** of such an equation is an ordered list of numbers that, when substituted for the variables in the order they appear, produces a true statement. For instance, $(1, 4)$ is a solution of the equation $2x + 3y = 14$ because substituting $x = 1$ and $y = 4$ produces the true statement $2(1) + 3(4) = 14$.

Many applications involve **systems of linear equations,** such as these two:

Two equations in two variables	Three equations in four variables
	$2x + y + z \quad\;\; = 3$
$5x - 3y = 7$	$x + y + z + w = 5$
$2x + 4y = 8$	$-4x + \quad\;\; z + w = 0.$

A **solution of a system** is a solution that satisfies *all* the equations in the system. For instance, in the right-hand system of equations on page 270, (1, 0, 1, 3) is a solution of all three equations (check it) and hence is a solution of the system. By contrast, (1, 1, 0, 3) is a solution of the first two equations, but not the third. Hence, (1, 1, 0, 3) is not a solution of the system.

This chapter presents methods for solving such systems, including matrix methods. Matrix algebra and other applications of matrices are also discussed.

6.1 Systems of Two Linear Equations in Two Variables

The graph of a linear equation in two variables is a straight line. The coordinates of each point on the graph represent a solution of the equation (Section 2.1). Thus, the solution of a system of two such equations is represented by the point or points where the two lines intersect. There are exactly three geometric possibilities for two lines: They intersect at a single point, or they coincide, or they are distinct and parallel. As illustrated in Figure 6.1, each of these geometric possibilities leads to a different number of solutions for the system.

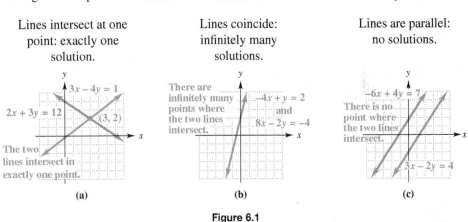

Lines intersect at one point: exactly one solution.	Lines coincide: infinitely many solutions.	Lines are parallel: no solutions.
(a)	(b)	(c)

Figure 6.1

The Substitution Method

Example 1 illustrates the substitution method for solving a system of two equations in two variables.

Example 1   Solve the system

$$2x - y = 1$$
$$3x + 2y = 4.$$

Solution   Begin by solving the first equation for y:

$$2x - y = 1$$
$$-y = -2x + 1 \qquad \text{Subtract } 2x \text{ from both sides.}$$
$$y = 2x - 1. \qquad \text{Multiply both sides by } -1.$$

Substitute this expression for y in the second equation and solve for x:

$$3x + 2y = 4$$
$$3x + 2(2x - 1) = 4 \qquad \text{Substitute } 2x - 1 \text{ for } y.$$
$$3x + 4x - 2 = 4 \qquad \text{Multiply out the left side.}$$
$$7x - 2 = 4 \qquad \text{Combine like terms.}$$
$$7x = 6 \qquad \text{Add 2 to both sides.}$$
$$x = 6/7. \qquad \text{Divide both sides by 7.}$$

Therefore, every solution of the system must have $x = 6/7$. To find the corresponding solution for y, substitute $x = 6/7$ in one of the two original equations and solve for y. We shall use the first equation.

$$2x - y = 1$$

$$2\left(\frac{6}{7}\right) - y = 1 \qquad \text{Substitute } 6/7 \text{ for } x.$$

$$\frac{12}{7} - y = 1 \qquad \text{Multiply out the left side.}$$

$$-y = -\frac{12}{7} + 1 \qquad \text{Subtract } 12/7 \text{ from both sides.}$$

$$y = \frac{12}{7} - 1 = \frac{5}{7}. \qquad \text{Multiply both sides by } -1.$$

Hence, the solution of the original system is $x = 6/7$ and $y = 5/7$. We would have obtained the same solution if we had substituted $x = 6/7$ in the second equation of the original system, as you can easily verify.

The substitution method is useful when at least one of the equations has a variable with coefficient 1. That is why we solved for y in the first equation of Example 1. If we had solved for x in the first equation or for x or y in the second, we would have had a lot more fractions to deal with.

TECHNOLOGY TIP   A graphing calculator can be used to solve systems of two equations in two variables. Solve each of the given equations for y and graph them on the same screen. In Example 1, for instance we would graph

$$y_1 = 2x - 1 \qquad \text{and} \qquad y_2 = \frac{-3x + 4}{2}.$$

Use the intersection finder to determine the point where the graphs intersect (the solution of the system), as shown in Figure 6.2. Note that this is an *approximate* solution, rather than the exact solution found algebraically in Example 1.

The Elimination Method

The elimination method of solving systems of linear equations is often more convenient than substitution, as illustrated in the next four examples.

Example 2   Solve the system

$$5x + y = 4$$
$$3x + 2y = 1.$$

Solution   Multiply the first equation by -2, so that the coefficients of y in the two equations are negatives of each other:

$$-10x - 2y = -8 \qquad \text{First equation multiplied by } -2.$$
$$3x + 2y = 1. \qquad \text{Second equation as given.}$$

Any solution of this system of equations must also be a solution of the sum of the two equations:

$$
\begin{array}{rcl}
-10x - 2y &=& -8 \\
\underline{3x + 2y} &=& \underline{1} \\
-7x &=& -7 \qquad \text{Sum; variable } y \text{ is eliminated.} \\
x &=& 1. \qquad \text{Divide both sides by } -7.
\end{array}
$$

✓ **Checkpoint 1**

Use the substitution method to solve this system:

$$x - 2y = 3$$
$$2x + 3y = 13.$$

Answers to Checkpoint exercises are found at the end of the section.

Figure 6.2

To find the corresponding value of y, substitute $x = 1$ in one of the original equations, say the first one:

$$5x + y = 4$$
$$5(1) + y = 4 \qquad \text{Substitute 1 for } x.$$
$$y = -1. \qquad \text{Subtract 5 from both sides.}$$

Therefore, the solution of the original system is $(1, -1)$.

✓ **Checkpoint 2**

Use the elimination method to solve this system:
$$x + 2y = 4$$
$$3x - 4y = -8.$$

Example 3   Solve the system

$$3x - 4y = 1$$
$$2x + 3y = 12.$$

Solution   Multiply the first equation by 2 and the second equation by -3 to get

$$6x - 8y = 2 \qquad \text{First equation multiplied by 2.}$$
$$-6x - 9y = -36. \qquad \text{Second equation multiplied by } -3.$$

The multipliers 2 and -3 were chosen so that the coefficients of x in the two equations would be negatives of each other. Any solution of both these equations must also be a solution of their sum:

$$6x - 8y = 2$$
$$\underline{-6x - 9y = -36}$$
$$-17y = -34 \qquad \text{Sum; variable } x \text{ is eliminated.}$$
$$y = 2. \qquad \text{Divide both sides by } -17.$$

To find the corresponding value of x, substitute 2 for y in either of the original equations. We choose the first equation:

$$3x - 4y = 1$$
$$3x - 4(2) = 1 \qquad \text{Substitute 2 for } y.$$
$$3x - 8 = 1 \qquad \text{Simplify.}$$
$$3x = 9 \qquad \text{Add 8 to both sides.}$$
$$x = 3. \qquad \text{Divide both sides by 3.}$$

Therefore, the solution of the system is $(3, 2)$. The graphs of both equations of the system are shown in Figure 6.1(a). They intersect at the point $(3, 2)$, the solution of the system. ✓

✓ **Checkpoint 3**

Solve the system of equations
$$3x + 2y = -1$$
$$5x - 3y = 11.$$
Draw the graph of each equation on the same set of axes.

Dependent and Inconsistent Systems

A system of equations that has a unique solution, such as those in Examples 1–3, is called an **independent system.** Now we consider systems that have infinitely many solutions or no solutions at all.

Example 4   Solve the system

$$-4x + y = 2$$
$$8x - 2y = -4.$$

Solution   If you solve each equation in the system for y, you see that the two equations are actually the same:

$$-4x + y = 2 \qquad\qquad 8x - 2y = -4$$
$$y = 4x + 2 \qquad\qquad -2y = -8x - 4$$
$$y = 4x + 2.$$

So the two equations have the same graph, as shown in Figure 6.1(b), and the system has infinitely many solutions (namely, all solutions of $y = 4x + 2$). A system such as this is said to be **dependent.**

You do not have to analyze a system as was just done in order to find out that the system is dependent. The elimination method will warn you. For instance, if you attempt to eliminate x in the original system by multiplying both sides of the first equation by 2 and adding the results to the second equation, you obtain

$$
\begin{array}{ll}
-8x + 2y = 4 & \text{First equation multiplied by 2.} \\
\underline{8x - 2y = -4} & \text{Second equation as given.} \\
0 = 0. & \text{Both variables are eliminated.}
\end{array}
$$

The equation "$0 = 0$" is an algebraic indication that the system is dependent and has infinitely many solutions. ✓ 4

✓ **Checkpoint 4**

Solve the following system:
$$
\begin{array}{l}
3x - 4y = 13 \\
12x - 16y = 52.
\end{array}
$$

Example 5 Solve the system
$$
\begin{array}{l}
3x - 2y = 4 \\
-6x + 4y = 7.
\end{array}
$$

Solution The graphs of these equations are parallel lines (each has slope $3/2$), as shown in Figure 6.1(c). Therefore, the system has no solution. However, you do not need the graphs to discover this fact. If you try to solve the system algebraically by multiplying both sides of the first equation by 2 and adding the results to the second equation, you obtain

$$
\begin{array}{ll}
6x - 4y = 8 & \text{First equation multiplied by 2.} \\
\underline{-6x + 4y = 7} & \text{Second equation as given.} \\
0 = 15. & \text{False statement.}
\end{array}
$$

The false statement "$0 = 15$" is the algebraic signal that the system has no solution. A system with no solutions is said to be **inconsistent.** ✓ 5

✓ **Checkpoint 5**

Solve the system
$$
\begin{array}{l}
x - y = 4 \\
2x - 2y = 3.
\end{array}
$$

Draw the graph of each equation on the same set of axes.

Applications

In many applications, the answer is the solution of a system of equations. Solving the system is the easy part—*finding* the system, however, may take some thought.

Example 6 **Business** Eight hundred people attend a basketball game, and total ticket sales are $3102. If adult tickets are $6 and student tickets are $3, how many adults and how many students attended the game?

Solution Let x be the number of adults and y the number of students. Then

Number of adults + Number of students = Total attendance.

$$x + y = 800.$$

A second equation can be found by considering ticket sales:

Adult ticket sales + Student ticket sales = Total ticket sales

$$
\left(\begin{array}{c} \text{Price} \\ \text{per} \\ \text{ticket} \end{array} \right) \times \left(\begin{array}{c} \text{Number} \\ \text{of} \\ \text{adults} \end{array} \right) + \left(\begin{array}{c} \text{Price} \\ \text{per} \\ \text{ticket} \end{array} \right) \times \left(\begin{array}{c} \text{Number} \\ \text{of} \\ \text{students} \end{array} \right) = 3102
$$

$$6x + 3y = 3102.$$

✓ **Checkpoint 6**

(a) Use substitution or elimination to solve the system of equations in Example 6.

⬈ (b) Use technology to solve the system. (*Hint:* Solve each equation for y, graph both equations on the same screen, and use the intersection finder.)

To find x and y we must solve this system of equations:

$$x + y = 800$$
$$6x + 3y = 3102.$$

The system can readily be solved by hand or by using technology. See Checkpoint 6, which shows that 234 adults and 566 students attended the game. ✓6

6.1 Exercises

Determine whether the given ordered list of numbers is a solution of the system of equations.

1. $(-1, 3)$
$$2x + y = 1$$
$$-3x + 2y = 9$$

2. $(2, -.5)$
$$.5x + 8y = -3$$
$$x + 5y = -5$$

Use substitution to solve each system. (See Example 1.)

3. $3x - y = 1$
$$x + 2y = -9$$

4. $x + y = 7$
$$x - 2y = -5$$

5. $3x - 2y = 4$
$$2x + y = -1$$

6. $5x - 3y = -2$
$$-x - 2y = 3$$

Use elimination to solve each system. (See Examples 2–5.)

7. $x - 2y = 5$
$$2x + y = 3$$

8. $3x - y = 1$
$$-x + 2y = 4$$

9. $2x - 2y = 12$
$$-2x + 3y = 10$$

10. $3x + 2y = -4$
$$4x - 2y = -10$$

11. $x + 3y = -1$
$$2x - y = 5$$

12. $4x - 3y = -1$
$$x + 2y = 19$$

13. $2x + 3y = 15$
$$8x + 12y = 40$$

14. $2x + 5y = 8$
$$6x + 15y = 18$$

15. $2x - 8y = 2$
$$3x - 12y = 3$$

16. $3x - 2y = 4$
$$6x - 4y = 8$$

In Exercises 17 and 18, multiply both sides of each equation by a common denominator to eliminate the fractions. Then solve the system.

17. $\dfrac{x}{5} + 3y = 31$

$$2x - \dfrac{y}{5} = 8$$

18. $\dfrac{x}{2} + \dfrac{y}{3} = 8$

$$\dfrac{2x}{3} + \dfrac{3y}{2} = 17$$

19. Business When Neil Simon opened a new play, he had to decide whether to open the show on Broadway or off Broadway. For example, he decided to open his play *London Suite* off Broadway. From information provided by Emanuel Azenberg, his producer, the following equations were developed:

$$43,500x - y = 1,295,000$$
$$27,000x - y = 440,000,$$

where x represents the number of weeks that the show ran and y represents the profit or loss from the show. The first equation is for Broadway, and the second equation is for off Broadway.[*]

(a) Solve this system of equations to determine when the profit or loss from the show will be equal for each venue. What is the amount of that profit or loss?

✎ (b) Discuss which venue is favorable for the show.

20. Social Science One of the factors that contribute to the success or failure of a particular army during war is its ability to get new troops ready for service. It is possible to analyze the rate of change in the number of troops of two hypothetical armies with the simplified model

Rate of increase (Red Army) $= 200,000 - .5r - .3b$

Rate of increase (Blue Army) $= 350,000 - .5r - .7b,$

where r is the number of soldiers in the Red Army at a given time and b is the number of soldiers in the Blue Army at the same time. The factors .5 and .7 represent each army's efficiency at bringing new soldiers into the fight.*

(a) Solve this system of equations to determine the number of soldiers in each army when the rate of increase for each is zero.

(b) Describe what might be going on in a war when the rate of increase is zero.

21. **Social Science** According to U.S. Census Bureau projections through the year 2030, the population y of the given state in year x is approximated by

$$\text{Ohio:} \quad -5x + y = 11,400$$
$$\text{North Carolina:} \quad -140x + y = 8000,$$

where $x = 0$ corresponds to the year 2000 and y is in thousands. In what year do the two states have the same population?

22. **Social Science** The population y of the given state in year x is approximated by

$$\text{Florida:} \quad 50y - 21x = 800$$
$$\text{New York:} \quad 75y - x = 1425,$$

where $x = 0$ corresponds to the year 2000 and y is in millions. (Data from: U.S. Census Bureau.)

(a) Which state had the larger population in the year 2000?

(b) Which state is projected to have the larger population in the year 2030?

(c) In what year do the two states have the same population?

23. **Finance** On the basis of data from 2000 and 2010, median weekly earnings y in year x can be approximated for women and men by

$$\text{Women:} \quad 2y - 9x = 1248$$
$$\text{Men:} \quad 10y - 13x = 8110,$$

where $x = 0$ corresponds to the year 2000 and y is in constant 2010 dollars. If these equations remain valid in the future, when will the median weekly earnings for women and men be the same? (Data from: Bureau of Labor Statistics.)

24. **Health** The number of deaths y in year x can be approximated for diseases of the heart and malignant neoplasms (cancer) by

$$\text{Heart disease:} \quad 58x + 5y = 3555$$
$$\text{Cancer:} \quad -21x + 10y = 5530,$$

where $x = 0$ corresponds to the year 2000 and y is in thousands. According to these models (which are based on data from 2000 and 2010), when were deaths from heart disease equal to cancer deaths? (Data from: Centers for Disease Control and Prevention.)

25. **Business** A 200-seat theater charges $8 for adults and $5 for children. If all seats were filled and the total ticket income was $1435, how many adults and how many children were in the audience?

26. **Business** In November 2008, HBO released the complete series of *The Sopranos* on DVD. According to an ad in the *New York Times*, there were 86 episodes on 33 discs. If 5 discs were soundtracks and bonus material and 6 discs each had 4 episodes, how many discs had 2 episodes and how many had 3?

27. **Physical Science** A plane flies 3000 miles from San Francisco to Boston in 5 hours, with a tailwind all the way. The return trip on the same route, now with a headwind, takes 6 hours. Assuming both remain constant, find the speed of the plane and the speed of the wind. [*Hint:* If x is the plane's speed and y the wind speed (in mph), then the plane travels to Boston at $x + y$ mph because the plane and the wind go in the same direction; on the return trip, the plane travels at $x - y$ mph. (Why?)]

28. **Physical Science** A plane flying into a headwind travels 2200 miles in 5 hours. The return flight along the same route with a tailwind takes 4 hours. Find the wind speed and the plane's speed (assuming both are constant). (See the hint for Exercise 27.)

29. **Finance** Shirley Cicero has $16,000 invested in Boeing and GE stock. The Boeing stock currently sells for $30 a share and the GE stock for $70 a share. If GE stock triples in value and Boeing stock goes up 50%, her stock will be worth $34,500. How many shares of each stock does she own?

30. **Business** An apparel shop sells skirts for $45 and blouses for $35. Its entire stock is worth $51,750, but sales are slow and only half the skirts and two-thirds of the blouses are sold, for a total of $30,600. How many skirts and blouses are left in the store?

31. (a) Find the equation of the straight line through $(1, 2)$ and $(3, 4)$.

(b) Find the equation of the line through $(-1, 1)$ with slope 3.

(c) Find a point that lies on both of the lines in (a) and (b).

32. (a) Find an equation of the straight line through $(0, 9)$ and $(2, 1)$.

(b) Find an equation of the straight line through $(1, 5)$ with slope 2.

(c) Find a point that lies on both of the lines in (a) and (b).

✓**Checkpoint Answers**

1. $(5, 1)$ 2. $(0, 2)$

3. $(1, -2)$

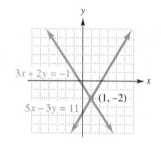

4. All ordered pairs that satisfy the equation $3x - 4y = 13$ (or $12x - 16y = 52$)

5. No solution

6. (a) $x = 234$ and $y = 566$

(b)

6.2 Larger Systems of Linear Equations

Two systems of equations are said to be **equivalent** if they have the same solutions. The basic procedure for solving a large system of equations is to transform the system into a simpler, equivalent system and then solve this simpler system.

Three operations, called **elementary operations,** are used to transform a system into an equivalent one:

1. **Interchange any two equations in the system.**

   Changing the order of the equations obviously does not affect the solutions of the equations or the system.

2. **Multiply an equation in the system by a nonzero constant.**

   Multiplying an equation by a nonzero constant does not change its solutions. So it does not change the solutions of the system.

3. **Replace an equation in the system by the sum of itself and a constant multiple of another equation.**

   We are not saying here that the replacement equation has the same solutions as the one it replaces—it doesn't—only that the new *system* has the same solutions as the original system (that is, the systems are equivalent).*

Example 1 shows how to use elementary operations on a system to eliminate certain variables and produce an equivalent system that is easily solved. The italicized statements provide an outline of the procedure. Here and later on, we use R_1 to denote the first equation in a system, R_2 the second equation, and so on.

Example 1   Solve the system

$$2x + y - z = 2$$
$$x + 3y + 2z = 1$$
$$x + y + z = 2.$$

Solution   First, *use elementary operations to produce an equivalent system in which 1 is the coefficient of x in the first equation.* One way to do this is to interchange the first two equations (another would be to multiply both sides of the first equation by $\frac{1}{2}$):

$$x + 3y + 2z = 1 \qquad \text{Interchange } R_1 \text{ and } R_2.$$
$$2x + y - z = 2$$
$$x + y + z = 2.$$

---

*This operation was used in a slightly different form in Section 6.1, when the sum of an equation and a constant multiple of another equation was found in order to eliminate one of the variables. See, for instance, Examples 2 and 3 of that section.

Next, *use elementary operations to produce an equivalent system in which the x-term has been eliminated from the second and third equations.* To eliminate the x-term from the second equation, replace the second equation by the sum of itself and -2 times the first equation:

$$
\begin{array}{rl}
-2R_1 & -2x - 6y - 4z = -2 \\
R_2 & 2x + y - z = 2 \\
\hline
-2R_1 + R_2 & -5y - 5z = 0
\end{array}
$$

$$
\begin{aligned}
x + 3y + 2z &= 1 \\
-5y - 5z &= 0 \qquad {\scriptstyle -2R_1 + R_2} \longleftarrow \\
x + y + z &= 2.
\end{aligned}
$$

To eliminate the x-term from the third equation of this last system, replace the third equation by the sum of itself and -1 times the first equation:

$$
\begin{array}{rl}
-1R_1 & -x - 3y - 2z = -1 \\
R_3 & x + y + z = 2 \\
\hline
-1R_1 + R_3 & -2y -z = 1
\end{array}
$$

$$
\begin{aligned}
x + 3y + 2z &= 1 \\
-5y - 5z &= 0 \\
-2y - z &= 1. \qquad {\scriptstyle -1R_1 + R_3} \longleftarrow
\end{aligned}
$$

Now that x has been eliminated from all but the first equation, we ignore the first equation and work on the remaining ones. *Use elementary operations to produce an equivalent system in which 1 is the coefficient of y in the second equation.* This can be done by multiplying the second equation in the system by $-\frac{1}{5}$:

$$
\begin{aligned}
x + 3y + 2z &= 1 \\
y + z &= 0 \qquad {\scriptstyle -\frac{1}{5}R_2} \\
-2y - z &= 1.
\end{aligned}
$$

Then *use elementary operations to obtain an equivalent system in which y has been eliminated from the third equation.* Replace the third equation by the sum of itself and 2 times the second equation:

$$
\begin{aligned}
x + 3y + 2z &= 1 \\
y + z &= 0 \\
z &= 1. \qquad {\scriptstyle 2R_2 + R_3}
\end{aligned}
$$

The solution of the third equation is obvious: $z = 1$. Now work backward in the system. Substitute 1 for z in the second equation and solve for y, obtaining $y = -1$. Finally, substitute 1 for z and -1 for y in the first equation and solve for x, obtaining $x = 2$. This process is known as **back substitution.** When it is finished, we have the solution of the original system, namely, $(2, -1, 1)$. It is always wise to check the solution by substituting the values for x, y, and z in *all* equations of the original system.

The procedure used in Example 1 to eliminate variables and produce a system in which back substitution works can be carried out with any system, as summarized below. In this summary, the first variable that appears in an equation with a nonzero coefficient is called the **leading variable** of that equation, and its nonzero coefficient is called the **leading coefficient.**

The Elimination Method for Solving Large Systems of Linear Equations

Use elementary operations to transform the given system into an equivalent one as follows:

1. Make the leading coefficient of the first equation 1 either by interchanging equations or by multiplying the first equation by a suitable constant.

2. Eliminate the leading variable of the first equation from each later equation by replacing the later equation by the sum of itself and a suitable multiple of the first equation.

3. Repeat Steps 1 and 2 for the second equation: Make its leading coefficient 1 and eliminate its leading variable from each later equation by replacing the later equation by the sum of itself and a suitable multiple of the second equation.

4. Repeat Steps 1 and 2 for the third equation, fourth equation, and so on, until it is not possible to go any further.

Then solve the resulting system by back substitution.

At various stages in the elimination process, you may have a choice of elementary operations that can be used. As long as the final result is a system in which back substitution can be used, the choice does not matter. To avoid unnecessary errors, choose elementary operations that minimize the amount of computation and, as far as possible, avoid complicated fractions. ☑₁

Matrix Methods

You may have noticed that the variables in a system of equations remain unchanged during the solution process. So we need to keep track of only the coefficients and the constants. For instance, consider the system in Example 1:

$$2x + y - z = 2$$
$$x + 3y + 2z = 1$$
$$x + y + z = 2.$$

This system can be written in an abbreviated form without listing the variables as

$$\begin{bmatrix} 2 & 1 & -1 & 2 \\ 1 & 3 & 2 & 1 \\ 1 & 1 & 1 & 2 \end{bmatrix}.$$

Such a rectangular array of numbers, consisting of horizontal **rows** and vertical **columns,** is called a **matrix** (plural, **matrices**). Each number in the array is an **element,** or **entry.** To separate the constants in the last column of the matrix from the coefficients of the variables, we sometimes use a vertical line, producing the following **augmented matrix:**

$$\left[\begin{array}{ccc|c} 2 & 1 & -1 & 2 \\ 1 & 3 & 2 & 1 \\ 1 & 1 & 1 & 2 \end{array}\right]. ☑₂$$

The rows of the augmented matrix can be transformed in the same way as the equations of the system, since the matrix is just a shortened form of the system. The following **row operations** on the augmented matrix correspond to the elementary operations used on systems of equations.

Performing any one of the following **row operations** on the augmented matrix of a system of linear equations produces the augmented matrix of an equivalent system:

1. Interchange any two rows.

2. Multiply each element of a row by a nonzero constant.

3. Replace a row by the sum of itself and a constant multiple of another row of the matrix.

✓ **Checkpoint 1**

Use the elimination method to solve each system.

(a) $2x + y = -1$
  $x + 3y = 2$

(b) $2x - y + 3z = 2$
  $x + 2y - z = 6$
  $-x - y + z = -5$

✓ **Checkpoint 2**

(a) Write the augmented matrix of the following system:

$$4x - 2y + 3z = 4$$
$$3x + 5y + z = -7$$
$$5x - y + 4z = 6.$$

(b) Write the system of equations associated with the following augmented matrix:

$$\left[\begin{array}{cc|c} 2 & -2 & -2 \\ 1 & 1 & 4 \\ 3 & 5 & 8 \end{array}\right].$$

Row operations on a matrix are indicated by the same notation we used for elementary operations on a system of equations. For example, $2R_3 + R_1$ indicates the sum of 2 times row 3 and row 1.

Checkpoint 3

Perform the given row operations on the matrix

$$\begin{bmatrix} -1 & 5 \\ 3 & -2 \end{bmatrix}.$$

(a) Interchange R_1 and R_2.

(b) Find $2R_1$.

(c) Replace R_2 by $-3R_1 + R_2$.

(d) Replace R_1 by $2R_2 + R_1$.

Example 2   Use matrices to solve the system

$$x - 2y = 6 - 4z$$
$$x + 13z = 6 - y$$
$$-2x + 6y - z = -10.$$

Solution   First, put the system in the required form, with the constants on the right side of the equals sign and the terms with variables *in the same order* in each equation on the left side of the equals sign. Then write the augmented matrix of the system.

$$\begin{array}{rcrcl} x & - & 2y & + & 4z = & 6 \\ x & + & y & + & 13z = & 6 \\ -2x & + & 6y & - & z = & -10 \end{array} \qquad \begin{bmatrix} 1 & -2 & 4 & 6 \\ 1 & 1 & 13 & 6 \\ -2 & 6 & -1 & -10 \end{bmatrix}.$$

The matrix method is the same as the elimination method, except that row operations are used on the augmented matrix instead of elementary operations on the corresponding system of equations, as shown in the following side-by-side comparison:

Equation Method   **Matrix Method**

Replace the second equation by the sum of itself and -1 times the first equation:

Replace the second row by the sum of itself and -1 times the first row:

$$\begin{array}{rcl} x - 2y + 4z = & 6 \\ 3y + 9z = & 0 \\ -2x + 6y - z = & -10. \end{array} \quad \leftarrow -1R_1 + R_2 \rightarrow \quad \begin{bmatrix} 1 & -2 & 4 & 6 \\ 0 & 3 & 9 & 0 \\ -2 & 6 & -1 & -10 \end{bmatrix}.$$

Replace the third equation by the sum of itself and 2 times the first equation:

Replace the third row by the sum of itself and 2 times the first row:

$$\begin{array}{rcl} x - 2y + 4z = 6 \\ 3y + 9z = 0 \\ 2y + 7z = 2. \end{array} \quad \leftarrow 2R_1 + R_3 \rightarrow \quad \begin{bmatrix} 1 & -2 & 4 & 6 \\ 0 & 3 & 9 & 0 \\ 0 & 2 & 7 & 2 \end{bmatrix}.$$

Multiply both sides of the second equation by $\frac{1}{3}$:

Multiply each element of row 2 by $\frac{1}{3}$:

$$\begin{array}{rcl} x - 2y + 4z = 6 \\ y + 3z = 0 \\ 2y + 7z = 2. \end{array} \quad \leftarrow \frac{1}{3} R_2 \rightarrow \quad \begin{bmatrix} 1 & -2 & 4 & 6 \\ 0 & 1 & 3 & 0 \\ 0 & 2 & 7 & 2 \end{bmatrix}.$$

Replace the third equation by the sum of itself and -2 times the second equation:

Replace the third row by the sum of itself and -2 times the second row:

$$\begin{array}{rcl} x - 2y + 4z = 6 \\ y + 3z = 0 \\ z = 2. \end{array} \quad \leftarrow -2R_2 + R_3 \rightarrow \quad \begin{bmatrix} 1 & -2 & 4 & 6 \\ 0 & 1 & 3 & 0 \\ 0 & 0 & 1 & 2 \end{bmatrix}.$$

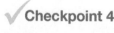**Checkpoint 4**

Complete the matrix solution of the system with this augmented matrix:

$$\begin{bmatrix} 1 & 1 & 1 & 2 \\ 1 & -2 & 1 & -1 \\ 0 & 3 & 1 & 5 \end{bmatrix}.$$

Now use back substitution:

$$z = 2 \qquad\qquad y + 3(2) = 0 \qquad\qquad x - 2(-6) + 4(2) = 6$$
$$y = -6 \qquad\qquad x + 20 = 6$$
$$x = -14.$$

The solution of the system is $(-14, -6, 2)$.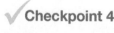

A matrix, such as the last one in Example 2, is said to be in **row echelon form** when

all rows consisting entirely of zeros (if any) are at the bottom;

the first nonzero entry in each row is 1 (called a *leading* 1); and

each leading 1 appears to the right of the leading 1s in any preceding rows.

When a matrix in row echelon form is the augmented matrix of a system of equations, as in Example 2, the system can readily be solved by back substitution. So the matrix solution method amounts to transforming the augmented matrix of a system of equations into a matrix in row echelon form.

The Gauss–Jordan Method

The **Gauss–Jordan method** is a variation on the matrix elimination method used in Example 2. It replaces the back substitution used there with additional elimination of variables, as illustrated in the next example.

Example 3   Use the Gauss–Jordan method to solve the system in Example 2.

Solution   First, set up the augmented matrix. Then apply the same row operations used in Example 2 until you reach the final row echelon matrix, which is

$$\left[\begin{array}{ccc|c} 1 & -2 & 4 & 6 \\ 0 & 1 & 3 & 0 \\ 0 & 0 & 1 & 2 \end{array}\right].$$

Now use additional row operations to make the entries (other than the 1s) in columns two and three into zeros. Make the first two entries in column three 0 as follows:

$$\left[\begin{array}{ccc|c} 1 & -2 & 4 & 6 \\ 0 & 1 & 0 & -6 \\ 0 & 0 & 1 & 2 \end{array}\right] \qquad -3R_3 + R_2$$

$$\left[\begin{array}{ccc|c} 1 & -2 & 0 & -2 \\ 0 & 1 & 0 & -6 \\ 0 & 0 & 1 & 2 \end{array}\right] \qquad -4R_3 + R_1$$

Now make the first entry in column two 0.

$$\left[\begin{array}{ccc|c} 1 & 0 & 0 & -14 \\ 0 & 1 & 0 & -6 \\ 0 & 0 & 1 & 2 \end{array}\right]. \qquad 2R_2 + R_1$$

The last matrix corresponds to the system $x = -14, y = -6, z = 2$. So the solution of the original system is $(-14, -6, 2)$. This solution agrees with what we found in Example 2.

The final matrix in the Gauss–Jordan method is said to be in **reduced row echelon form,** meaning that it is in row echelon form *and* every column containing a leading 1 has zeros in all its other entries, as in Example 3. As we saw there, the solution of the system can be read directly from the reduced row echelon matrix.

In the Gauss–Jordan method, row operations may be performed in any order, but it is best to transform the matrix systematically. Either follow the procedure in Example 3 (which first puts the system into a form in which back substitution can be used and then eliminates additional variables) or work column by column from left to right, as in Checkpoint 5. ✓ 5

✓ **Checkpoint 5**

Use the Gauss–Jordan method to solve the system

$$x + 2y = 11$$
$$-4x + y = -8$$
$$5x + y = 19$$

as instructed in parts (a)–(g). Give the shorthand notation for the required row operations in parts (b)–(f) and the new matrix in each step.

(a)   Set up the augmented matrix.

(b)   Get 0 in row 2, column 1.

(c)   Get 0 in row 3, column 1.

(d)   Get 1 in row 2, column 2.

(e)   Get 0 in row 1, column 2.

(f)   Get 0 in row 3, column 2.

(g)   List the solution of the system.

Technology and Systems of Equations

When working by hand, it is usually better to use the matrix elimination method (Example 2), because errors with back substitution are less likely to occur than errors in performing the additional row operations needed in the Gauss–Jordan method. When you are using technology, however, the Gauss–Jordan method (Example 3) is more efficient: The solution can be read directly from the final reduced row echelon matrix without any "hand work," as illustrated in the next example.

 Example 4   Use a graphing calculator to solve the system in Example 2.

Solution   There are three ways to proceed.

Matrix Elimination Method   Enter the augmented matrix of the system into the calculator (Figure 6.3). Use REF (in the MATH or OPS submenu of the MATRIX menu) to put this matrix in row echelon form (Figure 6.4). The system corresponding to this matrix is

$$x - 3y + .5z = 5$$
$$y + 3.125z = .25$$
$$z = 2.$$

Because the calculator used a different sequence of row operations than was used in Example 2, it produced a different row echelon matrix (and corresponding system). However, back substitution shows that the solutions of this system are the same ones found in Example 2:

$$z = 2 \qquad y + 3.125(2) = .25 \qquad x - 3(-6) + .5(2) = 5$$
$$y + 6.25 = .25 \qquad x + 18 + 1 = 5$$
$$y = -6 \qquad x = -14.$$

As you can see, a significant amount of hand work is involved in this method, so it is not recommended.

Gauss–Jordan Method   Enter the augmented matrix (Figure 6.3). Use RREF (in same menu as REF) to produce the same reduced row echelon matrix obtained in Example 3 (Figure 6.5). The solution of the system can be read directly from the matrix: $x = -14$, $y = -6, z = 2$.

System Solver Method   This is essentially the same as the Gauss–Jordan method, with an extra step at the beginning. Call up the solver (see the Technology Tip on the next page) and enter the number of variables and equations. The solver will display an appropriately sized matrix, with all entries 0. Change the entries so that the matrix becomes the augmented matrix of the system (Figure 6.6). Press SOLVE and the solution will appear (Figure 6.7). The calculator uses the variables x_1, x_2, and x_3 instead of x, y, and z.

Figure 6.3

Figure 6.4

Figure 6.5

 Checkpoint 6

On a graphing calculator, use the Gauss–Jordan method or the system solver to solve

$$x - y + 5z = -6$$
$$4x + 2y + 4z = 4$$
$$x - 5y + 8z = -17$$
$$x + 3y + 2z = 5.$$

Figure 6.6

Figure 6.7

TECHNOLOGY TIP Many graphing calculators have system solvers. Select PLYSMLT2 in the APPS menu of TI-84+, SIMULT on the TI-86 keyboard, or EQUA in the Casio main menu. *Note:* The TI-86 and Casio solvers work only for systems that have the same number of variables as equations *and* have a unique solution (so they cannot be used in Checkpoint 6 or in Examples 5–8).

Example 5   Use a graphing calculator to solve the system

$$
\begin{aligned}
x + 2y - z &= 0 \\
3x - y + z &= 6 \\
7x + 28y - 8z &= -5 \\
5x + 3y - z &= 6.
\end{aligned}
$$

Solution   Enter the augmented matrix into the calculator (Figure 6.8). Then use RREF to put this matrix in reduced row echelon form (Figure 6.9). In Figure 6.9, you must use the arrow key to scroll over to see the full decimal expansions in the right-hand column. This inconvenience can be avoided on TI calculators by using FRAC (in the MATH menu), as in Figure 6.10.

```
[A]
   [1   2   -1    0 ]
   [3  -1    1    6 ]
   [7  28   -8   -5 ]
   [5   3   -1    6 ]
```

Figure 6.8

```
rref([A])
   [1   0   0   1.571428571 ]
   [0   1   0   -.2857142857]
   [0   0   1            1  ]
   [0   0   0            0  ]
```

Figure 6.9

```
rref([A])▶Frac
   [1   0   0   11/7 ]
   [0   1   0   -2/7 ]
   [0   0   1    1   ]
   [0   0   0    0   ]
```

Figure 6.10

✓ Checkpoint 7

Use a graphing calculator to solve the following system:

$$
\begin{aligned}
x + 3y &= 4 \\
4x + 8y &= 4 \\
6x + 12y &= 6.
\end{aligned}
$$

The answers can now be read from the last column of the matrix in Figure 6.10: $x = 11/7$, $y = -2/7, z = 1$. ✓₇

Inconsistent and Dependent Systems

Recall that a system of equations in two variables may have exactly one solution, an infinite number of solutions, or no solutions at all. This fact was illustrated geometrically in Figure 6.1. The same thing is true for systems with three or more variables (and the same terminology is used): A system has exactly one solution (an **independent system**), an infinite number of solutions (a **dependent system**), or no solutions at all (an **inconsistent system**).

Example 6   Solve the system

$$
\begin{aligned}
2x + 4y &= 4 \\
3x + 6y &= 8 \\
2x + y &= 7.
\end{aligned}
$$

Solution   There are several possible ways to proceed.

Manual Method   Write the augmented matrix and perform row operations to obtain a first column whose entries (from top to bottom) are 1, 0, 0:

$$
\begin{bmatrix}
2 & 4 & | & 4 \\
3 & 6 & | & 8 \\
2 & 1 & | & 7
\end{bmatrix}
$$

$$\begin{bmatrix} 1 & 2 & | & 2 \\ 3 & 6 & | & 8 \\ 2 & 1 & | & 7 \end{bmatrix} \quad \tfrac{1}{2}R_1$$

$$\begin{bmatrix} 1 & 2 & | & 2 \\ 0 & 0 & | & 2 \\ 2 & 1 & | & 7 \end{bmatrix}. \quad -3R_1 + R_2$$

Stop! The second row of the matrix denotes the equation $0x + 0y = 2$. Since the left side of this equation is always 0 and the right side is 2, it has no solution. Therefore, the original system has no solution.

rref([A])
$$\begin{bmatrix} 1 & 0 & 0 \\ 0 & 1 & 0 \\ 0 & 0 & 1 \end{bmatrix}$$

Figure 6.11

Calculator Method Enter the augmented matrix into a graphing calculator and use RREF to put it into reduced row echelon form, as in Figure 6.11. The last row of that matrix corresponds to $0x + 0y = 1$, which has no solution. Hence, the original system has no solution. ✔8

✔ **Checkpoint 8**

Solve each system.

(a) $x - y = 4$
      $-2x + 2y = 1$

(b) $3x - 4y = 0$
      $2x + y = 0$

Whenever the solution process produces a row whose elements are all 0 *except* the last one, as in Example 6, the system is inconsistent and has no solutions. However, if a row with a 0 for *every* entry is produced, it corresponds to an equation such as $0x + 0y + 0z = 0$, which has infinitely many solutions. So the system may have solutions, as in the next example.

Example 7   Solve the system

$$\begin{aligned} 2x - 3y + 4z &= 6 \\ x - 2y + z &= 9 \\ y + 2z &= -12. \end{aligned}$$

Solution Use matrix elimination as far as possible, beginning with the augmented matrix of the system:

$$\begin{bmatrix} 2 & -3 & 4 & | & 6 \\ 1 & -2 & 1 & | & 9 \\ 0 & 1 & 2 & | & -12 \end{bmatrix}$$

$$\begin{bmatrix} 1 & -2 & 1 & | & 9 \\ 2 & -3 & 4 & | & 6 \\ 0 & 1 & 2 & | & -12 \end{bmatrix} \quad \text{Interchange } R_1 \text{ and } R_2.$$

$$\begin{bmatrix} 1 & -2 & 1 & | & 9 \\ 0 & 1 & 2 & | & -12 \\ 0 & 1 & 2 & | & -12 \end{bmatrix} \quad -2R_1 + R_2$$

$$\begin{bmatrix} 1 & -2 & 1 & | & 9 \\ 0 & 1 & 2 & | & -12 \\ 0 & 0 & 0 & | & 0 \end{bmatrix}. \qquad \begin{aligned} x - 2y + z &= 9 \\ y + 2z &= -12. \end{aligned}$$
$$-R_2 + R_3$$

The last augmented matrix above represents the system shown to its right. Since there are only two rows in the matrix, it is not possible to continue the process. The fact that the corresponding system has one variable (namely, z) that is not the leading variable of an equation indicates a dependent system. To find its solutions, first solve the second equation for y:

$$y = -2z - 12.$$

Now substitute the result for y in the first equation and solve for x:

$$x - 2y + z = 9$$
$$x - 2(-2z - 12) + z = 9$$
$$x + 4z + 24 + z = 9$$
$$x + 5z = -15$$
$$x = -5z - 15.$$

Each choice of a value for z leads to values for x and y. For example,

$$\text{if } z = 1, \quad \text{then } x = -20 \quad \text{and} \quad y = -14;$$
$$\text{if } z = -6, \quad \text{then } x = 15 \quad \text{and} \quad y = 0;$$
$$\text{if } z = 0, \quad \text{then } x = -15 \quad \text{and} \quad y = -12.$$

There are infinitely many solutions of the original system, since z can take on infinitely many values. The solutions are all ordered triples of the form

$$(-5z - 15, -2z - 12, z),$$

where z is any real number.

✓ Checkpoint 9

Use the following values of z to find additional solutions for the system of Example 7.

(a) $z = 7$

(b) $z = -14$

(c) $z = 5$

Figure 6.12

Since both x and y in Example 7 were expressed in terms of z, the variable z is called a **parameter.** If we had solved the system in a different way, x or y could have been the parameter. The system in Example 7 had one more variable than equations. If there are two more variables than equations, there usually will be two parameters, and so on.

Example 8   Row operations were used to reduce the augmented matrix of a system of three equations in four variables $(x, y, z, \text{and } w)$ to the reduced row echelon matrix in Figure 6.12. Solve the system.

Solution   First write out the system represented by the matrix:

$$x + \qquad\qquad 9w = -12$$
$$y - \qquad w = \quad 4$$
$$z - 2w = \quad 1.$$

Let w be the parameter. Solve the first equation for x, the second for y, and the third for z:

$$x = -9w - 12; \qquad y = w + 4; \qquad z = 2w + 1.$$

The solutions are given by $(-9w - 12, w + 4, 2w + 1, w)$, where w is any real number.

TECHNOLOGY TIP   When the system solvers on TI-86 and Casio produce an error message, the system might be inconsistent (no solutions) or dependent (infinitely many solutions). You must use RREF or manual methods to solve the system.

    The TI-84+ solver usually solves dependent systems directly; Figure 6.13 shows its solutions for Example 7. When the message "no solution found" is displayed, as in Figure 6.14, select RREF at the bottom of the screen to display the reduced row echelon matrix of the system. From that, you can determine the solutions (if there are any) or that no solutions are possible.

Figure 6.13

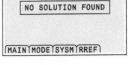

Figure 6.14

6.2 Exercises

Obtain an equivalent system by performing the stated elementary operation on the system. (See Example 1.)

1. Interchange equations 1 and 2.

$$2x - 4y + 5z = 1$$
$$x \quad\quad - 3z = 2$$
$$5x - 8y + 7z = 6$$
$$3x - 4y + 2z = 3$$

2. Interchange equations 1 and 3.

$$2x - 2y + \quad z = -6$$
$$3x + \quad y + 2z = \quad 2$$
$$x + \quad y - 2z = \quad 0$$

3. Multiply the second equation by -1.

$$3x \quad\quad + z + 2w + 18v = 0$$
$$4x - y + \quad\quad w + 24v = 0$$
$$7x - y + z + 3w + 42v = 0$$
$$4x \quad\quad + z + 2w + 24v = 0$$

4. Multiply the third equation by $1/2$.

$$x + 2y + 4z = 3$$
$$x \quad\quad + 2z = 0$$
$$2x + 4y + \quad z = 3$$

5. Replace the second equation by the sum of itself and -2 times the first equation.

$$x + y + 2z + 3w = 1$$
$$2x + y + 3z + 4w = 1$$
$$3x + y + 4z + 5w = 2$$

6. Replace the third equation by the sum of itself and -1 times the first equation.

$$x + 2y + 4z = \quad 6$$
$$y + \quad z = \quad 1$$
$$x + 3y + 5z = 10$$

7. Replace the third equation by the sum of itself and -2 times the second equation.

$$x + 12y - 3z + 4w = 10$$
$$2y + 3z + \quad w = \quad 4$$
$$4y + 5z + 2w = \quad 1$$
$$6y - 2z - 3w = \quad 0$$

8. Replace the third equation by the sum of itself and 3 times the second equation.

$$2x + 2y - 4z + \quad w = -5$$
$$2y + 4z - \quad w = \quad 2$$
$$-6y - 4z + 2w = \quad 6$$
$$2y + 5z - 3w = \quad 7$$

Solve the system by back substitution. (See Example 1.)

9.
$$x + 3y - 4z + 2w = \quad 1$$
$$y + \quad z - \quad w = \quad 4$$
$$2z + 2w = -6$$
$$3w = \quad 9$$

10.
$$x + \quad\quad 5z + 6w = \quad 10$$
$$y + 3z - 2w = \quad 4$$
$$z - 4w = -6$$
$$2w = \quad 4$$

11.
$$2x + 2y - 4z + \quad w = -5$$
$$3y + 4z - \quad w = \quad 0$$
$$2z - 7w = -6$$
$$5w = \quad 15$$

12.
$$3x - 2y - 4z + 2w = \quad 6$$
$$2y + 5z - 3w = \quad 7$$
$$3z + 4w = \quad 0$$
$$3w = \quad 15$$

Write the augmented matrix of each of the given systems. Do not solve the systems. (See Example 2.)

13.
$$2x + \quad y + \quad z = \quad 3$$
$$3x - 4y + 2z = -5$$
$$x + \quad y + \quad z = \quad 2$$

14.
$$3x + 4y - 2z - 3w = 0$$
$$x - 3y + 7z + 4w = 9$$
$$2x \quad\quad + 5z - 6w = 0$$

Write the system of equations associated with each of the given augmented matrices. Do not solve the systems.

15.
$$\begin{bmatrix} 2 & 3 & 8 & 20 \\ 1 & 4 & 6 & 12 \\ 0 & 3 & 5 & 10 \end{bmatrix}$$

16.
$$\begin{bmatrix} 3 & 2 & 6 & 18 \\ 2 & -2 & 5 & 7 \\ 1 & 0 & 5 & 20 \end{bmatrix}$$

Use the indicated row operation to transform each matrix. (See Examples 2 and 3.)

17. Interchange R_2 and R_3.

$$\begin{bmatrix} 1 & 2 & 3 & -1 \\ 6 & 5 & 4 & 6 \\ 2 & 0 & 7 & -4 \end{bmatrix}$$

18. Replace R_3 by $-3R_1 + R_3$.

$$\begin{bmatrix} 1 & 5 & 2 & 0 & -1 \\ 8 & 5 & 4 & 6 & 6 \\ 3 & 0 & 7 & 1 & -4 \end{bmatrix}$$

19. Replace R_2 by $2R_1 + R_2$.

$$\begin{bmatrix} -4 & -3 & 1 & -1 & 2 \\ 8 & 2 & 5 & 0 & 6 \\ 0 & -2 & 9 & 4 & 5 \end{bmatrix}$$

20. Replace R_3 by $\frac{1}{4}R_3$.

$$\begin{bmatrix} 2 & 5 & 1 & -1 \\ -4 & 0 & 4 & 6 \\ 6 & 0 & 8 & -4 \end{bmatrix}$$

In Exercises 21–24, the reduced row echelon form of the augmented matrix of a system of equations is given. Find the solutions of the system. (See Example 3.)

21. $\begin{bmatrix} 1 & 0 & 0 & 0 & | & 3/2 \\ 0 & 1 & 0 & 0 & | & 17 \\ 0 & 0 & 1 & 0 & | & -5 \\ 0 & 0 & 0 & 1 & | & 0 \end{bmatrix}$

22. $\begin{bmatrix} 1 & 0 & 0 & 0 & 0 & | & 6 \\ 0 & 1 & 0 & 0 & 0 & | & 4 \\ 0 & 0 & 1 & 0 & 0 & | & 5 \\ 0 & 0 & 0 & 0 & 1 & | & 2 \\ 0 & 0 & 0 & 0 & 0 & | & 1 \end{bmatrix}$

23. $\begin{bmatrix} 1 & 0 & 0 & 1 & | & 12 \\ 0 & 1 & 0 & 2 & | & -3 \\ 0 & 0 & 1 & 0 & | & -5 \\ 0 & 0 & 0 & 0 & | & 0 \end{bmatrix}$

24. $\begin{bmatrix} 1 & 0 & 0 & 0 & | & 7 \\ 0 & 1 & 0 & 0 & | & 2 \\ 0 & 0 & 1 & 0 & | & -5 \\ 0 & 0 & 0 & 1 & | & 3 \\ 0 & 0 & 0 & 0 & | & 0 \\ 0 & 0 & 0 & 0 & | & 0 \end{bmatrix}$

In Exercises 25–30, perform row operations on the augmented matrix as far as necessary to determine whether the system is independent, dependent, or inconsistent. (See Examples 6–8.)

25.
$x + 2y \quad\quad = 0$
$\quad\quad y - z = 2$
$x + y + z = -2$

26.
$x + 2y + z = 0$
$\quad\quad y + 2z = 0$
$x + y - z = 0$

27.
$x + 2y + 4z = 6$
$\quad\quad y + z = 1$
$x + 3y + 5z = 10$

28.
$x + y + 2z + 3w = 1$
$2x + y + 3z + 4w = 1$
$3x + y + 4z + 5w = 2$

29.
$a - 3b - 2c = -3$
$3a + 2b - c = 12$
$-a - b + 4c = 3$

30.
$2x + 2y + 2z = 6$
$3x - 3y - 4z = -1$
$x + y + 3z = 11$

Write the augmented matrix of the system and use the matrix method to solve the system. (See Examples 2 and 4.)

31.
$-x + 3y + 2z = 0$
$2x - y - z = 3$
$x + 2y + 3z = 0$

32.
$3x + 7y + 9z = 0$
$x + 2y + 3z = 2$
$x + 4y + z = 2$

33.
$x - 2y + 4z = 6$
$x + 2y + 13z = 6$
$-2x + 6y - z = -10$

34.
$x - 2y + 5z = -6$
$x + 2y + 3z = 0$
$x + 3y + 2z = 5$

35.
$x + y + z = 200$
$x - 2y = 0$
$2x + 3y + 5z = 600$
$2x - y + z = 200$

36.
$2x - y + 2z = 3$
$-x + 2y - z = 0$
$3y - 2z = 1$
$x + y - z = 1$

37.
$x + y + z = 5$
$2x + y - z = 2$
$x - y + z = -2$

38.
$2x + y + 3z = 9$
$-x - y + z = 1$
$3x - y + z = 9$

Use the Gauss–Jordan method to solve each of the given systems of equations. (See Examples 3–5.)

39.
$x + 2y + z = 5$
$2x + y - 3z = -2$
$3x + y + 4z = -5$

40.
$3x - 2y + z = 6$
$3x + y - z = -4$
$-x + 2y - 2z = -8$

41.
$x + 3y - 6z = 7$
$2x - y + 2z = 0$
$x + y + 2z = -1$

42.
$x = 1 - y$
$2x = z$
$2z = -2 - y$

43.
$x - 2y + 4z = 9$
$x + y + 13z = 6$
$-2x + 6y - z = -10$

44.
$x - y + 5z = -6$
$3x + 3y - z = 10$
$x + 2y + 3z = 5$

Solve the system by any method.

45.
$x + 3y + 4z = 14$
$2x - 3y + 2z = 10$
$3x - y + z = 9$
$4x + 2y + 5z = 9$

46.
$4x - y + 3z = -2$
$3x + 5y - z = 15$
$-2x + y + 4z = 14$
$x + 6y + 3z = 29$

47.
$x + 8y + 8z = 8$
$3x - y + 3z = 5$
$-2x - 4y - 6z = 5$

48.
$3x - 2y - 8z = 1$
$9x - 6y - 24z = -2$
$x - y + z = 1$

49.
$5x + 3y + 4z = 19$
$3x - y + z = -4$

50.
$3x + y - z = 0$
$2x - y + 3z = -7$

51.
$x - 2y + z = 5$
$2x + y - z = 2$
$-2x + 4y - 2z = 2$

52.
$2x + 3y + z = 9$
$4x + y - 3z = -7$
$6x + 2y - 4z = -8$

53.
$-8x - 9y = 11$
$24x + 34y = 2$
$16x + 11y = -57$

54.
$2x + y = 7$
$x - y = 3$
$x + 3y = 4$

55.
$x + 2y = 3$
$2x + 3y = 4$
$3x + 4y = 5$
$4x + 5y = 6$

56.
$x - y = 2$
$x + y = 4$
$2x + 3y = 9$
$3x - 2y = 6$

57.
$x + y - z = -20$
$2x - y + z = 11$

58.
$4x + 3y + z = 1$
$-2x - y + 2z = 0$

59.
$2x + y + 3z - 2w = -6$
$4x + 3y + z - w = -2$
$x + y + z + w = -5$
$-2x - 2y - 2z + 2w = -10$

60.
$x + y + z + w = -1$
$-x + 4y + z - w = 0$
$x - 2y + z - 2w = 11$
$-x - 2y + z + 2w = -9$

61.
$x + 2y - z = 3$
$3x + y + w = 4$
$2x - y + z + w = 2$

62. $\begin{aligned} x - 2y - z - 3w &= -3 \\ -x + y + z &= 2 \\ 4y + 3z - 6w &= -2 \end{aligned}$

63. $\dfrac{3}{x} - \dfrac{1}{y} + \dfrac{4}{z} = -13$

$\dfrac{1}{x} + \dfrac{2}{y} - \dfrac{1}{z} = 12$

$\dfrac{4}{x} - \dfrac{1}{y} + \dfrac{3}{z} = -7$

[*Hint:* Let $u = 1/x, v = 1/y$, and $w = 1/z$, and solve the resulting system.]

64. $\dfrac{1}{x+1} - \dfrac{2}{y-3} + \dfrac{3}{z-2} = 4$

$\dfrac{5}{y-3} - \dfrac{10}{z-2} = -5$

$\dfrac{-3}{x+1} + \dfrac{4}{y-3} - \dfrac{1}{z-2} = -2$

[*Hint:* Let $u = 1/(x+1), v = 1/(y-3)$, and $w = 1/(z-2)$.]

Work these exercises.

65. Social Science   The population y in year x of the county listed is approximated by:

     Calhoun County, IL: $x + 20y = 102$

     Martin County, TX: $-x + 10y = 48$

     Schley County, GA: $y = 5,$

where $x = 0$ corresponds to the year 2010 and y is in thousands. When did all three counties have the same population? What was that population? (Data from: U.S. Census Bureau.)

66. Social Science   The population y in year x of the greater metropolitan area listed is approximated by the given equation in which $x = 0$ corresponds to the year 2010 and y is in thousands:

     Portland, OR: $-32x + y = 2226$

     Cambridge, MA: $-22x + y = 2246$

     Charlotte, NC: $-73x + 2y = 4434.$

In what year did all three metropolitan areas have the same population? (Data from: U.S. Census Bureau.)

67. Business   A band concert is attended by x adults, y teenagers, and z preteen children. These numbers satisfy the following equations:

$$x + 1.25y + .25z = 457.5$$
$$x + .6y + .4z = 390$$
$$3.16x + 3.48y + .4z = 1297.2.$$

How many adults, teenagers, and children were present?

68. Business   The owner of a small business borrows money on three separate credit cards: x dollars on Mastercard, y dollars on Visa, and z dollars on American Express. These amounts satisfy the following equations:

$$1.18x + 1.15y + 1.09z = 11{,}244.25$$
$$3.54x - .55y + .27z = 3{,}732.75$$
$$.06x + .05y + .03z = 414.75.$$

How much did the owner borrow on each card?

Work these problems.

69. Graph the equations in the given system. Then explain why the graphs show that the system is inconsistent:

$$2x + 3y = 8$$
$$x - y = 4$$
$$5x + y = 7.$$

70. Explain why the graphs of the equations in the given system suggest that the system is independent:

$$-x + y = 1$$
$$-2x + y = 0$$
$$x + y = 3.$$

71. Find constants a, b, and c such that the points $(2, 3)$, $(-1, 0)$, and $(-2, 2)$ lie on the graph of the equation $y = ax^2 + bx + c$. (*Hint:* Since $(2, 3)$ is on the graph, we must have $3 = a(2^2) + b(2) + c$; that is, $4a + 2b + c = 3$. Similarly, the other two points lead to two more equations. Solve the resulting system for a, b, and c.)

72. Explain why a system with more variables than equations cannot have a unique solution (that is, be an independent system). (*Hint:* When you apply the elimination method to such a system, what must happen?)

✓**Checkpoint Answers**

1. (a) $(-1, 1)$ **(b)** $(3, 1, -1)$

2. (a) $\left[\begin{array}{ccc|c} 4 & -2 & 3 & 4 \\ 3 & 5 & 1 & -7 \\ 5 & -1 & 4 & 6 \end{array}\right]$

     (b) $\begin{aligned} 2x - 2y &= -2 \\ x + y &= 4 \\ 3x + 5y &= 8 \end{aligned}$

3. (a) $\left[\begin{array}{cc} 3 & -2 \\ -1 & 5 \end{array}\right]$ **(b)** $\left[\begin{array}{cc} -2 & 10 \\ 3 & -2 \end{array}\right]$

   (c) $\left[\begin{array}{cc} -1 & 5 \\ 6 & -17 \end{array}\right]$ **(d)** $\left[\begin{array}{cc} 5 & 1 \\ 3 & -2 \end{array}\right]$

4. $(-1, 1, 2)$

5. (a) $\left[\begin{array}{cc|c} 1 & 2 & 11 \\ -4 & 1 & -8 \\ 5 & 1 & 19 \end{array}\right]$ **(b)** $4R_1 + R_2 \left[\begin{array}{cc|c} 1 & 2 & 11 \\ 0 & 9 & 36 \\ 5 & 1 & 19 \end{array}\right]$

   (c) $-5R_1 + R_3 \left[\begin{array}{cc|c} 1 & 2 & 11 \\ 0 & 9 & 36 \\ 0 & -9 & -36 \end{array}\right]$

   (d) $\dfrac{1}{9}R_2 \left[\begin{array}{cc|c} 1 & 2 & 11 \\ 0 & 1 & 4 \\ 0 & -9 & -36 \end{array}\right]$

(e) $-2R_2 + R_1$ $\begin{bmatrix} 1 & 0 & | & 3 \\ 0 & 1 & | & 4 \\ 0 & -9 & | & -36 \end{bmatrix}$

(f) $9R_2 + R_3$ $\begin{bmatrix} 1 & 0 & | & 3 \\ 0 & 1 & | & 4 \\ 0 & 0 & | & 0 \end{bmatrix}$

(g) $(3, 4)$

6. $(1, 2, -1)$

7. $(-5, 3)$

8. **(a)** No solution   **(b)** $(0, 0)$

9. **(a)** $(-50, -26, 7)$ **(b)** $(55, 16, -14)$

   (c) $(-40, -22, 5)$

6.3 Applications of Systems of Linear Equations

There are no hard and fast rules for solving applied problems, but it is usually best to begin by identifying the unknown quantities and letting each be represented by a variable. Then look at the given data to find one or more relationships among the unknown quantities that lead to equations. If the equations are all linear, use the techniques of the preceding sections to solve the system.

Example 1   **Business**   The U-Drive Rent-a-Truck Company plans to spend $5 million on 200 new vehicles. Each van will cost $20,000, each small truck $25,000, and each large truck $35,000. Past experience shows that U-Drive needs twice as many vans as small trucks. How many of each kind of vehicle can the company buy?

Solution   Let x be the number of vans, y the number of small trucks, and z the number of large trucks. Then

$$\left(\begin{matrix}\text{Number of}\\\text{vans}\end{matrix}\right) + \left(\begin{matrix}\text{Number of}\\\text{small trucks}\end{matrix}\right) + \left(\begin{matrix}\text{Number of}\\\text{large trucks}\end{matrix}\right) = \text{Total number of vehicles}$$

$$x + y + z = 200. \tag{1}$$

Similarly,

$$\left(\begin{matrix}\text{Cost of } x\\\text{vans}\end{matrix}\right) + \left(\begin{matrix}\text{Cost of } y\\\text{small trucks}\end{matrix}\right) + \left(\begin{matrix}\text{Cost of } z\\\text{large trucks}\end{matrix}\right) = \text{Total cost}$$

$$20{,}000x + 25{,}000y + 35{,}000z = 5{,}000{,}000.$$

Dividing both sides by 5000 produces the equivalent equation

$$4x + 5y + 7z = 1000. \tag{2}$$

Finally, the number of vans is twice the number of small trucks; that is, $x = 2y$, or equivalently,

$$x - 2y = 0. \tag{3}$$

We must solve the system given by equations (1)–(3):

$$\begin{aligned} x + y + z &= 200 \\ 4x + 5y + 7z &= 1000 \\ x - 2y \, &= 0. \end{aligned}$$

Manual Method   Form the augmented matrix and transform it into row echelon form:

$$\begin{bmatrix} 1 & 1 & 1 & | & 200 \\ 4 & 5 & 7 & | & 1000 \\ 1 & -2 & 0 & | & 0 \end{bmatrix}$$

$$\begin{bmatrix} 1 & 1 & 1 & | & 200 \\ 0 & 1 & 3 & | & 200 \\ 0 & -3 & -1 & | & -200 \end{bmatrix} \quad \begin{matrix} -4R_1 + R_2 \\ -R_1 + R_3 \end{matrix}$$

$$\begin{bmatrix} 1 & 1 & 1 & | & 200 \\ 0 & 1 & 3 & | & 200 \\ 0 & 0 & 8 & | & 400 \end{bmatrix} \quad 3R_2 + R_3$$

$$\begin{bmatrix} 1 & 1 & 1 & | & 200 \\ 0 & 1 & 3 & | & 200 \\ 0 & 0 & 1 & | & 50 \end{bmatrix}. \quad \tfrac{1}{8}R_3$$

This row echelon matrix corresponds to the system

$$x + y + z = 200$$
$$y + 3z = 200$$
$$z = 50.$$

Use back substitution to solve this system:

$$z = 50 \qquad \begin{aligned} y + 3z &= 200 \\ y + 3(50) &= 200 \\ y + 150 &= 200 \\ y &= 50 \end{aligned} \qquad \begin{aligned} x + y + z &= 200 \\ x + 50 + 50 &= 200 \\ x + 100 &= 200 \\ x &= 100. \end{aligned}$$

Therefore, U-Drive should buy 100 vans, 50 small trucks, and 50 large trucks.

rref([A])
$$\begin{bmatrix} 1 & 0 & 0 & 100 \\ 0 & 1 & 0 & 50 \\ 0 & 0 & 1 & 50 \end{bmatrix}$$

Figure 6.15

Calculator Method   Enter the augmented matrix of the system into the calculator. Use RREF to change it into reduced row echelon form, as in Figure 6.15. The answers may be read directly from the matrix: $x = 100$ vans, $y = 50$ small trucks, and $z = 50$ large trucks. ✓ 1

✓ **Checkpoint 1**

In Example 1, suppose that U-Drive can spend only $2 million on 150 new vehicles and the company needs three times as many vans as small trucks. Write a system of equations to express these conditions.

Example 2   **Finance**   Ellen McGillicuddy plans to invest a total of $100,000 in a money market account, a bond fund, an international stock fund, and a domestic stock fund. She wants 60% of her investment to be conservative (money market and bonds). She wants the amount in international stocks to be one-fourth of the amount in domestic stocks. Finally, she needs an annual return of $4000. Assuming she gets annual returns of 2.5% on the money market account, 3.5% on the bond fund, 5% on the international stock fund, and 6% on the domestic stock fund, how much should she put in each investment?

Solution   Let x be the amount invested in the money market account, y the amount in the bond fund, z the amount in the international stock fund, and w the amount in the domestic stock fund. Then

$$x + y + z + w = \text{total amount invested} = 100{,}000. \qquad \textbf{(4)}$$

Use her annual return to get a second equation:

$$\begin{pmatrix} 2.5\% \text{ return} \\ \text{on money} \\ \text{market} \end{pmatrix} + \begin{pmatrix} 3.5\% \text{ return} \\ \text{on bond} \\ \text{fund} \end{pmatrix} + \begin{pmatrix} 5\% \text{ return on} \\ \text{international} \\ \text{stock fund} \end{pmatrix} + \begin{pmatrix} 6\% \text{ return} \\ \text{on domestic} \\ \text{stock fund} \end{pmatrix} = 4000$$

$$.025x \quad + \quad .035y \quad + \quad .05z \quad + \quad .06w \quad = 4000. \qquad \textbf{(5)}$$

Since Ellen wants the amount in international stocks to be one-fourth of the amount in domestic stocks, we have

$$z = \frac{1}{4}w, \quad \text{or equivalently,} \quad z - .25w = 0. \tag{6}$$

Finally, the amount in conservative investments is $x + y$, and this quantity should be equal to 60% of $100,000—that is,

$$x + y = 60,000. \tag{7}$$

Now solve the system given by equations (4)–(7):

$$
\begin{aligned}
x + \quad y + \quad z + \quad w &= 100,000 \\
.025x + .035y + .05z + .06w &= 4,000 \\
z - .25w &= 0 \\
x + \quad y \qquad\qquad &= 60,000.
\end{aligned}
$$

Manual Method Write the augmented matrix of the system and transform it into row echelon form, as in Checkpoint 2.

The final matrix in Checkpoint 2 represented the system

$$
\begin{aligned}
x + y + \quad z + \quad w &= 100,000 \\
y + 2.5z + 3.5w &= 150,000 \\
z - .25w &= 0 \\
w &= 32,000.
\end{aligned}
$$

Back substitution shows that

$$w = 32,000 \qquad z = .25w = .25(32,000) = 8000$$
$$y = -2.5z - 3.5w + 150,000 = -2.5(8000) - 3.5(32,000) + 150,000 = 18,000$$
$$x = -y - z - w + 100,000 = -18,000 - 8000 - 32,000 + 100,000 = 42,000.$$

Therefore, Ellen should put $42,000 in the money market account, $18,000 in the bond fund, $8000 in the international stock fund, and $32,000 in the domestic stock fund.

Calculator Method Enter the augmented matrix of the system into the calculator. Use RREF to change it into reduced row echelon form, as in Figure 6.16. The answers can easily be read from this matrix: $x = 42,000$, $y = 18,000$, $z = 8000$, and $w = 32,000$.

✓**Checkpoint 2**

(a) Write the augmented matrix of the system given by equations (4)–(7) of Example 2.

(b) List a sequence of row operations that transforms this matrix into row echelon form.

(c) Display the final row echelon form matrix.

```
rref([A])
[1  0  0  0   42000]
[0  1  0  0   18000]
[0  0  1  0    8000]
[0  0  0  1   32000]
```

Figure 6.16

Example 3 **Business** An animal feed is to be made from corn, soybeans, and cottonseed. Determine how many units of each ingredient are needed to make a feed that supplies 1800 units of fiber, 2800 units of fat, and 2200 units of protein, given that 1 unit of each ingredient provides the numbers of units shown in the table below. The table states, for example, that a unit of corn provides 10 units of fiber, 30 units of fat, and 20 units of protein.

	Corn	Soybeans	Cottonseed	Totals
Units of Fiber	10	20	30	1800
Units of Fat	30	20	40	2800
Units of Protein	20	40	25	2200

Solution Let x represent the required number of units of corn, y the number of units of soybeans, and z the number of units of cottonseed. Since the total amount of fiber is to be 1800, we have

$$10x + 20y + 30z = 1800.$$

The feed must supply 2800 units of fat, so

$$30x + 20y + 40z = 2800.$$

Finally, since 2200 units of protein are required, we have

$$20x + 40y + 25z = 2200.$$

Thus, we must solve this system of equations:

$$10x + 20y + 30z = 1800$$
$$30x + 20y + 40z = 2800 \tag{8}$$
$$20x + 40y + 25z = 2200.$$

Now solve the system, either manually or with technology.

Manual Method Write the augmented matrix and use row operations to transform it into row echelon form, as in Checkpoint 3. The resulting matrix represents the following system: ✓3

$$x + 2y + 3z = 180$$
$$y + \frac{5}{4}z = 65$$
$$z = 40. \tag{9}$$

Back substitution now shows that

$$z = 40, \quad y = 65 - \frac{5}{4}(40) = 15, \quad \text{and} \quad x = 180 - 2(15) - 3(40) = 30.$$

Thus, the feed should contain 30 units of corn, 15 units of soybeans, and 40 units of cottonseed.

Calculator Method Enter the augmented matrix of the system into the calculator (top of Figure 6.17). Use RREF to transform it into reduced row echelon form (bottom of Figure 6.17), which shows that $x = 30$, $y = 15$, and $z = 40$.

✓ **Checkpoint 3**

(a) Write the augmented matrix of system (8) of Example 3.

(b) List a sequence of row operations that transforms this matrix into row echelon form.

(c) Display the final row echelon form matrix.

```
[10  20  30  1800]
[30  20  40  2800]
[20  40  25  2200]
rref([A])
      [1  0  0  30]
      [0  1  0  15]
      [0  0  1  40]
```

Figure 6.17

Example 4 **Social Science** The table shows Census Bureau projections for the population of the United States (in millions).

Year	2020	2040	2050
U.S. Population	334	380	400

(a) Use the given data to construct a quadratic function that gives the U.S. population (in millions) in year x.

Solution Let $x = 0$ correspond to the year 2000. Then the table represents the data points (20,334), (40,380), and (50,400). We must find a function of the form

$$f(x) = ax^2 + bx + c$$

whose graph contains these three points. If (20,334) is to be on the graph, we must have $f(20) = 334$; that is,

$$a(20)^2 + b(20) + c = 334$$
$$400a + 20b + c = 334.$$

The other two points lead to these equations:

$$f(40) = 380 \qquad\qquad f(50) = 400$$
$$a(40)^2 + b(40) + c = 380 \qquad a(50)^2 + b(50) + c = 400$$
$$1600a + 40b + c = 380 \qquad 2500a + 50b + c = 400.$$

Now work by hand or use technology to solve the following system:

$$400a + 20b + c = 334$$
$$1600a + 40b + c = 380$$
$$2500a + 50b + c = 400.$$

```
[400   20   1   334]
[1600  40   1   380]
[2500  50   1   400]
rref([A])
       [1   0   0   -.01]
       [0   1   0   2.9 ]
       [0   0   1   280 ]
```

Figure 6.18

The reduced row echelon form of the augmented matrix in Figure 6.18 shows that the solution is $a = -.01$, $b = 2.9$, and $c = 280$. So the function is

$$f(x) = -.01x^2 + 2.9x + 280.$$

(b) Use this model to estimate the U.S. population in the year 2030.

Solution The year 2030 corresponds to $x = 30$, so the U.S. population is projected to be

$$f(30) = -.01(30)^2 + 2.9(30) + 280 = 358 \text{ million.}$$

Example 5   **Business**   Kelly Karpet Kleaners sells rug-cleaning machines. The EZ model weighs 10 pounds and comes in a 10-cubic-foot box. The compact model weighs 20 pounds and comes in an 8-cubic-foot box. The commercial model weighs 60 pounds and comes in a 28-cubic-foot box. Each of Kelly's delivery vans has 248 cubic feet of space and can hold a maximum of 440 pounds. In order for a van to be fully loaded, how many of each model should it carry?

Solution Let x be the number of EZ, y the number of compact, and z the number of commercial models carried by a van. Then we can summarize the given information in this table.

Model	Number	Weight	Volume
EZ	x	10	10
Compact	y	20	8
Commercial	z	60	28
Total for a load		440	248

Since a fully loaded van can carry 440 pounds and 248 cubic feet, we must solve this system of equations:

$$10x + 20y + 60z = 440 \qquad \text{Weight equation}$$
$$10x + 8y + 28z = 248. \qquad \text{Volume equation}$$

The augmented matrix of the system is

$$\begin{bmatrix} 10 & 20 & 60 & | & 440 \\ 10 & 8 & 28 & | & 248 \end{bmatrix}.$$

```
rref([A])▶Frac
       [1   0   2/3   12]
       [0   1   8/3   16]
```

Figure 6.19

If you are working by hand, transform the matrix into row echelon form and use back substitution. If you are using a graphing calculator, use RREF to transform the matrix into reduced row echelon form, as in Figure 6.19 (which also uses FRAC in the MATH menu to eliminate long decimals).

The system corresponding to Figure 6.19 is

$$x + \frac{2}{3}z = 12$$

$$y + \frac{8}{3}z = 16,$$

which is easily solved: $x = 12 - \frac{2}{3}z$ and $y = 16 - \frac{8}{3}z$.

Hence, all solutions of the system are given by $\left(12 - \frac{2}{3}z, 16 - \frac{8}{3}z, z\right)$. The only solutions that apply in this situation, however, are those given by $z = 0, 3$, and 6, because all other values of z lead to fractions or negative numbers. (You can't deliver part of a box or a negative number of boxes). Hence, there are three ways to have a fully loaded van:

Solution	Van Load
(12, 16, 0)	12 EZ, 16 compact, 0 commercial
(10, 8, 3)	10 EZ, 8 compact, 3 commercial
(8, 0, 6)	8 EZ, 0 compact, 6 commercial.

6.3 Exercises

Use systems of equations to work these applied problems. (See Examples 1–5.)

1. **Business**   The U-Drive Rent-a-Truck Company of Example 1 learns that each van now costs $25,000, each small truck costs $30,000, and each large truck costs $40,000. The company still needs twice as many vans as small trucks and wants to spend $5 million, but it decides to buy only 175 vehicles. How many of each kind should it buy?

2. **Finance**   Suppose that Ellen McGillicuddy in Example 2 finds that her annual return on the international stock fund will be only 4%. Now how much should she put in each investment?

3. **Health**   To meet consumer demand, the animal feed in Example 3 now supplies only 2400 units of fat. How many units of corn, soybeans, and cottonseed are now needed?

4. **Business**   Suppose that Kelly Karpet Kleaners in Example 5 finds a way to pack the EZ model in an 8-cubic-foot box. Now how many of each model should a fully loaded van carry?

5. **Business**   Mario took clothes to the cleaners three times last month. First, he brought 3 shirts and 1 pair of slacks and paid $10.96. Then he brought 7 shirts, 2 pairs of slacks, and a sports coat and paid $30.40. Finally, he brought 4 shirts and 1 sports coat and paid $14.45. How much was he charged for each shirt, each pair of slacks, and each sports coat?

6. **Business**   A minor league baseball park has 7000 seats. Box seats cost $6, grandstand seats cost $4, and bleacher seats cost $2. When all seats are sold, the revenue is $26,400. If the number of box seats is one-third the number of bleacher seats, how many seats of each type are there?

7. **Business**   Tickets to a band concert cost $5 for adults, $3 for teenagers, and $2 for preteens. There were 570 people at the concert, and total ticket receipts were $1950. Three-fourths as many teenagers as preteens attended. How many adults, teenagers, and preteens attended?

8. **Business**   Shipping charges at an online bookstore are $4 for one book, $6 for two books, and $7 for three to five books. Last week, there were 6400 orders of five or fewer books, and total shipping charges for these orders were $33,600. The number of shipments with $7 charges was 1000 less than the number with $6 charges. How many shipments were made in each category (one book, two books, three-to-five books)?

9. **Finance**   An investor wants to invest $30,000 in corporate bonds that are rated AAA, A, and B. The lower rated ones pay higher interest, but pose a higher risk as well. The average yield is 5% on AAA bonds, 6% on A bonds, and 10% on B bonds. Being conservative, the investor wants to have twice as much in AAA bonds as in B bonds. How much should she invest in each type of bond to have an interest income of $2000?

10. **Finance**   Makayla borrows $10,000. Some is from her friend at 8% annual interest, twice as much as that from her bank at 9%, and the remainder from her insurance company at 5%. She pays a total of $830 in interest for the first year. How much did she borrow from each source?

11. **Business**   Pretzels cost $3 per pound, dried fruit $4 per pound, and nuts $8 per pound. How many pounds of each should be used to produce 140 pounds of trail mix costing $6 per pound in which there are twice as many pretzels (by weight) as dried fruit?

12. **Business**   An auto manufacturer sends cars from two plants, I and II, to dealerships A and B, located in a midwestern city.

Plant I has a total of 28 cars to send, and plant II has 8. Dealer *A* needs 20 cars, and dealer *B* needs 16. Transportation costs based on the distance of each dealership from each plant are $220 from I to *A*, $300 from I to *B*, $400 from II to *A*, and $180 from II to *B*. The manufacturer wants to limit transportation costs to $10,640. How many cars should be sent from each plant to each of the two dealerships?

13. **Natural Science** An animal breeder can buy four types of tiger food. Each case of Brand *C* contains 25 units of fiber, 30 units of protein, and 30 units of fat. Each case of Brand *B* contains 50 units of fiber, 30 units of protein, and 20 units of fat. Each case of Brand *C* contains 75 units of fiber, 30 units of protein, and 20 units of fat. Each case of Brand *D* contains 100 units of fiber, 60 units of protein, and 30 units of fat. How many cases of each brand should the breeder mix together to obtain a food that provides 1200 units of fiber, 600 units of protein, and 400 units of fat?

14. **Physical Science** The stopping distance for a car traveling 25 mph is 61.7 feet, and for a car traveling 35 mph it is 106 feet. The stopping distance in feet can be described by the equation $y = ax^2 + bx$, where *x* is the speed in mph. (Data from: *National Traffic Safety Institute Student Workbook*, 1993, p. 7.)

    (a) Find the values of *a* and *b*.

    (b) Use your answers from part (a) to find the stopping distance for a car traveling 55 mph.

15. **Finance** An investor plans to invest $70,000 in a mutual fund, corporate bonds, and a fast-food franchise. She plans to put twice as much in bonds as in the mutual fund. On the basis of past performance, she expects the mutual fund to pay a 2% dividend, the bonds 6%, and the franchise 10%. She would like a dividend income of $4800. How much should she put in each of three investments?

16. **Business** According to data from a Texas agricultural report, the amounts of nitrogen (lb/acre), phosphate (lb/acre), and labor (hr/acre) needed to grow honeydews, yellow onions, and lettuce are given by the following table:[*]

	Honeydews	Yellow Onions	Lettuce
Nitrogen	120	150	180
Phosphate	180	80	80
Labor	4.97	4.45	4.65

    (a) If a farmer has 220 acres, 29,100 pounds of nitrogen, 32,600 pounds of phosphate, and 480 hours of labor, can he use all of his resources completely? If so, how many acres should he allot for each crop?

    (b) Suppose everything is the same as in part (a), except that 1061 hours of labor are available. Is it possible to use all of his resources completely? If so, how many acres should he allot for each crop?

17. **Health** Computer-aided tomography (CAT) scanners take X-rays of a part of the body from different directions and put the information together to create a picture of a cross-section of

the body.[†] The amount by which the energy of the X-ray decreases, measured in linear-attenuation units, tells whether the X-ray has passed through healthy tissue, tumorous tissue, or bone, on the basis of the following table:

Type of Tissue	Linear-Attenuation Values
Healthy tissue	.1625–.2977
Tumorous tissue	.2679–.3930
Bone	.3857–.5108

The part of the body to be scanned is divided into cells. If an X-ray passes through more than one cell, the total linear-attenuation value is the sum of the values for the cells. For example, in the accompanying figure, let *a*, *b*, and *c* be the values for cells *A*, *B*, and *C*, respectively. Then the attenuation value for beam 1 is $a + b$ and for beam 2 is $a + c$.

    (a) Find the attenuation value for beam 3.

    (b) Suppose that the attenuation values are .8, .55, and .65 for beams 1, 2, and 3, respectively. Set up and solve the system of three equations for *a*, *b*, and *c*. What can you conclude about cells *A*, *B*, and *C*?

18. **Health** (Refer to Exercise 17.) Four X-ray beams are aimed at four cells, as shown in the following figure:

    (a) Suppose the attenuation values for beams 1, 2, 3, and 4 are .60, .75, .65, and .70, respectively. Do we have enough information to determine the values of *a*, *b*, *c*, and *d*? Explain.

    (b) Suppose we have the data from part (a), as well as the following values for *d*. Find the values for *a*, *b*, and *c*, and make conclusions about cells *A*, *B*, *C*, and *D* in each case.
    (i) .33
    (ii) .43

    (c) Two X-ray beams are added as shown in the figure. In addition to the data in part (a), we now have attenuation values

---

[*]Miguel Paredes, Mohammad Fatehi, and Richard Hinthorn, "The Transformation of an Inconsistent Linear System into a Consistent System," *AMATYC Review*, 13, no. 2 (spring 1992).

[†]Exercises 17 and 18 are based on the article "Medical Applications of Systems of Linear Equations," by David Jabon, Penny Coffman, Gail Nord, John Nord, and Bryce W. Wilson, *Mathematics Teacher* 89, no. 5 (May 1996) pp. 398–402; 408–410.

of .85 and .50 for beams 5 and 6, respectively. Find the values for a, b, c, and d, and make conclusions about cells A, B, C, and D.

Beam 1 Beam 2

19. **Physical Science** During rush hours, substantial traffic congestion is encountered at the intersections shown in the figure. (The arrows indicate one-way streets.)

The city wishes to improve the signals at these corners to speed the flow of traffic. The traffic engineers first gather data. As the figure shows, 700 cars per hour come down M Street to intersection A, and 300 cars per hour come down 10th Street to intersection A. x_1 of these cars leave A on M Street, and x_4 cars leave A on 10th Street.

The number of cars entering A must equal the number leaving, so that

$$x_1 + x_4 = 700 + 300,$$

or

$$x_1 + x_4 = 1000.$$

For intersection B, x_1 cars enter on M Street and x_2 on 11th Street. The figure shows that 900 cars leave B on 11th Street and 200 cars leave B on M Street. So, we have

$$x_1 + x_2 = 900 + 200$$
$$x_1 + x_2 = 1100.$$

(a) Write two equations representing the traffic entering and leaving intersections C and D.

(b) Solve the system of four equations, using x_4 as the parameter.

(c) On the basis of your solution to part (b), what are the largest and smallest possible values for the number of cars leaving intersection A on 10th Street?

(d) Answer the question in part (c) for the other three variables.

(e) Verify that you could have discarded any one of the four original equations without changing the solution. What does this tell you about the original problem?

20. **Physical Science** The diagram shows the traffic flow at four intersections during rush hour, as in Exercise 19.

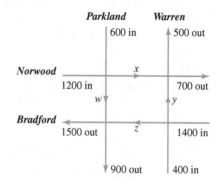

(a) What are the possible values of x, y, z, and w that will avoid any congestion? (Use w as the parameter.)

(b) What are the possible values of w?

A graphing calculator or other technology is recommended for the following exercises.

21. **Health** The table shows the calories, sodium, and protein in one cup of various kinds of soup.

	Progresso™ Hearty Chicken Rotini	Healthy Choice™ Hearty Chicken	Campbell's™ Chunky Chicken Noodle
Calories	100	130	110
Sodium (mg)	960	480	890
Protein (g)	7	9	8

How many cups of each kind of soup should be mixed together to produce 10 servings of soup, each of which provides 171 calories, 1158 milligrams of sodium, and 12.1 grams of protein? What is the serving size (in cups)? (*Hint:* In 10 servings, there must be 1710 calories, 11,580 milligrams of sodium, and 121 grams of protein.)

22. **Health** The table shows the calories, sodium, and fat in 1 ounce of various snack foods (all produced by Planters™):

	Sweet N' Crunchy Peanuts	Dry Roasted Honey Peanuts	Kettle Roasted Honey BBQ Peanuts
Calories	140	160	180
Sodium (mg)	20	110	55
Fat (g)	8	13	15

How many ounces of each kind of snack should be combined to produce 10 servings, each of which provides 284 calories, 93 milligrams of sodium, and 20.6 grams of fat? What is the serving size?

23. **Finance** An investment firm recommends that a client invest in bonds rated AAA, A, and B. The average yield on AAA bonds is 6%, on A bonds 7%, and on B bonds 10%. The client wants to invest twice as much in AAA bonds as in B bonds.

How much should be invested in each type of bond under the following conditions?

(a) The total investment is $25,000, and the investor wants an annual return of $1810 on the three investments.

(b) The values in part (a) are changed to $30,000 and $2150, respectively.

(c) The values in part (a) are changed to $40,000 and $2900, respectively.

24. **Business** An electronics company produces transistors, resistors, and computer chips. Each transistor requires 3 units of copper, 1 unit of zinc, and 2 units of glass. Each resistor requires 3, 2, and 1 unit of the three materials, and each computer chip requires 2, 1, and 2 units of these materials, respectively. How many of each product can be made with the following amounts of materials?

(a) 810 units of copper, 410 of zinc, and 490 of glass

(b) 765 units of copper, 385 of zinc, and 470 of glass

(c) 1010 units of copper, 500 of zinc, and 610 of glass

Work these exercises. (See Example 4.)

25. **Social Science** The table shows Census Bureau projections for the female population of the United States (in millions).

Year	2015	2035	2040
Female Population	163	187	192

(a) Find a quadratic function $f(x) = ax^2 + bx + c$ that gives the female population (in millions) in year x, where $x = 0$ corresponds to the year 2000.

(b) Estimate the female population in the year 2020.

26. **Social Science** The table shows Census Bureau projections for the male population of the United States (in millions).

Year	2015	2035	2040
Male Population	158	183	188

(a) Find a quadratic function $f(x) = ax^2 + bx + c$ that gives the male population (in millions) in year x, where $x = 0$ corresponds to the year 2000.

(b) Estimate the male population in the year 2020.

27. **Business** At a pottery factory, fuel consumption for heating the kilns varies with the size of the order being fired. In the past, the company recorded the figures in the table.

x = Number of Platters	y = Fuel Cost per Platter
6	$2.80
8	2.48
10	2.24

(a) Find an equation of the form $y = ax^2 + bx + c$ whose graph contains the three points corresponding to the data in the table.

(b) How many platters should be fired at one time in order to minimize the fuel cost per platter? What is the minimum fuel cost per platter?

28. **Health** The number of Alzheimer's cases in people 85 and older was 2 million in 2004 and is projected to be 3 million in 2025 and 8 million in 2050. (Data from: Alzheimer's Association.)

(a) Let $x = 0$ correspond to 2000. Find a quadratic function that models the given data.

(b) How many people 85 or older will have Alzheimer's disease in 2020 and in 2034?

(c) In the year you turn 85, how many people your age or older are expected to have Alzheimer's disease?

29. **Physical Science** For certain aircraft, there exists a quadratic relationship between an airplane's maximum speed S (in knots) and its ceiling C—its highest altitude possible (in thousands of feet). (Data from: D. Sanders, *Statistics: A First Course*, Fifth Edition [McGraw Hill, 1995].) The following table lists three airplanes that conform to this relationship:

Airplane	Maximum Speed	Ceiling
Hawkeye	320	33
Corsair	600	40
Tomcat	1283	50

(a) If the relationship between C and S is written as $C = aS^2 + bS + c$, use a linear system of equations to determine the constants $a, b,$ and c.

(b) A new aircraft of this type has a ceiling of 45,000 feet. Predict its top speed.

30. **Natural Science** The concentration (in parts per million) of carbon dioxide (a greenhouse gas) has been measured at Mauna Loa, Hawaii since 1959. The concentrations are known to have increased quadratically. The following table lists readings for three years. (Data from: National Oceanic and Atmospheric Administration.)

Year	1960	1989	2012
Carbon Dioxide	317	353	394

(a) Use the given data to construct a quadratic function that gives the concentration in year x. Let $x = 0$ correspond to the year 1959, so the table represents the data points (1,317), (30,353), and (53,394).

(b) Use this model to estimate the carbon dioxide concentration in the year 2019.

✓**Checkpoint Answers**

1. $x + y + z = 150$
   $4x + 5y + 7z = 400$
   $x - 3y = 0$

2. (a) $\begin{bmatrix} 1 & 1 & 1 & 1 & 100{,}000 \\ .025 & .035 & .05 & .06 & 4000 \\ 0 & 0 & 1 & -.25 & 0 \\ 1 & 1 & 0 & 0 & 60{,}000 \end{bmatrix}$

(b) Many sequences are possible, including this one:

Replace R_2 by $-.025R_1 + R_2$;

replace R_4 by $-R_1 + R_4$;

replace R_2 by $\dfrac{1}{.01}R_2$;

replace R_4 by $R_3 + R_4$;

replace R_4 by $\dfrac{-1}{1.25}R_4$.

(c) $\begin{bmatrix} 1 & 1 & 1 & 1 & 100{,}000 \\ 0 & 1 & 2.5 & 3.5 & 150{,}000 \\ 0 & 0 & 1 & -.25 & 0 \\ 0 & 0 & 0 & 1 & 32{,}000 \end{bmatrix}$

3. (a) $\begin{bmatrix} 10 & 20 & 30 & 1800 \\ 30 & 20 & 40 & 2800 \\ 20 & 40 & 25 & 2200 \end{bmatrix}$

(b) Many sequences are possible, including this one:

Replace R_1 by $\dfrac{1}{10}R_1$;

replace R_2 by $\dfrac{1}{10}R_2$;

replace R_3 by $\dfrac{1}{5}R_3$;

replace R_2 by $-3R_1 + R_2$;

replace R_3 by $-4R_1 + R_3$;

replace R_2 by $-\dfrac{1}{4}R_2$;

replace R_3 by $-\dfrac{1}{7}R_3$.

(c) $\begin{bmatrix} 1 & 2 & 3 & 180 \\ 0 & 1 & \dfrac{5}{4} & 65 \\ 0 & 0 & 1 & 40 \end{bmatrix}$

6.4 Basic Matrix Operations

Until now, we have used matrices only as a convenient shorthand to solve systems of equations. However, matrices are also important in the fields of management, natural science, engineering, and social science as a way to organize data, as Example 1 demonstrates.

Example 1 **Business** The EZ Life Company manufactures sofas and armchairs in three models: *A*, *B*, and *C*. The company has regional warehouses in New York, Chicago, and San Francisco. In its August shipment, the company sends 10 model *A* sofas, 12 model *B* sofas, 5 model *C* sofas, 15 model *A* chairs, 20 model *B* chairs, and 8 model *C* chairs to each warehouse.

These data might be organized by first listing them as follows:

Sofas	10 model *A*	12 model *B*	5 model *C*;
Chairs	15 model *A*	20 model *B*	8 model *C*.

Alternatively, we might tabulate the data:

		MODEL		
		A	**B**	**C**
FURNITURE	Sofa	10	12	5
	Chair	15	20	8

With the understanding that the numbers in each row refer to the type of furniture (sofa or chair) and the numbers in each column refer to the model (*A*, *B*, or *C*), the same information can be given by a matrix as follows:

$$M = \begin{bmatrix} 10 & 12 & 5 \\ 15 & 20 & 8 \end{bmatrix}$$

✓ **Checkpoint 1**

Rewrite matrix *M* in Example 1 in a matrix with three rows and two columns.

A matrix with *m* horizontal rows and *n* vertical columns has dimension, or size, $m \times n$. The number of rows is always given first.

Example 2

(a) The matrix $\begin{bmatrix} 6 & 5 \\ 3 & 4 \\ 5 & -1 \end{bmatrix}$ is a 3 × 2 matrix.

(b) $\begin{bmatrix} 5 & 8 & 9 \\ 0 & 5 & -3 \\ -4 & 0 & 5 \end{bmatrix}$ is a 3 × 3 matrix.

(c) $[1 \quad 6 \quad 5 \quad -2 \quad 5]$ is a 1 × 5 matrix.

(d) A graphing calculator displays a 4 × 1 matrix like this:

✓ Checkpoint 2

Give the size of each of the following matrices.

(a) $\begin{bmatrix} 2 & 1 & -5 & 6 \\ 3 & 0 & 7 & -4 \end{bmatrix}$

(b) $\begin{bmatrix} 1 & 2 & 3 \\ 4 & 5 & 6 \\ 9 & 8 & 7 \end{bmatrix}$

✓ Checkpoint 3

Use the numbers 2, 5, −8, and 4 to write

(a) a row matrix;

(b) a column matrix;

(c) a square matrix.

A matrix with only one row, as in Example 2(c), is called a **row matrix,** or **row vector.** A matrix with only one column, as in Example 2(d), is called a **column matrix,** or **column vector.** A matrix with the same number of rows as columns is called a **square matrix.** The matrix in Example 2(b) is a square matrix, as are

$$A = \begin{bmatrix} -5 & 6 \\ 8 & 3 \end{bmatrix} \quad \text{and} \quad B = \begin{bmatrix} 0 & 0 & 0 & 0 \\ -2 & 4 & 1 & 3 \\ 0 & 0 & 0 & 0 \\ -5 & -4 & 1 & 8 \end{bmatrix}.$$

When a matrix is denoted by a single letter, such as the matrix A above, the element in row i and column j is denoted a_{ij}. For example, $a_{21} = 8$ (the element in row 2, column 1). Similarly, in matrix B, $b_{42} = -4$ (the element in row 4, column 2).

Addition

The matrix given in Example 1,

$$M = \begin{bmatrix} 10 & 12 & 5 \\ 15 & 20 & 8 \end{bmatrix},$$

shows the August shipment from the EZ Life plant to each of its warehouses. If matrix N below gives the September shipment to the New York warehouse, what is the total shipment for each item of furniture to the New York warehouse for the two months?

$$N = \begin{bmatrix} 45 & 35 & 20 \\ 65 & 40 & 35 \end{bmatrix}$$

If 10 model A sofas were shipped in August and 45 in September, then altogether 55 model A sofas were shipped in the two months. Adding the other corresponding entries gives a new matrix, Q, that represents the total shipment to the New York warehouse for the two months:

$$Q = \begin{bmatrix} 55 & 47 & 25 \\ 80 & 60 & 43 \end{bmatrix}$$

It is convenient to refer to Q as the *sum* of M and N.

The way these two matrices were added illustrates the following definition of addition of matrices:

> ## Matrix Addition
>
> The **sum** of two $m \times n$ matrices X and Y is the $m \times n$ matrix $X + Y$ in which each element is the sum of the corresponding elements of X and Y.

It is important to remember that only matrices that are the same size can be added.

Example 3 Find each sum if possible.

(a) $\begin{bmatrix} 5 & -6 \\ 8 & 9 \end{bmatrix} + \begin{bmatrix} -4 & 6 \\ 8 & -3 \end{bmatrix} = \begin{bmatrix} 5 + (-4) & -6 + 6 \\ 8 + 8 & 9 + (-3) \end{bmatrix} = \begin{bmatrix} 1 & 0 \\ 16 & 6 \end{bmatrix}.$

(b) The matrices

$$A = \begin{bmatrix} 5 & 8 \\ 6 & 2 \end{bmatrix} \quad \text{and} \quad B = \begin{bmatrix} 3 & 9 & 1 \\ 4 & 2 & 5 \end{bmatrix}$$

are of different sizes, so it is not possible to find the sum $A + B$. ✔4

✓ **Checkpoint 4**

Find each sum when possible.

(a) $\begin{bmatrix} 2 & 5 & 7 \\ 3 & -1 & 4 \end{bmatrix}$
$+ \begin{bmatrix} -1 & 2 & 0 \\ 10 & -4 & 5 \end{bmatrix}$

(b) $\begin{bmatrix} 1 \\ 2 \\ 3 \end{bmatrix} + \begin{bmatrix} 2 & -1 \\ 4 & 5 \\ 6 & 0 \end{bmatrix}$

(c) $[5 \quad 4 \quad -1] + [-5 \quad 2 \quad 3]$

TECHNOLOGY TIP Graphing calculators can find matrix sums, as illustrated in Figure 6.20.

Figure 6.20

Example 4 **Business** The September shipments of the three models of sofas and chairs from the EZ Life Company to the New York, San Francisco, and Chicago warehouses are given respectively in matrices N, S, and C as follows:

$$N = \begin{bmatrix} 45 & 35 & 20 \\ 65 & 40 & 35 \end{bmatrix}; \quad S = \begin{bmatrix} 30 & 32 & 28 \\ 43 & 47 & 30 \end{bmatrix}; \quad C = \begin{bmatrix} 22 & 25 & 38 \\ 31 & 34 & 35 \end{bmatrix}.$$

What was the total amount shipped to the three warehouses in September?

Solution The total of the September shipments is represented by the sum of the three matrices N, S, and C:

$$N + S + C = \begin{bmatrix} 45 & 35 & 20 \\ 65 & 40 & 35 \end{bmatrix} + \begin{bmatrix} 30 & 32 & 28 \\ 43 & 47 & 30 \end{bmatrix} + \begin{bmatrix} 22 & 25 & 38 \\ 31 & 34 & 35 \end{bmatrix}$$

$$= \begin{bmatrix} 97 & 92 & 86 \\ 139 & 121 & 100 \end{bmatrix}.$$

✓ **Checkpoint 5**

From the result of Example 4, find the total number of the following shipped to the three warehouses.

(a) Model A chairs

(b) Model B sofas

(c) Model C chairs

For example, from this sum, the total number of model C sofas shipped to the three warehouses in September was 86. ✔5

Example 5 **Health** A drug company is testing 200 patients to see if Painoff (a new headache medicine) is effective. Half the patients receive Painoff and half receive a placebo. The data on the first 50 patients is summarized in this matrix:

$$
\begin{array}{cc}
 & \text{Pain Relief Obtained} \\
 & \text{Yes} \quad \text{No}
\end{array}
$$

$$
\begin{array}{c}
\text{Patient took Painoff} \\
\text{Patient took placebo}
\end{array}
\begin{bmatrix}
22 & 3 \\
8 & 17
\end{bmatrix}
$$

For example, row 2 shows that, of the people who took the placebo, 8 got relief, but 17 did not. The test was repeated on three more groups of 50 patients each, with the results summarized by these matrices:

$$
\begin{bmatrix} 21 & 4 \\ 6 & 19 \end{bmatrix};
\begin{bmatrix} 19 & 6 \\ 10 & 15 \end{bmatrix};
\begin{bmatrix} 23 & 2 \\ 3 & 22 \end{bmatrix}.
$$

The total results of the test can be obtained by adding these four matrices:

$$
\begin{bmatrix} 22 & 3 \\ 8 & 17 \end{bmatrix} +
\begin{bmatrix} 21 & 4 \\ 6 & 19 \end{bmatrix} +
\begin{bmatrix} 19 & 6 \\ 10 & 15 \end{bmatrix} +
\begin{bmatrix} 23 & 2 \\ 3 & 22 \end{bmatrix} =
\begin{bmatrix} 85 & 15 \\ 27 & 73 \end{bmatrix}.
$$

Because 85 of 100 patients got relief with Painoff and only 27 of 100 did so with the placebo, it appears that Painoff is effective. ✓6

✓**Checkpoint 6**

Later, it was discovered that the data in the last group of 50 patients in Example 5 was invalid. Use a matrix to represent the total test results after those data were eliminated.

Subtraction

Subtraction of matrices can be defined in a manner similar to matrix addition.

Matrix Subtraction

The **difference** of two $m \times n$ matrices X and Y is the $m \times n$ matrix $X - Y$ in which each element is the difference of the corresponding elements of X and Y.

Example 6 Find the following.

(a) $\begin{bmatrix} 1 & 2 & 3 \\ 0 & -1 & 5 \end{bmatrix} - \begin{bmatrix} -2 & 3 & 0 \\ 1 & -7 & 2 \end{bmatrix}$

Solution

$$
\begin{bmatrix} 1 & 2 & 3 \\ 0 & -1 & 5 \end{bmatrix} - \begin{bmatrix} -2 & 3 & 0 \\ 1 & -7 & 2 \end{bmatrix} =
\begin{bmatrix} 1 - (-2) & 2 - 3 & 3 - 0 \\ 0 - 1 & -1 - (-7) & 5 - 2 \end{bmatrix}
$$

$$
= \begin{bmatrix} 3 & -1 & 3 \\ -1 & 6 & 3 \end{bmatrix}.
$$

(b) $\begin{bmatrix} 8 & 6 & -4 \end{bmatrix} - \begin{bmatrix} 3 & 5 & -8 \end{bmatrix}$

Solution

$$
\begin{bmatrix} 8 & 6 & -4 \end{bmatrix} - \begin{bmatrix} 3 & 5 & -8 \end{bmatrix} = \begin{bmatrix} 8 - 3 & 6 - 5 & -4 - (-8) \end{bmatrix}
$$

$$
= \begin{bmatrix} 5 & 1 & 4 \end{bmatrix}.
$$

✓**Checkpoint 7**

Find each of the following differences when possible.

(a) $\begin{bmatrix} 2 & 5 \\ -1 & 0 \end{bmatrix} - \begin{bmatrix} 6 & 4 \\ 3 & -2 \end{bmatrix}$

(b) $\begin{bmatrix} 1 & 5 & 6 \\ 2 & 4 & 8 \end{bmatrix} - \begin{bmatrix} 2 & 1 \\ 10 & 3 \end{bmatrix}$

(c) $\begin{bmatrix} 5 & -4 & 1 \end{bmatrix} - \begin{bmatrix} 6 & 0 & -3 \end{bmatrix}$

(c) $\begin{bmatrix} -2 & 5 \\ 0 & 1 \end{bmatrix} - \begin{bmatrix} 3 \\ 5 \end{bmatrix}$

Solution The matrices are of different sizes and thus cannot be subtracted. ✓7

↗ **TECHNOLOGY TIP**
Graphing calculators can do matrix subtraction, as illustrated in Figure 6.21.

[B]
$$\begin{bmatrix} -4 & 5 & Ø & 2 \\ 6 & 3 & -7 & 1 \end{bmatrix}$$
[C]
$$\begin{bmatrix} 4 & 12 & 8 & -5 \\ 2 & 8 & 5 & Ø \end{bmatrix}$$

[B]−[C]
$$\begin{bmatrix} -8 & -7 & -8 & 7 \\ 4 & -5 & -12 & 1 \end{bmatrix}$$

Figure 6.21

Example 7 **Business** During September, the Chicago warehouse of the EZ Life Company shipped out the following numbers of each model, where the entries in the matrix have the same meaning as given earlier:

$$K = \begin{bmatrix} 5 & 10 & 8 \\ 11 & 14 & 15 \end{bmatrix}.$$

What was the Chicago warehouse's inventory on October 1, taking into account only the number of items received and sent out during the previous month?

Solution The number of each kind of item received during September is given by matrix C from Example 4; the number of each model sent out during September is given by matrix K. The October 1 inventory is thus represented by the matrix $C - K$:

$$C - K = \begin{bmatrix} 22 & 25 & 38 \\ 31 & 34 & 35 \end{bmatrix} - \begin{bmatrix} 5 & 10 & 8 \\ 11 & 14 & 15 \end{bmatrix} = \begin{bmatrix} 17 & 15 & 30 \\ 20 & 20 & 20 \end{bmatrix}.$$

Scalar Multiplication

Suppose one of the EZ Life Company warehouses receives the following order, written in matrix form, where the entries have the same meaning as given earlier:

$$\begin{bmatrix} 5 & 4 & 1 \\ 3 & 2 & 3 \end{bmatrix}.$$

Later, the store that sent the order asks the warehouse to send six more of the same order. The six new orders can be written as one matrix by multiplying each element in the matrix by 6, giving the product

$$6\begin{bmatrix} 5 & 4 & 1 \\ 3 & 2 & 3 \end{bmatrix} = \begin{bmatrix} 30 & 24 & 6 \\ 18 & 12 & 18 \end{bmatrix}.$$

In work with matrices, a real number, like the 6 in the preceding multiplication, is called a **scalar.**

[A]
$$\begin{bmatrix} 3 & -4 \\ 5 & 2 \end{bmatrix}$$
2[A]
$$\begin{bmatrix} 6 & -8 \\ 1Ø & 4 \end{bmatrix}$$

Figure 6.22

✓**Checkpoint 8**

Find each product.

(a) $-3\begin{bmatrix} 4 & -2 \\ 1 & 5 \end{bmatrix}$

(b) $4\begin{bmatrix} 2 & 4 & 7 \\ 8 & 2 & 1 \\ 5 & 7 & 3 \end{bmatrix}$

Scalar Multiplication

The **product** of a scalar k and a matrix X is the matrix kX in which each element is k times the corresponding element of X.

Example 8

(a) $(-3)\begin{bmatrix} 2 & -5 \\ 1 & 7 \\ 4 & -6 \end{bmatrix} = \begin{bmatrix} -6 & 15 \\ -3 & -21 \\ -12 & 18 \end{bmatrix}.$

(b) Graphing calculators can also do scalar multiplication (Figure 6.22). ✓ 8

↺ Recall that the *negative* of a real number a is the number $-a = (-1)a$. The negative of a matrix is defined similarly.

To compute the negative of matrix A on a calculator, use the "negative" key ($-$), as shown in Figure 6.23.

Figure 6.23

✓ **Checkpoint 9**

Let A and B be the matrices in Example 9. Find

(a) $A + (-B)$;

(b) $A - B$.

(c) What can you conclude from parts (a) and (b)?

The **negative** (or *additive inverse*) of a matrix A is the matrix $(-1)A$ which is obtained by multiplying each element of A by -1. It is denoted $-A$.

Example 9   Find $-A$ and $-B$ when

$$A = \begin{bmatrix} 1 & 2 & 3 \\ 0 & -1 & 5 \end{bmatrix} \quad \text{and} \quad B = \begin{bmatrix} -2 & 3 & 0 \\ 1 & -7 & 2 \end{bmatrix}.$$

Solution   By the preceding definition,

$$-A = \begin{bmatrix} -1 & -2 & -3 \\ 0 & 1 & -5 \end{bmatrix} \quad \text{and} \quad -B = \begin{bmatrix} 2 & -3 & 0 \\ -1 & 7 & -2 \end{bmatrix}. \quad ✓_9$$

A matrix consisting only of zeros is called a **zero matrix** and is denoted O. There is an $m \times n$ zero matrix for each pair of values of m and n—for instance,

$$\begin{bmatrix} 0 & 0 \\ 0 & 0 \end{bmatrix}; \qquad \begin{bmatrix} 0 & 0 & 0 & 0 \\ 0 & 0 & 0 & 0 \end{bmatrix}.$$

2 × 2 zero matrix   2 × 4 zero matrix

The negative of a matrix and zero matrices have the following properties, as illustrated in Checkpoint 9 and Exercises 28–30.

Let A and B be any $m \times n$ matrices and let O be the $m \times n$ zero matrix. Then

$$A + (-B) = A - B;$$
$$A + (-A) = O = A - A;$$
$$A + O = A = O + A.$$

6.4 Exercises

Find the size of each of the given matrices. Identify any square, column, or row matrices. Give the negative (additive inverse) of each matrix. (See Examples 2 and 9.)

1. $\begin{bmatrix} 7 & -8 & 4 \\ 0 & 13 & 9 \end{bmatrix}$

2. $\begin{bmatrix} -7 & 23 \\ 5 & -6 \end{bmatrix}$

3. $\begin{bmatrix} -3 & 0 & 11 \\ 1 & \frac{1}{4} & -7 \\ 5 & -3 & 9 \end{bmatrix}$

4. $[6 \quad -4 \quad \frac{2}{3} \quad 12 \quad 2]$

5. $\begin{bmatrix} 7 \\ 11 \end{bmatrix}$

6. $[-5]$

7. If A is a 5×3 matrix and $A + B = A$, what do you know about B?

8. If C is a 3×3 matrix and D is a 3×4 matrix, then $C + D$ is _____.

Perform the indicated operations where possible. (See Examples 3–7.)

9. $\begin{bmatrix} 1 & 2 & 7 & -1 \\ 8 & 0 & 2 & -4 \end{bmatrix} + \begin{bmatrix} -8 & 12 & -5 & 5 \\ -2 & -3 & 0 & 0 \end{bmatrix}$

10. $\begin{bmatrix} 1 & 7 \\ 2 & -3 \\ 3 & 7 \end{bmatrix} + \begin{bmatrix} 2 & 8 \\ 6 & 8 \\ -1 & 9 \end{bmatrix}$

11. $\begin{bmatrix} -1 & -5 & 9 \\ 2 & 2 & 3 \end{bmatrix} + \begin{bmatrix} 4 & 4 & -7 \\ 1 & -1 & 2 \end{bmatrix}$

12. $\begin{bmatrix} 2 & 4 \\ -8 & 2 \end{bmatrix} + \begin{bmatrix} 9 & -5 \\ 8 & 5 \end{bmatrix}$

13. $\begin{bmatrix} -3 & -2 & 5 \\ 3 & 9 & 0 \end{bmatrix} - \begin{bmatrix} 1 & 5 & -2 \\ -3 & 6 & 8 \end{bmatrix}$

14. $\begin{bmatrix} 0 & -2 \\ 1 & 9 \\ -5 & -9 \end{bmatrix} - \begin{bmatrix} 8 & 6 \\ 9 & 17 \\ 3 & -1 \end{bmatrix}$

15. $\begin{bmatrix} 9 & 1 \\ 0 & -3 \\ 4 & 10 \end{bmatrix} - \begin{bmatrix} 1 & 9 & -4 \\ -1 & 1 & 0 \end{bmatrix}$

16. $\begin{bmatrix} 3 & -8 & 0 \\ 1 & 5 & -7 \end{bmatrix} - \begin{bmatrix} 2 & 6 \\ 9 & -4 \end{bmatrix}$

Let $A = \begin{bmatrix} -2 & 0 \\ 5 & 3 \end{bmatrix}$ and $B = \begin{bmatrix} 0 & 2 \\ 4 & -6 \end{bmatrix}$. Find each of the following. (See Examples 8 and 9.)

17. $2A$

18. $-3B$

19. $-4B$

20. $5A$

21. $-4A + 5B$

22. $3A - 10B$

Let $A = \begin{bmatrix} 1 & -2 \\ 4 & 3 \end{bmatrix}$ and $B = \begin{bmatrix} 2 & -1 \\ 0 & 5 \end{bmatrix}$. Find a matrix X satisfying the given equation.

23. $2X = 2A + 3B$

24. $3X = A - 3B$

Using matrices

$$O = \begin{bmatrix} 0 & 0 \\ 0 & 0 \end{bmatrix}, P = \begin{bmatrix} m & n \\ p & q \end{bmatrix}, T = \begin{bmatrix} r & s \\ t & u \end{bmatrix}, and\ X = \begin{bmatrix} x & y \\ z & w \end{bmatrix},$$

verify that the statements in Exercises 25–30 are true.

25. $X + T$ is a 2 × 2 matrix.

26. $X + T = T + X$ (commutative property of addition of matrices).

27. $X + (T + P) = (X + T) + P$ (associative property of addition of matrices).

28. $X + (-X) = O$ (inverse property of addition of matrices).

29. $P + O = P$ (identity property of addition of matrices).

30. Which of the preceding properties are valid for matrices that are not square?

Work the following exercises. (See Example 1.)

31. **Business** When ticket holders fail to attend, major league sports teams lose the money these fans would have spent on refreshments, souvenirs, etc. The percentage of fans who don't show up is 16% in basketball and hockey, 20% in football, and 18% in baseball. The lost revenue per fan is $18.20 in basketball, $18.25 in hockey, $19 in football, and $15.40 in baseball. The total annual lost revenue is $22.7 million in basketball, $35.8 million in hockey, $51.9 million in football, and $96.3 million in baseball. Express this information in matrix form; specify what the rows and columns represent. (Data from: American Demographics.)

32. **Finance** In both 2010 and 2011, 66% of college graduates had student loan debt. The average debt was $25,250 in 2010 and rose to $26,600 in 2011. The unemployment rate for 2011 graduates was 8.8%, down slightly from 9.1% in 2010. Write

this information as a 3 × 2 matrix, labeling rows and columns. (Data from: ProjectOnStudentDebt.org.)

33. **Health** The shortage of organs for transplants is a continuing problem in the United States. At the end of 2009, there were 2674 adults waiting for a heart transplant, 1799 for a lung transplant, 15,094 for a liver transplant, and 79,397 for a kidney transplant. Corresponding figures for 2010 were 2874, 1759, 15,394, and 83,919, respectively. In 2011, the figures were 2813, 1630, 15,330, and 86,547, respectively. Express this information as a matrix, labeling rows and columns. (Data from: Organ Procurement and Transplant Network and Scientific Registry of Transplant Recipients.)

34. **Finance** Median household debt varies by age group. Median secured debt (backed by collateral) is $76,500 for individuals under 35 years old, $128,500 for 35–44 year-olds, $99,000 for 45–54 year-olds, $85,000 for 55–64 year olds, and $50,000 for those 65 and older. The corresponding figures for unsecured debt (including credit card debt) are $9700, $8400, $8000, $6000, and $3450. Round all dollar amounts to the nearest thousand and then write this information (in thousands) in matrix form, labeling rows and columns. (Data from: U.S. Census Bureau.)

Work these exercises.

35. **Business** There are three convenience stores in Gambier. This week, Store I sold 88 loaves of bread, 48 quarts of milk, 16 jars of peanut butter, and 112 pounds of cold cuts. Store II sold 105 loaves of bread, 72 quarts of milk, 21 jars of peanut butter, and 147 pounds of cold cuts. Store III sold 60 loaves of bread, 40 quarts of milk, no peanut butter, and 50 pounds of cold cuts.

(a) Use a 3 × 4 matrix to express the sales information for the three stores.

(b) During the following week, sales on these products at Store I increased by 25%, sales at Store II increased by one-third, and sales at Store III increased by 10%. Write the sales matrix for that week.

(c) Write a matrix that represents total sales over the two-week period.

36. **Social Science** The following table gives educational attainment as a percent of the U.S. population 25 years and older in various years. (Data from: U.S. Census Bureau.)

	MALE		FEMALE	
Year	Four Years of High School or More	Four Years of College or More	Four Years of High School or More	Four Years of College or More
1940	22.7%	5.5%	26.3%	3.8%
1970	55.0%	14.1%	55.4%	8.2%
2000	84.2%	27.8%	84.0%	23.6%
2012	87.3%	31.4%	88.0%	30.6%

(a) Write a 2 × 4 matrix for the educational attainment of males.

(b) Write a 2 × 4 matrix for the educational attainment of females.

(c) Use the matrices from parts (a) and (b) to write a matrix showing how much more (or less) males have reached educational attainment than females.

37. Social Science The tables give the death rates (per million person-trips) for male and female drivers for various ages and numbers of passengers:[*]

MALE DRIVERS

Age	Number of Passengers			
	0	**1**	**2**	**≥3**
16	2.61	4.39	6.29	9.08
17	1.63	2.77	4.61	6.92
30–59	.92	.75	.62	.54

FEMALE DRIVERS

Age	Number of Passengers			
	0	**1**	**2**	**≥3**
16	1.38	1.72	1.94	3.31
17	1.26	1.48	2.82	2.28
30–59	.41	.33	.27	.40

(a) Write a matrix A for the death rate of male drivers.

(b) Write a matrix B for the death rate of female drivers.

(c) Use the matrices from parts (a) and (b) to write a matrix showing the difference between the death rates of males and females.

38. Social Science Use matrix operations on the matrices found in Exercise 37(a) and (b) to obtain one matrix that gives the combined death rates for males and females (per million person-trips) of drivers of various ages, with varying numbers of passengers. $\left[\textit{Hint: Consider } \frac{1}{2}(A + B). \right]$

[*]Li-Hui Chen, Susan Baker, Elisa Braver, and Guohua Li, "Carrying Passengers as a Risk Factor for Crashes Fatal to 16- and 17-Year-Old Drivers," *JAMA* 283, no. 12 (March 22/29, 2000): 1578–1582.

✓ **Checkpoint Answers**

1. $\begin{bmatrix} 10 & 15 \\ 12 & 20 \\ 5 & 8 \end{bmatrix}$

2. (a) 2×4 (b) 3×3

3. (a) $[2 \quad 5 \quad -8 \quad 4]$

(b) $\begin{bmatrix} 2 \\ 5 \\ -8 \\ 4 \end{bmatrix}$ (c) $\begin{bmatrix} 2 & 5 \\ -8 & 4 \end{bmatrix}$ or $\begin{bmatrix} 2 & -8 \\ 5 & 4 \end{bmatrix}$
(Other answers are possible.)

4. (a) $\begin{bmatrix} 1 & 7 & 7 \\ 13 & -5 & 9 \end{bmatrix}$ (b) Not possible

(c) $[0 \quad 6 \quad 2]$

5. (a) 139   (b) 92   (c) 100

6. $\begin{bmatrix} 62 & 13 \\ 24 & 51 \end{bmatrix}$

7. (a) $\begin{bmatrix} -4 & 1 \\ -4 & 2 \end{bmatrix}$ (b) Not possible

(c) $[-1 \quad -4 \quad 4]$

8. (a) $\begin{bmatrix} -12 & 6 \\ -3 & -15 \end{bmatrix}$ (b) $\begin{bmatrix} 8 & 16 & 28 \\ 32 & 8 & 4 \\ 20 & 28 & 12 \end{bmatrix}$

9. (a) $\begin{bmatrix} 3 & -1 & 3 \\ -1 & 6 & 3 \end{bmatrix}$ (b) $\begin{bmatrix} 3 & -1 & 3 \\ -1 & 6 & 3 \end{bmatrix}$

(c) $A + (-B) = A - B$.

6.5 Matrix Products and Inverses

To understand the reasoning behind the definition of matrix multiplication, look again at the EZ Life Company. Suppose sofas and chairs of the same model are often sold as sets, with matrix W showing the number of each model set in each warehouse:

$$\begin{array}{c} \\ \text{New York} \\ \text{Chicago} \\ \text{San Francisco} \end{array} \begin{array}{ccc} A & B & C \\ \begin{bmatrix} 10 & 7 & 3 \\ 5 & 9 & 6 \\ 4 & 8 & 2 \end{bmatrix} \end{array} = W.$$

If the selling price of a model A set is $800, of a model B set is $1000, and of a model C set is $1200, find the total value of the sets in the New York warehouse as follows:

Type	Number of Sets		Price of Set		Total
A	10	×	$ 800	=	$ 8,000
B	7	×	1000	=	7,000
C	3	×	1200	=	3,600
			Total for New York		$18,600

✓ **Checkpoint 1**

In this example of the EZ Life Company, find the total value of the New York sets if model A sets sell for $1200, model B for $1600, and model C for $1300.

The total value of the three kinds of sets in New York is $18,600. ✓

The work done in the preceding table is summarized as

$$10(\$800) + 7(\$1000) + 3(\$1200) = \$18,600.$$

In the same way, the Chicago sets have a total value of

$$5(\$800) + 9(\$1000) + 6(\$1200) = \$20,200,$$

and in San Francisco, the total value of the sets is

$$4(\$800) + 8(\$1000) + 2(\$1200) = \$13,600.$$

The selling prices can be written as a column matrix P and the total value in each location as a column matrix V:

$$P = \begin{bmatrix} 800 \\ 1000 \\ 1200 \end{bmatrix} \quad \text{and} \quad V = \begin{bmatrix} 18,600 \\ 20,200 \\ 13,600 \end{bmatrix}.$$

Consider how the first row of the matrix W and the single column P lead to the first entry of V:

$$\underset{W}{\begin{bmatrix} 10 & 7 & 3 \\ 5 & 9 & 6 \\ 4 & 8 & 2 \end{bmatrix}} \underset{P}{\begin{bmatrix} 800 \\ 1000 \\ 1200 \end{bmatrix}} \quad 10(800) + 7(1000) + 3(1200) = \underset{V}{\begin{bmatrix} 18,600 \\ 20,200 \\ 13,600 \end{bmatrix}}.$$

Product of first entries + Product of second entries + Product of third entries

Similarly, adding the products of corresponding entries in the second row of W and the column P produces the second entry in V. The third entry in V is obtained in the same way by using the third row of W and column P. This suggests that it is reasonable to *define* the product WP to be V:

$$WP = \begin{bmatrix} 10 & 7 & 3 \\ 5 & 9 & 6 \\ 4 & 8 & 2 \end{bmatrix} \begin{bmatrix} 800 \\ 1000 \\ 1200 \end{bmatrix} = \begin{bmatrix} 18,600 \\ 20,200 \\ 13,600 \end{bmatrix} = V.$$

Note the sizes of the matrices here: The product of a 3×3 matrix and a 3×1 matrix is a 3×1 matrix.

Multiplying Matrices

In order to define matrix multiplication in the general case, we first define the **product of a row of a matrix and a column of a matrix** (with the same number of entries in each) to be the *number* obtained by multiplying the corresponding entries (first by first, second by second, etc.) and adding the results. For instance,

$$[3 \quad -2 \quad 1] \cdot \begin{bmatrix} 4 \\ 5 \\ 0 \end{bmatrix} = 3 \cdot 4 + (-2) \cdot 5 + 1 \cdot 0 = 12 - 10 + 0 = 2.$$

Now **matrix multiplication** is defined as follows.

Matrix Multiplication

Let A be an $m \times n$ matrix and let B be an $n \times k$ matrix. The **product matrix** AB is the $m \times k$ matrix whose entry in the ith row and jth column is

the product of the ith row of A and the jth column of B.

⚠ CAUTION Be careful when multiplying matrices. Remember that the number of *columns* of *A* must equal the number of *rows* of *B* in order to get the product matrix *AB*. The final product will have as many rows as *A* and as many columns as *B*.

Example 1 Suppose matrix *A* is 2 × 2 and matrix *B* is 2 × 4. Can the product *AB* be calculated? If so, what is the size of the product?

Solution The following diagram helps decide the answers to these questions:

The product *AB* can be calculated because *A* has two columns and *B* has two rows. The product will be a 2 × 4 matrix. ✓ 2

✓ **Checkpoint 2**

Matrix *A* is 4 × 6 and matrix *B* is 2 × 4.

(a) Can *AB* be found? If so, give its size.

(b) Can *BA* be found? If so, give its size.

Example 2 Find the product *CD* when

$$C = \begin{bmatrix} -3 & 4 & 1 \\ 5 & 0 & 4 \end{bmatrix} \quad \text{and} \quad D = \begin{bmatrix} -6 & 4 \\ 2 & 3 \\ 3 & -2 \end{bmatrix}.$$

Solution Here, matrix *C* is 2 × 3 and matrix *D* is 3 × 2, so matrix *CD* can be found and will be 2 × 2.

Step 1 row 1, column 1

$$\begin{bmatrix} -3 & 4 & 1 \\ 5 & 0 & 4 \end{bmatrix}\begin{bmatrix} -6 & 4 \\ 2 & 3 \\ 3 & -2 \end{bmatrix} \quad (-3) \cdot (-6) + 4 \cdot 2 + 1 \cdot 3 = 29.$$

Hence, 29 is the entry in row 1, column 1, of *CD*, as shown in Step 5 below.

Step 2 row 1, column 2

$$\begin{bmatrix} -3 & 4 & 1 \\ 5 & 0 & 4 \end{bmatrix}\begin{bmatrix} -6 & 4 \\ 2 & 3 \\ 3 & -2 \end{bmatrix} \quad (-3) \cdot 4 + 4 \cdot 3 + 1 \cdot (-2) = -2.$$

So −2 is the entry in row 1, column 2, of *CD*, as shown in Step 5. Continue in this manner to find the remaining entries of *CD*.

Step 3 row 2, column 1

$$\begin{bmatrix} -3 & 4 & 1 \\ 5 & 0 & 4 \end{bmatrix}\begin{bmatrix} -6 & 4 \\ 2 & 3 \\ 3 & -2 \end{bmatrix} \quad 5 \cdot (-6) + 0 \cdot 2 + 4 \cdot 3 = -18.$$

Step 4 row 2, column 2

$$\begin{bmatrix} -3 & 4 & 1 \\ 5 & 0 & 4 \end{bmatrix}\begin{bmatrix} -6 & 4 \\ 2 & 3 \\ 3 & -2 \end{bmatrix} \quad 5 \cdot 4 + 0 \cdot 3 + 4 \cdot (-2) = 12.$$

Step 5   The product is

$$CD = \begin{bmatrix} -3 & 4 & 1 \\ 5 & 0 & 4 \end{bmatrix} \begin{bmatrix} -6 & 4 \\ 2 & 3 \\ 3 & -2 \end{bmatrix} = \begin{bmatrix} 29 & -2 \\ -18 & 12 \end{bmatrix}. \checkmark_3$$

✓ **Checkpoint 3**

Find the product CD, given that

$$C = \begin{bmatrix} 1 & 3 & 5 \\ 2 & -4 & -1 \end{bmatrix}$$

and

$$D = \begin{bmatrix} 2 & -1 \\ 4 & 3 \\ 1 & -2 \end{bmatrix}.$$

Example 3   Find BA, given that

$$A = \begin{bmatrix} 1 & 7 \\ -3 & 2 \end{bmatrix} \quad \text{and} \quad B = \begin{bmatrix} 1 & 0 & -1 \\ 3 & 1 & 4 \end{bmatrix}.$$

Since B is a 2×3 matrix and A is a 2×2 matrix, the product BA is not defined.

TECHNOLOGY TIP Graphing calculators can find matrix products. However, if you use a graphing calculator to try to find the product in Example 3, the calculator will display an error message.

✓ **Checkpoint 4**

Give the size of each of the following products, if the product can be found.

(a) $\begin{bmatrix} 2 & 4 \\ 6 & 8 \end{bmatrix} \begin{bmatrix} 1 & 2 & 3 \\ 0 & -1 & 2 \end{bmatrix}$

(b) $\begin{bmatrix} 1 & 2 \\ 5 & 10 \\ 12 & 7 \end{bmatrix} \begin{bmatrix} 2 & 4 \\ 3 & 6 \\ 9 & 1 \end{bmatrix}$

(c) $\begin{bmatrix} 5 \\ 2 \\ 4 \end{bmatrix} \begin{bmatrix} 1 & 0 & 6 \end{bmatrix}$

Matrix multiplication has some similarities to the multiplication of numbers.

> For any matrices A, B, and C such that all the indicated sums and products exist, matrix multiplication is associative and distributive:
>
> $$A(BC) = (AB)C; A(B + C) = AB + AC; (B + C)A = BA + CA.$$

However, there are important differences between matrix multiplication and the multiplication of numbers. (See Exercises 19–22 at the end of this section.) In particular, matrix multiplication is *not* commutative.

> If A and B are matrices such that the products AB and BA exist,
>
> $$AB \text{ may not equal } BA.$$

Figure 6.24 shows an example of this situation.

```
[A]
          [1  -4]
          [3   2]
[B]
          [-2  4]
          [ 5  3]
```
```
[A][B]
          [-22  -8]
          [  4  18]
[B][A]
          [10  16]
          [14 -14]
```

Figure 6.24

Example 4   **Business**   A contractor builds three kinds of houses, models A, B, and C, with a choice of two styles, Spanish or contemporary. Matrix P shows the number of each kind of house planned for a new 100-home subdivision:

$$\begin{array}{c} \\ \text{Model } A \\ \text{Model } B \\ \text{Model } C \end{array} \begin{array}{cc} \text{Spanish} & \text{Contemporary} \\ \begin{bmatrix} 0 & 30 \\ 10 & 20 \\ 20 & 20 \end{bmatrix} \end{array} = P.$$

The amounts for each of the exterior materials used depend primarily on the style of the house. These amounts are shown in matrix Q (concrete is measured in cubic yards, lumber in units of 1000 board feet, brick in thousands, and shingles in units of 100 square feet):

$$
\begin{array}{c}
 \\
\text{Spanish} \\
\text{Contemporary}
\end{array}
\begin{array}{cccc}
\text{Concrete} & \text{Lumber} & \text{Brick} & \text{Shingles} \\
\end{array}
$$

$$
\begin{array}{c}
\text{Spanish} \\
\text{Contemporary}
\end{array}
\left[
\begin{array}{cccc}
10 & 2 & 0 & 2 \\
50 & 1 & 20 & 2
\end{array}
\right] = Q.
$$

Matrix R gives the cost for each kind of material:

$$
\begin{array}{c}
 \\
\text{Concrete} \\
\text{Lumber} \\
\text{Brick} \\
\text{Shingles}
\end{array}
\begin{array}{c}
\text{Cost per Unit} \\
\left[
\begin{array}{c}
20 \\
180 \\
60 \\
25
\end{array}
\right]
\end{array} = R.
$$

(a) What is the total cost for each model of house?

Solution   First find the product PQ, which shows the amount of each material needed for each model of house:

$$
PQ = \left[
\begin{array}{cc}
0 & 30 \\
10 & 20 \\
20 & 20
\end{array}
\right]
\left[
\begin{array}{cccc}
10 & 2 & 0 & 2 \\
50 & 1 & 20 & 2
\end{array}
\right]
$$

$$
PQ =
\begin{array}{cccc}
\text{Concrete} & \text{Lumber} & \text{Brick} & \text{Shingles} \\
\end{array}
$$

$$
PQ = \left[
\begin{array}{cccc}
1500 & 30 & 600 & 60 \\
1100 & 40 & 400 & 60 \\
1200 & 60 & 400 & 80
\end{array}
\right]
\begin{array}{l}
\text{Model } A \\
\text{Model } B. \\
\text{Model } C
\end{array}
$$

Now multiply PQ and R, the cost matrix, to get the total cost for each model of house:

$$
\left[
\begin{array}{cccc}
1500 & 30 & 600 & 60 \\
1100 & 40 & 400 & 60 \\
1200 & 60 & 400 & 80
\end{array}
\right]
\left[
\begin{array}{c}
20 \\
180 \\
60 \\
25
\end{array}
\right] =
\begin{array}{c}
\text{Cost} \\
\left[
\begin{array}{c}
72{,}900 \\
54{,}700 \\
60{,}800
\end{array}
\right]
\end{array}
\begin{array}{l}
\text{Model } A \\
\text{Model } B. \\
\text{Model } C
\end{array}
$$

(b) How much of each of the four kinds of material must be ordered?

Solution   The totals of the columns of matrix PQ will give a matrix whose elements represent the total amounts of each material needed for the subdivision. Call this matrix T and write it as a row matrix:

$$
T = [3800 \quad 130 \quad 1400 \quad 200].
$$

(c) What is the total cost for material?

Solution   Find the total cost of all the materials by taking the product of matrix T, the matrix showing the total amounts of each material, and matrix R, the cost matrix. [To multiply these and get a 1×1 matrix representing total cost, we must multiply a 1×4 matrix by a 4×1 matrix. This is why T was written as a row matrix in (b).] So, we have

$$
TR = [3800 \quad 130 \quad 1400 \quad 200]
\left[
\begin{array}{c}
20 \\
180 \\
60 \\
25
\end{array}
\right] = [188{,}400].
$$

(d) Suppose the contractor builds the same number of homes in five subdivisions. What is the total amount of each material needed for each model in this case?

✓**Checkpoint 5**

Let matrix A be

$$
\begin{array}{c}
 \\
\text{Brand}
\end{array}
\begin{array}{c}
 \\
\begin{array}{cc} X \\ Y \end{array}
\end{array}
\begin{array}{c}
\text{Vitamin} \\
\begin{array}{ccc} \text{C} & \text{E} & \text{K} \end{array} \\
\begin{bmatrix} 2 & 7 & 5 \\ 4 & 6 & 9 \end{bmatrix}
\end{array}
$$

and matrix B be

$$
\begin{array}{c}
 \\
\text{Vitamin}
\end{array}
\begin{array}{c}
\begin{array}{c} \text{C} \\ \text{E} \\ \text{K} \end{array}
\end{array}
\begin{array}{c}
\text{Cost} \\
\begin{array}{cc} X & Y \end{array} \\
\begin{bmatrix} 12 & 14 \\ 18 & 15 \\ 9 & 10 \end{bmatrix}
\end{array}.
$$

(a) What quantities do matrices A and B represent?

(b) What quantities does the product AB represent?

(c) What quantities does the product BA represent?

Solution Determine the total amount of each material for each model for all five subdivisions. Multiply PQ by the scalar 5 as follows:

$$
5\begin{bmatrix} 1500 & 30 & 600 & 60 \\ 1100 & 40 & 400 & 60 \\ 1200 & 60 & 400 & 80 \end{bmatrix} = \begin{bmatrix} 7500 & 150 & 3000 & 300 \\ 5500 & 200 & 2000 & 300 \\ 6000 & 300 & 2000 & 400 \end{bmatrix}.
$$

We can introduce notation to help keep track of the quantities a matrix represents. For example, we can say that matrix P from Example 4 represents models/styles, matrix Q represents styles/materials, and matrix R represents materials/cost. In each case, the meaning of the rows is written first and the columns second. When we found the product PQ in Example 4, the rows of the matrix represented models and the columns represented materials. Therefore, we can say that the matrix product PQ represents models/materials. The common quantity, styles, in both P and Q was eliminated in the product PQ. Do you see that the product $(PQ)R$ represents models/cost?

In practical problems, this notation helps decide in what order to multiply two matrices so that the results are meaningful. In Example 4(c), we could have found either product RT or product TR. However, since T represents subdivisions/materials and R represents materials/cost, the product TR gives subdivisions/cost. ✓₅

Identity Matrices

Recall from Section 1.1 that the real number 1 is the identity element for multiplication of real numbers: For any real number a, $a \cdot 1 = 1 \cdot a = a$. In this section, an **identity matrix** I is defined that has properties similar to those of the number 1.

If I is to be the identity matrix, the products AI and IA must both equal A. The 2×2 identity matrix that satisfies these conditions is

$$
I = \begin{bmatrix} 1 & 0 \\ 0 & 1 \end{bmatrix}. \quad ✓_6
$$

To check that I is really the 2×2 identity matrix, let

$$
A = \begin{bmatrix} a & b \\ c & d \end{bmatrix}.
$$

✓**Checkpoint 6**

Let $A = \begin{bmatrix} 3 & -2 \\ 4 & -1 \end{bmatrix}$ and

$I = \begin{bmatrix} 1 & 0 \\ 0 & 1 \end{bmatrix}$.

Find IA and AI.

Then AI and IA should both equal A:

$$
AI = \begin{bmatrix} a & b \\ c & d \end{bmatrix}\begin{bmatrix} 1 & 0 \\ 0 & 1 \end{bmatrix} = \begin{bmatrix} a(1)+b(0) & a(0)+b(1) \\ c(1)+d(0) & c(0)+d(1) \end{bmatrix} = \begin{bmatrix} a & b \\ c & d \end{bmatrix} = A;
$$

$$
IA = \begin{bmatrix} 1 & 0 \\ 0 & 1 \end{bmatrix}\begin{bmatrix} a & b \\ c & d \end{bmatrix} = \begin{bmatrix} 1(a)+0(c) & 1(b)+0(d) \\ 0(a)+1(c) & 0(b)+1(d) \end{bmatrix} = \begin{bmatrix} a & b \\ c & d \end{bmatrix} = A.
$$

This verifies that I has been defined correctly. (It can also be shown that I is the only 2×2 identity matrix.)

The identity matrices for 3×3 matrices and 4×4 matrices are, respectively,

$$
I = \begin{bmatrix} 1 & 0 & 0 \\ 0 & 1 & 0 \\ 0 & 0 & 1 \end{bmatrix} \quad \text{and} \quad I = \begin{bmatrix} 1 & 0 & 0 & 0 \\ 0 & 1 & 0 & 0 \\ 0 & 0 & 1 & 0 \\ 0 & 0 & 0 & 1 \end{bmatrix}.
$$

By generalizing these findings, an identity matrix can be found for any n by n matrix. This identity matrix will have 1s on the main diagonal from upper left to lower right, with all other entries equal to 0.

Inverse Matrices

🖊 **TECHNOLOGY TIP**
An $n \times n$ identity matrix can be displayed on most graphing calculators by using IDENTITY n or IDENT n or IDENMAT(n). Look in the MATH or OPS submenu of the TI MATRIX menu, or the OPTN MAT menu of Casio.

Recall that for every nonzero real number a, the equation $ax = 1$ has a solution, namely, $x = 1/a = a^{-1}$. Similarly, for a square matrix A, we consider the matrix equation $AX = I$.

This equation does not always have a solution, but when it does, we use special terminology. If there is a matrix A^{-1} satisfying

$$AA^{-1} = I,$$

(that is, A^{-1} is a solution of $AX = I$), then A^{-1} is called the **inverse matrix** of A. In this case, it can be proved that $A^{-1}A = I$ and that A^{-1} is unique (that is, a square matrix has no more than one inverse). When a matrix has an inverse, it can be found by using the row operations given in Section 6.2, as we shall see later.

CAUTION   Only square matrices have inverses, but not every square matrix has one. A matrix that does not have an inverse is called a **singular matrix**. Note that the symbol A^{-1} (read "*A*-inverse") does *not* mean $1/A$; the symbol A^{-1} is just the notation for the inverse of matrix A. There is no such thing as matrix division.

Example 5   Given matrices A and B as follows, determine whether B is the inverse of A:

$$A = \begin{bmatrix} 1 & 2 \\ 4 & 6 \end{bmatrix}; \qquad B = \begin{bmatrix} -3 & 1 \\ 2 & -\frac{1}{2} \end{bmatrix}.$$

Solution B is the inverse of A if $AB = I$ and $BA = I$, so we find those products:

$$AB = \begin{bmatrix} 1 & 2 \\ 4 & 6 \end{bmatrix}\begin{bmatrix} -3 & 1 \\ 2 & -\frac{1}{2} \end{bmatrix} = \begin{bmatrix} 1 & 0 \\ 0 & 1 \end{bmatrix} = I;$$

$$BA = \begin{bmatrix} -3 & 1 \\ 2 & -\frac{1}{2} \end{bmatrix}\begin{bmatrix} 1 & 2 \\ 4 & 6 \end{bmatrix} = \begin{bmatrix} 1 & 0 \\ 0 & 1 \end{bmatrix} = I.$$

Therefore, B is the inverse of A; that is, $A^{-1} = B$. (It is also true that A is the inverse of B, or $B^{-1} = A$.) ✓ 7

✓**Checkpoint 7**

Given $A = \begin{bmatrix} 2 & 1 \\ 3 & 8 \end{bmatrix}$ and $B = \begin{bmatrix} -1 & 3 \\ 1 & -2 \end{bmatrix}$, determine whether they are inverses.

Example 6   Find the multiplicative inverse of

$$A = \begin{bmatrix} 2 & 4 \\ 1 & -1 \end{bmatrix}.$$

Solution   Let the unknown inverse matrix be

$$A^{-1} = \begin{bmatrix} x & y \\ z & w \end{bmatrix}.$$

By the definition of matrix inverse, $AA^{-1} = I$, or

$$AA^{-1} = \begin{bmatrix} 2 & 4 \\ 1 & -1 \end{bmatrix}\begin{bmatrix} x & y \\ z & w \end{bmatrix} = \begin{bmatrix} 1 & 0 \\ 0 & 1 \end{bmatrix}.$$

Use matrix multiplication to get

$$\begin{bmatrix} 2x + 4z & 2y + 4w \\ x - z & y - w \end{bmatrix} = \begin{bmatrix} 1 & 0 \\ 0 & 1 \end{bmatrix}.$$

Setting corresponding elements equal to each other gives the system of equations

$$2x + 4z = 1 \tag{1}$$
$$2y + 4w = 0 \tag{2}$$
$$x - z = 0 \tag{3}$$
$$y - w = 1. \tag{4}$$

Since equations (1) and (3) involve only x and z, while equations (2) and (4) involve only y and w, these four equations lead to two systems of equations:

$$\begin{aligned} 2x + 4z &= 1 \\ x - z &= 0 \end{aligned} \quad \text{and} \quad \begin{aligned} 2y + 4w &= 0 \\ y - w &= 1. \end{aligned}$$

Writing the two systems as augmented matrices gives

$$\begin{bmatrix} 2 & 4 & | & 1 \\ 1 & -1 & | & 0 \end{bmatrix} \quad \text{and} \quad \begin{bmatrix} 2 & 4 & | & 0 \\ 1 & -1 & | & 1 \end{bmatrix}.$$

Note that the row operations needed to transform both matrices are the same because the first two columns of both matrices are identical. Consequently, we can save time by combining these matrices into the single matrix

$$\begin{bmatrix} 2 & 4 & | & 1 & 0 \\ 1 & -1 & | & 0 & 1 \end{bmatrix}. \tag{5}$$

Columns 1–3 represent the first system and columns 1, 2, and 4 represent the second system. Now use row operations as follows:

$$\begin{bmatrix} 1 & -1 & | & 0 & 1 \\ 2 & 4 & | & 1 & 0 \end{bmatrix} \qquad \text{Interchange } R_1 \text{ and } R_2.$$

$$\begin{bmatrix} 1 & -1 & | & 0 & 1 \\ 0 & 6 & | & 1 & -2 \end{bmatrix} \qquad -2R_1 + R_2$$

$$\begin{bmatrix} 1 & -1 & | & 0 & 1 \\ 0 & 1 & | & \frac{1}{6} & -\frac{1}{3} \end{bmatrix} \qquad \frac{1}{6}R_2$$

$$\begin{bmatrix} 1 & 0 & | & \frac{1}{6} & \frac{2}{3} \\ 0 & 1 & | & \frac{1}{6} & -\frac{1}{3} \end{bmatrix}. \qquad R_2 + R_1 \tag{6}$$

The left half of the augmented matrix in equation (6) is the identity matrix, so the Gauss–Jordan process is finished and the solutions can be read from the right half of the augmented matrix. The numbers in the first column to the right of the vertical bar give the values of x and z. The second column to the right of the bar gives the values of y and w. That is,

$$\begin{bmatrix} 1 & 0 & | & x & y \\ 0 & 1 & | & z & w \end{bmatrix} = \begin{bmatrix} 1 & 0 & | & \frac{1}{6} & \frac{2}{3} \\ 0 & 1 & | & \frac{1}{6} & -\frac{1}{3} \end{bmatrix},$$

so that

$$A^{-1} = \begin{bmatrix} x & y \\ z & w \end{bmatrix} = \begin{bmatrix} \frac{1}{6} & \frac{2}{3} \\ \frac{1}{6} & -\frac{1}{3} \end{bmatrix}.$$

Check by multiplying A and A^{-1}. The result should be I:

$$AA^{-1} = \begin{bmatrix} 2 & 4 \\ 1 & -1 \end{bmatrix}\begin{bmatrix} \frac{1}{6} & \frac{2}{3} \\ \frac{1}{6} & -\frac{1}{3} \end{bmatrix} = \begin{bmatrix} \frac{1}{3}+\frac{2}{3} & \frac{4}{3}-\frac{4}{3} \\ \frac{1}{6}-\frac{1}{6} & \frac{2}{3}+\frac{1}{3} \end{bmatrix} = \begin{bmatrix} 1 & 0 \\ 0 & 1 \end{bmatrix} = I.$$

Thus, the original augmented matrix in equation (5) has A as its left half and the identity matrix as its right half, while the final augmented matrix in equation (6), at the end of the Gauss–Jordan process, has the identity matrix as its left half and the inverse matrix A^{-1} as its right half:

$$[A \mid I] \to [I \mid A^{-1}].$$

✓ **Checkpoint 8**

Carry out the process in Example 6 on a graphing calculator as follows: Enter matrix (5) in the example as matrix [B] on the calculator. Then find RREF [B]. What is the result?

The procedure in Example 6 can be generalized as follows.

Inverse Matrix

To obtain an **inverse matrix** A^{-1} for any $n \times n$ matrix A for which A^{-1} exists, follow these steps:

1. Form the augmented matrix $[A \mid I]$, where I is the $n \times n$ identity matrix.
2. Perform row operations on $[A \mid I]$ to get a matrix of the form $[I \mid B]$.
3. Matrix B is A^{-1}.

Example 7   Find A^{-1} if

$$A = \begin{bmatrix} 1 & 0 & 1 \\ 2 & -2 & -1 \\ 5 & 0 & 0 \end{bmatrix}.$$

Solution   First write the augmented matrix $[A \mid I]$:

$$[A \mid I] = \begin{bmatrix} 1 & 0 & 1 & 1 & 0 & 0 \\ 2 & -2 & -1 & 0 & 1 & 0 \\ 5 & 0 & 0 & 0 & 0 & 1 \end{bmatrix}.$$

Transform the left side of this matrix into the 3×3 identity matrix:

$$\begin{bmatrix} 1 & 0 & 1 & 1 & 0 & 0 \\ 0 & -2 & -3 & -2 & 1 & 0 \\ 0 & 0 & -5 & -5 & 0 & 1 \end{bmatrix} \quad \begin{aligned} &-2R_1 + R_2 \\ &-5R_1 + R_3 \end{aligned}$$

$$\begin{bmatrix} 1 & 0 & 1 & 1 & 0 & 0 \\ 0 & 1 & \frac{3}{2} & 1 & -\frac{1}{2} & 0 \\ 0 & 0 & 1 & 1 & 0 & -\frac{1}{5} \end{bmatrix} \quad \begin{aligned} &-\tfrac{1}{2}R_2 \\ &-\tfrac{1}{5}R_3 \end{aligned}$$

$$\begin{bmatrix} 1 & 0 & 0 & 0 & 0 & \frac{1}{5} \\ 0 & 1 & 0 & -\frac{1}{2} & -\frac{1}{2} & \frac{3}{10} \\ 0 & 0 & 1 & 1 & 0 & -\frac{1}{5} \end{bmatrix}. \quad \begin{aligned} &-1R_3 + R_1 \\ &-\tfrac{3}{2}R_3 + R_2 \end{aligned}$$

Looking at the right half of the preceding matrix, we see that

$$A^{-1} = \begin{bmatrix} 0 & 0 & \frac{1}{5} \\ -\frac{1}{2} & -\frac{1}{2} & \frac{3}{10} \\ 1 & 0 & -\frac{1}{5} \end{bmatrix}.$$

Verify that AA^{-1} is I.

The best way to find matrix inverses on a graphing calculator is illustrated in the next example.

Example 8   Use a graphing calculator to find the inverse of the following matrices (if they have inverses):

$$A = \begin{bmatrix} 1 & 0 & 1 \\ 2 & -2 & -1 \\ 5 & 0 & 0 \end{bmatrix} \quad \text{and} \quad B = \begin{bmatrix} 2 & 4 \\ 3 & 6 \end{bmatrix}.$$

Solution   Enter matrix A into the calculator [Figure 6.25(a)]. Then use the x^{-1} key to find the inverse matrix, as in Figure 6.25(b). (Using $\wedge$ and -1 for the inverse results in an error message on most calculators.) Note that Figure 6.25(b) agrees with the answer we found working by hand in Example 7.

(a)   (b)

Figure 6.25

Now enter matrix B into the calculator and use the x^{-1} key. The result is an error message (Figure 6.26), which indicates that the matrix is singular; it does not have an inverse. (If you were working by hand, you would have found that the appropriate system of equations has no solution.)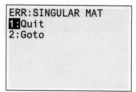

✓ Checkpoint 9 ◢

Use a graphing calculator to find the inverses of these matrices (if they exist).

(a) $A = \begin{bmatrix} 1 & 2 & 3 \\ 4 & -1 & 0 \\ 5 & 1 & 3 \end{bmatrix}$

(b) $B = \begin{bmatrix} 2 & 3 \\ -1 & 4 \end{bmatrix}$

```
ERR:SINGULAR MAT
1:Quit
2:Goto
```

Figure 6.26

◢ **TECHNOLOGY TIP** Because of round-off error, a graphing calculator may sometimes display an "inverse" for a matrix that doesn't actually have one. So always verify your results by multiplying A and A^{-1}. If the product is not the identity matrix, then A does not have an inverse.

6.5 Exercises

In Exercises 1–6, the sizes of two matrices A and B are given. Find the sizes of the product AB and the product BA whenever these products exist. (See Example 1.)

1. A is 2×2 and B is 2×2.

2. A is 3×3 and B is 3×2.

3. A is 3×5 and B is 5×3.

4. A is 4×3 and B is 3×6.

5. A is 4×2 and B is 3×4.

6. A is 7×3 and B is 2×7.

7. To find the product matrix AB, the number of _____ of A must be the same as the number of _____ of B.

8. The product matrix AB has the same number of _____ as A and the same number of _____ as B.

Find each of the following matrix products, if they exist. (See Examples 2 and 3.)

9. $\begin{bmatrix} 1 & 2 \\ 3 & 4 \end{bmatrix}\begin{bmatrix} -1 \\ 3 \end{bmatrix}$

10. $\begin{bmatrix} -2 & 5 \\ 7 & 0 \end{bmatrix}\begin{bmatrix} 2 \\ 6 \end{bmatrix}$

11. $\begin{bmatrix} 2 & 2 & -1 \\ 5 & 0 & 1 \end{bmatrix}\begin{bmatrix} 0 & -2 \\ -1 & 5 \\ 0 & 2 \end{bmatrix}$

12. $\begin{bmatrix} -9 & 3 & 1 \\ 3 & 0 & 0 \end{bmatrix}\begin{bmatrix} 2 \\ -1 \\ 4 \end{bmatrix}$

13. $\begin{bmatrix} -4 & 1 \\ 2 & -3 \end{bmatrix}\begin{bmatrix} 1 & 0 \\ 0 & 1 \end{bmatrix}$

14. $\begin{bmatrix} 1 & 0 \\ 0 & 1 \end{bmatrix}\begin{bmatrix} 3 & -2 \\ 1 & -5 \end{bmatrix}$

15. $\begin{bmatrix} 1 & 0 & 0 \\ 0 & 1 & 0 \\ 0 & 0 & 1 \end{bmatrix}\begin{bmatrix} 3 & -5 & 7 \\ -2 & 1 & 6 \\ 0 & -3 & 4 \end{bmatrix}$

16. $\begin{bmatrix} -8 & 9 \\ 3 & -4 \\ -1 & 6 \end{bmatrix}\begin{bmatrix} 1 & 0 & 0 \\ 0 & 1 & 0 \end{bmatrix}$

17. $\begin{bmatrix} 1 & 2 & 3 \\ 4 & 0 & 6 \\ 7 & 8 & 9 \end{bmatrix}\begin{bmatrix} -1 & 4 \\ 7 & 0 \\ 1 & 2 \end{bmatrix}$

18. $\begin{bmatrix} -2 & 0 & 3 \\ 4 & -3 & -1 \end{bmatrix}\begin{bmatrix} 2 & 0 & -1 & 5 \\ 0 & 1 & 0 & -1 \\ 4 & 2 & 5 & -4 \end{bmatrix}$

In Exercises 19–21, use the matrices

$$A = \begin{bmatrix} -3 & -9 \\ 2 & 6 \end{bmatrix} \quad and \quad B = \begin{bmatrix} 4 & 6 \\ 2 & 3 \end{bmatrix}.$$

19. Show that $AB \neq BA$. Hence, matrix multiplication is not commutative.

20. Show that $(A + B)^2 \neq A^2 + 2AB + B^2$.

21. Show that $(A + B)(A - B) \neq A^2 - B^2$.

22. Show that $D^2 = D$, where

$$D = \begin{bmatrix} 1 & 0 & 0 \\ \frac{1}{2} & 0 & \frac{1}{2} \\ 0 & 0 & 1 \end{bmatrix}.$$

Given matrices

$$P = \begin{bmatrix} m & n \\ p & q \end{bmatrix}, \quad X = \begin{bmatrix} x & y \\ z & w \end{bmatrix}, \quad and \quad T = \begin{bmatrix} r & s \\ t & u \end{bmatrix},$$

verify that the statements in Exercises 23–26 are true.

23. $(PX)T = P(XT)$ (associative property)

24. $P(X + T) = PX + PT$ (distributive property)

25. $k(X + T) = kX + kT$ for any real number k

26. $(k + h)P = kP + hP$ for any real numbers k and h

Determine whether the given matrices are inverses of each other by computing their product. (See Example 5.)

27. $\begin{bmatrix} 5 & 2 \\ 3 & -1 \end{bmatrix}$ and $\begin{bmatrix} -1 & 2 \\ 3 & -4 \end{bmatrix}$ **28.** $\begin{bmatrix} 3 & 2 \\ 7 & 5 \end{bmatrix}$ and $\begin{bmatrix} 5 & 0 \\ -7 & 3 \end{bmatrix}$

29. $\begin{bmatrix} 3 & -1 \\ -4 & 2 \end{bmatrix}$ and $\begin{bmatrix} 1 & \frac{1}{2} \\ 2 & \frac{3}{2} \end{bmatrix}$ **30.** $\begin{bmatrix} 3 & 5 \\ 7 & 9 \end{bmatrix}$ and $\begin{bmatrix} -\frac{9}{8} & \frac{5}{8} \\ \frac{7}{8} & -\frac{3}{8} \end{bmatrix}$

31. $\begin{bmatrix} 1 & 1 & 1 \\ 2 & 3 & 0 \\ 1 & 2 & 1 \end{bmatrix}$ and $\begin{bmatrix} 1.5 & .5 & -1.5 \\ -1 & 0 & 1 \\ .5 & -.5 & .5 \end{bmatrix}$

32. $\begin{bmatrix} 2 & 5 & 4 \\ 1 & 4 & 3 \\ 1 & 3 & 2 \end{bmatrix}$ and $\begin{bmatrix} 1 & 2 & 1 \\ -5 & 8 & 2 \\ 7 & -11 & -3 \end{bmatrix}$

Find the inverse, if it exists, for each of the given matrices. (See Examples 6 and 7.)

33. $\begin{bmatrix} 2 & -3 \\ -1 & 2 \end{bmatrix}$ **34.** $\begin{bmatrix} 2 & 1 \\ 1 & 1 \end{bmatrix}$

35. $\begin{bmatrix} -1 & 2 \\ 1 & -1 \end{bmatrix}$ **36.** $\begin{bmatrix} 1 & 2 \\ 3 & 4 \end{bmatrix}$

37. $\begin{bmatrix} 1 & 2 \\ 3 & 6 \end{bmatrix}$ **38.** $\begin{bmatrix} -3 & -5 \\ 6 & 10 \end{bmatrix}$

39. $\begin{bmatrix} 1 & -1 & 0 \\ -1 & 2 & 3 \\ 1 & 0 & 2 \end{bmatrix}$ **40.** $\begin{bmatrix} 0 & 1 & -1 \\ 2 & -2 & -1 \\ -1 & 1 & 1 \end{bmatrix}$

41. $\begin{bmatrix} 1 & 4 & 3 \\ 1 & -3 & -2 \\ 2 & 5 & 4 \end{bmatrix}$ **42.** $\begin{bmatrix} 1 & -1 & 4 \\ 0 & 1 & 3 \\ 2 & -3 & 4 \end{bmatrix}$

43. $\begin{bmatrix} 1 & 2 & 0 \\ 3 & -1 & 2 \\ -2 & 3 & -2 \end{bmatrix}$ **44.** $\begin{bmatrix} 1 & 0 & -5 \\ 4 & -7 & 3 \\ 3 & -7 & 8 \end{bmatrix}$

✒ *Use a graphing calculator to find the inverse of each matrix. (See Example 8.)*

45. $\begin{bmatrix} 1 & 2 & 3 \\ 1 & 4 & 2 \\ 0 & 1 & -1 \end{bmatrix}$ **46.** $\begin{bmatrix} 2 & 2 & -4 \\ 2 & 6 & 0 \\ -3 & -3 & 5 \end{bmatrix}$

47. $\begin{bmatrix} 1 & 0 & -2 & 0 \\ -2 & 1 & 2 & 2 \\ 3 & -1 & -2 & -3 \\ 0 & 1 & 4 & 1 \end{bmatrix}$ **48.** $\begin{bmatrix} 1 & 1 & 0 & 2 \\ 2 & -1 & 1 & -1 \\ 3 & 3 & 2 & -2 \\ 1 & 2 & 1 & 0 \end{bmatrix}$

A graphing calculator or other technology is recommended for part (c) of Exercises 49–51.

49. Social Science Population estimates and projections (in millions) for several regions of the world and the average birth and death rates per million people for those regions are shown in the tables below. (Data from: United Nations Population Fund.)

	Asia	Europe	Latin America	North America
2000	3719	727	521	313
2010	4164	738	590	345
2020	4566	744	652	374

	Births	Deaths
Asia	.019	.007
Europe	.011	.011
Latin America	.019	.006
North America	.024	.008

(a) Write the information in the first table as a 3×4 matrix A.

(b) Write the information in the second table as a 4×2 matrix B.

(c) Find the matrix product AB.

(d) Explain what AB represents.

(e) According to matrix AB, what was the total number of births in these four regions combined in 2010? What total number of deaths is projected for 2020?

50. Business A restaurant has a main location and a traveling food truck. The first matrix A shows the number of managers and associates employed. The second matrix B shows the average annual cost of salary and benefits (in thousands of dollars).

$$\begin{array}{c} \\ \text{Restaurant} \\ \text{Food Truck} \end{array} \begin{array}{cc} \text{Managers} & \text{Associates} \\ \begin{bmatrix} 5 & 25 \\ 1 & 4 \end{bmatrix} \end{array} = A$$

$$\begin{array}{c} \\ \text{Managers} \\ \text{Associates} \end{array} \begin{array}{cc} \text{Salary} & \text{Benefits} \\ \begin{bmatrix} 41 & 6 \\ 20 & 2 \end{bmatrix} \end{array} = B$$

(a) Find the matrix product AB.

(b) Explain what AB represents.

(c) According to matrix AB, what is the total cost of salaries for all employees (managers and associates) at the restaurant? What is the total cost of benefits for all employees at the food truck?

51. Social Science Population estimates and projections (in millions) for the BRIC countries (Brazil, Russia, India, China) and birth and death rates per million people for those countries are shown in the tables on the next page. (Data from: United Nations Population Fund.)

	2010	2020
Brazil	195	210
Russia	143	141
India	1225	1387
China	1341	1388

	Births	Deaths
Brazil	.016	.006
Russia	.011	.014
India	.023	.008
China	.013	.007

(a) Write the information in the first table as a 2 × 4 matrix *A*.

(b) Write the information in the second table as a 4 × 2 matrix *B*.

(c) Find the matrix product *AB*.

(d) Explain what *AB* represents.

(e) According to matrix *AB*, what was the total number of deaths in the BRIC countries in 2010? What total number of births is projected for 2020?

52. Business The first table shows the number of employees (in millions) in various sectors of the U.S. economy over a 3-year period. The second table gives the average weekly wage per employee (in dollars) in each sector over the same period. (Data from: Bureau of Labor Statistics.)

	2007	2008	2009
Private	114.0	113.2	106.9
Local Government	14.0	14.2	14.2
State Government	4.6	4.6	4.6
Federal Government	2.7	2.8	2.8

	2007	2008	2009
Private	853	873	868
Local Government	784	813	830
State Government	883	923	937
Federal Government	1248	1275	1303

(a) Write the information in the first table as a 4 × 3 matrix *A*.

(b) Write the information in the second table as a 3 × 4 matrix *B*.

(c) Explain what each of the following entries in *AB* represents: row 1, column 1; row 2, column 2; row 3, column 3; row 4, column 4. Do any of the other entries represent anything meaningful?

(d) What was the total weekly payroll (in dollars) for the federal government over the 3-year period?

53. Business The four departments of Stagg Enterprises need to order the following amounts of the same products:

	Paper	Tape	Ink Cartridges	Memo Pads	Pens
Department 1	10	4	3	5	6
Department 2	7	2	2	3	8
Department 3	4	5	1	0	10
Department 4	0	3	4	5	5

The unit price (in dollars) of each product is as follows for two suppliers:

Product	Supplier *A*	Supplier *B*
Paper	9	12
Tape	6	6
Ink Cartridges	24	18
Memo Pads	4	4
Pens	8	12

(a) Use matrix multiplication to get a matrix showing the comparative costs for each department for the products from the two suppliers.

(b) Find the total cost to buy products from each supplier. From which supplier should the company make the purchase?

54. Health The first table shows the number of live births (in thousands). The second table shows infant mortality rates (deaths per 1000 live births). (Data from: U.S. Center for Health Statistics.)

	2008	2009	2010
Black	671	658	636
White	3274	3173	3069

	2008	2009	2010
Black	12.7	12.6	11.6
White	5.6	5.3	5.2

(a) Write the information in the first table as a 3 × 2 matrix *C*.

(b) Write the information in the second table as a 2 × 3 matrix *D*.

(c) Find the matrix product *DC*.

(d) Which entry in *DC* gives the total number of black infant deaths from 2008 to 2010?

(e) Which entry in *DC* gives the total number of white infant deaths from 2008 to 2010?

55. Business Burger Barn's three locations sell hamburgers, fries, and soft drinks. Barn I sells 900 burgers, 600 orders of fries, and 750 soft drinks each day. Barn II sells 1500 burgers a day and Barn III sells 1150. Soft drink sales number 900 a day at Barn II and 825 a day at Barn III. Barn II sells 950 orders of fries per day and Barn III sells 800.

(a) Write a 3 × 3 matrix *S* that displays daily sales figures for all locations.

(b) Burgers cost $3.00 each, fries $1.80 an order, and soft drinks $1.20 each. Write a 1×3 matrix P that displays the prices.

(c) What matrix product displays the daily revenue at each of the three locations?

(d) What is the total daily revenue from all locations?

56. **Business** The Perulli Candy Company makes three types of chocolate candy: Cheery Cherry, Mucho Mocha, and Almond Delight. The company produces its products in San Diego, Mexico City, and Managua, using two main ingredients: chocolate and sugar.

(a) Each kilogram of Cheery Cherry requires .5 kilogram of sugar and .2 kilogram of chocolate; each kilogram of Mucho Mocha requires .4 kilogram of sugar and .3 kilogram of chocolate; and each kilogram of Almond Delight requires .3 kilogram of sugar and .3 kilogram of chocolate. Put this information into a 2×3 matrix, labeling the rows and columns.

(b) The cost of 1 kilogram of sugar is $3 in San Diego, $2 in Mexico City, and $1 in Managua. The cost of 1 kilogram of chocolate is $3 in San Diego, $3 in Mexico City, and $4 in Managua. Put this information into a matrix in such a way that when you multiply it with your matrix from part (a), you get a matrix representing the cost by ingredient of producing each type of candy in each city.

(c) Multiply the matrices in parts (a) and (b), labeling the product matrix.

(d) From part (c), what is the combined cost of sugar and chocolate required to produce 1 kilogram of Mucho Mocha in Managua?

(e) Perulli Candy needs to quickly produce a special shipment of 100 kilograms of Cheery Cherry, 200 kilograms of Mucho Mocha, and 500 kilograms of Almond Delight, and it decides to select one factory to fill the entire order. Use matrix multiplication to determine in which city the total cost of sugar and chocolate combined required to produce the order is the smallest.

✓ Checkpoint Answers

1. $27,100

2. (a) No (b) Yes; 2×6

3. $CD = \begin{bmatrix} 19 & -2 \\ -13 & -12 \end{bmatrix}$

4. (a) 2×3 (b) Not possible (c) 3×3

5. (a) $A = $ brand/vitamin;

   $B = $ vitamin/cost.

   (b) $AB = $ brand/cost.

   (c) Not meaningful, although the product BA can be found.

6. $IA = \begin{bmatrix} 3 & -2 \\ 4 & -1 \end{bmatrix} = A$, and $AI = \begin{bmatrix} 3 & -2 \\ 4 & -1 \end{bmatrix} = A$.

7. No, because $AB \neq I$.

8. RREF [B] is matrix (6) in the example.

9. (a) No inverse

   (b) Use the FRAC key (if you have one) to simplify the answer, which is

   $$B^{-1} = \begin{bmatrix} 4/11 & -3/11 \\ 1/11 & 2/11 \end{bmatrix}.$$

6.6 Applications of Matrices

This section gives a variety of applications of matrices.

Solving Systems with Matrices

Consider this system of linear equations:

$$2x - 3y = 4$$
$$x + 5y = 2.$$

Let

$$A = \begin{bmatrix} 2 & -3 \\ 1 & 5 \end{bmatrix}, \quad X = \begin{bmatrix} x \\ y \end{bmatrix}, \quad \text{and} \quad B = \begin{bmatrix} 4 \\ 2 \end{bmatrix}.$$

Since

$$AX = \begin{bmatrix} 2 & -3 \\ 1 & 5 \end{bmatrix} \begin{bmatrix} x \\ y \end{bmatrix} = \begin{bmatrix} 2x - 3y \\ x + 5y \end{bmatrix} \quad \text{and} \quad B = \begin{bmatrix} 4 \\ 2 \end{bmatrix},$$

the original system is equivalent to the single matrix equation $AX = B$. Similarly, any system of linear equations can be written as a matrix equation $AX = B$. The matrix A is called the **coefficient matrix**. ✓₁

A matrix equation $AX = B$ can be solved if A^{-1} exists. Assuming that A^{-1} exists and using the facts that $A^{-1}A = I$ and $IX = X$, along with the associative property of multiplication of matrices, gives

$$AX = B$$
$$A^{-1}(AX) = A^{-1}B \qquad \text{Multiply both sides by } A^{-1}.$$
$$(A^{-1}A)X = A^{-1}B \qquad \text{Associative property}$$
$$IX = A^{-1}B \qquad \text{Inverse property}$$
$$X = A^{-1}B. \qquad \text{Identity property}$$

When multiplying by matrices on both sides of a matrix equation, be careful to multiply in the same order on both sides, since multiplication of matrices is not commutative (unlike the multiplication of real numbers). This discussion is summarized below.

> Suppose that a system of equations with the same number of equations as variables is written in matrix form as $AX = B$, where A is the square matrix of coefficients, X is the column matrix of variables, and B is the column matrix of constants. If A has an inverse, then the unique solution of the system is $X = A^{-1}B$.*

Example 1 Consider this system of equations:

$$x + y + z = 2$$
$$2x + 3y = 5$$
$$x + 2y + z = -1.$$

(a) Write the system as a matrix equation.

Solution We have these three matrices:

Coefficient Matrix   *Matrix of Variables*   *Matrix of Constants*

$$A = \begin{bmatrix} 1 & 1 & 1 \\ 2 & 3 & 0 \\ 1 & 2 & 1 \end{bmatrix}, \quad X = \begin{bmatrix} x \\ y \\ z \end{bmatrix}, \quad \text{and} \quad B = \begin{bmatrix} 2 \\ 5 \\ -1 \end{bmatrix}.$$

So the matrix equation is

$$AX = B$$
$$\begin{bmatrix} 1 & 1 & 1 \\ 2 & 3 & 0 \\ 1 & 2 & 1 \end{bmatrix} \begin{bmatrix} x \\ y \\ z \end{bmatrix} = \begin{bmatrix} 2 \\ 5 \\ -1 \end{bmatrix}.$$

✓ **Checkpoint 1**

Write the matrix of coefficients, the matrix of variables, and the matrix of constants for the system

$$2x + 6y = -14$$
$$-x - 2y = 3.$$

---

*If A does not have an inverse, then the system either has no solution or has an infinite number of solutions. Use the methods of Sections 6.1 or 6.2.

(b) Find A^{-1} and solve the equation.

Solution   Use Exercise 31 of Section 6.5, technology, or the method of Section 6.5 to find that

$$A^{-1} = \begin{bmatrix} 1.5 & .5 & -1.5 \\ -1 & 0 & 1 \\ .5 & -.5 & .5 \end{bmatrix}.$$

Hence,

$$X = A^{-1}B = \begin{bmatrix} 1.5 & .5 & -1.5 \\ -1 & 0 & 1 \\ .5 & -.5 & .5 \end{bmatrix}\begin{bmatrix} 2 \\ 5 \\ -1 \end{bmatrix} = \begin{bmatrix} 7 \\ -3 \\ -2 \end{bmatrix}.$$

Thus, the solution of the original system is $(7, -3, -2)$. ✓2

✓ **Checkpoint 2**

Use the inverse matrix to solve the system in Example 1 if the constants for the three equations are 12, 0, and 8, respectively.

Example 2   Use the inverse of the coefficient matrix to solve the system

$$x + 1.5y = 8$$
$$2x + 3y = 10.$$

Solution   The coefficient matrix is $A = \begin{bmatrix} 1 & 1.5 \\ 2 & 3 \end{bmatrix}$. A graphing calculator will indicate that A^{-1} does not exist. If we try to carry out the row operations, we see why:

$$\begin{bmatrix} 1 & 1.5 & | & 1 & 0 \\ 2 & 3 & | & 0 & 1 \end{bmatrix}$$

$$\begin{bmatrix} 1 & 1.5 & | & 1 & 0 \\ 0 & 0 & | & -2 & 1 \end{bmatrix}. \qquad {\scriptstyle -2R_1 + R_2}$$

The next step cannot be performed because of the zero in the second row, second column. Verify that the original system has no solution. ✓3

✓ **Checkpoint 3**

Solve the system in Example 2 if the constants are, respectively, 3 and 6.

Input–Output Analysis

An interesting application of matrix theory to economics was developed by Nobel Prize winner Wassily Leontief. His application of matrices to the interdependencies in an economy is called **input–output analysis.** In practice, input–output analysis is very complicated, with many variables. We shall discuss only simple examples with just a few variables.

Input–output models are concerned with the production and flow of goods and services. A typical economy is composed of a number of different sectors (such as manufacturing, energy, transportation, agriculture, etc.). Each sector requires input from other sectors (and possibly from itself) to produce its output. For instance, manufacturing output requires energy, transportation, and manufactured items (such as tools and machinery). If an economy has n sectors, then the inputs required by the various sectors from each other to produce their outputs can be described by an $n \times n$ matrix called the **input–output matrix** (or the **technological matrix**).

Example 3   **Economics**   Suppose a simplified economy involves just three sectors—agriculture, manufacturing, and transportation—all in appropriate units. The production of 1 unit of agriculture requires $\frac{1}{2}$ unit of manufacturing and $\frac{1}{4}$ unit of transportation. The production of 1 unit of manufacturing requires $\frac{1}{4}$ unit of agriculture and $\frac{1}{4}$ unit of transportation. The production of 1 unit of transportation requires $\frac{1}{3}$ unit of agriculture and $\frac{1}{4}$ unit of manufacturing. Write the input–output matrix of this economy.

Solution Since there are three sectors in the economy, the input–output matrix A is 3×3. Each row and each column is labeled by a sector of the economy, as shown below. The first column lists the units from each sector of the economy that are required to produce one unit of agriculture. The second column lists the units required from each sector to produce 1 unit of manufacturing, and the last column lists the units required from each sector to produce 1 unit of transportation.

Output

| | Agriculture | Manufacturing | Transportation |

$$
\begin{array}{r}
\\
\textit{Input} \quad
\begin{array}{r}
\text{Agriculture} \\
\text{Manufacturing} \\
\text{Transportation}
\end{array}
\end{array}
\begin{bmatrix}
0 & \frac{1}{4} & \frac{1}{3} \\
\frac{1}{2} & 0 & \frac{1}{4} \\
\frac{1}{4} & \frac{1}{4} & 0
\end{bmatrix} = A.
$$

✓ **Checkpoint 4**

Write a 2 × 2 input–output matrix in which 1 unit of electricity requires $\frac{1}{2}$ unit of water and $\frac{1}{3}$ unit of electricity, while 1 unit of water requires no water but $\frac{1}{4}$ unit of electricity.

Example 3 is a bit unrealistic in that no sector of the economy requires any input from itself. In an actual economy, most sectors require input from themselves as well as from other sectors to produce their output (as discussed in the paragraph preceding Example 3). Nevertheless, it is easier to learn the basic concepts from simplified examples, so we shall continue to use them.

The input–output matrix gives only a partial picture of an economy. We also need to know the amount produced by each sector and the amount of the economy's output that is used up by the sectors themselves in the production process. The remainder of the total output is available to satisfy the needs of consumers and others outside the production system.

Example 4 **Economics** Consider the economy whose input–output matrix A was found in Example 3.

(a) Suppose this economy produces 60 units of agriculture, 52 units of manufacturing, and 48 units of transportation. Write this information as a column matrix.

Solution Listing the sectors in the same order as the rows of input–output matrix, we have

$$
X = \begin{bmatrix} 60 \\ 52 \\ 48 \end{bmatrix}.
$$

The matrix X is called the **production matrix.**

(b) How much from each sector is used up in the production process?

Solution Since $\frac{1}{4}$ unit of agriculture is used to produce each unit of manufacturing and there are 52 units of manufacturing output, the amount of agriculture used up by manufacturing is $\frac{1}{4} \times 52 = 13$ units. Similarly $\frac{1}{3}$ unit of agriculture is used to produce a unit of transportation, so $\frac{1}{3} \times 48 = 16$ units of agriculture are used up by transportation. Therefore $13 + 16 = 29$ units of agriculture are used up in the economy's production process.

A similar analysis shows that the economy's production process uses up

$$
\underset{\substack{\text{agricul-} \\ \text{ture}}}{\frac{1}{2} \times 60} + \underset{\substack{\text{transpor-} \\ \text{tation}}}{\frac{1}{4} \times 48} = 30 + 12 = 42 \text{ units of manufacturing}
$$

and

$$
\underset{\substack{\text{agricul-} \\ \text{ture}}}{\frac{1}{4} \times 60} + \underset{\substack{\text{manufac-} \\ \text{turing}}}{\frac{1}{4} \times 52} = 15 + 13 = 28 \text{ units of transportation.}
$$

(c) Describe the conclusions of part (b) in terms of the input–output matrix A and the production matrix X.

Solution The matrix product AX gives the amount from each sector that is used up in the production process, as shown here [with selected entries color coded as in part (b)]:

$$AX = \begin{bmatrix} 0 & \frac{1}{4} & \frac{1}{3} \\ \frac{1}{2} & 0 & \frac{1}{4} \\ \frac{1}{4} & \frac{1}{4} & 0 \end{bmatrix} \begin{bmatrix} 60 \\ 52 \\ 48 \end{bmatrix} = \begin{bmatrix} 0 \cdot 60 + \frac{1}{4} \cdot 52 + \frac{1}{3} \cdot 48 \\ \frac{1}{2} \cdot 60 + 0 \cdot 52 + \frac{1}{4} \cdot 48 \\ \frac{1}{4} \cdot 60 + \frac{1}{4} \cdot 52 + 0 \cdot 48 \end{bmatrix}$$

$$= \begin{bmatrix} \frac{1}{4} \cdot 52 + \frac{1}{3} \cdot 48 \\ \frac{1}{2} \cdot 60 + \frac{1}{4} \cdot 48 \\ \frac{1}{4} \cdot 60 + \frac{1}{4} \cdot 52 \end{bmatrix} = \begin{bmatrix} 29 \\ 42 \\ 28 \end{bmatrix}.$$

(d) Find the matrix $D = X - AX$ and explain what its entries represent.

Solution From parts (a) and (c), we have

$$D = X - AX = \begin{bmatrix} 60 \\ 52 \\ 48 \end{bmatrix} - \begin{bmatrix} 29 \\ 42 \\ 28 \end{bmatrix} = \begin{bmatrix} 31 \\ 10 \\ 20 \end{bmatrix}.$$

The matrix D lists the amount of each sector that is *not* used up in the production process and hence is available to groups outside the production process (such as consumers). For example, 60 units of agriculture are produced and 29 units are used up in the process, so the difference $60 - 29 = 31$ is the amount of agriculture that is available to groups outside the production process. Similar remarks apply to manufacturing and transportation. The matrix D is called the **demand matrix.** Matrices A and D show that the production of 60 units of agriculture, 52 units of manufacturing, and 48 units of transportation would satisfy an outside demand of 31 units of agriculture, 10 units of manufacturing, and 20 units of transportation. �5

✓ **Checkpoint 5**

(a) Write a 2×1 matrix X to represent the gross production of 9000 units of electricity and 12,000 units of water.

(b) Find AX, using A from Checkpoint 4.

(c) Find D, using $D = X - AX$.

Example 4 illustrates the general situation. In an economy with n sectors, the input–output matrix A is $n \times n$. The production matrix X is a column matrix whose n entries are the outputs of each sector of the economy. The demand matrix D is also a column matrix with n entries. This matrix is defined by

$$D = X - AX.$$

D lists the amount from each sector that is available to meet the demands of consumers and other groups outside the production process.

In Example 4, we knew the input–output matrix A and the production matrix X and used them to find the demand matrix D. In practice, however, this process is reversed: The input–output matrix A and the demand matrix D are known, and we must find the production matrix X needed to satisfy the required demands. Matrix algebra can be used to solve the equation $D = X - AX$ for X:

$$D = X - AX$$
$$D = IX - AX \qquad \text{Identity property}$$
$$D = (I - A)X. \qquad \text{Distributive property}$$

If the matrix $I - A$ has an inverse, then

$$X = (I - A)^{-1}D.$$

Example 5   **Economics**   Suppose, in the three-sector economy of Examples 3 and 4, there is a demand for 516 units of agriculture, 258 units of manufacturing, and 129 units of transportation. What should production be for each sector?

Solution The demand matrix is

$$D = \begin{bmatrix} 516 \\ 258 \\ 129 \end{bmatrix}.$$

Find the production matrix by first calculating $I - A$:

$$I - A = \begin{bmatrix} 1 & 0 & 0 \\ 0 & 1 & 0 \\ 0 & 0 & 1 \end{bmatrix} - \begin{bmatrix} 0 & \frac{1}{4} & \frac{1}{3} \\ \frac{1}{2} & 0 & \frac{1}{4} \\ \frac{1}{4} & \frac{1}{4} & 0 \end{bmatrix} = \begin{bmatrix} 1 & -\frac{1}{4} & -\frac{1}{3} \\ -\frac{1}{2} & 1 & -\frac{1}{4} \\ -\frac{1}{4} & -\frac{1}{4} & 1 \end{bmatrix}.$$

Using a calculator with matrix capability or row operations, find the inverse of $I - A$:

$$(I - A)^{-1} = \begin{bmatrix} 1.3953 & .4961 & .5891 \\ .8372 & 1.3643 & .6202 \\ .5581 & .4651 & 1.3023 \end{bmatrix}.$$

(The entries are rounded to four decimal places.[*]) Since $X = (I - A)^{-1}D$.

$$X = \begin{bmatrix} 1.3953 & .4961 & .5891 \\ .8372 & 1.3643 & .6202 \\ .5581 & .4651 & 1.3023 \end{bmatrix} \begin{bmatrix} 516 \\ 258 \\ 129 \end{bmatrix} = \begin{bmatrix} 924 \\ 864 \\ 576 \end{bmatrix}$$

(rounded to the nearest whole numbers).

From the last result, we see that the production of 924 units of agriculture, 864 units of manufacturing, and 576 units of transportation is required to satisfy demands of 516, 258, and 129 units, respectively.

Example 6 **Economics** An economy depends on two basic products: wheat and oil. To produce 1 metric ton of wheat requires .25 metric ton of wheat and .33 metric ton of oil. The production of 1 metric ton of oil consumes .08 metric ton of wheat and .11 metric ton of oil. Find the production that will satisfy a demand of 500 metric tons of wheat and 1000 metric tons of oil.

Solution The input–output matrix is

$$\begin{array}{cc} & \text{Wheat} \quad \text{Oil} \\ A = & \begin{bmatrix} .25 & .08 \\ .33 & .11 \end{bmatrix} \begin{array}{l} \text{Wheat} \\ \text{Oil} \end{array} \end{array},$$

and we also have

$$I - A = \begin{bmatrix} 1 & 0 \\ 0 & 1 \end{bmatrix} - \begin{bmatrix} .25 & .08 \\ .33 & .11 \end{bmatrix} = \begin{bmatrix} .75 & -.08 \\ -.33 & .89 \end{bmatrix}.$$

Next, use technology or the methods of Section 6.5 to calculate $(I - A)^{-1}$:

$$(I - A)^{-1} = \begin{bmatrix} 1.3882 & .1248 \\ .5147 & 1.1699 \end{bmatrix} \quad \text{(rounded)}.$$

The demand matrix is

$$D = \begin{bmatrix} 500 \\ 1000 \end{bmatrix}.$$

---

[*]Although we show the matrix $(I - A)^{-1}$ with entries rounded to four decimal places, we did not round off in calculating $(I - A)^{-1}D$. If the rounded figures are used, the numbers in the product may vary slightly in the last digit.

Consequently, the production matrix is

$$X = (I - A)^{-1}D = \begin{bmatrix} 1.3882 & .1248 \\ .5147 & 1.1699 \end{bmatrix}\begin{bmatrix} 500 \\ 1000 \end{bmatrix} = \begin{bmatrix} 819 \\ 1427 \end{bmatrix},$$

where the production numbers have been rounded to the nearest whole numbers. The production of 819 metric tons of wheat and 1427 metric tons of oil is required to satisfy the indicated demand.

Checkpoint 6

A simple economy depends on just two products: beer and pretzels.

(a) Suppose $\frac{1}{2}$ unit of beer and $\frac{1}{2}$ unit of pretzels are needed to make 1 unit of beer, and $\frac{3}{4}$ unit of beer is needed to make 1 unit of pretzels. Write the technological matrix A for the economy.

(b) Find $I - A$.

(c) Find $(I - A)^{-1}$.

(d) Find the gross production X that will be needed to get a net production of

$$D = \begin{bmatrix} 100 \\ 1000 \end{bmatrix}.$$

TECHNOLOGY TIP If you are using a graphing calculator to determine X, you can calculate $(I - A)^{-1}D$ in one step without finding the intermediate matrices $I - A$ and $(I - A)^{-1}$.

Code Theory

Governments need sophisticated methods of coding and decoding messages. One example of such an advanced code uses matrix theory. This code takes the letters in the words and divides them into groups. (Each space between words is treated as a letter; punctuation is disregarded.) Then, numbers are assigned to the letters of the alphabet. For our purposes, let the letter a correspond to 1, b to 2, and so on. Let the number 27 correspond to a space.

For example, the message

mathematics is for the birds

can be divided into groups of three letters each:

mat   hem   ati   cs−   is−   for   −th   e−b   ird   s−−

(We used − to represent a space.) We now write a column matrix for each group of three symbols, using the corresponding numbers instead of letters. For example, the first four groups can be written as

$$\overset{mat}{\begin{bmatrix} 13 \\ 1 \\ 20 \end{bmatrix}}, \quad \overset{hem}{\begin{bmatrix} 8 \\ 5 \\ 13 \end{bmatrix}}, \quad \overset{ati}{\begin{bmatrix} 1 \\ 20 \\ 9 \end{bmatrix}}, \quad \overset{cs-}{\begin{bmatrix} 3 \\ 19 \\ 27 \end{bmatrix}}.$$

The entire message consists of ten 3×1 column matrices:

$$\begin{bmatrix} 13 \\ 1 \\ 20 \end{bmatrix}, \begin{bmatrix} 8 \\ 5 \\ 13 \end{bmatrix}, \begin{bmatrix} 1 \\ 20 \\ 9 \end{bmatrix}, \begin{bmatrix} 3 \\ 19 \\ 27 \end{bmatrix}, \begin{bmatrix} 9 \\ 19 \\ 27 \end{bmatrix}, \begin{bmatrix} 6 \\ 15 \\ 18 \end{bmatrix}, \begin{bmatrix} 27 \\ 20 \\ 8 \end{bmatrix}, \begin{bmatrix} 5 \\ 27 \\ 2 \end{bmatrix}, \begin{bmatrix} 9 \\ 18 \\ 4 \end{bmatrix}, \begin{bmatrix} 19 \\ 27 \\ 27 \end{bmatrix}.$$

Checkpoint 7

Write the message "*when*" using 2×1 matrices.

Although you could transmit these matrices, a simple substitution code such as this is very easy to break.

To get a more reliable code, we choose a 3×3 matrix M that has an inverse. Suppose we choose

$$M = \begin{bmatrix} 1 & 3 & 3 \\ 1 & 4 & 3 \\ 1 & 3 & 4 \end{bmatrix}.$$

Then encode each message group by multiplying by M—that is,

$$\begin{bmatrix} 1 & 3 & 3 \\ 1 & 4 & 3 \\ 1 & 3 & 4 \end{bmatrix}\begin{bmatrix} 13 \\ 1 \\ 20 \end{bmatrix} = \begin{bmatrix} 76 \\ 77 \\ 96 \end{bmatrix}, \quad \begin{bmatrix} 1 & 3 & 3 \\ 1 & 4 & 3 \\ 1 & 3 & 4 \end{bmatrix}\begin{bmatrix} 8 \\ 5 \\ 13 \end{bmatrix} = \begin{bmatrix} 62 \\ 67 \\ 75 \end{bmatrix},$$

$$\begin{bmatrix} 1 & 3 & 3 \\ 1 & 4 & 3 \\ 1 & 3 & 4 \end{bmatrix}\begin{bmatrix} 1 \\ 20 \\ 9 \end{bmatrix} = \begin{bmatrix} 88 \\ 108 \\ 97 \end{bmatrix},$$

and so on. The coded message consists of the ten 3×1 column matrices

$$\begin{bmatrix} 76 \\ 77 \\ 96 \end{bmatrix}, \begin{bmatrix} 62 \\ 67 \\ 75 \end{bmatrix}, \begin{bmatrix} 88 \\ 108 \\ 97 \end{bmatrix}, \ldots, \begin{bmatrix} 181 \\ 208 \\ 208 \end{bmatrix}.$$

The message would be sent as a string of numbers:

$$76, 77, 96, 62, 67, 75, 88, 108, 97, \ldots, 181, 208, 208.$$

Note that the same letter may be encoded by different numbers. For instance, the first *a* in "mathematics" is 77 and the second *a* is 88. This makes the code harder to break. ✓8

The receiving agent rewrites the message as the ten 3×1 column matrices shown in color previously. The agent then decodes the message by multiplying each of these column matrices by the matrix M^{-1}. Verify that

$$M^{-1} = \begin{bmatrix} 7 & -3 & -3 \\ -1 & 1 & 0 \\ -1 & 0 & 1 \end{bmatrix}.$$

So the first two matrices of the coded message are decoded as

$$\begin{bmatrix} 7 & -3 & -3 \\ -1 & 1 & 0 \\ -1 & 0 & 1 \end{bmatrix} \begin{bmatrix} 76 \\ 77 \\ 96 \end{bmatrix} = \begin{bmatrix} 13 \\ 1 \\ 20 \end{bmatrix} \begin{matrix} m \\ a \\ t \end{matrix}$$

and

$$\begin{bmatrix} 7 & -3 & -3 \\ -1 & 1 & 0 \\ -1 & 0 & 1 \end{bmatrix} \begin{bmatrix} 62 \\ 67 \\ 75 \end{bmatrix} = \begin{bmatrix} 8 \\ 5 \\ 13 \end{bmatrix} \begin{matrix} h \\ e \\ m \end{matrix}.$$

The other blocks are decoded similarly.

✓**Checkpoint 8**

Use the following matrix to find the 2×1 matrices to be transmitted for the message in Checkpoint 7:

$$\begin{bmatrix} 2 & 1 \\ 5 & 0 \end{bmatrix}.$$

Routing

The diagram in Figure 6.27 shows the pathways connecting five buildings on a college campus. We can represent the pathways via matrix A, where the entries represent the number of pathways connecting two buildings without passing through another building. From the diagram, we see that there are two pathways connecting building 1 to building 2 without passing through buildings 3, 4, or 5. This information is entered in row one, column two, and again in row two, column one of matrix A:

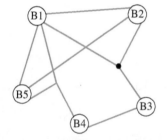

Figure 6.27

$$A = \begin{bmatrix} 0 & 2 & 1 & 1 & 2 \\ 2 & 0 & 1 & 0 & 1 \\ 1 & 1 & 0 & 1 & 0 \\ 1 & 0 & 1 & 0 & 1 \\ 2 & 1 & 0 & 1 & 0 \end{bmatrix}.$$

Note that there are no pathways connecting each building to itself, so the main diagonal of the matrix from upper left to lower right consists entirely of zeros.

We can also investigate the number of ways to go from building 1 to building 3 by going through exactly one other building. This can happen by going from building 1 to building 2 two ways, and then from building 2 to building 3. Another way is to go from building 1 to building 4 and then from building 4 to building 3. Thus, there are three total ways to go from building 1 to building 3 by going through exactly one other building.

The matrix A^2 shows the number of ways to travel between any two buildings by going through exactly one other building.

$$A^2 = \begin{bmatrix} 10 & 3 & 3 & 3 & 3 \\ 3 & 6 & 2 & 4 & 4 \\ 3 & 2 & 3 & 1 & 4 \\ 3 & 4 & 1 & 3 & 2 \\ 3 & 4 & 4 & 2 & 6 \end{bmatrix}.$$

We ignore the values down the main diagonal for travel from one building into itself. We notice that the entry in row one, column three has a value of 3. This coincides with what we learned earlier—that there are three ways to go from building 1 to building 3 that go through exactly one other building.

We can also find the number of ways to walk between any two buildings by passing through exactly two other buildings by calculating A^3. Additionally, $A + A^2$ gives the number of ways to walk between two buildings with at most one intermediate building. ✓₉

The diagram can be given many other interpretations. For example, the lines could represent lines of mutual influence between people or nations, or they could represent communication lines, such as telephone lines.

✓ **Checkpoint 9**

Use a graphing calculator to find the following.

(a) A^3

(b) $A + A^2$

6.6 Exercises

Solve the matrix equation AX = B for X. (See Example 1.)

1. $A = \begin{bmatrix} 1 & -1 \\ 5 & 6 \end{bmatrix}, B = \begin{bmatrix} 4 \\ -2 \end{bmatrix}$

2. $A = \begin{bmatrix} 1 & 2 \\ 1 & 5 \end{bmatrix}, B = \begin{bmatrix} -3 \\ 5 \end{bmatrix}$

3. $A = \begin{bmatrix} 3 & 1 \\ 4 & 2 \end{bmatrix}, B = \begin{bmatrix} 3 & 4 \\ 5 & 6 \end{bmatrix}$

4. $A = \begin{bmatrix} 1 & 4 \\ 2 & 7 \end{bmatrix}, B = \begin{bmatrix} 0 & 8 \\ 4 & 1 \end{bmatrix}$

5. $A = \begin{bmatrix} 2 & 1 & 0 \\ -4 & -1 & 3 \\ 3 & 1 & -2 \end{bmatrix}, B = \begin{bmatrix} 1 \\ 4 \\ 0 \end{bmatrix}$

6. $A = \begin{bmatrix} 3 & -1 & 0 \\ 0 & 1 & 2 \\ 9 & 0 & 5 \end{bmatrix}, B = \begin{bmatrix} -3 \\ 6 \\ 12 \end{bmatrix}$

Use the inverse of the coefficient matrix to solve each system of equations. (See Example 1.)

7.
$x + 2y + 3z = 10$
$2x + 3y + 2z = 6$
$-x - 2y - 4z = -1$

8.
$-x + y - 3z = 3$
$2x + 4y - 4z = 6$
$-x + y + 4z = -1$

9.
$x + 4y + 3z = -12$
$x - 3y - 2z = 0$
$2x + 5y + 4z = 7$

10.
$5x + 2z = 3$
$2x + 2y + z = 4$
$-3x + y - z = 5$

11.
$x + 2y + 3z = 4$
$x + 4y + 2z = 8$
$y - z = -4$

12.
$2x + 2y - 4z = 12$
$2x + 6y = 16$
$-3x - 3y + 5z = -20$

13.
$x + y + 2w = 3$
$2x - y + z - w = 3$
$3x + 3y + 2z - 2w = 5$
$x + 2y + z = 3$

14.
$x - 2z = 4$
$-2x + y + 2z + 2w = -8$
$3x - y - 2z - 3w = 12$
$y + 4z + w = -4$

Use matrix algebra to solve the given matrix equations for X. Check your work.

15. $N = X - MX; N = \begin{bmatrix} 8 \\ -12 \end{bmatrix}, M = \begin{bmatrix} 0 & 1 \\ -2 & 1 \end{bmatrix}$

16. $A = BX + X; A = \begin{bmatrix} 4 & 6 \\ -2 & 2 \end{bmatrix}, B = \begin{bmatrix} -2 & -2 \\ 3 & 3 \end{bmatrix}$

To complete these exercises, write a system of equations and use the inverse of the coefficient matrix to solve the system.

17. Business Donovan's Dandy Furniture makes dining room furniture. A buffet requires 15 hours for cutting, 20 hours for assembly, and 5 hours for finishing. A chair requires 5 hours for cutting, 8 hours for assembly, and 5 hours for finishing. A table requires 10 hours for cutting, 6 hours for assembly, and 6 hours for finishing. The cutting department has 4900 hours of labor available each week, the assembly department has 6600 hours available, and the finishing department has 3900 hours available. How many pieces of each type of furniture should be produced each week if the factory is to run at full capacity?

18. Natural Science A hospital dietician is planning a special diet for a certain patient. The total amount per meal of food groups A, B, and C must equal 400 grams. The diet should include one-third as much of group A as of group B, and the sum of the amounts of group A and group C should equal twice the amount of group B.

(a) How many grams of each food group should be included?

(b) Suppose we drop the requirement that the diet include one-third as much of group A as of group B. Describe the set of all possible solutions.

(c) Suppose that, in addition to the conditions given in part (a), foods A and B cost 2 cents per gram, food C costs 3 cents per gram, and a meal must cost $8. Is a solution possible?

19. Natural Science Three species of bacteria are fed three foods: I, II, and III. A bacterium of the first species consumes 1.3 units each of foods I and II and 2.3 units of food III each day. A bacterium of the second species consumes 1.1 units of food I, 2.4 units of food II, and 3.7 units of food III each day. A bacterium of the third species consumes 8.1 units of I, 2.9 units of II, and 5.1 units of III each day. If 16,000 units of I, 28,000 units of II, and 44,000 units of III are supplied each day, how many of each species can be maintained in this environment?

20. Business A company produces three combinations of mixed vegetables, which sell in 1-kilogram packages. Italian style combines .3 kilogram of zucchini, .3 of broccoli, and .4 of carrots. French style combines .6 kilogram of broccoli and .4 of carrots. Oriental style combines .2 kilogram of zucchini, .5 of broccoli, and .3 of carrots. The company has a stock of 16,200 kilograms of zucchini, 41,400 kilograms of broccoli, and 29,400 kilograms of carrots. How many packages of each style should the company prepare in order to use up its supplies?

21. Business A national chain of casual clothing stores recently sent shipments of jeans, jackets, sweaters, and shirts to its stores in various cities. The number of items shipped to each city and their total wholesale cost are shown in the table. Find the wholesale price of one pair of jeans, one jacket, one sweater, and one shirt.

City	Jeans	Jackets	Sweaters	Shirts	Total Cost
Cleveland	3000	3000	2200	4200	$507,650
St. Louis	2700	2500	2100	4300	459,075
Seattle	5000	2000	1400	7500	541,225
Phoenix	7000	1800	600	8000	571,500

22. Health A 100-bed nursing home provides two levels of long-term care: regular and maximum. Patients at each level have a choice of a private room or a less expensive semiprivate room. The tables show the number of patients in each category at various times last year. The total daily costs for all patients were

$24,040 in January, $23,926 in April, $23,760 in July, and $24,042 in October. Find the daily cost of each of the following: a private room (regular care), a private room (maximum care), a semiprivate room (regular care), and a semiprivate room (maximum care).

	REGULAR-CARE PATIENTS	
Month	Semiprivate	Private
January	22	8
April	26	8
July	24	14
October	20	10

	MAXIMUM-CARE PATIENTS	
Month	Semiprivate	Private
January	60	10
April	54	12
July	56	6
October	62	8

Find the production matrix for the given input–output and demand matrices. (See Examples 3–6.).

23. $A = \begin{bmatrix} .1 & .03 \\ .07 & .6 \end{bmatrix}, D = \begin{bmatrix} 5 \\ 10 \end{bmatrix}$

24. $A = \begin{bmatrix} \frac{1}{2} & \frac{2}{5} \\ \frac{1}{4} & \frac{1}{5} \end{bmatrix}, D = \begin{bmatrix} 2 \\ 4 \end{bmatrix}$

Exercises 25 and 26 refer to Example 6.

25. Business If the demand is changed to 690 metric tons of wheat and 920 metric tons of oil, how many units of each commodity should be produced?

26. Business Change the technological matrix so that the production of 1 metric ton of wheat requires $\frac{1}{5}$ metric ton of oil (and no wheat) and the production of 1 metric ton of oil requires $\frac{1}{3}$ metric ton of wheat (and no oil). To satisfy the same demand matrix, how many units of each commodity should be produced?

Work these problems. (See Examples 3–6.)

27. Business A simplified economy has only two industries: the electric company and the gas company. Each dollar's worth of the electric company's output requires $.40 of its own output and $.50 of the gas company's output. Each dollar's worth of the gas company's output requires $.25 of its own output and $.60 of the electric company's output. What should the production of electricity and gas be (in dollars) if there is a $12 million demand for gas and a $15 million demand for electricity?

28. Business A two-segment economy consists of manufacturing and agriculture. To produce 1 unit of manufacturing output requires .40 unit of its own output and .20 unit of agricultural output. To produce 1 unit of agricultural output requires .30 unit of its own output and .40 unit of manufacturing output. If there is a demand of 240 units of manufacturing and 90 units of agriculture, what should be the output of each segment?

29. **Business** A primitive economy depends on two basic goods: yams and pork. The production of 1 bushel of yams requires $\frac{1}{4}$ bushel of yams and $\frac{1}{2}$ of a pig. To produce 1 pig requires $\frac{1}{6}$ bushel of yams. Find the amount of each commodity that should be produced to get

   (a) 1 bushel of yams and 1 pig;

   (b) 100 bushels of yams and 70 pigs.

30. **Business** A simplified economy is based on agriculture, manufacturing, and transportation. Each unit of agricultural output requires .4 unit of its own output, .3 unit of manufacturing output, and .2 unit of transportation output. One unit of manufacturing output requires .4 unit of its own output, .2 unit of agricultural output, and .3 unit of transportation output. One unit of transportation output requires .4 unit of its own output, .1 unit of agricultural output, and .2 unit of manufacturing output. There is demand for 35 units of agricultural, 90 units of manufacturing, and 20 units of transportation output. How many units should each segment of the economy produce?

31. **Business** In his work *Input–Output Economics*, Leontief provides an example of a simplified economy with just three sectors: agriculture, manufacturing, and households (that is, the sector of the economy that produces labor).[*] It has the following input–output matrix:

	Agriculture	Manufacturing	Households
Agriculture	.25	.40	.133
Manufacturing	.14	.12	.100
Households	.80	3.60	.133

   (a) How many units from each sector does the manufacturing sector require to produce 1 unit?

   (b) What production levels are needed to meet a demand of 35 units of agriculture, 38 units of manufacturing, and 40 units of households?

   (c) How many units of agriculture are used up in the economy's production process?

32. **Business** A much simplified version of Leontief's 42-sector analysis of the 1947 American economy has the following input–output matrix:[†]

	Agriculture	Manufacturing	Households
Agriculture	.245	.102	.051
Manufacturing	.099	.291	.279
Households	.433	.372	.011

   (a) What information about the needs of agricultural production is given by column 1 of the matrix?

(b) Suppose the demand matrix (in billions of dollars) is

$$D = \begin{bmatrix} 2.88 \\ 31.45 \\ 30.91 \end{bmatrix}.$$

Find the amount of each commodity that should be produced.

33. **Business** An analysis of the 1958 Israeli economy is simplified here by grouping the economy into three sectors, with the following input–output matrix:[‡]

	Agriculture	Manufacturing	Energy
Agriculture	.293	0	0
Manufacturing	.014	.207	.017
Energy	.044	.010	.216

   (a) How many units from each sector does the energy sector require to produce one unit?

   (b) If the economy's production (in thousands of Israeli pounds) is 175,000 of agriculture, 22,000 of manufacturing, and 12,000 of energy, how much is available from each sector to satisfy the demand from consumers and others outside the production process?

   (c) The actual 1958 demand matrix is

$$D = \begin{bmatrix} 138,213 \\ 17,597 \\ 1786 \end{bmatrix}.$$

How much must each sector produce to meet this demand?

34. **Business** The 1981 Chinese economy can be simplified to three sectors: agriculture, industry and construction, and transportation and commerce.[§] The input–output matrix is

	Agri.	Industry/Constr.	Trans./Commerce
Agri.	.158	.156	.009
Industry/Constr.	.136	.432	.071
Trans./Commerce	.013	.041	.011

   The demand [in 100,000 *renminbi* (RMB), the unit of money in China] is

$$D = \begin{bmatrix} 106,674 \\ 144,739 \\ 26,725 \end{bmatrix}.$$

   (a) Find the amount each sector should produce.

   (b) Interpret the economic value of an increase in demand of 1 RMB in agriculture exports.

35. **Business** The 1987 economy of the state of Washington has been simplified to four sectors: natural resource, manufacturing,

[*]Wassily Leontief, *Input–Output Economics*, 2d ed. (Oxford University Press, 1986), pp. 19–27.

[†]Ibid., pp. 6–9.

[‡]Ibid., pp. 174–175.

[§]*Input–Output Tables of China: 1981*, China Statistical Information and Consultancy Service Centre, 1987, pp. 17–19.

trade and services, and personal consumption. The input–output matrix is as follows:[*]

	Natural Resources	Manufacturing	Trade and Services	Personal Consumption
Natural Resources	.1045	.0428	.0029	.0031
Manufacturing	.0826	.1087	.0584	.0321
Trade and Services	.0867	.1019	.2032	.3555
Personal Consumption	.6253	.3448	.6106	.0798

Suppose the demand (in millions of dollars) is

$$D = \begin{bmatrix} 450 \\ 300 \\ 125 \\ 100 \end{bmatrix}.$$

Find the amount each sector should produce.

36. Business The 1963 economy of the state of Nebraska has been condensed to six sectors; livestock, crops, food products, mining and manufacturing, households, and other. The input–output matrix is as follows:[†]

$$\begin{bmatrix} .178 & .018 & .411 & 0 & .005 & 0 \\ .143 & .018 & .088 & 0 & .001 & 0 \\ .089 & 0 & .035 & 0 & .060 & .003 \\ .001 & .010 & .012 & .063 & .007 & .014 \\ .141 & .252 & .088 & .089 & .402 & .124 \\ .188 & .156 & .103 & .255 & .008 & .474 \end{bmatrix}.$$

(a) Find the matrix $(I - A)^{-1}$ and interpret the value in row two, column one, of this matrix.

(b) Suppose the demand (in millions of dollars) is

$$D = \begin{bmatrix} 1980 \\ 650 \\ 1750 \\ 1000 \\ 2500 \\ 3750 \end{bmatrix}.$$

Find the dollar amount each sector should produce.

37. Business Input–output analysis can also be used to model how changes in one city can affect cities that are connected with it in some way. For example, if a large manufacturing company shuts down in one city, it is very likely that the economic welfare of all of the cities around it will suffer. Consider three Pennsylvania communities: Sharon, Farrell, and Hermitage.

Due to their proximity to each other, residents of these three communities regularly spend time and money in the other communities. Suppose that we have gathered information in the form of an input–output matrix

$$\begin{bmatrix} .2 & .1 & .1 \\ .1 & .1 & 0 \\ .5 & .6 & .7 \end{bmatrix}.$$

This matrix can be thought of as the likelihood that a person from a particular community will spend money in each of the communities.[‡]

(a) Treat this matrix like an input–output matrix and calculate $(I - A)^{-1}$, where A is the given input–output matrix.

(b) Interpret the entries of this inverse matrix.

38. Social Science Use the method discussed in this section to encode the message

Anne is home.

Break the message into groups of two letters and use the matrix

$$M = \begin{bmatrix} 1 & 3 \\ 2 & 7 \end{bmatrix}.$$

39. Social Science Use the matrix of Exercise 38 to encode the message

Head for the hills!

40. Social Science Decode the following message, which was encoded by using the matrix M of Exercise 38:

$$\begin{bmatrix} 90 \\ 207 \end{bmatrix}, \begin{bmatrix} 39 \\ 87 \end{bmatrix}, \begin{bmatrix} 26 \\ 57 \end{bmatrix}, \begin{bmatrix} 66 \\ 145 \end{bmatrix}, \begin{bmatrix} 61 \\ 142 \end{bmatrix}, \begin{bmatrix} 89 \\ 205 \end{bmatrix}.$$

Work these routing problems.

41. Social Science Use matrix A in the discussion on routing (pages 324–325) to find A^2. Then answer the following questions: How many ways are there to travel from

(a) city 1 to city 3 by passing through exactly one city?

(b) city 2 to city 4 by passing through exactly one city?

(c) city 1 to city 3 by passing through at most one city?

(d) city 2 to city 4 by passing through at most one city?

42. Social Science The matrix A^3 (see Exercise 41) was found in Checkpoint 9 of the text. Use it to answer the following questions.

(a) How many ways are there to travel between cities 1 and 4 by passing through exactly two cities?

(b) How many ways are there to travel between cities 1 and 4 by passing through at most two cities?

43. Business A small telephone system connects three cities. There are four lines between cities 3 and 2, three lines connecting city 3 with city 1, and two lines between cities 1 and 2.

(a) Write a matrix B to represent this information.

(b) Find B^2.

[*]Robert Chase, Philip Bourque, and Richard Conway, Jr., *The 1987 Washington State Input–Output Study*, Report to the Graduate School of Business Administration, University of Washington, September 1993.

[†]F. Charles Lamphear and Theodore Roesler, "1970 Nebraska Input–Output Tables," *Nebraska Economic and Business Report No. 10*, Bureau of Business Research, University of Nebraska, Lincoln.

[‡]The idea for this problem came from an example created by Thayer Watkins, Department of Economics, San Jose State University.

(c) How many lines that connect cities 1 and 2 go through exactly one other city (city 3)?

(d) How many lines that connect cities 1 and 2 go through at most one other city?

44. Business The figure shows four southern cities served by Supersouth Airlines.

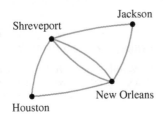

(a) Write a matrix to represent the number of nonstop routes between cities.

(b) Find the number of one-stop flights between Houston and Jackson.

(c) Find the number of flights between Houston and Shreveport that require at most one stop.

(d) Find the number of one-stop flights between New Orleans and Houston.

45. Natural Science The figure shows a food web. The arrows indicate the food sources of each population. For example, cats feed on rats and on mice.

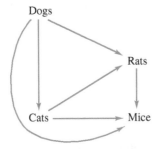

(a) Write a matrix C in which each row and corresponding column represent a population in the food chain. Enter a 1 when the population in a given row feeds on the population in the given column.

(b) Calculate and interpret C^2.

✓ Checkpoint Answers

1. $A = \begin{bmatrix} 2 & 6 \\ -1 & -2 \end{bmatrix}$, $X = \begin{bmatrix} x \\ y \end{bmatrix}$, and $B = \begin{bmatrix} -14 \\ 3 \end{bmatrix}$.

2. $(6, -4, 10)$

3. $(3 - 1.5y, y)$ for all real numbers y

4.

	Elec.	Water
Elec.	$\frac{1}{3}$	$\frac{1}{4}$
Water	$\frac{1}{2}$	0

5. (a) $\begin{bmatrix} 9000 \\ 12{,}000 \end{bmatrix}$ **(b)** $\begin{bmatrix} 6000 \\ 4500 \end{bmatrix}$ **(c)** $\begin{bmatrix} 3000 \\ 7500 \end{bmatrix}$

6. (a) $\begin{bmatrix} \frac{1}{2} & \frac{3}{4} \\ \frac{1}{2} & 0 \end{bmatrix}$ **(b)** $\begin{bmatrix} \frac{1}{2} & -\frac{3}{4} \\ -\frac{1}{2} & 1 \end{bmatrix}$

(c) $\begin{bmatrix} 8 & 6 \\ 4 & 4 \end{bmatrix}$ **(d)** $\begin{bmatrix} 6800 \\ 4400 \end{bmatrix}$

7. $\begin{bmatrix} 23 \\ 8 \end{bmatrix}, \begin{bmatrix} 5 \\ 14 \end{bmatrix}$

8. $\begin{bmatrix} 54 \\ 115 \end{bmatrix}, \begin{bmatrix} 24 \\ 25 \end{bmatrix}$

9. (a) $[A]^3$
```
[18  26  16  16  26]
[26  12  13   9  16]
[16  13   6  10   9]
[16   9  10   6  13]
[26  16   9  13  12]
```

(b) $[A]+[A]^2$
```
[10   5   4   4   5]
[ 5   6   3   4   5]
[ 4   3   3   2   4]
[ 4   4   2   3   3]
[ 5   5   4   3   6]
```

CHAPTER 6 Summary and Review

Key Terms and Symbols

6.1 linear equation
system of linear equations
solution of a system
substitution method
elimination method
independent system
dependent system
inconsistent system

6.2 equivalent systems
elementary operations
elimination method
row

column
matrix (matrices)
element (entry)
augmented matrix
row operations
row echelon form
Gauss–Jordan method
reduced row echelon form
independent system
inconsistent system
dependent system
parameter

6.3 applications of systems of
linear equations

6.4 row matrix (row vector)
column matrix (column
vector)
square matrix
additive inverse of a
matrix
zero matrix
scalar
product of a scalar and a
matrix

6.5 product matrix
identity matrix
inverse matrix
singular matrix

6.6 coefficient matrix
input–output analysis
input–output matrix
production matrix
demand matrix
code theory
routing theory

Chapter 6 Key Concepts

Solving Systems of Equations

The following **elementary operations** are used to transform a system of equations into a simpler equivalent system:

1. Interchange any two equations.
2. Multiply both sides of an equation by a nonzero constant.
3. Replace an equation by the sum of itself and a constant multiple of another equation in the system.

The **elimination method** is a systematic way of using elementary operations to transform a system into an equivalent one that can be solved by **back substitution.** See Section 6.2 for details.

The matrix version of the elimination method uses the following **matrix row operations,** which correspond to using elementary row operations with back substitution on a system of equations:

1. Interchange any two rows.
2. Multiply each element of a row by a nonzero constant.
3. Replace a row by the sum of itself and a constant multiple of another row in the matrix.

The **Gauss–Jordan method** is an extension of the elimination method for solving a system of linear equations. It uses row operations on the augmented matrix of the system. See Section 6.2 for details.

Operations on Matrices

The **sum** of two $m \times n$ matrices X and Y is the $m \times n$ matrix $X + Y$ in which each element is the sum of the corresponding elements of X and Y. The **difference** of two $m \times n$ matrices X and Y is the $m \times n$ matrix $X - Y$ in which each element is the difference of the corresponding elements of X and Y.

The **product** of a scalar k and a matrix X is the matrix kX, with each element being k times the corresponding element of X.

The **product matrix** AB of an $m \times n$ matrix A and an $n \times k$ matrix B is the $m \times k$ matrix whose entry in the ith row and jth column is the product of the ith row of A and the jth column of B.

The **inverse matrix** A^{-1} for any $n \times n$ matrix A for which A^{-1} exists is found as follows: Form the augmented matrix $[A\,|\,I]$, and perform row operations on $[A\,|\,I]$ to get the matrix $[I\,|\,A^{-1}]$.

Chapter 6 Review Exercises

Solve each of the following systems.

1. $-5x - 3y = -3$
   $2x + y = 4$

2. $3x - y = 8$
   $2x + 3y = 6$

3. $3x - 5y = 16$
   $2x + 3y = -2$

4. $\dfrac{1}{4}x - \dfrac{1}{3}y = -\dfrac{1}{4}$
   $\dfrac{1}{10}x + \dfrac{2}{5}y = \dfrac{2}{5}$

5. Business Abigail Henderson plans to buy shares of two stocks. One costs \$32 per share and pays dividends of \$1.20 per share. The other costs \$23 per share and pays dividends of \$1.40 per share. She has \$10,100 to spend and wants to earn dividends of \$540. How many shares of each stock should she buy?

6. Business Emma Henderson has money in two investment funds. Last year, the first fund paid a dividend of 8% and the second a dividend of 2%, and she received a total of \$780. This year, the first fund paid a 10% dividend and the second only 1%, and she received \$810. How much does she have invested in each fund?

Solve each of the following systems.

7. $x - 2y = 1$
   $4x + 4y = 2$
   $10x + 8y = 4$

8. $4x - y - 2z = 4$
   $x - y - \dfrac{1}{2}z = 1$
   $2x - y - z = 8$

9. $3x + y - z = 3$
   $x \quad\;\; + 2z = 6$
   $-3x - y + 2z = 9$

10. $x + y - 4z = 0$
   $2x + y - 3z = 2$

Solve each of the following systems by using matrix methods.

11. $x + \;\; z = -3$
   $y - z = 6$
   $2x + 3z = 5$

12. $2x + 3y + 4z = 8$
   $-x + y - 2z = -9$
   $2x + 2y + 6z = 16$

13. $x - 2y + 5z = 3$
   $4x + 3y - 4z = 1$
   $3x + 5y - 9z = 7$

14. $5x - 8y + z = 1$
   $3x - 2y + 4z = 3$
   $10x - 16y + 2z = 3$

15. $x - 2y + 3z = 4$
   $2x + y - 4z = 3$
   $-3x + 4y - z = -2$

16. $3x + 2y - 6z = 3$
   $x + y + 2z = 2$
   $2x + 2y + 5z = 0$

17. Finance You are given \$144 in one-, five-, and ten-dollar bills. There are 35 bills. There are two more ten-dollar bills than five-dollar bills. How many bills of each type are there?

18. Social Science A social service agency provides counseling, meals, and shelter to clients referred by sources I, II, and III. Clients from source I require an average of \$100 for food, \$250 for shelter, and no counseling. Source II clients require an average of \$100 for counseling, \$200 for food, and nothing for shelter. Source III clients require an average of $100 for counseling, $150 for food, and $200 for shelter. The agency has funding of $25,000 for counseling, $50,000 for food, and $32,500 for shelter. How many clients from each source can be served?

19. Business A small business makes woven blankets, rugs, and skirts. Each blanket requires 24 hours for spinning the yarn, 4 hours for dying the yarn, and 15 hours for weaving. Rugs require 30, 5, and 18 hours, and skirts require 12, 3, and 9 hours, respectively. If there are 306, 59, and 201 hours available for spinning, dying, and weaving, respectively, how many of each item can be made? (*Hint:* Simplify the equations you write, if possible, before solving the system.)

20. Business Each week at a furniture factory, 2000 work hours are available in the construction department, 1400 work hours in the painting department, and 1300 work hours in the packing department. Producing a chair requires 2 hours of construction, 1 hour of painting, and 2 hours for packing. Producing a table requires 4 hours of construction, 3 hours of painting, and 3 hours for packing. Producing a chest requires 8 hours of construction, 6 hours of painting, and 4 hours for packing. If all available time is used in every department, how many of each item are produced each week?

For each of the following, find the dimensions of the matrix and identify any square, row, or column matrices.

21. $\begin{bmatrix} 2 & 3 \\ 5 & 9 \end{bmatrix}$

22. $\begin{bmatrix} 2 & -1 \\ 4 & 6 \\ 5 & 7 \end{bmatrix}$

23. $[12 \quad 4 \quad -8 \quad -1]$

24. $\begin{bmatrix} -7 & 5 & 6 & 4 \\ 3 & 2 & -1 & 2 \\ -1 & 12 & 8 & -1 \end{bmatrix}$

25. $\begin{bmatrix} 6 & 8 & 10 \\ 5 & 3 & -2 \end{bmatrix}$

26. $\begin{bmatrix} -9 \\ 15 \\ 4 \end{bmatrix}$

27. Finance The closing stock price, change in price, and volume of stocks traded for the following companies were reported on January 3, 2013: Apple Inc.: $542.10; −$6.93; and 12,605,900. Nike Inc.: $52.37; $.53; and 3,616,100. Verizon Communications Inc.: $44.06; −$.21; and 11,227,700. Write these data as a 3 × 3 matrix. (Data from: www.morningstar.com.)

28. Natural Science The activities of a grazing animal can be classified roughly into three categories: grazing, moving, and resting. Suppose horses spend 8 hours grazing, 8 moving, and 8 resting; cattle spend 10 grazing, 5 moving, and 9 resting; sheep spend 7 grazing, 10 moving, and 7 resting; and goats spend 8 grazing, 9 moving, and 7 resting. Write this information as a 4 × 3 matrix.

Given the matrices

$A = \begin{bmatrix} 4 & 6 \\ -2 & -2 \\ 5 & 9 \end{bmatrix}$, $B = \begin{bmatrix} 1 & 2 & -3 \\ 2 & 3 & 0 \\ 0 & 1 & 4 \end{bmatrix}$, $C = \begin{bmatrix} 5 & 0 \\ -1 & 3 \\ 4 & 7 \end{bmatrix}$,

$D = \begin{bmatrix} 6 \\ 1 \\ 0 \end{bmatrix}$, $E = [1 \quad 3 \quad -4]$, $F = \begin{bmatrix} -1 & 2 \\ 6 & 7 \end{bmatrix}$, *and*

$G = \begin{bmatrix} 2 & 5 \\ 1 & 6 \end{bmatrix}$,

find each of the following (if possible).

29. $-B$ **30.** $-D$ **31.** $A + 2C$ **32.** $F + 3G$

33. $2B - 5C$ **34.** $D + E$ **35.** $3A - 2C$ **36.** $G - 2F$

37. Finance Refer to Exercise 27. Write a 3 × 2 matrix giving just the change in price and volume data for the three companies. The next day's changes in price and volume for the same three companies were: −$15.10 and 21,226,200; $.51 and 3,397,000; $.24 and 14,930,400. Write a 3 × 2 matrix to represent these new price change and volume figures. Use matrix addition to find the total change in price and volume of stock traded for the two days. (Data from: www.morningstar.com.)

38. Business An oil refinery in Tulsa sent 110,000 gallons of oil to a Chicago distributor, 73,000 to a Dallas distributor, and 95,000 to an Atlanta distributor. Another refinery in New Orleans sent the following respective amounts to the same three distributors: 85,000, 108,000, and 69,000. The next month, the two refineries sent the same distributors new shipments of oil as follows: from Tulsa, 58,000 to Chicago, 33,000 to Dallas, and 80,000 to Atlanta; from New Orleans, 40,000, 52,000, and 30,000, respectively.

(a) Write the monthly shipments from the two distributors to the three refineries as 3 × 2 matrices.

(b) Use matrix addition to find the total amounts sent to the refineries from each distributor.

Use the matrices shown before Exercise 29 to find each of the following (if possible).

39. AG **40.** EB **41.** GA

42. CA **43.** AGF **44.** EBD

45. Health In a study, the numbers of head and neck injuries among hockey players wearing full face shields and half face shields were compared. Injury rates were recorded per 1000 athlete exposures for specific injuries that caused a player to miss one or more events.[*]

Players wearing a half shield had the following rates of injury:

Head and face injuries, excluding concussions: 3.54; Concussions: 1.53; Neck injuries: .34; Other injuries: 7.53.

Players wearing a full shield had the following injury rates:

Head and face injuries, excluding concussions: 1.41; Concussions: 1.57; Neck injuries: .29; Other injuries: 6.21.

[*]Brian Benson, Nicholas Nohtadi, Sarah Rose, and Willem Meeuwisse, "Head and Neck Injuries among Ice Hockey Players Wearing Full Face Shields vs. Half Face Shields," *JAMA*, 282, no. 24, (December 22/29, 1999): 2328–2332.

If an equal number of players in a large league wear each type of shield and the total number of athlete exposures for the league in a season is 8000, use matrix operations to estimate the total number of injuries of each type.

46. **Business** An office supply manufacturer makes two kinds of paper clips: standard and extra large. To make a unit of standard paper clips requires $\frac{1}{4}$ hour on a cutting machine and $\frac{1}{2}$ hour on a machine that shapes the clips. A unit of extra-large paper clips requires $\frac{1}{3}$ hour on each machine.

   (a) Write this information as a 2×2 matrix (size/machine).

   (b) If 48 units of standard and 66 units of extra-large clips are to be produced, use matrix multiplication to find out how many hours each machine will operate. (*Hint:* Write the units as a 1×2 matrix.)

47. **Finance** The cost per share of stock was $61.17 for Coca-Cola Bottling Co. Consolidated, $60.50 for Starbucks Corporation, and $96.21 for Anheuser-Busch, as reported on April 26, 2013. The dividend per share was $1.00, $.84, and $1.88, respectively. Your stock portfolio consists of 100 shares of Coca-Cola, 500 shares of Starbucks, and 200 shares of Anheuser-Busch. (Data from: www.morningstar.com.)

   (a) Write the cost per share and dividend per share data as a 3×2 matrix.

   (b) Write the number of shares of each stock as a 1×3 matrix.

   (c) Use matrix multiplication to find the total cost and total dividend earnings of this portfolio.

48. **Finance** Matthew's stock portfolio consists of 4000 shares of The New York Times Company, 1000 shares of Coffee Holding Co. Inc., 5000 shares of Barnes & Noble Inc., and 2000 shares of Columbia Sportswear Company. On April 26, 2013, the cost per share for each of these stocks was $9.45, $6.59, $18.21, and $60.70, respectively, and the dividend per share for each of these stocks was $0, $.24, $0, and $.88, respectively. (Data from: www.morningstar.com.)

   (a) Write the cost per share and dividend per share data as a 4×2 matrix.

   (b) Write the number of shares of each stock as a 1×4 matrix.

   (c) Use matrix multiplication to find the total cost and total dividend earnings of this portfolio.

49. If $A = \begin{bmatrix} 3 & 0 \\ 2 & 1 \end{bmatrix}$, find a matrix B such that both AB and BA are defined and $AB \neq BA$.

50. Is it possible to do Exercise 49 if $A = \begin{bmatrix} 4 & 0 \\ 0 & 4 \end{bmatrix}$? Explain.

Find the inverse of each of the following matrices, if an inverse exists for that matrix.

51. $\begin{bmatrix} -2 & 2 \\ 0 & 5 \end{bmatrix}$

52. $\begin{bmatrix} 3 & -1 \\ -5 & 2 \end{bmatrix}$

53. $\begin{bmatrix} 6 & 4 \\ 3 & 2 \end{bmatrix}$

54. $\begin{bmatrix} 15 & -12 \\ 5 & -4 \end{bmatrix}$

55. $\begin{bmatrix} 2 & 0 & 6 \\ 1 & -1 & 0 \\ 0 & 1 & -3 \end{bmatrix}$

56. $\begin{bmatrix} 2 & -1 & 0 \\ 1 & 0 & 2 \\ 1 & -4 & 0 \end{bmatrix}$

57. $\begin{bmatrix} 2 & 3 & 5 \\ -2 & -3 & -5 \\ 1 & 4 & 2 \end{bmatrix}$

58. $\begin{bmatrix} 1 & 3 & 6 \\ 4 & 0 & 9 \\ 5 & 15 & 30 \end{bmatrix}$

59. $\begin{bmatrix} 1 & 3 & -2 & -1 \\ 0 & 1 & 1 & 2 \\ -1 & -1 & 1 & -1 \\ 1 & -1 & -3 & -2 \end{bmatrix}$

60. $\begin{bmatrix} 3 & 2 & 0 & -1 \\ 2 & 0 & 1 & 2 \\ 1 & 2 & -1 & 0 \\ 2 & -1 & 1 & 1 \end{bmatrix}$

Refer again to the matrices shown before Exercise 29 to find each of the following (if possible).

61. F^{-1}

62. G^{-1}

63. $(G - F)^{-1}$

64. $(F + G)^{-1}$

65. B^{-1}

66. Explain why the matrix $\begin{bmatrix} a & 0 \\ c & 0 \end{bmatrix}$, where a and c are nonzero constants, cannot have an inverse.

Solve each of the following matrix equations $AX = B$ for X.

67. $A = \begin{bmatrix} -3 & 4 \\ -1 & 2 \end{bmatrix}$, $B = \begin{bmatrix} 3 \\ -1 \end{bmatrix}$

68. $A = \begin{bmatrix} 1 & 3 \\ -2 & 4 \end{bmatrix}$, $B = \begin{bmatrix} 9 \\ 6 \end{bmatrix}$

69. $A = \begin{bmatrix} 1 & 0 & 2 \\ -1 & 1 & 0 \\ 3 & 0 & 4 \end{bmatrix}$, $B = \begin{bmatrix} 8 \\ 4 \\ -6 \end{bmatrix}$

70. $A = \begin{bmatrix} 2 & 4 & 0 \\ 1 & -2 & 0 \\ 0 & 0 & 3 \end{bmatrix}$, $B = \begin{bmatrix} 72 \\ -24 \\ 48 \end{bmatrix}$

Use the method of matrix inverses to solve each of the following systems.

71. $x + y = -2$
    $2x + 5y = 2$

72. $5x - 3y = -2$
    $2x + 7y = -9$

73. $2x + y = 10$
    $3x - 2y = 8$

74. $x - 2y = 7$
    $3x + y = 7$

75. $x + y + z = 1$
    $2x - y = -2$
    $3y + z = 2$

76. $x = -3$
    $y + z = 6$
    $2x - 3z = -9$

77. $3x - 2y + 4z = 4$
    $4x + y - 5z = 2$
    $-6x + 4y - 8z = -2$

78. $-2x + 3y - z = 1$
    $5x - 7y + 8z = 4$
    $6x - 9y + 3z = 2$

Solve each of the following problems by any method.

79. **Business** A wine maker has two large casks of wine. One is 9% alcohol and the other is 14% alcohol. How many liters of

each wine should be mixed to produce 40 liters of wine that is 12% alcohol?

80. Business A gold merchant has some 12-carat gold (12/24 pure gold) and some 22-carat gold (22/24 pure). How many grams of each could be mixed to get 25 grams of 15-carat gold?

81. Natural Science A chemist has a 40% acid solution and a 60% solution. How many liters of each should be used to get 40 liters of a 45% solution?

82. Business How many pounds of tea worth $4.60 a pound should be mixed with tea worth $6.50 a pound to get 10 pounds of a mixture worth $5.74 a pound?

83. Business A machine in a pottery factory takes 3 minutes to form a bowl and 2 minutes to form a plate. The material for a bowl costs $.25, and the material for a plate costs $.20. If the machine runs for 8 hours and exactly $44 is spent for material, how many bowls and plates can be produced?

84. Physical Science A boat travels at a constant speed a distance of 57 kilometers downstream in 3 hours and then turns around and travels 55 kilometers upstream in 5 hours. What are the speeds of the boat and the current?

85. Business Henry Miller invests $50,000 three ways—at 8%, $8\frac{1}{2}$%, and 11%. In total, he receives $4436.25 per year in interest. The interest on the 11% investment is $80 more than the interest on the 8% investment. Find the amount he has invested at each rate.

86. Business Tickets to the homecoming football game cost $4 for students, $10 for alumni, $12 for other adults, and $6 for children. The total attendance was 3750, and the ticket receipts were $29,100. Six times more students than children attended. The number of alumni was $\frac{4}{5}$ of the number of students. How many students, alumni, other adults, and children were at the game?

87. Given the input–output matrix $A = \begin{bmatrix} 0 & \frac{1}{4} \\ \frac{1}{2} & 0 \end{bmatrix}$ and the demand matrix $D = \begin{bmatrix} 2100 \\ 1400 \end{bmatrix}$, find each of the following.

(a) $I - A$

(b) $(I - A)^{-1}$

(c) The production matrix X

88. Business An economy depends on two commodities: goats and cheese. It takes $\frac{2}{3}$ unit of goats to produce 1 unit of cheese and $\frac{1}{2}$ unit of cheese to produce 1 unit of goats.

(a) Write the input–output matrix for this economy.

(b) Find the production required to satisfy a demand of 400 units of cheese and 800 units of goats.

✎ *Use technology to do Exercises 89–91.*

89. Business In a simple economic model, a country has two industries: agriculture and manufacturing. To produce $1 of agricultural output requires $.10 of agricultural output and $.40 of manufacturing output. To produce $1 of manufacturing output

requires $.70 of agricultural output and $.20 of manufacturing output. If agricultural demand is $60,000 and manufacturing demand is $20,000, what must each industry produce? (Round answers to the nearest whole number.)

90. Business Here is the input–output matrix for a small economy:

	Agriculture	Services	Mining	Manufacturing
Agriculture	.02	.9	0	.001
Services	0	.4	0	.06
Mining	.01	.02	.06	.07
Manufacturing	.25	.9	.9	.4

(a) How many units from each sector does the service sector require to produce 1 unit?

(b) What production levels are needed to meet a demand for 760 units of agriculture, 1600 units of services, 1000 units of mining, and 2000 units of manufacturing?

(c) How many units of manufacturing production are used up in the economy's production process?

91. Use this input–output matrix to answer the questions below.

	Agriculture	Construction	Energy	Manufacturing	Transportation
Agriculture	.18	.017	.4	.005	0
Construction	.14	.018	.09	.001	0
Energy	.9	0	.4	.06	.002
Manufacturing	.19	.16	.1	.008	.5
Transportation	.14	.25	.9	.4	.12

(a) How many units from each sector does the energy sector require to produce 1 unit?

(b) If the economy produces 28,067 units of agriculture, 9383 units of construction, 51,372 units of energy, 61,364 units of manufacturing, and 90,403 units of transportation, how much is available from each sector to satisfy the demand from consumers and others outside the production system?

(c) A new demand matrix for the economy is

$$\begin{bmatrix} 2400 \\ 850 \\ 1400 \\ 3200 \\ 1800 \end{bmatrix}.$$

How much must each sector produce to meet this demand?

92. Business The following matrix represents the number of direct flights between four cities:

$$\begin{array}{c} \\ A \\ B \\ C \\ D \end{array} \begin{array}{c} A\ B\ C\ D \\ \begin{bmatrix} 0 & 1 & 0 & 1 \\ 1 & 0 & 0 & 1 \\ 0 & 0 & 0 & 1 \\ 1 & 1 & 1 & 0 \end{bmatrix} \end{array}.$$

(a) Find the number of one-stop flights between cities A and C.

(b) Find the total number of flights between cities B and C that are either direct or one stop.

(c) Find the matrix that gives the number of two-stop flights between these cities.

93. Social Science Use the matrix $M = \begin{bmatrix} 2 & 6 \\ 1 & 4 \end{bmatrix}$ to encode the message "leave now."

94. What matrix should be used to decode the answer to the previous exercise?

Case Study 6 Matrix Operations and Airline Route Maps

Airline route maps are usually published on airline Web sites, as well as in in-flight magazines. The purpose of these maps is to show what cities are connected to each other by nonstop flights provided by the airline. We can think of these maps as another type of **graph,** and we can use matrix operations to answer questions of interest about the graph. To study these graphs, a bit of terminology will be helpful. In this context, a **graph** is a set of points called **vertices** or **nodes** and a set of lines called **edges** connecting some pairs of vertices. Two vertices connected by an edge are said to be **adjacent.** Suppose, for example, that Stampede Air is a short-haul airline serving the state of Texas whose route map is shown in Figure 1 below. The vertices are the cities to which Stampede Air flies, and two vertices are connected if there is a nonstop flight between them.

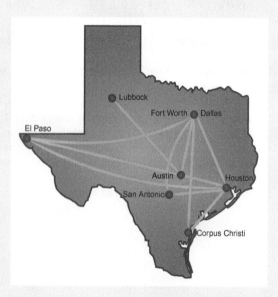

Figure 1 Stampede Air route map

Some natural questions arise about graphs. It might be important to know if two vertices are connected by a sequence of two edges, even if they are not connected by a single edge. In the route map, Huston and Lubbock are connected by a two-edge sequence, meaning that a passenger would have to stop in Austin while flying between those cities on Stampede Air. It might be important to know if it is possible to get from a vertex to another vertex in a given number of flights. In the example, a passenger on Stampede Air can get from any city in the company's network to any other city, given enough flights. But how many flights are enough? This is another issue of interest: What is the minimum number of steps required to get from one vertex to another? What is the minimum number of steps required to get from any vertex on the graph to any other? While these questions are relatively easy to answer for a small graph, as the number of vertices and edges grows, it becomes harder to keep track of all the different ways the vertices are connected. Matrix notation and computation can help to answer these questions.

The **adjacency matrix** for a graph with n vertices is an $n \times n$ matrix whose (i, j) entry is 1 if the ith and jth vertices are connected and 0 if they are not. If the vertices in the Stampede Air graph respectively correspond to Austin (A), El Paso (E), Houston (H), Dallas-Fort Worth (D), San Antonio (S), Corpus Christi (C), and Lubbock (L), then the adjacency matrix for Stampede Air is as follows.

$$A = \begin{array}{c} \\ \\ \\ \\ \end{array} \begin{array}{c} A\ \ E\ \ H\ \ D\ \ S\ \ C\ \ L \\ \begin{bmatrix} 0 & 1 & 1 & 1 & 0 & 0 & 1 \\ 1 & 0 & 1 & 1 & 0 & 0 & 0 \\ 1 & 1 & 0 & 1 & 1 & 1 & 0 \\ 1 & 1 & 1 & 0 & 1 & 1 & 0 \\ 0 & 0 & 1 & 1 & 0 & 0 & 0 \\ 0 & 0 & 1 & 1 & 0 & 0 & 0 \\ 1 & 0 & 0 & 0 & 0 & 0 & 0 \end{bmatrix} \begin{array}{c} A \\ E \\ H \\ D\cdot \\ S \\ C \\ L \end{array} \end{array}$$

Adjacency matrices can be used to address the questions about graphs raised earlier. Which vertices are connected by a two-edge sequence? How many different two-edge sequences connect each pair of vertices? Consider the matrix A^2, which is A multiplied by itself. For example, let the (6, 2) entry in the matrix A^2 be named b_{62}. This entry in A^2 is the product of the 6th row of A and the 2nd column of A, or

$$b_{62} = a_{61}a_{12} + a_{62}a_{22} + a_{63}a_{32} + a_{64}a_{42} + a_{65}a_{52} + a_{66}a_{62} + a_{67}a_{72}$$
$$= 0 \cdot 1 + 0 \cdot 0 + 1 \cdot 1 + 1 \cdot 1 + 0 \cdot 0 + 0 \cdot 0 + 0 \cdot 0$$
$$= 2,$$

which happens to be the number of two-flight sequences that connect city 6 (Corpus Christi) and city 2 (El Paso). A careful look at Figure 1 confirms this fact. This calculation works because, in order for a two-flight sequence to occur between Corpus Christi and El Paso, Corpus Christi and El Paso must each connect to an intermediate city. Since Corpus Christi connects to Houston and Houston connects to El Paso, $a_{63}a_{32} = 1 \cdot 1 = 1$. Thus, there is one two-flight sequence between Corpus Christi and El Paso that passes through Houston. Since Corpus Christi does not connect to Austin (city 1), but Austin does connect with El Paso, $a_{61}a_{12} = 0 \cdot 1 = 0$. Hence, there is no two-flight sequence from Corpus Christi to El Paso that passes through Austin. To find the total number of two-flight sequences between Corpus Christi and El Paso, simply sum over all intermediate points. Notice that this sum, which is

$$a_{61}a_{12} + a_{62}a_{22} + a_{63}a_{32} + a_{64}a_{42} + a_{65}a_{52} + a_{66}a_{62} + a_{67}a_{72},$$

is just b_{62}, the (6, 2) entry in the matrix A^2. So we see that the number of two-step sequences between vertex i and vertex j in a graph with adjacency matrix A is the (i, j) entry in A^2. A more general result is the following:

> **The number of k-step sequences between vertex i and vertex j in a graph with adjacency matrix A is the (i, j) entry in A^k.**

If A is the adjacency matrix for Figure 1, then

$$A^2 = \begin{array}{c} \\ \\ \\ \\ \\ \\ \\ \end{array} \begin{array}{cccccccc} & A & E & H & D & S & C & L \\ \left[\begin{array}{ccccccc} 4 & 2 & 2 & 2 & 2 & 2 & 0 \\ 2 & 3 & 2 & 2 & 2 & 2 & 1 \\ 2 & 2 & 5 & 4 & 1 & 1 & 1 \\ 2 & 2 & 4 & 5 & 1 & 1 & 1 \\ 2 & 2 & 1 & 1 & 2 & 2 & 0 \\ 2 & 2 & 1 & 1 & 2 & 2 & 0 \\ 0 & 1 & 1 & 1 & 0 & 0 & 1 \end{array} \right] & \begin{array}{c} A \\ E \\ H \\ D \\ S \\ C \\ L \end{array} \end{array}$$

and

$$A^3 = \begin{array}{cccccccc} & A & E & H & D & S & C & L \\ \left[\begin{array}{ccccccc} 6 & 8 & 12 & 12 & 4 & 4 & 4 \\ 8 & 6 & 11 & 11 & 4 & 4 & 2 \\ 12 & 11 & 10 & 11 & 9 & 9 & 2 \\ 12 & 11 & 11 & 10 & 9 & 9 & 2 \\ 4 & 4 & 9 & 9 & 2 & 2 & 2 \\ 4 & 4 & 9 & 9 & 2 & 2 & 2 \\ 4 & 2 & 2 & 2 & 2 & 2 & 0 \end{array} \right] & \begin{array}{c} A \\ E \\ H \\ D \\ S \\ C \\ L \end{array} \end{array}.$$

Since the (6, 3) entry in A^2 is 1, there is one two-step sequence from Corpus Christi to Houston. Likewise, there are four three-step

sequences between El Paso and San Antonio, since the (2, 5) entry in A^3 is 4.

In observing the figure, note that some two-step or three-step sequences may not be meaningful. On the Stampede Air route map, Dallas-Fort Worth is reachable in two steps from Austin (via El Paso or Houston), but in reality this does not matter, since there is a non-stop flight between the two cities. A better question to ask of a graph might be, "What is the least number of edges that must be traversed to go from vertex i to vertex j?"

To answer this question, consider the matrix $S_k = A + A^2 + \cdots + A^k$. The (i, j) entry in this matrix tallies the number of ways to get from vertex i to vertex j in k steps or less. If such a trip is impossible, this entry will be zero. Thus, to find the shortest number of steps between the vertices, continue to compute S_k as k increases; the first k for which the (i, j) entry in S_k is nonzero is the shortest number of steps between i and j. Note that although the shortest number of steps may be computed, the method does not determine what those steps are.

Exercises

1. Which Stampede Air cities may be reached by a two-flight sequence from San Antonio? Which may be reached by a three-flight sequence?

2. It was shown previously that there are four three-step sequences between El Paso and San Antonio. Describe these three-step sequences.

3. Which trips in the Stampede Air network take the greatest number of flights?

4. Suppose that Vacation Air is an airline serving Jacksonville, Orlando, West Palm Beach, Miami, and Tampa, Florida. The route map is given in Figure 2. Produce an adjacency matrix B for this map, listing the cities in the order given.

Figure 2 Vacation Air route map

5. Find B^2, the square of the adjacency matrix found in Exercise 4. What does this matrix tell you?

6. Find $B + B^2$. What can you conclude from this calculation?

Extended Project

Visit the website dir.yahoo.com/business_and_economy/shopping_and_services/travel_and_transportation/airlines/. This site includes links to many obscure and smaller airlines, as well as the more well-known carriers. Find a small regional airline that serves your area and use their route map to produce an adjacency matrix. Determine which trips using this airline take the largest number of flights. How many flights did these trips take? Prepare a report that includes an overview of the airline, the route map, an explanation of the adjacency matrix, and your findings about which trips take the largest number of flights.

Solutions to Prerequisite Skills Test and Calculus Readiness Test

Prerequisite Skills Test

1. We must find a common denominator before subtracting. Since 6 can be written as a fraction as $\frac{6}{1}$, then 2 can be the common denominator.

$$\frac{5}{2} - 6 = \frac{5}{2} - \frac{6}{1}$$

$$= \frac{5}{2} - \frac{6(2)}{2} = \frac{5}{2} - \frac{12}{2}$$

$$= \frac{5 - 12}{2} = \frac{-7}{2}.$$

2. Division of fraction implies that we multiply by the reciprocal. In this case, we multiply $\frac{1}{2}$ by the reciprocal of $\frac{2}{5}$, which is $\frac{5}{2}$. We obtain

$$\frac{1}{2} \div \frac{2}{5} = \frac{1}{2} \cdot \frac{5}{2} = \frac{1 \cdot 5}{2 \cdot 2} = \frac{5}{4}.$$

3. We rewrite 3 as a fraction as $\frac{3}{1}$ and then multiply by the reciprocal.

$$\frac{1}{3} \div \frac{3}{1} = \frac{1}{3} \cdot \frac{1}{3} = \frac{1 \cdot 1}{3 \cdot 3} = \frac{1}{9}.$$

4. We perform the operation inside the parenthesis first. We have

$$2 \div 6 = \frac{2}{6} = \frac{1}{3}.$$

Thus,

$$7 + 2 - 3(2 \div 6) = 7 + 2 - 3\left(\frac{1}{3}\right).$$

We then perform the multiplication and see that

$$3\left(\frac{1}{3}\right) = \frac{3}{1} \cdot \frac{1}{3} = \frac{3(1)}{1(3)} = \frac{3}{3} = 1.$$

So we now have

$$7 + 2 - 3\left(\frac{1}{3}\right) = 7 + 2 - 1.$$

Performing addition and subtraction from left to right, we obtain $9 - 1 = 8$.

5. We begin by performing the multiplication on the numerator. We obtain

$$\frac{2 \times 3 + 12}{1 + 5} - 1 = \frac{6 + 12}{1 + 5} - 1.$$

Next, we perform addition in the numerator and addition in the denominator.

$$\frac{6 + 12}{1 + 5} - 1 = \frac{18}{6} - 1.$$

Next, we perform the division and realize that $\frac{18}{6} = 3$, to obtain $3 - 1 = 2$.

6. False. We add the numerator values together to obtain

$$\frac{4 + 3}{3} = \frac{7}{3} \neq 5.$$

7. False. We obtain a common denominator of 35 to obtain

$$\frac{5}{7} + \frac{7}{5} = \frac{5(5)}{35} + \frac{7(7)}{35} = \frac{25}{35} + \frac{49}{35} = \frac{25 + 49}{35} = \frac{74}{35} \neq 1.$$

8. False. We write 1 as a fraction with the same denominator as $\frac{3}{5}$, namely $1 = \frac{5}{5}$. Thus, we have

$$\frac{3}{5} + 1 = \frac{3}{5} + \frac{5}{5} = \frac{8}{5} \neq \frac{6}{5}.$$

9. Since n represents the number of shoes that Alicia has, we can add 2 to n to obtain the number of shoes for Manuel. Thus we are looking for the expression $n + 2$ for the number of shoes for Manuel.

10. We can say x represents David's age. Since Selina's age is 6 more than David, Selina's age is $x + 6$. The two ages together then are

$$x + (x + 6) = 42.$$

If we combine like terms, we have

$$2x + 6 = 42.$$

We can solve for x by adding -6 to each side to obtain

$$2x + 6 - 6 = 42 - 6$$
$$2x = 36.$$

We then divide each side by 2 to obtain

$$x = 18.$$

Thus, David's age is 18 and Selina's age is $18 + 6 = 24$.

11. If the sweater is reduced by 20%, then its sale price is $100 - 20 = 80\%$ of the original price. To obtain the new price we first convert 80% to a decimal to obtain .80 and then multiply by the price of the sweater to obtain

$$.80(\$72) = \$57.60$$

12. When we plot points, the first coordinate is the value for the x-axis and the second value is for the y-axis. For points A, B, and C, we obtain

13. Similarly, we plot points D, E, and F to obtain

14. (a) 4.27659 has a value of 2 in the tenths place, and the value after that is 7, so we round up to obtain 4.3 to the nearest tenth.

(b) 245.984 has a 5 in the units place and a 9 in the tenths place, so we round up the units place to obtain 246 to the nearest unit.

15. (a) 16.38572 has an 8 in the hundredths place and a 5 in the thousandths place, so we round up to obtain 16.39 to the nearest hundredth.

(b) 1,763,304.42 has a 3 in the thousands place and the following digit is also a 3, so we do not round up and obtain 1,763,000 rounded to the nearest thousand.

16. (a) Writing 34 million dollars as a numerical value is $34 \cdot 1,000,000 = \$34,000,000$.

(b) Writing 2.2 thousand dollars as a numerical value is $2.2 \cdot 1000 = \$2,200$.

17. (a) 17 hundred thousand as a numerical value is $17 \cdot 100,000 = 1,700,000$.

(b) Three and a quarter billion as a numerical value is $3.25 \cdot 1,000,000,000 = 3,250,000,000$.

18. There is no solution to $\dfrac{5}{0}$ because a 0 in the denominator indicates the fraction is undefined.

19. Yes, it is. If a car is traveling 60 miles in one hour, it is traveling 60 miles in 60 minutes, which equates to 1 mile per minute.

20. -9 is greater than -900.

Calculus Readiness Test

1. $(7x^4 - 8x^3 + 2x^2 - 3) - (9x^4 - 2x^2 + 5x + 6)$
$= (7x^4 - 9x^4) + (-8x^3 - 0) + (2x^2 - (-2x^2)) + (0 - 5x) + (-3 - 6)$
$= -2x^4 - 8x^3 + 4x^2 - 5x - 9$
(See Section 1.2, Example 7.)

2. $\dfrac{-6}{3x + 4} + \dfrac{2}{x} = \dfrac{-6}{3x + 4} \cdot \dfrac{x}{x} + \dfrac{2}{x} \cdot \dfrac{3x + 4}{3x + 4} = \dfrac{-6x}{x(3x + 4)} + \dfrac{2(3x + 4)}{x(3x + 4)}$
$= \dfrac{-6x}{3x^2 + 4x} + \dfrac{6x + 8}{3x^2 + 4x} = \dfrac{8}{3x^2 + 4x}$
(See Section 1.4, Example 5.)

3. $(3x + 7)(5x - 8) = (3x)(5x) + (3x)(-8) + (7)(5x) + (7)(-8)$
$= 15x^2 - 24x + 35x - 56 = 15x^2 + 11x - 56$
(See Section 1.2, Example 10.)

4. $(7x + 3)(6x^2 + x - 8) = 7x(6x^2 + x - 8) + 3(6x^2 + x - 8)$
$= (42x^3 + 7x^2 - 56x) + (18x^2 + 3x - 24) = 42x^3 + 25x^2 - 53x - 24$
(See Section 1.2, Example 8.)

5. $\dfrac{(x^5y^{-5})^3}{(x^2\sqrt{y})^6} = \dfrac{(x^5)^3(y^{-5})^3}{(x^2)^6(y^{1/2})^6} = \dfrac{x^{15}y^{-15}}{x^{12}y^3} = \dfrac{x^{15}}{x^{12}y^3y^{15}} = \dfrac{x^{15-12}}{y^{3+15}} = \dfrac{x^3}{y^{18}}$

(See Section 1.5, Example 8.)

6. $(8x - 9)^2 = (8x - 9)(8x - 9) = 64x^2 - 72x - 72x + 81 = 64x^2 - 144x + 81$

(See Section 1.2, Example 10.)

7. $9x^2 - 49 = (3x)^2 - 7^2 = (3x + 7)(3x - 7)$

(See Section 1.3, Example 7.)

8. $9x - 4 = 8 + 7(x - 5)$

$\Rightarrow 9x - 4 = 8 + 7x - 35$

$\Rightarrow 9x - 7x = 8 - 35 - (-4)$

$\Rightarrow 2x = -23$

$\Rightarrow x = -\dfrac{23}{2}$

(See Section 1.6, Example 2.)

9. $3x^2 + 2x + 8 = 20x - 7$

$\Rightarrow 3x^2 + 2x - 20x + 8 + 7 = 0$

$\Rightarrow 3x^2 - 18x + 15 = 0$

$\Rightarrow 3(x^2 - 6x + 5) = 0$

$\Rightarrow 3(x - 5)(x - 1) = 0$

$\Rightarrow x - 5 = 0 \quad \text{or} \quad x - 1 = 0$

$\Rightarrow x = 5 \quad \text{or} \quad x = 1$

(See Section 1.7, Example 2.)

10. $x^2 - x - 6 < 0$

First solve $x^2 - x - 6 = 0 \Rightarrow (x + 2)(x - 3) = 0 \Rightarrow x = -2$ or $x = 3$. The numbers -2 and 3 divide the number line into three regions. Test one number in each region to determine that $(x + 2)(x - 3) < 0$ when $-2 < x < 3$.

(See Section 2.5, Example 3.)

11. $5e^{x-3} - 1 = 9$

$\Rightarrow 5e^{x-3} = 10$

$\Rightarrow e^{x-3} = 2$

$\Rightarrow \ln(e^{x-3}) = \ln(2)$

$\Rightarrow x - 3 = \ln(2)$

$\Rightarrow x = \ln(2) + 3$

(See Section 4.4, Example 6.)

12. $\ln(5x + 1) = 2$

$\Rightarrow e^{\ln(5x+1)} = e^2$

$\Rightarrow 5x + 1 = e^2$

$\Rightarrow 5x = e^2 - 1$

$\Rightarrow x = \dfrac{e^2 - 1}{5}$

(See Section 4.4, Example 2.)

13. $f(-2) = 5(-2)^3 - 3(-2)^2 + 9(-2) + 60$

$= 5(-8) - 3(4) + 9(-2) + 60$

$= -40 - 12 - 18 + 60$

$= -10$

(See Section 3.1, Example 8.)

14. $f(x) = 0$

$\Rightarrow 6x^2 - 7x - 20 = 0$

$\Rightarrow (3x + 4)(2x - 5) = 0$

$\Rightarrow 3x + 4 = 0 \quad \text{or} \quad 2x - 5 = 0$

$\Rightarrow x = -4/3 \quad \text{or} \quad x = 5/2$

(See Section 1.7, Example 2.)

15. $y - y_1 = m(x - x_1)$

$\Rightarrow y - (-3) = -5(x - 8)$

$\Rightarrow y + 3 = -5x + 40$

$\Rightarrow y = -5x + 37$

(See Section 2.2, Example 9.)

Answers to Selected Exercises

Chapter 1

Section 1.1 (Page 8)

1. True   **3.** Answers vary with the calculator, but $2{,}508{,}429{,}787/798{,}458{,}000$ is the best.   **5.** Distributive property
7. Identity property of addition   **9.** Associative property of addition
11. Answers vary.   **13.** -39 **15.** -2 **17.** 45.6
19. About $.9167$ **21.** -12 **23.** 0 **25.** 4 **27.** -1
29. $\dfrac{2040}{523}, \dfrac{189}{37}, \sqrt{27}, \dfrac{4587}{691}, 6.735, \sqrt{47}$ **31.** $12 < 18.5$
33. $x \geq 5.7$ **35.** $z \leq 7.5$ **37.** $<$ **39.** $<$ **41.** a lies to the right of b or is equal to b.   **43.** $c < a < b$
45.

47.

49.

51. -3 **53.** -19 **55.** $=$ **57.** $=$ **59.** $=$ **61.** $>$
63. $7 - a$ **65.** Answers vary.   **67.** Answers vary.   **69.** 1
71. 9 **73.** 7 **75.** 49.9 **77.** 3.8 **79.** 35.7
81. $2005, 2006, 2008, 2010, 2011$ **83.** $2007, 2008, 2009, 2010, 2011$

Section 1.2 (Page 16)

1. $1{,}973{,}822.685$ **3.** 289.0991339 **5.** Answers vary.   **7.** 4^5
9. $(-6)^7$ **11.** $(5u)^{28}$ **13.** Degree 4; coefficients: $6.2, -5, 4, -3, 3.7$; constant term 3.7 **15.** 3 **17.** $-x^3 + x^2 - 13x$
19. $-6y^2 + 3y + 6$ **21.** $-6x^2 + 4x - 4$ **23.** $-18m^3 - 54m^2 + 9m$
25. $12z^3 + 14z^2 - 7z + 5$ **27.** $12k^2 + 16k - 3$
29. $6y^2 + 13y + 5$ **31.** $18k^2 - 7kq - q^2$
33. $4.34m^2 + 5.68m - 4.42$ **35.** $-k + 3$
37. $R = 5000x; C = 200{,}000 + 1800x; P = 3200x - 200{,}000$
39. $R = 9750x; C = -3x^2 + 3480x + 259{,}675;$
$P = 3x^2 + 6270x - 259{,}675$ **41. (a)** $\$265$ million
(b) About $\$212$ million   **43. (a)** $\$948$ million
(b) About $\$883$ million   **45.** About $\$1712$ million
47. About $\$1163$ million   **49.** False   **51.** True   **53.** $.866$
55. $.505$ **57. (a)** Approximately $60{,}501{,}067$ cu ft
(b) The shape becomes a rectangular box with a square base, with volume $b^2 h$. **(c)** Yes   **59. (a)** $0, 1, 2, 3,$ or no degree (if one is the negative of the other) **(b)** $0, 1, 2, 3,$ or no degree (if they are equal) **(c)** 6
61. Between $40{,}000$ and $45{,}000$ calculators

Section 1.3 (Page 23)

1. $12x(x - 2)$ **3.** $r(r^2 - 5r + 1)$ **5.** $6z(z^2 - 2z + 3)$
7. $(2y - 1)^2(14y - 4) = 2(2y - 1)^2(7y - 2)$
9. $(x + 5)^4(x^2 + 10x + 28)$ **11.** $(x + 1)(x + 4)$
13. $(x + 3)(x + 4)$ **15.** $(x + 3)(x - 2)$ **17.** $(x - 1)(x + 3)$
19. $(x - 4)(x + 1)$ **21.** $(z - 7)(z - 2)$ **23.** $(z + 4)(z + 6)$
25. $(2x - 1)(x - 4)$ **27.** $(3p - 4)(5p - 1)$ **29.** $(2z - 5)(2z - 3)$
31. $(2x + 1)(3x - 4)$ **33.** $(5y - 2)(2y + 5)$ **35.** $(2x - 1)(3x + 4)$
37. $(3a + 5)(a - 1)$ **39.** $(x + 9)(x - 9)$ **41.** $(3p - 2)^2$
43. $(r - 2t)(r + 5t)$ **45.** $(m - 4n)^2$ **47.** $(2u + 3)^2$
49. Cannot be factored   **51.** $(2r + 3v)(2r - 3v)$ **53.** $(x + 2y)^2$
55. $(3a + 5)(a - 6)$ **57.** $(7m + 2n)(3m + n)$
59. $(y - 7z)(y + 3z)$ **61.** $(11x + 8)(11x - 8)$
63. $(a - 4)(a^2 + 4a + 16)$ **65.** $(2r - 3s)(4r^2 + 6rs + 9s^2)$
67. $(4m + 5)(16m^2 - 20m + 25)$ **69.** $(10y - z)(100y^2 + 10yz + z^2)$

71. $(x^2 + 3)(x^2 + 2)$ **73.** $b^2(b + 1)(b - 1)$
75. $(x + 2)(x - 2)(x^2 + 3)$ **77.** $(4a^2 + 9b^2)(2a + 3b)(2a - 3b)$
79. $x^2(x^2 + 2)(x^4 - 2x^2 + 4)$ **81.** Answers vary.
83. Answers vary.

Section 1.4 (Page 29)

1. $\dfrac{x}{7}$ **3.** $\dfrac{5}{7p}$ **5.** $\dfrac{5}{4}$ **7.** $\dfrac{4}{w + 6}$ **9.** $\dfrac{y - 4}{3y^2}$ **11.** $\dfrac{m - 2}{m + 3}$
13. $\dfrac{x + 3}{x + 1}$ **15.** $\dfrac{3}{16a}$ **17.** $\dfrac{3y}{x^2}$ **19.** $\dfrac{5}{4c}$ **21.** $\dfrac{3}{4}$ **23.** $\dfrac{3}{10}$
25. $\dfrac{2(a + 4)}{a - 3}$ **27.** $\dfrac{k + 2}{k + 3}$ **29.** Answers vary.   **31.** $\dfrac{3}{35z}$
33. $\dfrac{4}{3}$ **35.** $\dfrac{20 + x}{5x}$ **37.** $\dfrac{3m - 2}{m(m - 1)}$ **39.** $\dfrac{37}{5(b + 2)}$
41. $\dfrac{33}{20(k - 2)}$ **43.** $\dfrac{7x - 1}{(x - 3)(x - 1)(x + 2)}$
45. $\dfrac{y^2}{(y + 4)(y + 3)(y + 2)}$ **47.** $\dfrac{x + 1}{x - 1}$ **49.** $\dfrac{-1}{x(x + h)}$
51. (a) $\dfrac{\pi x^2}{4x^2}$ **(b)** $\dfrac{\pi}{4}$ **53. (a)** $\dfrac{x^2}{25x^2}$ **(b)** $\dfrac{1}{25}$
55. $\dfrac{-7.2x^2 + 6995x + 230{,}000}{1000x}$ **57.** About $\$2.95$ million
59. No   **61.** $\$3.99$ **63.** $\$10{,}537.68$

Section 1.5 (Page 41)

1. 49 **3.** $16c^2$ **5.** $32/x^5$ **7.** $108u^{12}$ **9.** $1/7$
11. $-1/7776$ **13.** $-1/y^3$ **15.** $9/16$ **17.** b^3/a **19.** 7
21. About 1.55 **23.** -16 **25.** $81/16$ **27.** $4^2/5^3$ **29.** 4^3
31. 4^8 **33.** z^3 **35.** $\dfrac{p}{9}$ **37.** $\dfrac{q^5}{r^3}$ **39.** $\dfrac{8}{25p^7}$
41. $2^{5/6}p^{3/2}$ **43.** $2p + 5p^{5/3}$ **45.** $\dfrac{1}{3y^{2/3}}$ **47.** $\dfrac{a^{1/2}}{49b^{5/2}}$
49. $x^{7/6} - x^{11/6}$ **51.** $x - y$ **53.** (f)   **55.** (h)   **57.** (g)
59. (c)   **61.** 5 **63.** 5 **65.** 21 **67.** $\sqrt{77}$ **69.** $5\sqrt{3}$
71. $-\sqrt{2}$ **73.** $15\sqrt{5}$ **75.** 3 **77.** $-3 - 3\sqrt{2}$
79. $4 + \sqrt{3}$ **81.** $\dfrac{7}{11 + 6\sqrt{2}}$ **83. (a)** 14 **(b)** 85 **(c)** 58.0
85. About $\$10.2$ billion   **87.** About $\$10.6$ billion   **89.** About 180.6
91. About 168.7 **93.** About 5.8 million   **95.** About 7.3 million
97. About 30.4 million   **99.** About 87.1 million

Section 1.6 (Page 50)

1. 4 **3.** 7 **5.** $-10/9$ **7.** 4 **9.** $\dfrac{40}{7}$ **11.** $\dfrac{26}{3}$ **13.** $-\dfrac{12}{5}$
15. $-\dfrac{59}{6}$ **17.** $-\dfrac{9}{4}$ **19.** $x = .72$ **21.** $r \approx -13.26$
23. $\dfrac{b - 5a}{2}$ **25.** $x = \dfrac{3b}{a + 5}$ **27.** $V = \dfrac{k}{P}$ **29.** $g = \dfrac{V - V_0}{t}$
31. $B = \dfrac{2A}{h} - b$ or $B = \dfrac{2A - bh}{h}$ **33.** $-2, 3$ **35.** $-8, 2$
37. $\dfrac{5}{2}, \dfrac{7}{2}$ **39.** 10 hrs   **41.** $23°$ **43.** $71.6°$ **45.** 2010

47. 2015   **49.** 2010   **51.** 2016   **53.** 2012   **55.** 2016
57. 4779 thousand   **59.** 3074 thousand   **61.** $205.41
63. $21,000   **65.** $70,000 for first plot; $50,000 for the second
67. About 409,091 per month   **69.** 25,772,733   **71.** $\frac{400}{3}$ L
73. About 105 miles   **75.** 83 mph   **77.** 2.9 gallons of premium and 12.7 gallons of regular

Section 1.7 (Page 58)

1. $-4, 14$ **3.** $0, -6$ **5.** $0, 2$ **7.** $-7, -8$ **9.** $\frac{1}{2}, 3$

11. $-\frac{1}{2}, \frac{1}{3}$ **13.** $\frac{5}{2}, 4$ **15.** $-5, -2$ **17.** $\frac{4}{3}, -\frac{4}{3}$ **19.** $0, 1$

21. $2 \pm \sqrt{7}$ **23.** $\frac{1 \pm 2\sqrt{5}}{4}$ **25.** $\frac{-7 \pm \sqrt{41}}{4}; -.1492, -3.3508$

27. $\frac{-1 \pm \sqrt{5}}{4}; .3090, -.8090$ **29.** $\frac{-5 \pm \sqrt{65}}{10}; .3062, -1.3062$

31. No real-number solutions   **33.** $-\frac{5}{2}, 1$ **35.** No real-number

solutions   **37.** $-5, \frac{3}{2}$ **39.** 1   **41.** 2   **43.** $x \approx .4701$ or 1.8240

45. $x \approx -1.0376$ or $.6720$ **47. (a)** 30 mph **(b)** About 35 mph
(c) About 44 mph   **49. (a)** 2007 **(b)** 2009
51. (a) About $7.6 trillion **(b)** 2007   **53.** About 1.046 ft
55. (a) $x + 20$ **(b)** Northbound: $5x$; eastbound: $5(x + 20)$ or $5x + 100$
(c) $(5x)^2 + (5x + 100)^2 = 300^2$ **(d)** About 31.23 mph and 51.23 mph
57. (a) $150 - x$ **(b)** $x(150 - x) = 5000$ **(c)** Length 100 m; width 50 m
59. 9 ft by 12 ft   **61.** 6.25 sec   **63. (a)** About 3.54 sec **(b)** 2.5 sec
(c) 144 ft   **65. (a)** 2 sec **(b)** 3/4 sec or 13/4 sec **(c)** It reaches the
given height twice: once on the way up and once on the way down.
67. $t = \dfrac{\sqrt{2Sg}}{g}$ **69.** $h = \dfrac{d^2\sqrt{kL}}{L}$

71. $R = \dfrac{-2Pr + E^2 \pm E\sqrt{E^2 - 4Pr}}{2P}$ **73. (a)** $x^2 - 2x = 15$

(b) $x = 5$ or $x = -3$ **(c)** $z = \pm\sqrt{5}$ **75.** $\pm\dfrac{\sqrt{6}}{2}$

77. $\pm\sqrt{\dfrac{3 + \sqrt{13}}{2}}$

Chapter 1 Review Exercises (Page 61)

Refer to Section	1.1	1.2	1.3	1.4	1.5	1.6	1.7
For Exercises	1–18, 81–84	19–24, 85–88	25–32	33–38, 89–90	39–60, 91–92	61–68, 93–94	69–80, 95–100

1. $0, 6$ **3.** $-12, -6, -\dfrac{9}{10}, -\sqrt{4}, 0, \dfrac{1}{8}, 6$

5. Commutative property of multiplication   **7.** Distributive property
9. $x \geq 9$ **11.** $-|3 - (-2)|, -|-2|, |6 - 4|, |8 + 1|$ **13.** -1
15.

17. $-\dfrac{7}{9}$ **19.** $4x^4 - 4x^2 + 11x$ **21.** $25k^2 - 4h^2$
23. $9x^2 + 24xy + 16y^2$ **25.** $k(2h^2 - 4h + 5)$
27. $a^2(5a + 2)(a + 2)$ **29.** $(12p + 13q)(12p - 13q)$
31. $(3y - 1)(9y^2 + 3y + 1)$ **33.** $\dfrac{9x^2}{4}$ **35.** 4   **37.** $\dfrac{(m - 1)^2}{3(m + 1)}$
39. $\dfrac{1}{5^3}$ or $\dfrac{1}{125}$ **41.** -1 **43.** 4^3 **45.** $\dfrac{1}{8}$ **47.** $\dfrac{7}{10}$ **49.** $\dfrac{1}{5^{2/3}}$
51. $3^{7/2}a^{5/2}$ **53.** 3   **55.** $3pq\sqrt[3]{2q^2}$ **57.** $-21\sqrt{3}$
59. $\sqrt{6} - \sqrt{3}$ **61.** $-\dfrac{1}{3}$ **63.** No solution   **65.** $x = \dfrac{3}{8a - 2}$

67. $-38, 42$ **69.** $-7 \pm \sqrt{5}$ **71.** $\dfrac{1}{2}, -2$ **73.** $-\dfrac{3}{2}, 7$
75. $\pm\dfrac{\sqrt{3}}{3}$ **77.** $r = \dfrac{-Rp \pm E\sqrt{Rp}}{p}$ **79.** $s = \dfrac{a \pm \sqrt{a^2 + 4K}}{2}$
81. 111%   **83.** $1118.75   **85. (a)** 2009 **(b)** 2012
87. 52.66 million   **89. (a)** 9.8824 million **(b)** 2013
91. (a) About $19.79 billion **(b)** About $31.27 billion   **93.** 11%
95. (a) 7182 **(b)** About 13.61 million   **97.** 3.2 feet
99. About 7.77 seconds

Case Study 1 (Page 64)

1. $218 + 508x$ **3.** Electric by $1880   **5.** $1529.10 + 50x$
7. LG by $29.10

Chapter 2

Section 2.1 (Page 72)

1. IV, II, I, III   **3.** Yes   **5.** No
7.   **9.**

11.

13. x-intercepts $-2.5, 3$; y-intercept 3   **15.** x-intercepts $-1, 2$;
y-intercept -2 **17.** x-intercept 4; y-intercept 3   **19.** x-intercept 12;
y-intercept -8 **21.** x-intercepts $3, -3$; y-intercept -9
23. x-intercepts $-5, 4$; y-intercept -20
25. no x-intercept; y-intercept 7
27.   **29.**

31.   **33.**

35.

37.

39.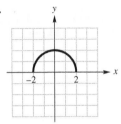

41. 2008; 20 million pounds　**43.** 2011
45. (a) About $1,250,000　**(b)** About $1,750,000
(c) About $4,250,000　**47. (a)** About $500,000
(b) About $1,000,000　**(c)** About $1,500,000　**49.** Beef: about
59 pounds; Chicken: about 83 pounds; Pork: about 47.5 pounds
51. 2001　**53.** About $507 billion　**55.** 2008–2015
57. $16.5; $21　**59.** $17.25; Day 14　**61.** No

63. 　**65.**

67. 　**69.** No;

71. $x \approx -1.1038$　**73.** $x \approx 2.1017$　**75.** $x \approx -1.7521$
77. About $6.99 trillion　**79.** About $45.41 trillion

Section 2.2 (Page 84)

1. $-\dfrac{3}{2}$　**3.** -2　**5.** $-\dfrac{5}{2}$　**7.** Not defined　**9.** $y = 4x + 5$

11. $y = -2.3x + 1.5$　**13.** $y = -\dfrac{3}{4}x + 4$　**15.** $m = 2; b = -9$

17. $m = 3; b = -2$　**19.** $m = \dfrac{2}{3}; b = -\dfrac{16}{9}$　**21.** $m = \dfrac{2}{3}; b = 0$

23. $m = 1; b = 5$　**25. (a)** C　**(b)** B　**(c)** B　**(d)** D

27. 　**29.**

31.

33. Perpendicular　**35.** Parallel　**37.** Neither　**39. (a)** $\dfrac{2}{5}, \dfrac{9}{8}, -\dfrac{5}{2}$

(b) Yes　**41.** $y = -\dfrac{2}{3}x$　**43.** $y = 3x - 3$　**45.** $y = 1$

47. $x = -2$　**49.** $y = 2x + 3$　**51.** $2y = 7x - 3$　**53.** $y = 5x$
55. $x = 6$　**57.** $y = 2x - 2$　**59.** $y = x - 6$　**61.** $y = -x + 2$
63. $1330.42　**65.** $6715.23　**67. (a)** $202.05 billion
(b) $270.5 billion　**(c)** 2015　**69. (a)** 384.6 thousand
(b) 366.6 thousand　**(c)** 2019　**71. (a)** $(5, 35.1), (11, 29.7)$
(b) $y = -.9x + 39.6$　**(c)** $31.5 billion　**(d)** 2016
73. (a) $y = .035x + .40$　**(b)** $.82　**75. (a)** $y = -964.5x + 36,845$
(b) 31,058　**77. (a)** The average decrease in time over 1 year; times
are going down, in general.　**(b)** 12.94 minutes

Section 2.3 (Page 93)

1. (a) $y = \dfrac{5}{9}(x - 32)$　**(b)** 10°C and 23.89°C　**3.** 463.89°C

5. $y = 4.66x + 173.64$; 210.92; 243.54
7. $y = .0625x + 6$; 6.625 million　**9.** 4 ft
11. (a) 22.2, –23.2, –12.6, 6.0, 7.6; –22.6, –41.4, –4.2, 41.0, 69.2;
sum $= 0$　**(b)** 1283.6; 8712　**(c)** Model 1　**13.** Yes
15. (a) $y = 5.90x + 146.59$　**(b)** $235.09 billion
17. (a) $y = -3.96x + 73.98$　**(b)** $10.62 billion
19. (a) $y = 2.37x - 2.02$　**(b)** $26.42 billion; $31.16 billion
21. (a) $y = -2.318x + 55.88$　**(b)** 41.972 thousand　**(c)** early 2012
(d) $r \approx -.972$

Section 2.4 (Page 100)

1. Answers vary.
3. $[-4, \infty)$
5. $(-\infty, 0)$

7. $\left(-\infty, \dfrac{10}{3}\right]$

9. $(-\infty, -8]$

11. $(-\infty, 3)$

13. $(-1, \infty)$

15. $(-\infty, 1]$

17. $\left(\dfrac{1}{5}, \infty\right)$

19. $(-5, 7)$

21. $\left[\dfrac{7}{3}, 5\right]$

23. $\left[-\dfrac{11}{2}, \dfrac{7}{2}\right]$

25. $\left[-\dfrac{17}{7}, \infty\right)$

27. $x \geq 2$ **29.** $-3 < x \leq 5$ **31.** $x \geq 400$ **33.** $x \geq 50$
35. Impossible to break even
37. $(-\infty, -7)$ or $(7, \infty)$ **39.** $[-5, 5]$

41. All real numbers   **43.** $\left(-\dfrac{3}{2}, \dfrac{5}{2}\right)$

45. $\left(-\infty, -\dfrac{3}{2}\right]$ or $\left[\dfrac{1}{4}, \infty\right)$

47. $76 \leq T \leq 90$ **49.** $40 \leq T \leq 82$
51. (a) $25.33 \leq R_L \leq 28.17; 36.58 \leq R_E \leq 40.92$
(b) $5699.25 \leq T_L \leq 6338.25; 8230.5 \leq T_E \leq 9207$ **53.** $35 \leq B \leq 43$
55. $0 < x \leq 8700; 8700 < x \leq 35,350; 35,350 < x \leq 85,650;$
$85,650 < x \leq 178,650; 178,650 < x \leq 388,350; x > 388,350$

Section 2.5 (Page 108)

1. $\left[-4, \dfrac{3}{2}\right]$ **3.** $(-\infty, -3)$ or $(-1, \infty)$

5. $\left[-2, \dfrac{1}{4}\right]$ **7.** $(-\infty, -1)$ or $\left(\dfrac{1}{4}, \infty\right)$

9. $[-6, 6]$ **11.** $(-\infty, 0)$ or $(16, \infty)$

13. $[-3, 0]$ or $[3, \infty)$ **15.** $[-7, -2]$ or $[2, \infty)$
17. $(-\infty, -5)$ or $(-1, 3)$ **19.** $\left(-\infty, -\dfrac{1}{2}\right)$ or $\left(0, \dfrac{4}{3}\right)$ **21.** No.
23. $(-.1565, 2.5565)$ **25.** $[-2.2635, .7556]$ or $[3.5079, \infty)$
27. $(.5, .8393)$ **29.** $(-\infty, 1)$ or $[4, \infty)$ **31.** $\left(\dfrac{7}{2}, 5\right)$
33. $(-\infty, 2)$ or $(5, \infty)$ **35.** $(-\infty, -1)$ **37.** $(-\infty, -2)$ or $(0, 3)$
39. $[-1, .5]$ **41.** $(8, \infty)$ **43.** $[52, 200]$ **45.** 2010 or higher
47. $[2006, 2011]$

Chapter 2 Review Exercises (Page 110)

Refer to Section	2.1	2.2	2.3	2.4	2.5
For Exercises	1–10	11–34	35–38	39–54	55–68

1. $(-2, 3), (0, -5), (3, -2), (4, 3)$
3.   **5.**

7.

9. (a) About 11:30 AM to about 7:30 PM   (b) From midnight until about
5 AM and after about 10:30 PM   **11.** Answers vary.   **13.** -3
15. $-\dfrac{1}{4}$ **17.** 3   **19.** 0   **21.** -3

23.

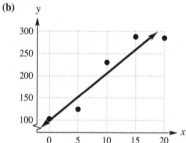

25. $3y = 2x - 13$ **27.** $4y = -5x + 17$
29. $x = -1$ **31.** $3y = 5x + 15$
33. (a) $y = .55x + 11.25$ (b) Positive; exports increased
(c) 18.95 million hectoliters
35. (a) $y = 1919x + 47,059$ (b) $y = 1917.38x + 47,051.26$
(c) $68,168; $68,142.44$; least–squares regression line is closer;
(d) $75, 811.96
37. (a) $y = 10.72x + 98.8$
(b)

(c) Yes   (d) $r \approx .953$ **39.** $\left(\dfrac{3}{8}, \infty\right)$ **41.** $\left(-\infty, \dfrac{1}{4}\right]$
43. $\left[-\dfrac{1}{2}, 2\right]$ **45.** $[-8, 8]$ **47.** $(-\infty, 2]$ or $[5, \infty)$
49. $\left[-\dfrac{9}{5}, 1\right]$ **51.** (d)   **53.** (a) $y = 75.4x + 1496$ (b) 2013
55. $(-3, 2)$ **57.** $(-\infty, -5]$ or $\left[\dfrac{3}{2}, \infty\right)$
59. $(-\infty, -5]$ or $[-2, 3]$ **61.** $[-2, 0)$ **63.** $\left(-1, \dfrac{3}{2}\right)$
65. $[-19, -5)$ or $(2, \infty)$ **67.** 2011 and 2012

Case Study 2 Exercises (Page 113)
1. $y = -146.1x + 2330$
3. $-389.8, -212.7, 96.4, 331.5, 525.6, 195.7, -41.2, -221.1, -217.0,$
$-137.9, 73.2$

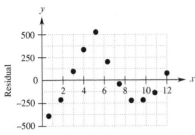

5. $y = .343x - 20.65$ **7.** $\hat{y} = \$-.07$; Cannot have a negative wage
9. $y = 0$; answers vary.

Chapter 3

Section 3.1 (Page 121)
1. Function   **3.** Function   **5.** Not a function   **7.** Function
9. $(-\infty, \infty)$ **11.** $(-\infty, \infty)$ **13.** $(-\infty, 0]$
15. All real numbers except 2   **17.** All real numbers except 2 and -2
19. All real numbers such that $x > -4$ and $x \neq 3$ **21.** $(-\infty, \infty)$
23. (a) 8 (b) 8 (c) 8 (d) 8   **25.** (a) 48 (b) 6 (c) 25.38
(d) 28.42   **27.** (a) $\sqrt{7}$ (b) 0 (c) $\sqrt{5.7}$ (d) Not defined
29. (a) 12 (b) 23 (c) 12.91 (d) 49.41   **31.** (a) $\dfrac{\sqrt{3}}{15}$
(b) Not defined (c) $\dfrac{\sqrt{1.7}}{6.29}$ (d) Not defined   **33.** (a) 13 (b) 9
(c) 6.5 (d) 24.01   **35.** (a) $6 - p$ (b) $6 + r$ (c) $3 - m$
37. (a) $\sqrt{4 - p}$ $(p \leq 4)$ (b) $\sqrt{4 + r}$ $(r \geq -4)$ (c) $\sqrt{1 - m}$ $(m \leq 1)$
39. (a) $p^3 + 1$ (b) $-r^3 + 1$ (c) $m^3 + 9m^2 + 27m + 28$
41. (a) $\dfrac{3}{p - 1}$ $(p \neq 1)$ (b) $\dfrac{3}{-r - 1}$ $(r \neq -1)$ (c) $\dfrac{3}{m + 2}$ $(m \neq -2)$
43. 2   **45.** $2x + h$
47.

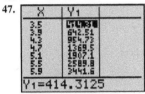

49. (a) \$1070 (b) \$4542.30 (c) \$8420.18   **51.** (a) \$-6.744 billion
(loss) (b) \$14.448 billion   **53.** (a) \$2347.9 million
(b) \$2299.9 million   **55.** $2050 - 500t$ **57.** (a) $c(x) = 1800 + .5x$
(b) $r(x) = 1.2x$ (c) $p(x) = .7x - 1800$
59.

Section 3.2 (Page 131)
1.

3.

$$f(x) = \begin{cases} x + 3 & \text{if } x \leq 1 \\ 4 & \text{if } x > 1 \end{cases}$$

5.

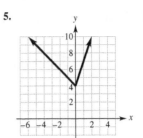

$$y = \begin{cases} 4 - x & \text{if } x \leq 0 \\ 3x + 4 & \text{if } x > 0 \end{cases}$$

7.

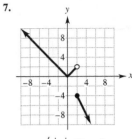

$$f(x) = \begin{cases} |x| & \text{if } x < 2 \\ -2x & \text{if } x \geq 2 \end{cases}$$

9.

$f(x) = |x - 4|$

11.

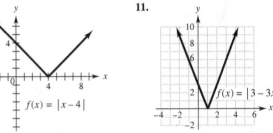

$f(x) = |3 - 3x|$

13.

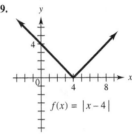

$y = -|x - 1|$

15.

$y = |x - 2| + 3$

17.

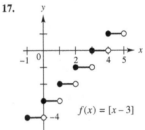

$f(x) = [x - 3]$

19.

$g(x) = [-x]$

21.

23.

$f(x) = 3 - 2x^2$

25.

$h(x) = x^3/10 + 2$

27.

$g(x) = \sqrt{-x}$

29.

$f(x) = \sqrt[3]{x}$

31.

33. Function   **35.** Not a function   **37.** Function

39.

41. $(1, -1)$ is on the graph; $(1, 3)$ is not on the graph

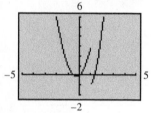

43. $x = -4, 2, 6$ **45.** Peak at $(.5078, .3938)$; valleys at $(-1.9826, -4.2009)$ and $(3.7248, -8.7035)$

47.

49. (a)

(b) \$7.879   **51. (a)** $f(x) = \begin{cases} 2x + 15.1 & \text{if } 0 \le x \le 30 \\ 10.5x - 240.1 & \text{if } x > 30 \end{cases}$

(b)

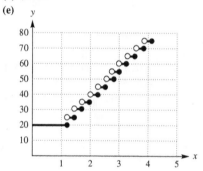

(c) 326.9   **(d)** 442.4   **53. (a)** No   **(b)** 1998, 2002, 2009   **(c)** 2009
55. (a) Yes   **(b)** The years 1990–2010   **(c)** [7750, 15400]
57. (a) 33; 44   **(b)** The figure has vertical line segments, which can't be part of the graph of a function. (Why?) To make the figure into the graph of f, delete the vertical line segments; then, for each horizontal segment of the graph, put a closed dot on the left end and an open circle on the right end (as in Figure 3.7).   **59. (a)** \$34.99   **(b)** \$24.99   **(c)** \$64.99
(d) \$74.99

(e)

61. There are many correct answers, including

Section 3.3 (Page 142)

1. Let $C(x)$ be the cost of renting a saw for x hours; $C(x) = 25 + 5x$.
3. Let $C(x)$ be the cost (in dollars) for x half hours; $C(x) = 8 + 2.5x$.
5. $C(x) = 36x + 200$ **7.** $C(x) = 120x + 3800$ **9.** \$48, \$15.60,
\$13.80   **11.** \$55.50, \$11.40, \$8.46   **13. (a)** $f(x) = -1916x + 16,615$
(b) 7035   **(c)** \$1916 per year   **15. (a)** $f(x) = -11,875x + 120,000$
(b) [0, 8]   **(c)** \$48,750   **17. (a)** \$80,000   **(b)** \$42.50   **(c)** \$122,500;
\$1,440,000   **(d)** \$122.50; \$45   **19. (a)** $C(x) = .097x + 1.32$
(b) \$98.32   **(c)** \$98.42   **(d)** \$.097, or 9.7¢   **(e)** \$.097, or 9.7¢
21. $R(x) = 1.77x + 2,310,000$ **23. (a)** $C(x) = 10x + 750$
(b) $R(x) = 35x$ **(c)** $P(x) = 25x - 750$ **(d)** \$1750
25. (a) $C(x) = 18x + 300$ **(b)** $R(x) = 28x$ **(c)** $P(x) = 10x - 300$
(d) \$700   **27. (a)** $C(x) = 12.50x + 20,000$ **(b)** $R(x) = 30x$
(c) $P(x) = 17.50x - 20,000$ **(d)** $-$18,250$ (a loss)   **29.** $(3, -1)$
31. $\left(-\dfrac{11}{4}, -\dfrac{61}{4}\right)$ **33. (a)** 200,000 policies ($x = 200$)

(b)

$R(x) = 125x$

$C(x) = 100x + 5000$

(c) Revenue: $12,500; cost: $15,000 **35. (a)** $C(x) = .126x + 1.5$
(b) $2.382 million **(c)** About 17.857 units **37.** Break-even
point is about 467 units; do not produce the item. **39.** Break-even
point is about 1037 units; produce the item. **41.** The percentage is
approximately 53% in 1998.
43. (a)

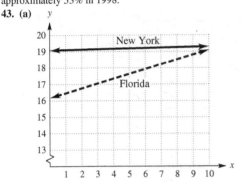

New York

Florida

(b) No **(c)** Yes; Late 2010 **45.** $140 **47.** 10 items
49. (a) $16 **(b)** $11 **(c)** $6 **(d)** 8 units **(e)** 4 units **(f)** 0 units
(g)

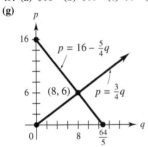

$p = 16 - \frac{5}{4}q$

$(8, 6)$ $p = \frac{3}{4}q$

(h) 0 units **(i)** $\frac{40}{3}$ units **(j)** $\frac{80}{3}$ units **(k)** See part (g). **(l)** 8 units

(m) $6
51. (a)

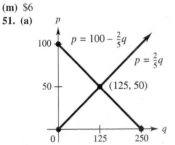

$p = 100 - \frac{2}{5}q$

$p = \frac{2}{5}q$

$(125, 50)$

(b) 125 units **(c)** 50¢ **(d)** [0, 125) **53.** Total cost increases when
more items are made (because it includes the cost of all previously made
items), so the graph cannot move downward. No; the average cost can
decrease as more items are made, so its graph can move downward.

Section 3.4 (Page 154)
1. Upward **3.** Downward **5.** (5, 7); downward
7. (−1, −9); upward **9.** i **11.** k **13.** j **15.** f

17. $f(x) = \frac{1}{4}(x - 1)^2 + 2$ **19.** $f(x) = (x + 1)^2 - 2$ **21.** (−3, 12)

23. (2, −7) **25.** x-intercepts 1, 3; y-intercept 9
27. x-intercepts −1, −3; y-intercept 6

29. (−2, 0), $x = -2$

$(-2, 0)$

$f(x) = (x + 2)^2$

31. (2, 2), $x = 2$

$(2, 2)$

$f(x) = x^2 - 4x + 6$
$f(x) = (x - 2)^2 + 2$

33. 54 **35. (a)** 10 milliseconds **(b)** 40 responses per millisecond
37. (a) 27 cases **(b)** Answers vary. **(c)** 15 cases
39. (a) About 12 books **(b)** 10 books **(c)** About 7 books **(d)** 0 books
(e) 5 books **(f)** About 7 books **(g)** 10 books **(h)** about 12 books
(i)

$p = \frac{1}{5}q^2$

$(10, 20)$

$p = -\frac{1}{5}q^2 + 40$

41. (a) $640 **(b)** $515 **(c)** $140
(d)

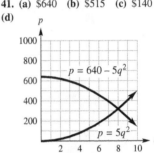

$p = 640 - 5q^2$

$p = 5q^2$

(e) 800 units **(f)** $320 **43.** 80; $3600 **45.** 30; $1500
47. 20 **49.** 10
51. (a) $R(x) = (100 - x)(200 + 4x)$
    $= 20,000 + 200x - 4x^2$
(b)

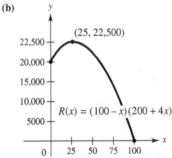

$(25, 22,500)$

$R(x) = (100 - x)(200 + 4x)$

(c) 25 seats **(d)** $22,500 **53.** 13 weeks; $96.10/hog
55. (a) $.013(x - 20)^2$ **(b)** About 4
57. (a) $f(x) = 3.9375(x - 4)^2 + 57.8$ **(b)** About $309.8 billion
59. 30 **61.** 200

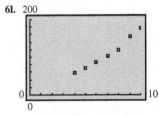

$f(x) = .034x^2 - 1.87x + 26.16$;
about 4

$f(x) = 1.808x^2 - 5.185x + 50.72$;
about $248.85 billion

63. (a) 11.3 and 88.7 **(b)** 50 **(c)** $3000 **(d)** $x < 11.3$ or $x > 88.7$
(e) $11.3 < x < 88.7$

Section 3.5 (Page 165)

1.

$f(x) = x^4$

3.

$h(x) = -.2x^5$

(b)

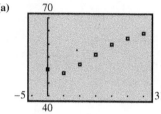

(c) Yes, the slope is always positive
33. $P(x) = .006x^3 - .13x^2 + .99x - 1.28$; $2.248 million

5. (a) Yes **(b)** No **(c)** No **(d)** Yes   **7. (a)** Yes **(b)** No
(c) Yes **(d)** No   **9.** d   **11.** b   **13.** e

15.

17.

35. (a)

(b) $g(x) = -.0016x^3 + .0765x^2 - .425x + 50.0$

(c)   Yes

19.

21.

(d) 62.9528 million
37. (a) $R(x) = -.0668x^3 + 1.708x^2 - 12.15x + 120.1$

(b) 110   Yes

23. $-3 \le x \le 5$ and $-20 \le y \le 5$ **25.** $-3 \le x \le 4$ and
$-35 \le y \le 20$ **27. (a)** $933.33 billion **(b)** $1200 billion
(c) $1145.8 billion **(d)** $787.5 billion

(e) 1400

39. $P(x) = -.0313x^3 + .773x^2 - 4.83x + 17.1$

29. (a) $54.785 million; $64.843 million; $99.578 million

(b)

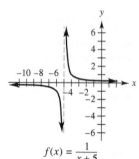

Section 3.6 (Page 175)

1. $x = -5, y = 0$ **3.** $x = -\dfrac{5}{2}, y = 0$

$f(x) = \dfrac{1}{x+5}$ $f(x) = \dfrac{-3}{2x+5}$

(c) Yes, because the slope is always positive.
31. (a) $53.615 million; $63.505 million; $97.33 million

5. $x = 1, y = 3$

$$f(x) = \frac{3x}{x-1}$$

7. $x = 4, y = 1$

$$f(x) = \frac{x+1}{x-4}$$

(e)

$$W = \frac{S(S-A)}{A}$$

(f) W becomes negative. The waiting time approaches 0 as A approaches 3. The formula does not apply for $A > 3$ because there will be no waiting if people arrive more than 3 min apart.

27.

$$y = \frac{900,000,000 - 30,000x}{x + 90,000}$$

Red Tranquilizers

30,000 reds; 10,000 blues

9. $x = 3; y = -1$

$$f(x) = \frac{2-x}{x-3}$$

11. $x = -2, y = \frac{3}{2}$

$$f(x) = \frac{3x+2}{2x+4}$$

29. (a) $C(x) = 2.6x + 40,000$

(b) $\overline{C}(x) = \dfrac{2.6x + 40,000}{x} = 2.6 + \dfrac{40,000}{x}$

(c) $y = 2.6$; the average cost may get close to, but will never equal, $2.60.

31. About 73.9

33. (a)

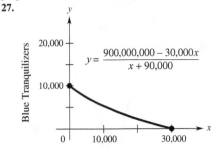

(b) They appear almost identical, because the parabola is an asymptote of the graph.

13. $x = -4, x = 2, y = 0$

$$h(x) = \frac{x+1}{x^2 + 2x - 8}$$

15. $x = -2, x = 2, y = 1$

$$f(x) = \frac{x^2 + 4}{x^2 - 4}$$

17. $x = -2, x = 1$ **19.** $x = -1, x = 5$

21. (a) $4300 **(b)** $10,033.33 **(c)** $17,200 **(d)** $38,700

(e) $81,700 **(f)** $210,700

(g) $425,700 **(h)** No

(i)

$$f(x) = \frac{4.3x}{100 - x}$$

Chapter 3 Review Exercises (Page 177)

Refer to Section	3.1	3.2	3.3	3.4	3.5	3.6
From Exercises	1–12	13–24	25–36	37–60	61–70	71–80

1. Not a function   **3.** Function   **5.** Not a function

7. (a) 23 **(b)** -9 **(c)** $4p - 1$ **(d)** $4r + 3$

9. (a) -28 **(b)** -12 **(c)** $-p^2 + 2p - 4$ **(d)** $-r^2 - 3$

11. (a) -13 **(b)** 3 **(c)** $-k^2 - 4k$ **(d)** $-9m^2 + 12m$

(e) $-k^2 + 14k - 45$ **(f)** $12 - 5p$

23. (a) $[0, \infty)$

(b)

$$f(x) = \frac{x}{1+x}$$

(c)

$$f(x) = \frac{x}{1 + x^2}$$

(d) Increasing b makes the next generation smaller when this generation is larger.   **25. (a)** 6 min **(b)** 1.5 min **(c)** .6 min **(d)** $A = 0$

13.

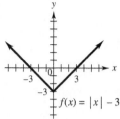

$f(x) = |x| - 3$

15.

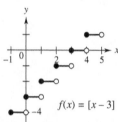

$f(x) = -|x + 1| + 3$

17.

$f(x) = [x - 3]$

19.

$f(x) = \begin{cases} -4x + 2 & \text{if } x \le 1 \\ 3x - 5 & \text{if } x > 1 \end{cases}$

21.

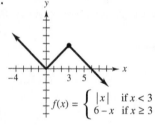

$f(x) = \begin{cases} |x| & \text{if } x < 3 \\ 6 - x & \text{if } x \ge 3 \end{cases}$

23.

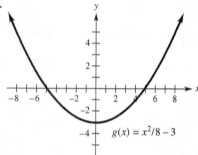

$g(x) = x^2/8 - 3$

25. (a)

(b) Domain: $(0, \infty)$ range: $\{65, 85, 105, 125, \ldots\}$ **(c)** 2 days
27. (a) decreasing; relatively flat   **(b)** $f(x) = -1.4x + 30$ **(c)** 13.2%
29. (a) $C(x) = 30x + 60$ **(b)** $30   **(c)** $30.60
31. (a) $C(x) = 30x + 85$ **(b)** $30   **(c)** $30.85
33. (a) $18,000   **(b)** $R(x) = 28x$ **(c)** 4500 cartridges   **(d)** $126,000
35. Equilibrium quantity is 36 million subscribers at a price of $12.95 per month.   **37.** Upward; (2, 6)   **39.** Downward; (−1, 8)

41.

Vertex (0, −9)

43.

Vertex (−1, −7)

45.

Vertex (−3, 14)

47.

Vertex (3, −8)

49. Minimum value; −11   **51.** Maximum value; 7
53. 161 weeks; $97.16   **55.** 2027; about 1391 million
57. (a) $f(x) = 25.82(x - 5)^2 + 3672$ **(b)** $44,984
59. (a) $g(x) = 9.738x^2 + 389x + 1096$
(b) 35,000

(c) $38,320.45

61.

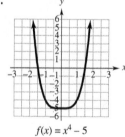

$f(x) = x^4 - 5$

63.

$f(x) = x(x - 4)(x + 1)$

65.

$f(x) = x^4 - 5x^2 - 6$

67. About 313,152; about $690.72 per thousand
69. (a) $404,963 million

(b) \$373,222 million   **(c)** $297x^3 - 6901x^2 + 50,400x - 79,159$
(d) \$31,741 million; \$45,113 million
71. $x = 3, y = 0$ **73.** $x = 2, y = 0$

$$f(x) = \frac{1}{x-3}$$

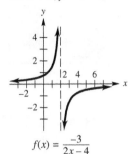

$$f(x) = \frac{-3}{2x-4}$$

75. $x = -\dfrac{1}{2}, x = \dfrac{3}{2}, y = 0$

$$g(x) = \frac{5x-2}{4x^2 - 4x - 3}$$

77. (a) About \$10.83   **(b)** About \$4.64   **(c)** About \$3.61
(d) About \$2.71
(e)

$$C(x) = \frac{650}{2x+40}$$

79. (a) $(10, 50)$

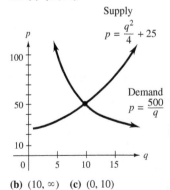

Supply
$$p = \frac{q^2}{4} + 25$$

Demand
$$p = \frac{500}{q}$$

(b) $(10, \infty)$ **(c)** $(0, 10)$

Case Study 3 Exercises (Page 182)

1. $f(x) = \dfrac{-20}{49}x^2 + 20$

3. $g(x) = \sqrt{625 - x^2}$; 50 ft

5. $h(x) = \sqrt{144 - x^2} + 8$; 8 ft   **7.** It will fit through the semicircular arch and Norman arch; to fit it through the parabolic arch, increase the width to 15 ft.

Chapter 4

Section 4.1 (Page 189)

1. Exponential   **3.** Quadratic   **5.** Exponential
7. (a) The graph is entirely above the x-axis and falls from left to right, crossing the y-axis at 1 and then getting very close to the x-axis.
(b) $(0, 1), (1, .6)$ **9. (a)** The graph is entirely above the x-axis and rises from left to right, less steeply than the graph of $f(x) = 2^x$.
(b) $(0, 1), (1, 2^{.5}) = (1, \sqrt{2})$ **11. (a)** The graph is entirely above the x-axis and falls from left to right, crossing the y-axis at 1 and then getting very close to the x-axis.   **(b)** $(0, 1), (1, e^{-1}) \approx (1, .367879)$
13.   **15.**

17.

19. (a)–(c)

(d) Answers vary.   **21.** 2.3   **23.** .75   **25.** .31
27. (a) $a > 1$ **(b)** Domain: $(-\infty, \infty)$; range: $(0, \infty)$
(c)

(d) Domain: $(-\infty, \infty)$; range: $(-\infty, 0)$
(e)

(f) Domain: $(-\infty, \infty)$; range: $(0, \infty)$ **29. (a)** 3   **(b)** $\dfrac{1}{3}$ **(c)** 9   **(d)** 1

31.

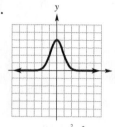

$$f(x) = 2^{-x^2 + 2}$$

33.

$$f(x) = x \cdot 2^x$$

35. (a)

t	0	1	2	3	4	5	6	7	8	9	10
y	1	1.06	1.12	1.19	1.26	1.34	1.42	1.50	1.59	1.69	1.79

(b)

$$y = (1.06)^t$$

37. (a) About \$141,892 **(b)** About \$64.10
39. (a) About 175 million **(b)** About 321 million
(c) About 355 million   **41. (a)** About .97 kg **(b)** About .75 kg
(c) About .65 kg **(d)** About 24,360 years   **43.** \$34,706.99
45. (a) About 6.2 billion **(b)** About 6.5 billion **(c)** About 8 billion
(d) Answers vary.   **47. (a)** China: About \$12.4 trillion; U.S: About
\$15.6 trillion **(b)** China: About \$27.2 trillion; U.S: About \$22.4 trillion
(c) China: About \$515.3 trillion; U.S: About \$86.3 trillion **(d)** 2016
49. (a) About 13.72 million **(b)** About 28.9 million
(c) First quarter of 2012   **51. (a)** About 1.2 billion
(b) About 2.1 billion **(c)** Fourth quarter of 2012
53. (a) About 12.6 mg **(b)** About 7.9 mg **(c)** In about 15.1 hours

Section 4.2 (Page 197)

1. (a) \$752.27 **(b)** \$707.39 **(c)** \$432.45 **(d)** \$298.98
(e) Answers vary.   **3. (a)** 2540 **(b)** About 9431 megawatts; about
59,177 megawatts   **5. (a)** $f(t) = 1000(1.046)^t$ **(b)** \$3078.17
(c) 2005   **7. (a)** $f(t) = 81.1(1.067)^t$ **(b)** About \$260.6 billion
(c) About \$410.3 billion   **9. (a)** Two-point: $f(t) = (.9763)^t$;
regression: $f(t) = .998(.976)^t$ **(b)** Two-point: \$.70; \$.65; regression:
\$.69; \$.64 **(c)** Two-point: 2038; regression: 2037
11. (a) Two-point: $f(t) = 257.6(.964)^t$; regression: $f(t) = 257.4(.963)^t$
(b) Two-point: about 165.9; about 143.3; regression: about 163.7; about
140.8 **(c)** Two-point: 2025; regression: 2025   **13. (a)** About 6 items
(b) About 23 items **(c)** 25 items   **15.** 2.6°C   **17. (a)** .13
(b) .23 **(c)** About 2 weeks
19. (a) About \$594.0 billion; about \$802.4 billion
(b) 1000

(c) 2011
21. (a) About \$91.89 billion; about \$96.86 billion

(b) 120

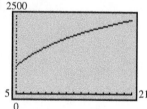

(c) No

Section 4.3 (Page 207)

1. a^y **3.** It is missing the value that equals b^y. If that value is x, the
expression should read $y = \log_b x$ **5.** $10^5 = 100,000$ **7.** $9^2 = 81$

9. $\log 96 = 1.9823$ **11.** $\log_3\left(\dfrac{1}{9}\right) = -2$ **13.** 3   **15.** 2

17. 3   **19.** -2 **21.** $\dfrac{1}{2}$ **23.** 8.77   **25.** 1.724

27. -4.991 **29.** Because $a^0 = 1$ for every valid base a.

31. $\log 24$ **33.** $\ln 5$ **35.** $\log\left(\dfrac{u^2 w^3}{v^6}\right)$ **37.** $\ln\left(\dfrac{(x+2)^2}{x+3}\right)$

39. $\dfrac{1}{2}\ln 6 + 2\ln m + \ln n$ **41.** $\dfrac{1}{2}\log x - \dfrac{5}{2}\log z$ **43.** $2u + 5v$

45. $3u - 2v$ **47.** 3.32112   **49.** 2.429777
51. Many correct answers, including, $b = 1, c = 2$.
53.

$$y = \ln(x+2)$$

55.

$$y = \log(x-3)$$

57. Answers vary.   **59.** $\ln 2.75 = 1.0116009$; $e^{1.0116009} = 2.75$
61. (a) 17.67 yr **(b)** 9.01 yr **(c)** 4.19 yr **(d)** 2.25 yr
63. (a) \$2219.63
(b) 2500

(c) Gradually increasing
65. (a) About 31.99 million; about 37.67 million
(b) 50

(c) Gradually increasing   **67.** 1.5887
69. (a) About \$441.15 billion; about \$737.74 billion **(b)** 2027
71. (a) About 24.8 gallons; about 21.9 **(b)** 2021

Section 4.4 (Page 216)

1. 8   **3.** 9   **5.** 11   **7.** $\dfrac{11}{6}$ **9.** $\dfrac{4}{9}$ **11.** 10

13. 5.2378   **15.** 10   **17.** $\dfrac{4+b}{4}$ **19.** $\dfrac{10^{2-b}-5}{6}$

21. Answers vary.   **23.** 4   **25.** $-\dfrac{5}{6}$ **27.** -4 **29.** -2

31. 2.3219   **33.** 2.710   **35.** -1.825 **37.** .597253

39. $-.123$ **41.** $\dfrac{\log d+3}{4}$ **43.** $\dfrac{\ln b+1}{2}$ **45.** 4

47. No solution   **49.** $-4,4$ **51.** 9   **53.** 1   **55.** $4,-4$
57. ± 2.0789 **59.** 1.386   **61.** Answers vary.   **63. (a)** 2009
(b) 2012   **65. (a)** 1992 $(x \approx 92.1518)$ **(b)** Mid-2007 $(x \approx 107.7364)$
(c) Mid-2041 $(x \approx 141.6168)$ **67. (a)** 1995   **(b)** 2022
69. (a) 25 g   **(b)** About 4.95 yr   **71.** About 3689 yr old
73. (a) Approximately $79{,}432{,}823i_0$ **(b)** Approximately $251{,}189i_0$
(c) About 316.23 times stronger   **75. (a)** 21   **(b)** 100   **(c)** 105
(d) 120   **(e)** 140   **77. (a)** 27.5%   **(b)** \$130.14

79. (a)

(b) 2002

Chapter 4 Review Exercises (Page 219)

Refer to Section	4.1	4.2	4.3	4.4
For Exercises	1–10	13–14, 55–58, 61–64	11–12, 15–40, 65–66	41–54, 59–60

1. (c)   **3.** (d)   **5.** $0 < a < 1$ **7.** All positive real numbers

9.

11.

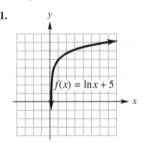

13. (a) About 412 thousand   **(b)** June 2012   **15.** $\log 340 = 2.53148$
17. $\ln 45 = 3.8067$ **19.** $10^4 = 10{,}000$ **21.** $e^{4.3957} = 81.1$

23. 5   **25.** 8.9   **27.** $\dfrac{1}{3}$ **29.** $\log 20x^6$ **31.** $\log\left(\dfrac{b^3}{c^2}\right)$

33. 4   **35.** 97   **37.** 5   **39.** 5   **41.** -2 **43.** -2
45. 1.416   **47.** -2.807 **49.** -3.305 **51.** .747
53. 28.463   **55. (a)** C   **(b)** A   **(c)** D   **(d)** B   **57. (a)** 10 g
(b) About 140 days   **(c)** About 243 days   **59. (a)** $10{,}000{,}000i_0$
(b) $3{,}162{,}278i_0$ **(c)** About 3.2 times stronger   **61.** $81.25°$ C
63. (a) $f(x) = 500(1.067)^x$ **(b)** $f(x) = 474.8(1.075)^x$
(c) Two-point: about 896 minutes; regression: about 910 minutes
(d) Two point and regression: May, 2013.

65. (a) $f(x) = 18 + 21.07 \ln x$ **(b)** $f(x) = 15.21 + 20.47 \ln x$
(c) Two point: about 64%; regression: about 60%
(d) Two point: 2016; regression: 2019

Case Study 4 Exercises (Page 224)

1.

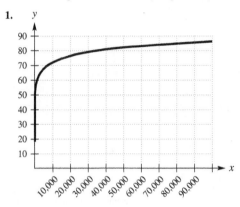

3. 66.6 years   **5.** About \$1383

7.

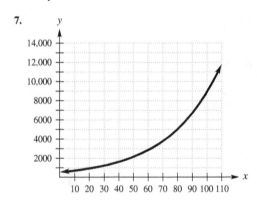

9. About \$2131; about \$8899

11.

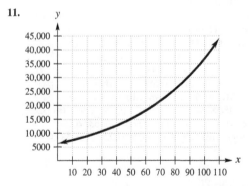

13. About \$18,168; about \$44,329

Chapter 5

Section 5.1 (Page 230)

1. Time and interest rate   **3.** \$133   **5.** \$217.48   **7.** \$86.26
9. \$158.82   **11.** \$31.25; \$187.50   **13.** \$234.38; \$4687.50
15. \$81.25; \$1625   **17.** \$12,105   **19.** \$6727.50
21. Answers vary.   **23.** \$14,354.07   **25.** \$15,089.46
27. \$19,996.25; about .07501%   **29.** \$15,491.86; about .105087%
31. \$19,752; about 5.0223%   **33.** \$15,117.92; about 5.0545%

35. (a) $9450 **(b)** $19,110 **37.** $3056.25 **39.** 5.0%
41. 4 months **43.** $1750.04 **45.** $5825.24 **47.** 3.5%
49. About 11.36% **51.** About 102.91%. Ouch! **53.** $13,725; yes
55. (a) $y_1 = 8t + 100$; $y_2 = 6t + 200$
(b) The graph of y_1 is a line with slope 8 and y-intercept 100. The graph of y_2 is a line with slope 6 and y-intercept 200.

(c)

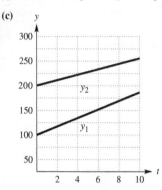

(d) The y-intercept of each graph indicates the amount invested. The slope of each graph is the annual amount of interest paid.

Section 5.2 (Page 241)

1. Answers vary. **3.** Interest rate and number of compounding periods
5. Answers vary. **7.** $1265.32; $265.32 **9.** $1204.75; $734.75
11. $9297.93; $2797.93 **13.** $10,090.41; $90.41
15. $5081.63; $81.63 **17.** $107,896.09; $7,896.09 **19.** 3.75%
21. 5.25% **23.** $23,824.92; $3824.92 **25.** $31,664.54; $1664.54
27. $10,000 **29.** $20,000 **31.** 4.04% **33.** 5.095%
35. $8954.58 **37.** $11,572.58 **39.** $4203.64 **41.** $9963.10
43. $4606.57 **45.** $465.85 **47.** $1000 now **49.** $21,570.27
51. Treasury note **53.** $1000 now **55.** 3.59%
57. Flagstar, 4.45%; Principal, 4.46%; Principal paid a higher APY
59. About $2,259,696 **61.** About $21,043 **63.** 23.4 years
65. 14.2 years **67.** About 11.9 years **69. (a)** $16,659.95
(b) $21,472.67 **71. (a)**

Section 5.3 (Page 249)

1. 21.5786 **3.** $119,625.61 **5.** $23,242.87 **7.** $72,482.38
9. About $205,490 **11.** About $310,831 **13.** $797.36
15. $4566.33 **17.** $152.53 **19.** 5.19% **21.** 5.223%
23. Answers vary. **25.** $6603.39 **27.** $234,295.32
29. $26,671.23 **31.** $3928.88 **33.** $620.46 **35.** $265.71
37. $280,686.25 **39. (a)** $173,497.86 **(b)** $144,493.82
(c) $29,004.04 **41. (a)** $552,539.96 **(b)** $854,433.28
43. $32,426.46 **45.** $284,527.35 **47. (a)** $256.08 **(b)** $247.81
49. $863.68 **51. (a)** $1200 **(b)** $3511.58 **53.** 6.5%
55. (a) Answers vary. **(b)** $24,000 **(c)** $603,229 **(d)** $84,000
(e) $460,884

Section 5.4 (Page 261)

1. Answers vary. **3.** $8693.71 **5.** $1,566,346.66
7. $11,468.10 **9.** $38,108.61 **11.** $557.68 **13.** $6272.14
15. $119,379.35 **17.** $97,122.49 **19.** $48,677.34
21. $15,537.76 **23.** $9093.14 **25.** $446.31 **27.** $11,331.18
29. $589.31 **31.** $979.21 **33.** $925.29
35. $594.72; $13,818.25 **37.** $947.69; $151,223.33 **39.** $6.80
41. $42.04 **43.** $30,669,881 **45.** $24,761,633
47. (a) $1465.42 **(b)** $214.58 **49.** $2320.83
51. $414.18; $14,701.60 **53. (a)** $2717.36 **(b)** 2
55. (a) $969.75 **(b)** $185,658.15 **(c)** $143,510
57. About $8143.79 **59.** $406.53 **61.** $663.22

63.

Payment Number	Amount of Payment	Interest for Period	Portion to Principal	Principal at End of Period
0	–	–	–	$4000.00
1	$1207.68	$320.00	$887.68	3112.32
2	1207.68	248.99	958.69	2153.63
3	1207.68	172.29	1035.39	1118.24
4	1207.70	89.46	1118.24	0

65.

Payment Number	Amount of Payment	Interest for Period	Portion to Principal	Principal at End of Period
0	–	–	–	$7184.00
1	$189.18	$71.84	117.34	7066.66
2	189.18	70.67	118.51	6948.15
3	189.18	69.48	119.70	6828.45
4	189.18	68.28	120.90	6707.55

Chapter 5 Review Exercises (Page 265)

Refer to Section	5.1	5.2	5.3	5.4
For Exercises	1–14	15–28, 65–66, 71	32–41, 67–70, 75–76	29–31, 42–64, 72–74, 77–79

1. $292.08 **3.** $62.05 **5.** $285; $3420 **7.** $7925.67
9. Answers vary. **11.** $78,742.54 **13.** About 4.082%
15. $5634.15; $2834.15 **17.** $20,402.98; $7499.53 **19.** $8532.58
21. $15,000 **23.** 5.0625% **25.** $18,207.65 **27.** $1088.54
29. $9706.74 **31.** Answers vary. **33.** $162,753.15
35. $22,643.29 **37.** Answers vary. **39.** $2619.29 **41.** $916.12
43. $31,921.91 **45.** $14,222.42 **47.** $136,340.32
49. $1194.02 **51.** $38,298.04 **53.** $3581.11 **55.** $435.66
57. $85,459.20 **59.** $81.98 **61.** $502.49
63. (a) $7,233,333.33 **(b)** $136,427,623.40
65. $2298.58 **67.** $24,818.76; $2418.76 **69.** $12,538.59
71. $5596.62 **73.** $3560.61 **75.** $222,221.02 **77. (d)**

Case Study 5 Exercises (Page 268)

1. (a) $22,549.94 **(b)** $36,442.38 **(c)** $66,402.34
3. (a) $40,722.37 **(b)** $41,090.49 **(c)** $41,175.24 **(d)** $41,216.62
(e) $41,218.03 **5. (a)** About 4.603% **(b)** About 5.866%
(c) About 7.681%

Chapter 6

Section 6.1 (Page 275)

1. Yes **3.** $(-1, -4)$ **5.** $\left(\dfrac{2}{7}, -\dfrac{11}{7}\right)$ **7.** $\left(\dfrac{11}{5}, -\dfrac{7}{5}\right)$
9. $(28, 22)$ **11.** $(2, -1)$ **13.** No solution **15.** $(4y + 1, y)$
for any real number y **17.** $(5, 10)$ **19. (a)** About 51.8 weeks;
$959,091 **(b)** Answers vary. **21.** 2025 **23.** 2058
25. 145 adults; 55 children **27.** Plane: 550 mph; wind: 50 mph
29. 300 of Boeing; 100 of GE **31. (a)** $y = x + 1$
(b) $y = 3x + 4$ **(c)** $\left(-\dfrac{3}{2}, -\dfrac{1}{2}\right)$

Section 6.2 (Page 286)

1. $\begin{aligned} x \quad\quad - 3z &= 2 \\ 2x - 4y + 5z &= 1 \\ 5x - 8y + 7z &= 6 \\ 3x - 4y + 2z &= 3 \end{aligned}$ **3.** $\begin{aligned} 3x \quad\quad + z + 2w + 18v &= 0 \\ -4x + y \quad\quad - w - 24v &= 0 \\ 7x - y + z + 3w + 42v &= 0 \\ 4x \quad\quad + z + 2w + 24v &= 0 \end{aligned}$

5.
$$x + y + 2z + 3w = 1$$
$$- y - z - 2w = -1$$
$$3x + y + 4z + 5w = 2$$

7.
$$x + 12y - 3z + 4w = 10$$
$$2y + 3z + w = 4$$
$$- z = -7$$
$$6y - 2z - 3w = 0$$

9. $(-68, 13, -6, 3)$ **11.** $\left(20, -9, \dfrac{15}{2}, 3\right)$ **13.** $\begin{bmatrix} 2 & 1 & 1 & | & 3 \\ 3 & -4 & 2 & | & -5 \\ 1 & 1 & 1 & | & 2 \end{bmatrix}$

15.
$$2x + 3y + 8z = 20$$
$$x + 4y + 6z = 12$$
$$3y + 5z = 10$$

17. $\begin{bmatrix} 1 & 2 & 3 & | & -1 \\ 2 & 0 & 7 & | & -4 \\ 6 & 5 & 4 & | & 6 \end{bmatrix}$

19. $\begin{bmatrix} -4 & -3 & 1 & -1 & | & 2 \\ 0 & -4 & 7 & -2 & | & 10 \\ 0 & -2 & 9 & 4 & | & 5 \end{bmatrix}$ **21.** $\left(\dfrac{3}{2}, 17, -5, 0\right)$

23. $(12 - w, -3 - 2w, -5, w)$ for any real number w **25.** Dependent

27. Inconsistent   **29.** Independent   **31.** $\left(\dfrac{3}{2}, \dfrac{3}{2}, -\dfrac{3}{2}\right)$

33. $(-.8, -1.8, .8)$ **35.** $(100, 50, 50)$ **37.** $(0, 3.5, 1.5)$

39. $(-3, 4, 0)$ **41.** $(1, 0, -1)$ **43.** $(-93, -31, 10)$

45. No solution   **47.** $(192, 125.5, -148.5)$

49. $\left(\dfrac{1 - z}{2}, \dfrac{11 - z}{2}, z\right)$ for any real number z **51.** No solution

53. $(-7, 5)$ **55.** $(-1, 2)$ **57.** $(-3, z - 17, z)$ for any real number z

59. $(-11.5, 13.75, -2.25, -5)$ **61.** No solution

63. $\left(\dfrac{1}{2}, \dfrac{1}{3}, -\dfrac{1}{4}\right)$ **65.** 2012; 5000 people

67. 220 adults; 150 teenagers; 200 children

69.

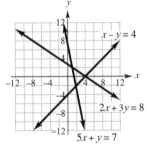

There is no point that is on all three lines.

71. $y = .75x^2 + .25x - .5$

Section 6.3 (Page 294)

1. 100 vans, 50 small trucks, 25 large trucks   **3.** 10 units of corn; 25 units of soybeans; 40 units of cottonseed   **5.** Shirt $1.99; slacks $4.99; sports coat $6.49   **7.** 220 adults; 150 teenagers; 200 preteens

9. $20,000 in AAA; $10,000 in B; none in A   **11.** 40 lb pretzels, 20 lb dried fruit, 80 lb nuts   **13.** Four possible solutions: (i) no cases of A and D; 12 cases of B; 8 cases of C; (ii) 1 of A; 8 of B; 9 of C; 1 of D; (iii) 2 of A; 4 of B; 10 of C; 2 of D; (iv) 3 of A; none of B; 11 of C; 3 of D

15. $13,750 in the mutual fund, $27,500 in bonds, and $28,750 in the franchise   **17.** (a) $b + c$ (b) .35, .45, .2; A is tumorous, B is bone, and C is healthy.

19. (a) $x_2 + x_3 = 700$
$\quad\quad x_3 + x_4 = 600$
(b) $(1000 - x_4, 100 + x_4, 600 - x_4, x_4)$ (c) 600; 0
(d) x_1: 1000; 400
$\quad x_2$: 700; 100
$\quad x_3$: 600; 0
(e) Answers vary.   **21.** 4 cups of Hearty Chicken Rotini, 5 cups of Hearty Chicken, and 6 cups of Chunky Chicken Noodle; serving size 1.5 cups

23. (a) $12,000 at 6%, $7000 at 7%, and $6000 at 10%
(b) $10,000 at 6%, $15,000 at 7%, and $5000 at 10%
(c) $20,000 at 6%, $10,000 at 7%, and $10,000 at 10%

25. (a) $f(x) = -.008x^2 + 1.6x + 140.8$ (b) 169.6 million

27. (a) $y = .01x^2 - .3x + 4.24$ (b) 15 platters; $1.99
29. (a) $C = -.0000108S^2 + .034896S + 22.9$ (b) About 864.7 knots

Section 6.4 (Page 303)

1. 2×3; $\begin{bmatrix} -7 & 8 & -4 \\ 0 & -13 & -9 \end{bmatrix}$ **3.** 3×3; square matrix; $\begin{bmatrix} 3 & 0 & -11 \\ -1 & -\frac{1}{4} & 7 \\ -5 & 3 & -9 \end{bmatrix}$ **5.** 2×1; column matrix; $\begin{bmatrix} -7 \\ -11 \end{bmatrix}$

7. B is a 5×3 zero matrix.   **9.** $\begin{bmatrix} -7 & 14 & 2 & 4 \\ 6 & -3 & 2 & -4 \end{bmatrix}$

11. $\begin{bmatrix} 3 & -1 & 2 \\ 3 & 1 & 5 \end{bmatrix}$ **13.** $\begin{bmatrix} -4 & -7 & 7 \\ 6 & 3 & -8 \end{bmatrix}$

15. Not defined   **17.** $\begin{bmatrix} -4 & 0 \\ 10 & 6 \end{bmatrix}$ **19.** $\begin{bmatrix} 0 & -8 \\ -16 & 24 \end{bmatrix}$

21. $\begin{bmatrix} 8 & 10 \\ 0 & -42 \end{bmatrix}$ **23.** $\begin{bmatrix} 4 & -\frac{7}{2} \\ 4 & \frac{21}{2} \end{bmatrix}$

25. $X + T = \begin{bmatrix} x & y \\ z & w \end{bmatrix} + \begin{bmatrix} r & s \\ t & u \end{bmatrix} = \begin{bmatrix} x + r & y + s \\ z + t & w + u \end{bmatrix}$; a 2×2 matrix

27. $X + (T + P) = \begin{bmatrix} x + (r + m) & y + (s + n) \\ z + (t + p) & w + (u + q) \end{bmatrix}$
$\quad\quad = \begin{bmatrix} (x + r) + m & (y + s) + n \\ (z + t) + p & (w + u) + q \end{bmatrix} = (X + T) + P$

29. $P + O = \begin{bmatrix} m + 0 & n + 0 \\ p + 0 & q + 0 \end{bmatrix} = \begin{bmatrix} m & n \\ p & q \end{bmatrix} = P$

31. Several possible correct answers, including

	Basketball	Hockey	Football	Baseball
Percent of no shows	16	16	20	18
Lost revenue per fan ($)	18.20	18.25	19	15.40
Lost annual revenue (millions $)	22.7	35.8	51.9	96.3

33.

	2009	2010	2011
Heart	2674	2874	2813
Lung	1799	1759	1630
Liver	15,094	15,394	15,330
Kidney	79,397	83,919	86,547

35. (a)

	Bread	Milk	Peanut Butter	Cold Cuts
I	88	48	16	112
II	105	72	21	147
III	60	40	0	50

(b) $\begin{bmatrix} 110 & 60 & 20 & 140 \\ 140 & 96 & 28 & 196 \\ 66 & 44 & 0 & 55 \end{bmatrix}$ (c) $\begin{bmatrix} 198 & 108 & 36 & 252 \\ 245 & 168 & 49 & 343 \\ 126 & 84 & 0 & 105 \end{bmatrix}$

37. (a) $A = \begin{bmatrix} 2.61 & 4.39 & 6.29 & 9.08 \\ 1.63 & 2.77 & 4.61 & 6.92 \\ .92 & .75 & .62 & .54 \end{bmatrix}$

(b) $B = \begin{bmatrix} 1.38 & 1.72 & 1.94 & 3.31 \\ 1.26 & 1.48 & 2.82 & 2.28 \\ .41 & .33 & .27 & .40 \end{bmatrix}$ (c) $\begin{bmatrix} 1.23 & 2.67 & 4.35 & 5.77 \\ .37 & 1.29 & 1.79 & 4.64 \\ .51 & .42 & .35 & .14 \end{bmatrix}$

Section 6.5 (Page 314)

1. 2×2; 2×2 **3.** 3×3; 5×5 **5.** AB does not exist; 3×2

7. columns; rows   **9.** $\begin{bmatrix} 5 \\ 9 \end{bmatrix}$ **11.** $\begin{bmatrix} -2 & 4 \\ 0 & -8 \end{bmatrix}$ **13.** $\begin{bmatrix} -4 & 1 \\ 2 & -3 \end{bmatrix}$

15. $\begin{bmatrix} 3 & -5 & 7 \\ -2 & 1 & 6 \\ 0 & -3 & 4 \end{bmatrix}$ **17.** $\begin{bmatrix} 16 & 10 \\ 2 & 28 \\ 58 & 46 \end{bmatrix}$

19. $AB = \begin{bmatrix} -30 & -45 \\ 20 & 30 \end{bmatrix}$, but $BA = \begin{bmatrix} 0 & 0 \\ 0 & 0 \end{bmatrix}$.

21. $(A + B)(A - B) = \begin{bmatrix} -7 & -24 \\ -28 & -33 \end{bmatrix}$, but $A^2 - B^2 = \begin{bmatrix} -37 & -69 \\ -8 & -3 \end{bmatrix}$.

23. $(PX)T = \begin{bmatrix} (mx + nz)r + (my + nw)t & (mx + nz)s + (my + nw)u \\ (px + qz)r + (py + qw)t & (px + qz)s + (py + qw)u \end{bmatrix}$.

$P(XT)$ is the same, so $(PX)T = P(XT)$.

25. $k(X + T) = k\begin{bmatrix} x + r & y + s \\ z + t & w + u \end{bmatrix}$

$= \begin{bmatrix} k(x + r) & k(y + s) \\ k(z + t) & k(w + u) \end{bmatrix}$

$= \begin{bmatrix} kx + kr & ky + ks \\ kz + kt & kw + ku \end{bmatrix}$

$= \begin{bmatrix} kx & ky \\ kz & kw \end{bmatrix} + \begin{bmatrix} kr & ks \\ kt & ku \end{bmatrix} = kX + kT$

27. No   **29.** Yes   **31.** Yes   **33.** $\begin{bmatrix} 2 & 3 \\ 1 & 2 \end{bmatrix}$ **35.** $\begin{bmatrix} 1 & 2 \\ 1 & 1 \end{bmatrix}$

37. No inverse   **39.** $\begin{bmatrix} -4 & -2 & 3 \\ -5 & -2 & 3 \\ 2 & 1 & -1 \end{bmatrix}$ **41.** $\begin{bmatrix} 2 & 1 & -1 \\ 8 & 2 & -5 \\ -11 & -3 & 7 \end{bmatrix}$

43. No inverse   **45.** $\begin{bmatrix} 6 & -5 & 8 \\ -1 & 1 & -1 \\ -1 & 1 & -2 \end{bmatrix}$ **47.** $\begin{bmatrix} \frac{1}{2} & -1 & -\frac{1}{2} & \frac{1}{2} \\ \frac{1}{2} & 4 & \frac{5}{2} & -\frac{1}{2} \\ -\frac{1}{4} & -\frac{1}{2} & -\frac{1}{4} & \frac{1}{4} \\ \frac{1}{2} & -2 & -\frac{3}{2} & \frac{1}{2} \end{bmatrix}$

49. (a) $A = \begin{bmatrix} 3719 & 727 & 521 & 313 \\ 4164 & 738 & 590 & 345 \\ 4566 & 744 & 652 & 374 \end{bmatrix}$

(b) $B = \begin{bmatrix} .019 & .007 \\ .011 & .011 \\ .019 & .006 \\ .024 & .008 \end{bmatrix}$ **(c)** $AB = \begin{bmatrix} 96 & 40 \\ 107 & 44 \\ 116 & 47 \end{bmatrix}$

(d) The rows represent the years 2000, 2010, 2020. Column 1 gives the total births (in millions) in those years and column 2 the total deaths (in millions)   **(e)** About 107 million; about 47 million

51. (a) $A = \begin{bmatrix} 195 & 143 & 1225 & 1341 \\ 210 & 141 & 1387 & 1388 \end{bmatrix}$ **(b)** $B = \begin{bmatrix} .016 & .006 \\ .011 & .014 \\ .023 & .008 \\ .013 & .007 \end{bmatrix}$

(c) $AB = \begin{bmatrix} 50 & 22 \\ 55 & 24 \end{bmatrix}$ **(d)** The rows represent the years 2010 and 2020. Column 1 gives the total births (in millions) in those years and column 2 the total deaths (in millions).   **(e)** About 22 million; about 55 million

53. (a) $\begin{array}{c} \\ \text{Dept. 1} \\ \text{Dept. 2} \\ \text{Dept. 3} \\ \text{Dept. 4} \end{array} \begin{array}{cc} A & B \\ \begin{bmatrix} 254 & 290 \\ 199 & 240 \\ 170 & 216 \\ 174 & 170 \end{bmatrix} \end{array}$ **(b)** supplier A: $797; supplier B: $916; buy from A.

55. (a) $\begin{array}{c} \\ \text{Burgers} \\ \text{Fries} \\ \text{Drinks} \end{array} \begin{array}{ccc} \text{I} & \text{II} & \text{III} \\ \begin{bmatrix} 900 & 1500 & 1150 \\ 600 & 950 & 800 \\ 750 & 900 & 825 \end{bmatrix} \end{array} = S$

(b) $\begin{array}{ccc} \text{Burgers} & \text{Fries} & \text{Drinks} \\ [\, 3.00 & 1.80 & 1.20\,] \end{array}$

(c) $PS = [4680 \quad 7290 \quad 5880]$ **(d)** $17,850

Section 6.6 (Page 325)

1. $\begin{bmatrix} 2 \\ -2 \end{bmatrix}$ **3.** $\begin{bmatrix} \frac{1}{2} & 1 \\ \frac{3}{2} & 1 \end{bmatrix}$ **5.** $\begin{bmatrix} -7 \\ 15 \\ -3 \end{bmatrix}$ **7.** $(-63, 50, -9)$

9. $(-31, -131, 181)$ **11.** $(-48, 8, 12)$ **13.** $(1, 0, 2, 1)$ **15.** $\begin{bmatrix} -6 \\ -14 \end{bmatrix}$

17. 60 buffets; 600 chairs; 100 tables   **19.** 2340 of the first species, 10,128 of the second species, 224 of the third species   **21.** jeans $34.50; jacket $72; sweater $44; shirt $21.75   **23.** $\begin{bmatrix} 6.43 \\ 26.12 \end{bmatrix}$ **25.** About 1073 metric tons of wheat, about 1431 metric tons of oil   **27.** Gas $98 million, electric $123 million   **29. (a)** $\frac{7}{4}$ bushels of yams, $\frac{15}{8} \approx 2$ pigs

(b) 167.5 bushels of yams, $153.75 \approx 154$ pigs   **31. (a)** .40 unit of agriculture, .12 unit of manufacturing, and 3.60 units of households **(b)** 848 units of agriculture, 516 units of manufacturing, and 2970 units of households   **(c)** About 813 units   **33. (a)** .017 unit of manufacturing and .216 unit of energy   **(b)** 123,725,000 pounds of agriculture, 14,792,000 pounds of manufacturing, 1,488,000 pounds of energy **(c)** 195,492,000 pounds of agriculture, 25,933,000 pounds of manufacturing, 13,580,000 pounds of energy   **35.** $532 million of natural resources, $481 million of manufacturing, $805 million of trade and services, $1185 million of personal consumption

37. (a) $\begin{bmatrix} 1.67 & .56 & .56 \\ .19 & 1.17 & .06 \\ 3.15 & 3.27 & 4.38 \end{bmatrix}$

(b) These multipliers imply that, if the demand for one community's output increases by $1, then the output of the other community will increase by the amount in the row and column of that matrix. For example, if the demand for Hermitage's output increases by $1, then output from Sharon will increase by $.56, from Farrell by $.06, and from Hermitage by $4.38.

39. $\begin{bmatrix} 23 \\ 51 \end{bmatrix}, \begin{bmatrix} 13 \\ 30 \end{bmatrix}, \begin{bmatrix} 45 \\ 96 \end{bmatrix}, \begin{bmatrix} 69 \\ 156 \end{bmatrix}, \begin{bmatrix} 87 \\ 194 \end{bmatrix}, \begin{bmatrix} 23 \\ 51 \end{bmatrix}, \begin{bmatrix} 51 \\ 110 \end{bmatrix}, \begin{bmatrix} 45 \\ 102 \end{bmatrix}, \begin{bmatrix} 69 \\ 157 \end{bmatrix}$

41. (a) 3   **(b)** 3   **(c)** 5   **(d)** 3

43. (a) $B = \begin{bmatrix} 0 & 2 & 3 \\ 2 & 0 & 4 \\ 3 & 4 & 0 \end{bmatrix}$ **(b)** $B^2 = \begin{bmatrix} 13 & 12 & 8 \\ 12 & 20 & 6 \\ 8 & 6 & 25 \end{bmatrix}$ **(c)** 12   **(d)** 14

45. (a) $C = \begin{array}{c} \\ \text{Dogs} \\ \text{Rats} \\ \text{Cats} \\ \text{Mice} \end{array} \begin{array}{cccc} \text{Dogs} & \text{Rats} & \text{Cats} & \text{Mice} \\ \begin{bmatrix} 0 & 1 & 1 & 1 \\ 0 & 0 & 0 & 1 \\ 0 & 1 & 0 & 1 \\ 0 & 0 & 0 & 0 \end{bmatrix} \end{array}$

(b) $\begin{bmatrix} 0 & 1 & 0 & 2 \\ 0 & 0 & 0 & 0 \\ 0 & 0 & 0 & 1 \\ 0 & 0 & 0 & 0 \end{bmatrix}$; C^2 gives the number of food sources once removed from the feeder.

Chapter 6 Review Exercises (Page 330)

Refer to Section	6.1	6.2	6.3	6.4	6.5	6.6
For Exercises	1–10	11–16	17–20, 79–86	21–38	39–66	67–78, 87–94

1. $(9, -14)$ **3.** $(2, -2)$ **5.** 100 shares of first stock; 300 shares of second stock   **7.** Inconsistent, no solution   **9.** $(-18, 69, 12)$ **11.** $(-14, 17, 11)$ **13.** No solution   **15.** $(4, 3, 2)$ **17.** 19 ones; 7 fives; 9 tens   **19.** 5 blankets; 3 rugs; 8 skirts   **21.** 2×2; square

23. 1×4; row   **25.** 2×3 **27.** $\begin{bmatrix} 542.10 & -6.93 & 12,605,900 \\ 52.37 & .53 & 3,616,100 \\ 44.06 & -.21 & 11,227,700 \end{bmatrix}$

29. $\begin{bmatrix} -1 & -2 & 3 \\ -2 & -3 & 0 \\ 0 & -1 & -4 \end{bmatrix}$ **31.** $\begin{bmatrix} 14 & 6 \\ -4 & 4 \\ 13 & 23 \end{bmatrix}$ **33.** Not defined

35. $\begin{bmatrix} 2 & 18 \\ -4 & -12 \\ 7 & 13 \end{bmatrix}$ **37.** $\begin{bmatrix} -6.93 & 12,605,900 \\ .53 & 3,616,100 \\ -.21 & 11,227,700 \end{bmatrix}$;

$\begin{bmatrix} -15.1 & 21,226,200 \\ .51 & 3,397,000 \\ .24 & 14,930,400 \end{bmatrix}$; $\begin{bmatrix} -22.03 & 33,832,100 \\ 1.04 & 7,013,100 \\ .03 & 26,158,100 \end{bmatrix}$

39. $\begin{bmatrix} 14 & 56 \\ -6 & -22 \\ 19 & 79 \end{bmatrix}$ **41.** Not defined   **43.** $\begin{bmatrix} 322 & 420 \\ -126 & -166 \\ 455 & 591 \end{bmatrix}$

45. About 20 head and face injuries; about 12 concussions; about 3 neck injuries; about 55 other injuries

47. (a) $\begin{array}{cc} \text{Cost} & \text{Earnings} \\ \begin{bmatrix} 61.17 & 1 \\ 60.50 & .84 \\ 96.21 & 1.88 \end{bmatrix} \end{array}$ (b) $[100 \quad 500 \quad 200]$

(c) Total cost $55,609; total dividend $896

49. Many correct answers, including $\begin{bmatrix} 1 & 2 \\ 3 & 4 \end{bmatrix}$ **51.** $\begin{bmatrix} -.5 & .2 \\ 0 & .2 \end{bmatrix}$

53. No inverse   **55.** $\begin{bmatrix} \frac{1}{4} & \frac{1}{2} & \frac{1}{2} \\ \frac{1}{4} & -\frac{1}{2} & \frac{1}{2} \\ \frac{1}{12} & -\frac{1}{6} & -\frac{1}{6} \end{bmatrix}$ **57.** No inverse

59. $\begin{bmatrix} -\frac{2}{3} & -\frac{17}{3} & -\frac{14}{3} & -3 \\ \frac{1}{3} & \frac{1}{3} & \frac{1}{3} & 0 \\ -\frac{1}{3} & -\frac{10}{3} & -\frac{7}{3} & -2 \\ 0 & 2 & 1 & 1 \end{bmatrix}$ **61.** $\begin{bmatrix} -\frac{7}{19} & \frac{2}{19} \\ \frac{6}{19} & \frac{1}{19} \end{bmatrix}$

63. $\begin{bmatrix} -\frac{1}{12} & -\frac{1}{4} \\ \frac{5}{12} & \frac{1}{4} \end{bmatrix}$ **65.** $\begin{bmatrix} -1.2 & 1.1 & -.9 \\ .8 & -.4 & .6 \\ -.2 & .1 & .1 \end{bmatrix}$ **67.** $\begin{bmatrix} -5 \\ -3 \end{bmatrix}$

69. $\begin{bmatrix} -22 \\ -18 \\ 15 \end{bmatrix}$ **71.** $(-4, 2)$ **73.** $(4, 2)$ **75.** $(-1, 0, 2)$

77. No inverse; no solution for the system   **79.** 16 liters of the 9%; 24 liters of the 14%   **81.** 30 liters of 40% solution; 10 liters of 60% solution   **83.** 80 bowls; 120 plates   **85.** $12,750 at 8%; $27,250 at 8.5%; $10,000 at 11%

87. (a) $\begin{bmatrix} 1 & -\frac{1}{4} \\ -\frac{1}{2} & 1 \end{bmatrix}$ (b) $\begin{bmatrix} \frac{8}{7} & \frac{2}{7} \\ \frac{4}{7} & \frac{8}{7} \end{bmatrix}$ (c) $\begin{bmatrix} 2800 \\ 2800 \end{bmatrix}$

89. Agriculture $140,909; manufacturing $95,455

91. (a) .4 unit agriculture; .09 unit construction; .4 unit energy; .1 unit manufacturing; .9 unit transportation   (b) 2000 units of agriculture; 600 units of construction; 1700 units of energy; 3700 units of manufacturing; 2500 units of transportation   (c) 29,049 units of agriculture; 9869 units of construction; 52,362 units of energy; 61,520 units of manufacturing; 90,987 units of transportation

93. $\begin{bmatrix} 54 \\ 32 \end{bmatrix}, \begin{bmatrix} 134 \\ 89 \end{bmatrix}, \begin{bmatrix} 172 \\ 113 \end{bmatrix}, \begin{bmatrix} 118 \\ 74 \end{bmatrix}, \begin{bmatrix} 208 \\ 131 \end{bmatrix}$

Case Study 6 Exercises (Page 335)

1. All Stampede Air cities except Lubbock may be reached by a two-flight sequence from San Antonio; all Stampede cities may be reached by a three-flight sequence.

3. The connection between Lubbock and Corpus Christi and the connection between Lubbock and San Antonio take three flights.

5. $B^2 = \begin{bmatrix} 2 & 1 & 1 & 1 & 1 \\ 1 & 1 & 1 & 1 & 0 \\ 1 & 1 & 1 & 1 & 0 \\ 1 & 1 & 1 & 2 & 1 \\ 1 & 0 & 0 & 1 & 4 \end{bmatrix}$; an entry is nonzero whenever there is a two-step sequence between the cities.

Index of Companies, Products, and Agencies

Index of Applications

Business

Physical Science

Social Science

Subject Index

Photo Credits

COMPOUND AMOUNT

If P dollars is deposited for n time periods at a compound interest rate i per period, the **compound amount** A is

$$A = P(1 + i)^n.$$

Consider an ordinary annuity of n payments of R dollars each at the end of consecutive interest periods with interest compounded at a rate of i per period. The **future value** S of the annuity is:

$$S = R\left[\frac{(1 + i)^n - 1}{i}\right].$$

The **present value** P of the annuity is:

$$P = R\left[\frac{1 - (1 + i)^{-n}}{i}\right].$$

The **matrix** version of the elimination method uses the following **matrix row operations** to obtain the augmented matrix of an equivalent system. They correspond to using elementary row operations on a system of equations.

1. Interchange any two rows.
2. Multiply each element of a row by a nonzero constant.
3. Replace a row by the sum of itself and a constant multiple of another row in the matrix.

UNION RULE

For any events E and F from a sample space S.

$$P(E \cup F) = P(E) + P(F) - P(E \cap F).$$

PROPERTIES OF PROBABILITY

Let S be a sample space consisting of n distinct outcomes $s_1, s_2, \ldots, s_n$. An acceptable probability assignment consists of assigning to each outcome s_1 a number p_1 (the probability of s_1) according to these rules.

1. The probability of each outcome is a number between 0 and 1.

$$0 \le p_1 \le 1, \quad 0 \le p_2 \le 1, \quad \ldots, \quad 0 \le p_n \le 1.$$

2. The sum of the probabilities of all possible outcomes is 1.

$$p_1 + p_2 + p_3 + \cdots + p_n = 1.$$

BAYES' FORMULA

For any events E and $F_1, F_2, \ldots, F_n$, from a sample space S, where $F_1 \cup F_2 \ldots \cup F_n = S$,

$$P(F_i | E) = \frac{P(F_i) \cdot P(E | F_i)}{P(F_1) \cdot P(E | F_1) + \cdots + P(F_n) \cdot P(E | F_n)}.$$

PERMUTATIONS

The number of permutations of n elements taken r at a time, where $r \leq n$, is

$$_nP_r = \frac{n!}{(n-r)!}.$$

COMBINATIONS

The number of combinations of n elements taken r at a time, where $r \leq n$, is

$$_nC_r = \binom{n}{r} = \frac{n!}{(n-r)!r!}.$$

BINOMIAL PROBABILITY

If p is the probability of success in a single trial of a binomial experiment, the probability of x successes and $n - x$ failures in n independent repeated trials of the experiment is

$$_nC_r p^x (1-p)^{n-x}.$$

MEAN

The mean of the n numbers, $x_1, x_2, x_3, \ldots, x_n$, is

$$\bar{x} = \frac{x_1 + x_2 + \cdots + x_n}{n} = \frac{\Sigma(x)}{n}.$$

SAMPLE STANDARD DEVIATION

The standard deviation of a sample of n numbers, $x_1, x_2, x_3, \ldots, x_n$, with mean $\bar{x}$, is

$$s = \sqrt{\frac{\Sigma(x - \bar{x})^2}{n-1}}.$$

BINOMIAL DISTRIBUTION

Suppose an experiment is a series of n independent repeated trials, where the probability of a success in a single trial is always p. Let x be the number of successes in the n trials. Then the probability that exactly x successes will occur in n trials is given by

$$_nC_r p^x (1-p)^{n-x}.$$

The mean μ and variance σ^2 of a binomial distribution are, respectively,

$$\mu = np \quad \text{and} \quad \sigma^2 = np(1-p).$$

The standard deviation is

$$\sigma = \sqrt{np(1-p)}.$$

The **derivative** of the function f is the function denoted f' whose value at the number x is defined to be the number

$$f'(x) = \lim_{h \to 0} \frac{f(x + h) - f(x)}{h},$$

provided this limit exists.

RULES FOR DERIVATIVES

Assume all indicated derivatives exist.

Constant Function   If $f(x) = k$, where k is any real number, then

$$f'(x) = 0.$$

Power Rule   If $f(x) = x^n$, for any real number n, then

$$f'(x) = n \cdot x^{n-1}.$$

Constant Times a Function   Let k be a real number. Then the derivative of $y = k \cdot f(x)$ is

$$y' = k \cdot f'(x).$$

Sum or Difference Rule   If $y = f(x) \pm g(x)$, then

$$y' = f'(x) \pm g'(x).$$

Product Rule   If $f(x) = g(x) \cdot k(x)$, then

$$f'(x) = g(x) \cdot k'(x) + k(x) \cdot g'(x).$$

Quotient Rule   If $f(x) = \dfrac{g(x)}{k(x)}$, and $k(x) \neq 0$, then

$$f'(x) = \frac{k(x) \cdot g'(x) - g(x) \cdot k'(x)}{[k(x)]^2}.$$

Chain Rule   Let $y = f[g(x)]$. Then

$$y' = f'[g(x)] \cdot g'(x).$$

Chain Rule (Alternative Form)   If y is a function of u, say $y = f(u)$, and if u is a function of x, say $u = g(x)$, then $y = f[g(x)]$, and

$$\frac{dy}{dx} = \frac{dy}{du} \cdot \frac{du}{dx}.$$

Generalized Power Rule   Let u be a function of x, and let $y = u^n$ for any real number n. Then

$$y' = n \cdot u^{n-1} \cdot u'.$$

Exponential Function   If $y = e^{g(x)}$, then

$$y' = g'(x) \cdot e^{g(x)}.$$

Natural Logarithmic Function   If $y = \ln |g(x)|$, then

$$y' = \frac{g'(x)}{g(x)}.$$

FIRST DERIVATIVE TEST

Assume that $a < c < b$ and that c is the only critical number for a function f in the interval $[a, b]$. Assume that f is differentiable for all x in $[a, b]$ except possibly at $x = c$.

1. If $f'(a) > 0$ and $f'(b) < 0$, then there is a local maximum at c.
2. If $f'(a) < 0$ and $f'(b) > 0$, then there is a local minimum at c.
3. If $f'(a)$ and $f'(b)$ are both positive, or both negative, then there is no local extremum at c.

SECOND DERIVATIVE TEST

Let c be a critical number of the function f such that $f'(c) = 0$ and $f''(x)$ exists for all x in some open interval containing c.

1. If $f''(c) > 0$, then f has a local minimum at c.
2. If $f''(c) < 0$, then f has a local maximum at c.
3. If $f''(c) = 0$, then this test gives no information; use the first derivative test.

BASIC INTEGRALS

$$\int x^n \, dx = \frac{1}{n+1} x^{n+1} + C \quad \text{(if } n \neq -1\text{)}$$

$$\int e^{kx} \, dx = \frac{1}{k} e^{kx} + C \quad \text{(if } k \text{ is any real number, } k \neq 0\text{)}$$

$$\int \frac{a}{x} \, dx = a \ln |x| + C \quad \text{(if } x \neq 0\text{)}$$

SUBSTITUTION METHOD

Form of the Integral	*Form of the Antiderivative*
1. $\int [u(x)]^n \cdot u'(x) \, dx, \ n \neq -1$	$\dfrac{[u(x)]^{n+1}}{n+1} + C$
2. $\int e^{u(x)} \cdot u'(x) \, dx$	$e^{u(x)} + C$
3. $\int \dfrac{u'(x) dx}{u(x)}$	$\ln |u(x)| + C$

TEST FOR LOCAL EXTREMA

Suppose $f(x, y)$ is a function such that f_{xx}, f_{yy}, f_{xy} all exist. Let (a, b) be a critical point for which

$$f_x(a, b) = 0 \quad \text{and} \quad f_y(a, b) = 0.$$

Let M be the number defined by

$$M = f_{xx}(a, b) \cdot f_{yy}(a, b) - [f_{xy}(a, b)]^2.$$

1. If $M > 0$ and $f_{xx}(a, b) < 0$, then f has a local maximum at (a, b).
2. If $M > 0$, and $f_{xx}(a, b) > 0$, then f has a local minimum at (a, b).
3. If $M < 0$, then f has a saddle point at (a, b).
4. If $M = 0$, the test gives no information.